MW00837402

Piping Stress Handbook

Second Edition

Gulf Publishing Company
Book Division
Houston, London, Paris, Tokyo

Piping Stress Handbook

Second Edition

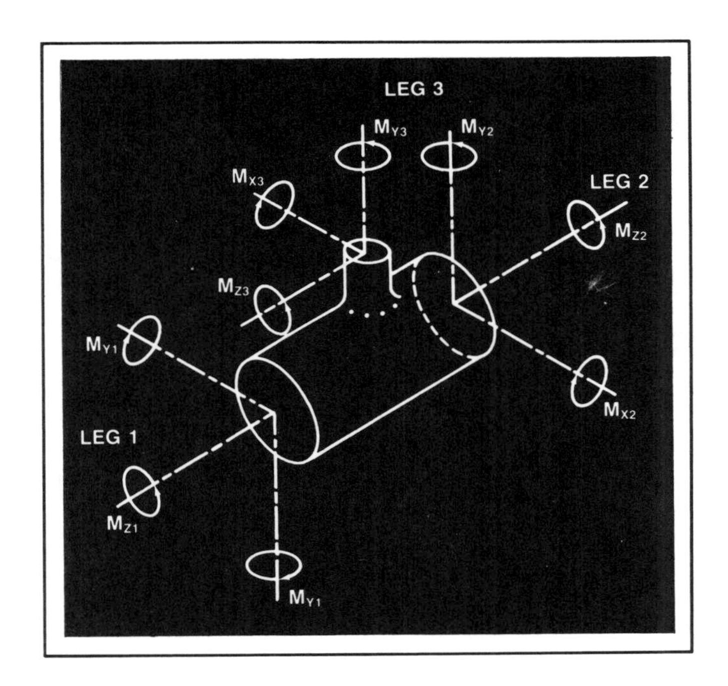

Victor Helguero M.

Dedicated to my mother, Blanca Maceda; my father, Victor Helguero B.; my brother, Guillermo Helguero; my wife, Maria Elena; and my children, who provide the essential inspiration for all my efforts.

Piping Stress Handbook

Second Edition

Library of Congress Cataloging-in-Publication Data

Helguero M., Victor.
Piping stress handbook.

Includes index.
1. Pipe lines—Design and construction—Handbooks, manuals, etc. I. Title.
TJ930.H397 1985 621.8′672 85-17716
ISBN 0-87201-703-6

ISBN 0-87201-703-6

Contents

Preface

Determining piping stresses for the design of petrochemical and power plant piping systems involves many complex mathematical calculations. These calculations can be solved with the aid of any one of several computer programs available provided they have the required capacity and an acceptable input/output format. The most formidable task facing the engineer is compiling the extensive amount of data needed to run the program. These data include physical properties, allowable stresses, valve weights and dimensions, stress intensification factors, thermal expansion coefficients, spring hangers and expansion joint selection, and piping wind loads.

This reference book provides formulas, technical data, and other pertinent design information not readily available in a single source for the piping stress analyst in the petrochemical industry who often has difficulty collecting the required data and solutions to complete a piping stress analysis. Depending on the magnitude and complexity of the job, the data needed to complete a given task may be scattered throughout a host of sources. The author's aim is to bring together in a single reference all the above material and present it in a convenient form.

Much of the information included in this book was obtained from the work of others; some was used in its original form, while some was rearranged for this application.

The author wishes to acknowledge his indebtedness to Mr. Robert Kingshill, Virender Shukla, and Timothy W. Calk for their assistance in preparing this handbook; and the American Society of Mechanical Engineers which generously permitted the author to use several equations to develop tabulations contained in this handbook.

Suggestions and criticism concerning errors that may remain in spite of all precautions will be greatly appreciated. They will contribute to the further improvement of this reference handbook.

Victor Helguero M., P.E.

1

Basic Theory of Pipe Stress and ANSI/ASME Codes B31.1, B31.3, B31.4, and B31.8 Pipe Stress Compliances

Pipe Stress Theory

To understand the basic criteria of the ANSI* pressure piping code, it will be useful to explain the way different stresses develop when a piping element is subjected to a number of loading conditions. There are four main stresses that affect a piping element, as shown in Figure 1-1. The following gives the intensity of these stresses and the manner in which they may be combined:

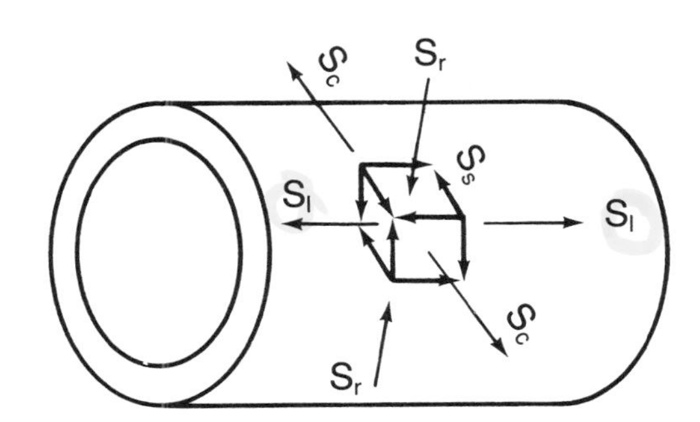

S_l = Longitudinal stress and the sum of three component parts (see Equation 1-1).
S_c = Circumferential stress
S_r = Radial stress
S_s = Shear stress

Figure 1-1. Stress-free-body diagram.

The bending stress due to temperature, weight of pipe, contents, insulation, snow and ice, wind or earthquake is calculated by the following equation:

$$S_b = \frac{\sqrt{(M_i I_i)^2 + (M_o I_o)^2}}{Z}$$

where
S_b = Bending stress
I_i = In-plane stress intensification factor
I_o = Out-of-plane stress intensification factor
M_i = In-plane moment, lb-in.
M_o = Out-of-plane moment, lb-in.
Z = Section modulus of pipe, in.^{3}

The direct longitudinal stress due to temperature and weight is calculated as follows:

$$S_{dl} = \frac{F_a}{A}$$

where
A = Metal pipe cross-sectional area, in.^{2}
F_a = Direct force, lb

The longitudinal stress due to internal pressure is calculated as follows:

$$S_p = \frac{PD}{4t}$$

where
P = Internal pressure
D = Outside diameter of pipe (see Chapter 10)
t = Pipe wall thickness (see Chapter 10)

$S_3 = 0$ (shear)

* For reasons of space these codes will be designated ANSI codes throughout the text of the book. Some readers may be more familiar with the designation ANSI/ASME as indicated in the headings.

Both significant stresses act in the same direction; therefore the stresses are "additive," i.e.

$$S_l = S_b + S_p + S_{dl} \quad (1\text{-}1)$$

Note: Longitudinal stresses due to temperature are excluded from the combination when doing code calculations.

Circumferential stress, S_c, is primarily due to internal pressure:

$$S_c = \frac{PD}{2t}$$

Radial stress, S_r, is primarily due to internal pressure, which is equal to P.

$$S_r = P$$

Shear stress, S_s, is the sum of two component parts: tortional stress and direct shear stress (the second stress is usually negligible). (This condition occurs in three-dimensional piping systems.)

$$S_s = \frac{T}{2Z} + 2.0\,\frac{F_s}{A}$$

where S_s = Shear stress
T = Torque, lb-in.
F_s = Resultant shear force
A = Cross-sectional area of pipe
Z = Section modulus of pipe
S_t = T/2Z, tortional stress

While the ANSI pressure piping code considers stresses due to thermal expansion separately from primary stresses due to pressure, weight, and external loadings, it is obvious that when combined stresses formulas and a specific yield criterion exist, stresses from all loadings should be included to determine the principal stresses before confirming them. Resultant principal stresses at the outside fiber are as follows:

$$S_1 = 1/2\,[S_l + S_c + \sqrt{4S_t^2 + (S_l - S_c)^2}]$$

$$S_2 = 1/2\,[S_l + S_c - \sqrt{4S_t^2 + (S_l - S_c)^2}]$$

To calculate the principal stresses use S_1 or S_2, whichever is greater, or the following equation:

$$\sqrt{4S_t^2 + (S_l - S_c)^2} \quad (1\text{-}2)$$

The preceding method is known as the maximum shear theory (Tresca) and is the preferred method of the ANSI Code. A second method, known as the distortion-energy theory (Von Mises), also provides good results but is not used by the Code:

$$\sqrt{3S_t^2 + S_l^2 + S_c^2 + S_lS_c}$$

Expansion Stresses

The ANSI pressure piping code recognizes that stress due to thermal expansion tends to diminish with time as a result of local yielding or creep. This reduction of stress will appear as a stress of opposite sign in the cold condition. This phenomenon is known as *self springing.* Cold springing is similar, and although the hot stresses tend to diminish with time, the sum of the hot and cold stresses for any one cycle will remain practically constant. This sum is called the *stress range,* and the code for pressure piping defines this allowable expansion stress range established for thermal expansion in terms of hot and cold tabular S values as:

$$S_a = F\,(1.25\,S_c + 0.25\,S_h)$$

where S_a = Allowable expansion stress range (see Chapters 3 and 4)
S_c = Allowable stress for the cold condition (see Chapters 3 and 4)
S_h = Allowable stress for the hot condition (see Chapters 3 and 4)
F = Stress range reduction factor for the cyclic condition

Total No. of Cycles Over Expected Life	F
7,000 and less	1.0
14,000 and less	0.9
22,000 and less	0.8
45,000 and less	0.7
100,000 and less	0.6
250,000 and less	0.5

The stress due to thermal expansion, which must not exceed the allowable expansion range, is called *expansion stress* and is defined by the piping code as:

$$S_e = \sqrt{(S_b)^2 + 4(S_t)^2}$$

See Equation 1-2, where $S_p = 0$ and $S_l = S_b$

The piping code further states that the sum of the longitudinal stresses due to pressure, weight, and other sustained external loadings shall not exceed S_h. If the longitudinal stress due to sustained loadings is less than S_h, the code permits the unused portion to be applied to extend the stress range available for expansion effects. Therefore, the code, in effect, permits a total equal to 1.25 $(S_c + S_h)$, for thermal expansion stress combined with stresses from other sustained loadings.

Cold Springing

A piping system may be *cold sprung,* or *prestressed,* to reduce anchor forces and moments caused by thermal expansion or contraction. This is accomplished by shortening or lengthening the overall length of pipe by any desired amount not in excess of the calculated expansion. The amount of cold spring (C. S.) is usually expressed as a percentage or fraction of the total expansion or contraction.

This procedure is recognized by the ANSI Code for pressure piping which states:

> The beneficial effect of judicious cold springing in assisting the system to attain its most favorable condition sooner is recognized. Inasmuch as the life of a system under cyclic condition depends primarily on the stress range rather than the stress level at any one time, no credit for cold spring is warranted with regard to stresses. In calculating end trusts and moments acting on equipment containing moving or removable parts with close clearances, the actual reactions at any one time rather than their range are significant, and credit accordingly is allowed for cold spring in the calculations of thrusts and moments.

The reactions (forces and moments) R_h and R_c in the hot and cold conditions, respectively, obtained as follows from the reactions, R, are derived from the flexibility calculations based on the modulus of elasticity at room temperature, E_c:

$$R_h = (1 - 2/3C)\left(\frac{E_h}{E_c}\right) R$$

$$R_c = CR$$

or

$$R_c = \left[1 - \frac{S_h}{S_e} \times \frac{E_c}{E_h}\right] R$$

These relationships apply only to two-anchor piping systems with no intermediate restraints (use whichever equation is greater) and with the further condition that

$$\frac{S_h}{S_e} \times \frac{E_c}{E_h} < 1$$

where
- C = Cold-spring factor varying from zero for no cold spring to one for 100% cold spring
- S_e = Maximum computed expansion stress
- E_c = Modulus of elasticity in the cold condition
- E_h = Modulus of elasticity in the hot condition
- R = Range of reactions corresponding to the full expansion range based on E_c

R_c and R_h represent the maximum reactions estimated to occur in the cold and hot conditions, respectively.

Thus, the ANSI piping code does not allow any credit for cold springing in the computation of stress. For reactions in the hot condition credit may be taken for two-thirds of the actual cold spring applied; however, the full amount of cold sping must be taken into account in computing reactions for the cold condition.

To understand the effects of stress range, self springing, and cold springing, see Figure 1-2.

ANSI B31.1 Power Piping Code Stress Compliances (1983)

The standard terms, used in the equations set forth in the ANSI code, are defined as follows:

- i = Stress intensification factor. The term (0.75i) shall never be taken as less than 1.0
- Z = Section modulus, in., $Z = r_m^2 t_n \pi$
- r_m = Mean radius, in.
- D_o = Outside diameter, in.
- t_n = Nominal wall thickness, in.

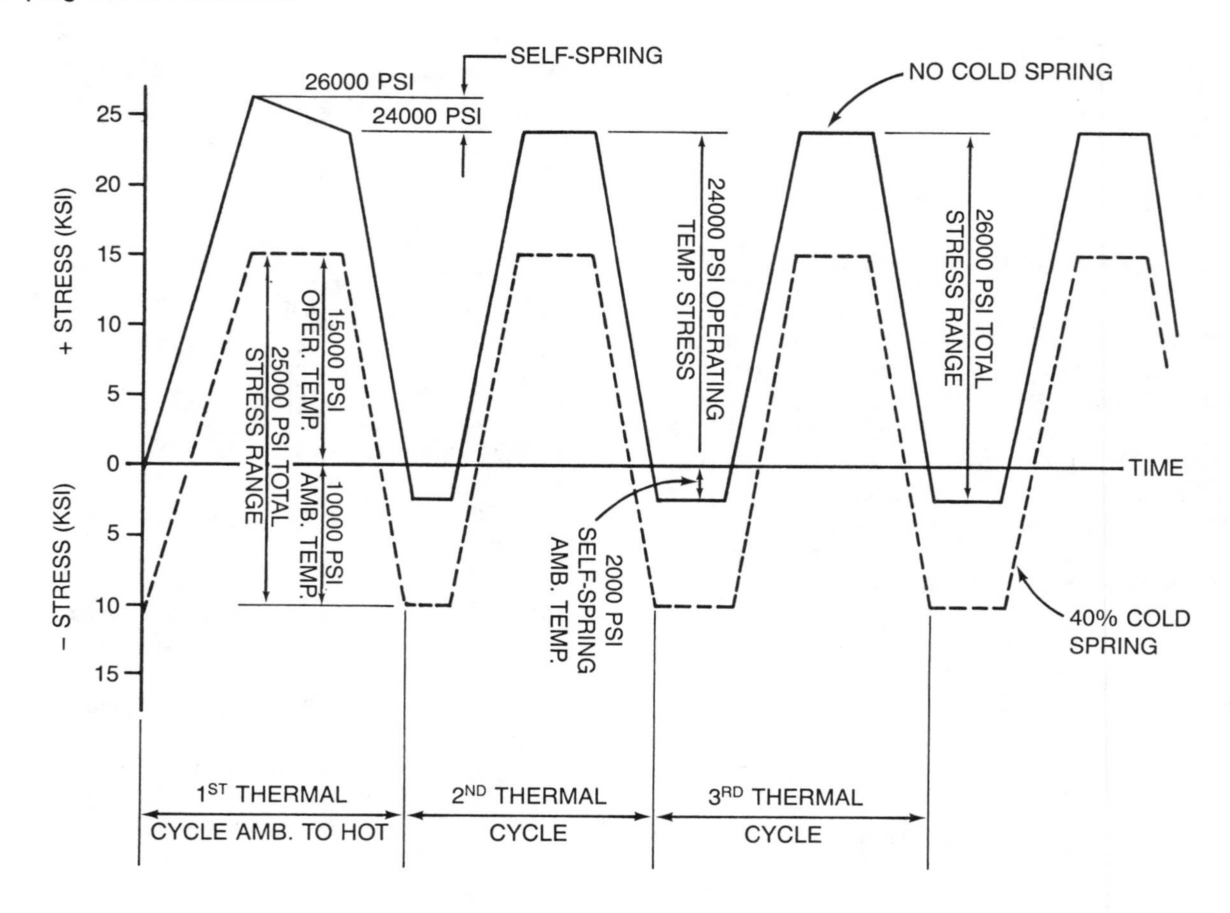

Figure 1-2. Stress-range curve with and without cold spring.

P = Internal design pressure
M_a = Resultant moment loading due to weight and other sustained loads, in.-lbs
M_b = Resultant moment loading due to occasional loads, including earthquake loads, trusts from relief/safety valve loads, in.-lbs
M_c = Range of resultant moments due to thermal expansion/contraction, in.-lbs
K = 1.15 for occasional loads acting less than 10% of the operation period
K = 1.20 for occasional loads acting less than 1% of the operation period
S_{lp} = Longitudinal stress due to pressure, psi
S_{ls} = Longitudinal stress due to sustained loads, psi
S_{lo} = Longitudinal stress due to occasional loads, psi
S_e = Thermal expansion stress due to thermal expansion and anchor displacements, psi
$S_{ls} + S_e$ = Longitudinal stress due to sustained loads plus the thermal expansion stress, psi
S_a = Allowable stress range for expansion stresses.
$S_a = f(1.25\ S_c + 0.25\ S_h)$
(see Chapter 4)
S_c = Basic material allowable stress at minimum temperature from allowable stress tables, psi
S_h = Basic material allowable stress at maximum temperature from allowable stress tables, psi
f = Stress range reduction factor for cyclic conditions for total number N of full-temperature cycles over total number of years of system operation (see "Expansion Stresses")
t_n = Wall thickness, in.
y = Coefficient having values as given in the ANSI Code B31.1, Table 104.1.2(A)
SE = Maximum allowable stress in material due to internal pressure and joint efficiency at the design temperature

Pressure Design

The minimum wall thickness for straight pipe under internal pressure and temperatures not exceeding those for various materials listed in the allowable stress tables, including allowances for mechanical strength, should not be less than that determined by this equation (Section 104.1.2, Equation 3):

$$t_m = \left[\frac{PD_o}{2(SE + PY)} + A\right] \quad \text{(see Chapter 7)}$$

The design pressure should not exceed:

$$P = \frac{2SE\,(t_m - A)}{D_o - 2Y\,(t_m - A)} \quad \text{(see Chapter 7)}$$

where t_m = minimum required wall thickness, in. (mm)

If pipe is ordered by its nominal thickness, the manufacturing tolerances must be taken into account. This minimum thickness must be increased to provide the increase of manufactured tolerance allowed by the applicable specification or required by the process. The next heavier commercial thickness should be selected.

External Pressure

To determine wall thickness and stiffening requirements for straight pipe under external pressure, the procedures outlined in paragraphs UG-28, UG-29, and UG-30 of Section VIII, Division 1 of the ASME Boiler and Pressure Vessel Code should be followed.

Longitudinal Stress

The internal pressure stress, S_{lp}, should be determined by the following equation:

$$S_{lp} = \frac{PD_o}{4t_n}$$

Thermal Expansion Stress

The thermal expansion stress is calculated using the following Code equation:

$$S_e = (iM_c/Z)$$

where M_c is combined in the following manner:

$$M_c = (M_x^2 + M_y^2 + M_z^2)^{1/2}$$

For full size outlet connections the equation is:

$$Z = \pi\, r_h^2 t_h$$

where t_h = Nominal wall thickness of the run pipe

For reduced outlet branch connections the equation is (see Figure 1-3):

$$Z = \pi\, r_b^2 t_s$$

where r_b = Branch mean cross sectional radius, in.
t_s = Effective branch wall thickness, in. = lesser of t_h or (i) t_b
t_b = Nominal branch wall thickness, in.
t_h = Nominal thickness of run pipe, in.

Sustained Longitudinal Stress

The sustained longitudinal stress, S_{ls}, is the algebraic summation of the longitudinal pressure stress and longitudinal sustained weight stress. S_{ls} is calculated using the following Code equation (Section 104.8.1, Equation 11):

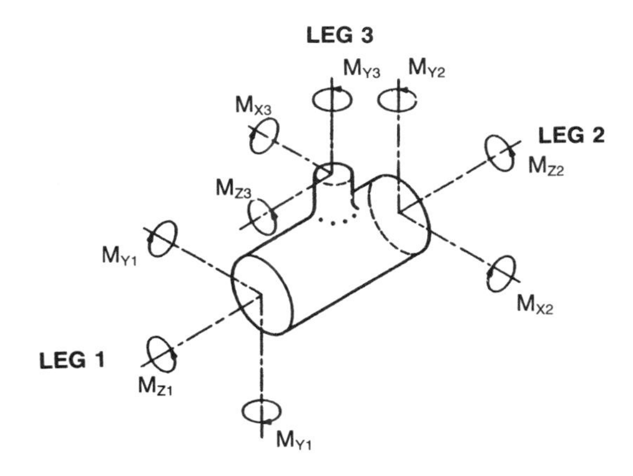

Figure 1-3. Header and branch connections.

$$S_{ls} = \frac{PD_o}{4t_n} + \frac{0.75iM_A}{Z} \leq 1.0Sh$$

(see Chapter 3 for S_h)

As can be seen from the equation, the longitudinal stress due to pressure, weight, and other sustained loads should be less than or equal to the S_h for the material.

Occasional Longitudinal Stress

The occasional longitudinal stress, S_{lo}, is the algebraic summation of the longitudinal sustained weight stress, the longitudinal pressure stress, and occasional stress. S_{lo} is calculated using the following Code equation (Section 104.8.2, Equation 12):

$$S_{lo} = \frac{PD_o}{4t_n} + \frac{0.75iM_a}{Z} + \frac{0.75iM_b}{Z} \leq K\ S_h$$

As can be seen from the equation, the longitudinal stress due to occasional loads should be less than or equal to k S_h.

Allowable Thermal Expansion Stress

The thermal expansion stress is calculated using the following Code equation (Section 104.8.3 (A), Equation 13):

$$S_e = iM_c/Z \leq S_a + f(S_h - S_l)$$ (see Chapter 3 for S_a)

As can be seen from the equation, the thermal expansion stress should be less than or equal to S_a.

Sustained-Plus-Thermal-Expansion Stress

The sustained-plus-thermal-expansion stress, $S_{ls} + S_e$, is the algebraic summation of the longitudinal stress due to sustained loads and the thermal expansion stress. $S_{ls} + S_e$ is calculated using the following equation:

$$S_{ls} + SE = \frac{PD_o}{4t_n} + \frac{0.75iM_a}{Z} + \frac{iM_c}{Z} \leq (S_h + S_a)$$

As can be seen from the equation, the sustained-plus-thermal-expansion stress should be less than or equal to the sum of S_h and S_a.

ANSI B31.3 Chemical Plant and Petroleum Refinery Piping Code Stress Compliances (1984)

Pressure Stress

The minimum allowed wall thickness is calculated by using the design pressure in the following equation:

$$t_m = \frac{(P)\ (O.\ D.)}{2\ (SE + yP)} + A$$ (see Chapter 6)

where

- P = Design pressure, psig
- O. D. = Actual pipe outside diameter, in.
- SE = Maximum allowable stress in material due to internal pressure and joint efficiency
- y = A coefficient having values as given in the ANSI Code, Table 304.1.1, A; normally 0.4
- .875 = A factor used to account to the industry's 12.5% mill tolerance on finished-wall thicknesses
- A = Allowance for corrosion, erosion, etc., in.

The allowed pressure is calculated by using:

$$P_{allow} = \frac{2\ (SE)\ (t_m - A)}{O.\ D. - 2y\ (t_m - A)}$$ (see Chapter 6)

where

- t_m = .875 × wall thickness, in.
- SE = Maximum allowable stress of the material for internal pressure considering the joint efficiency

Expansion Stress

The expansion stress is calculated using the Code equation (Section 319.4.4, Equation 17).

$$S_e = (S_b^2 + 4S_t^2)^{1/2}$$

where

- S_e = Computed expansion stress, psi
- S_b = Resultant bending stress, psi
- S_b = $[(i_iM_i)^2 + (i_oM_o)^2]^{1/2}/Z$
- S_t = Torsional stress, psi, = $M_t/2Z$
- M_i = In-plane bending moment, in.-lb
- M_o = Out-of-plane bending moment, in.-lb

M_t = Torsional moment on cross section, in.-lb
Z = Section modulus of pipe, $in.^3$
i = Stress intensification factor (see Chapter 5)

For branch connections, the resultant bending stress (S_b) is calculated using the Code equations (Section 319.4.4, Equations 19 and 20):

For the header (Legs 1 and 2 in Figure 1-3):

$$S_b = \frac{[(i_i M_i)^2 + (i_o M_o)^2]^{1/2}}{Z}$$

For the branch (Leg 3):

$$S_b = \frac{[(i_i M_i)^2 + (i_o M_o)^2]^{1/2}}{Z_e}$$

where S_b = Resultant bending stress, psi
Z_e = Effective section modulus for the branch, $in.^3$, $= r_m^2 t_s \pi$
r_m = Mean branch cross-sectional radius, in.
t_s = Effective branch wall thickness, in., = lesser of t_h and (i_o) (t_b)
t_h = Thickness of pipe matching run of tee or header exclusive of reinforcing pad or saddle, in.
t_b = Thickness of pipe matching branch, in.
i_o = Out-of-plane stress intensification factor
i_i = In-plane stress intensification factor

For elbows and miter bends, the resultant bending stresses (S_b) calculated using the Code equation (Section 319.4.4, Equation 18):

S_b = Resultant bending stress, psi

$$S_b = \frac{[(i_i M_i)^2 + (i_o M_o)^2]^{1/2}}{Z}$$

where i_i = In-plane stress intensification factor
i_o = Out-of-plane stress intensification factor
M_i = In-plane bending bending moment, in.-lb (see Figure 1-4)
M_o = Out-of-plane bending moment, in.-lb (see Figure 1-4)
Z = Section modulus of pipe, $in.^3$

A conservative equation generally utilized for the calculation of the allowable expansion stress range is given in the ANSI Code B31.3 Section 302.3.58d, Equation 1:

$$S_a = f\,(1.25\,S_c + .25\,S_h) \qquad \text{(see Chapter 4)}$$

ANSI B31.4 Liquid Petroleum Transportation Piping Code Stress Compliances

Pressure Stress

The minimum allowed wall-thickness pressure stress is calculated by using the internal pressure in the equation:

$$t_{allow} = \frac{P\,D_o}{2\,S} + A$$

where P = Pressure, psig
D_o = Actual pipe outside diameter, in.
A = Allowance for corrosion, erosion, etc., in.
S = (0.72) (E) (SMYS), psi
SMYS = Specified minimum yield strength, psi, Table 1-1
E = Weld joint factor, Table 1-2

Longitudinal Stress

The longitudinal pressure stress is computed in accordance with the Code using the equation:

$$S_{lp} = \frac{P\,D_o}{4t}$$

where S_{lp} = Longitudinal pressure stress, psi
P = Internal pressure, psig
t = Actual pipe wall thickness, in.
D_o = Nominal outside diameter of the pipe, in.

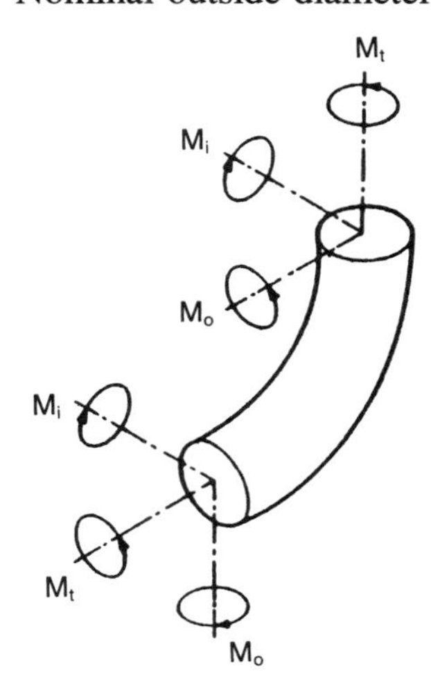

Figure 1-4. In-plane and out-of-plane bending moments.

Table 1-1
Tabulation of Examples of Allowable Stresses for Reference Use in Liquid Petroleum Transportation Piping Systems

Allowable stress values (S) shown in this Table are equal to 0.72 × E (weld joint factor) × specified minimum yield strength of the pipe.

Allowable stress values shown are for new pipe of known specification. Allowable stress values for new pipe of unknown specification, ASTM A 120 specification or used (reclaimed) pipe shall be determined in accordance with 402.3.1.

For some Code computations, particularly with regard to branch connections [see 404.3.1 (d) (3)] and expansion, flexibility, structural attachments, supports, and restraints (Chapter II, Part 5), the weld joint factor E need not be considered.

For specified minimum yield strength of other grades in approved specifications, refer to that particular specification.

Allowable stress value for cold worked pipe subsequently heated to 600 F or higher (welding excepted) shall be 75 percent of value listed in Table.

Definitions for the various types of pipe are given in 400.2.

Specification	Grade	Specified Min Yield Strength psi	Notes	(E) Weld Joint Factor	(S) Allowable Stress Value −20 F to 250 F psi
Seamless					
API 5L	A25	25,000	(1)	1.00	18,000
API 5L, ASTM A 53, ASTM A 106	A	30,000	(1) (2)	1.00	21,600
API 5L, ASTM A 53, ASTM A 106	B	35,000	(1) (2)	1.00	25,200
ASTM A 106	C	40,000	(1) (2)	1.00	28,800
ASTM A 524	I	35,000	(1)	1.00	25,200
ASTM A 524	II	30,000	(1)	1.00	21,600
API 5LU	U80	80,000	(1) (4)	1.00	57,600
API 5LU	U100	100,000	(1) (4)	1.00	72,000
API 5LX	X42	42,000	(1) (2) (4)	1.00	30,250
API 5LX	X46	46,000	(1) (2) (4)	1.00	33,100
API 5LX	X52	52,000	(1) (2) (4)	1.00	37,450
API 5LX	X56	56,000	(1) (4)	1.00	40,300
API 5LX	X60	60,000	(1) (4)	1.00	43,200
API 5LX	X65	65,000	(1) (4)	1.00	46,800
API 5LX	X70	70,000	(1) (4)	1.00	50,400
Furnace Welded-Butt Welded					
ASTM A 53		25,000	(1) (2)	0.60	10,800
API 5L Class I & Class II	A25	25,000	(1) (2) (3)	0.60	10,800
API 5L (Bessemer), ASTM A 53 (Bessemer)		30,000	(1) (2) (5)	0.60	12,950
Furnace Welded-Lap Welded					
API 5L Class I		25,000	(1) (2) (6)	0.80	14,400
API 5L Class II		28,000	(1) (2) (6)	0.80	16,150
API 5L (Bessemer)		30,000	(1) (2) (6)	0.80	17,300
API 5L Electric Furnace		25,000	(1) (2) (6)	0.80	14,400
Electric Resistance Welded and Electric Flash Welded					
API 5L	A25	25,000	(1) (7)	1.00	18,000
API 5L, ASTM A 53, ASTM A 135	A	30,000	(2)	0.85	18,360
API 5L, API 5LS, ASTM A 53, ASTM A 135	A	30,000	(1)	1.00	21,600
API 5L, ASTM A 53, ASTM A 135	B	35,000	(2)	0.85	21,420
API 5L, API 5LS, ASTM A 53, ASTM A 135	B	35,000	(1)	1.00	25,200
API 5LS, API 5LX	X42	42,000	(1) (2) (4)	1.00	30,250
API 5LS, API 5LX	X46	46,000	(1) (2) (4)	1.00	33,100
API 5LS, API 5LX	X52	52,000	(1) (2) (4)	1.00	37,450
API 5LS, API 5LX	X56	56,000	(1) (4)	1.00	40,300
API 5LS, API 5LX	X60	60,000	(1) (4)	1.00	43,200
API 5LS, API 5LX	X65	65,000	(1) (4)	1.00	46,800
API 5LS, API 5LX	X70	70,000	(1) (4)	1.00	50,400
API 5LU	U80	80,000	(1) (4)	1.00	57,600
API 5LU	U100	100,000	(1) (4)	1.00	72,000

Reproduced from ANSI/ASME Code B31.4-1979, Table 402.3.1. Reprinted courtesy of The American Society of Mechanical Engineers.

Table 1-1
Continued

Specification	Grade	Specified Min Yield Strength psi	Notes	(*E*) Weld Joint Factor	(*S*) Allowable Stress Value −20 F to 250 F psi
Electric Fusion Welded					
ASTM A 134	–	–		0.80	–
ASTM A 139	A	30,000	(1) (2)	0.80	17,300
ASTM A 139	B	35,000	(1) (2)	0.80	20,150
ASTM A 155	–	–	(2) (8)	0.90	–
ASTM A 155	–	–	(1) (8)	1.00	–
Submerged Arc Welded					
API 5L, API 5LS	A	30,000	(1)	1.00	21,600
API 5L, API 5LS	B	35,000	(1)	1.00	25,200
API 5LS, API 5LX	X42	42,000	(1) (2) (4)	1.00	30,250
API 5LS, API 5LX	X46	46,000	(1) (2) (4)	1.00	33,100
API 5LS, API 5LX	X52	52,000	(1) (2) (4)	1.00	37,450
API 5LS, API 5LX	X56	56,000	(1) (4)	1.00	40,300
API 5LS, API 5LX	X60	60,000	(1) (4)	1.00	43,200
API 5LS, API 5LX	X65	65,000	(1) (4)	1.00	46,800
API 5LS, API 5LX	X70	70,000	(1) (4)	1.00	50,400
API 5LU	U80	80,000	(1) (4)	1.00	57,600
API 5LU	U100	100,000	(1) (4)	1.00	72,000
ASTM A 381	Y35	35,000	(1) (2)	1.00	25,200
ASTM A 381	Y42	42,000	(1) (2)	1.00	30,250
ASTM A 381	Y46	46,000	(1) (2)	1.00	33,100
ASTM A 381	Y48	48,000	(1) (2)	1.00	34,550
ASTM A 381	Y50	50,000	(1)	1.00	36,000
ASTM A 381	Y52	52,000	(1)	1.00	37,450
ASTM A 381	Y60	60,000	(1)	1.00	43,200
ASTM A 381	Y65	65,000	(1)	1.00	46,800

NOTES
(1) Weld joint factor *E* (see Table 402.4.3) and allowable stress value are applicable to pipe manufactured after 1958.
(2) Weld joint factor *E* (see Table 402.4.3) and allowable stress value are applicable to pipe manufactured before 1959.
(3) Class II produced under API 5L 23rd Edition, 1968, or earlier has a specified minimum yield strength of 28,000 psi.
(4) Other grades provided for in API 5LS, API 5LU, and API 5LX not precluded.
(5) Manufacture was discontinued and process deleted from API 5L in 1969.
(6) Manufacture was discontinued and process deleted from API 5L in 1962.
(7) A25 is not produced in electric flash weld.
(8) See applicable plate specification for yield point and refer to 402.3.1 for calculation of (*S*).

Allowable Longitudinal Stress

The allowable stress value for additive longitudinal stresses is given by the Code in Section 419.6.4(c):

$$S_l \text{ (allow)} = 0.75\ S_a$$

where S_a = The allowable expansion stress range, psi
= 0.72 SMYS

where SMYS = Specified minimum yield strength, psi (see Table 1-1)

Allowable Expansion Stress Range for Unrestrained Piping

This is given by:

$$S_a = 0.72\ (\text{SMYS})$$

where SMYS = Specified minimum yield strength, psi (see Table 1-1)

Table 1-2
Weld Joint Factor *E*

Specification Number	Pipe Type (1)	Weld Joint Factor *E* Pipe Mfrd. Before 1959	Pipe Mfrd. After 1958
ASTM A 53	Seamless	1.00	1.00
	Electric-Resistance-Welded	0.85 (2)	1.00
	Furnace Lap-Welded	0.80	0.80
	Furnace Butt-Welded	0.60	0.60
ASTM A 106	Seamless	1.00	1.00
ASTM A 134	Electric-Fusion (Arc)-Welded single or double pass	0.80	0.80
ASTM A 135	Electric-Resistance-Welded	0.85 (2)	1.00
ASTM A 139	Electric-Fusion-Welded single or double pass	0.80	0.80
ASTM A 155	Electric-Fusion-Welded	0.90	1.00
ASTM A 381	Electric-Fusion-Welded, Double Submerged Arc-Welded	–	1.00
API 5L	Seamless	1.00	1.00
	Electric-Resistance-Welded	0.85 (2)	1.00
	Electric-Flash-Welded	0.85 (2)	1.00
	Electric-Induction-Welded	–	1.00
	Submerged Arc-Welded	–	1.00
	Furnace Lap-Welded	0.80	0.80 (3)
	Furnace Butt-Welded	0.60	0.60
API 5LS	Electric-Resistance-Welded	–	1.00
	Submerged Arc-Welded	–	1.00
API 5LX	Seamless	1.00	1.00
	Electric-Resistance-Welded	1.00	1.00
	Electric-Flash-Welded	1.00	1.00
	Electric-Induction-Welded	–	1.00
	Submerged Arc-Welded	1.00	1.00
API 5LU	Seamless	–	1.00
	Electric-Resistance-Welded	–	1.00
	Electric-Flash-Welded	–	1.00
	Electric-Induction-Welded	–	1.00
	Submerged Arc-Welded	–	1.00
Known	Known	(4)	(5)
Unknown	Seamless	1.00 (6)	1.00 (6)
Unknown	Electric-Resistance or Flash-Welded	0.85 (6)	1.00 (6)
Unknown	Electric-Fusion-Welded	0.80 (6)	0.80 (6)
Unknown	Furnace Lap-Welded or over 4½" OD	0.80 (7)	0.80 (7)
Unknown	Furnace Butt-Welded or 4½" OD and smaller	0.60 (8)	0.60 (8)

NOTES: (1) Definitions for the various pipe types (weld joints) are given in 400.2.

(2) A weld joint factor of 1.0 may be used for electric-resistance-welded or electric-flash-welded pipe manufactured prior to 1959 where (a) pipe furnished under this classification has been subjected to supplemental tests and/or heat treatments as agreed to by the supplier and the purchaser, and such supplemental tests and/or heat treatment demonstrate the strength characteristics of the weld to be equal to the minimum tensile strength specified for the pipe, or (b) pipe has been tested as required for a new pipeline in accordance with 437.4.1.

(3) Manufacture was discontinued and process deleted from API 5L in 1962.

(4) Factors shown above for pipe manufactured before 1959 apply for new or used (reclaimed) pipe if pipe specification and pipe type are known and it is known that pipe was manufactured before 1959 or not known whether manufactured after 1958.

(5) Factors shown above for pipe manufactured after 1958 apply for new or used (reclaimed) pipe if pipe specification and pipe type are known and it is known that pipe was manufactured after 1958.

(6) Factor applies for new or used pipe of unknown specification and ASTM A 120 if type of weld joint is known.

(7) Factor applies for new or used pipe of unknown specification and ASTM A 120 if type of weld joint is known to be furnace lap-welded, or for pipe over 4½ in. OD if type of joint is unknown.

(8) Factor applies for new or used pipe of unknown specification and ASTM A 120 if type of weld joint is known to be furnace butt-welded, or for pipe 4½ in. OD and smaller if type of joint is unknown.

Longitudinal Expansion Stress for Restrained Piping

For restrained piping, use the longitudinal expansion stress from the equation given in ANSI Code B31.4, Section 419.6.4 (b):

$$S_l = E\,(a)\,(T_2 - T_1) - v(S_h)$$

where
S_l = Longitudinal compressive stress, psi
E = Modulus of elasticity of steel, psi
S_h = Hoop stress due to fluid pressure, psi
T_1 = Temperature at time of installation, °F
T_2 = Maximum or minimum operating temperature, °F
a = Linear coefficient of thermal expansion, in./in./°F
v = Poisson's ratio = 0.3 for steel

Allowable Expansion Stress Range for Restrained Piping

This is calculated by using:

$$S_a = 0.90\,(SMYS)$$

where SMYS = Specified minimum yield strength of the pipe, psi (see Table 1-1)

The expansion stress for unrestrained piping is calculated by using:

$$S_e = [S_b^2 + 4S_t^2]^{1/2}$$

where
S_e = Computed expansion stress, psi
$S_b = \dfrac{[(i_iM_i)^2 + (i_oM_o)^2]^{1/2}}{Z}$ = equivalent bending stress, psi
$S_t = M_t/2Z$ = torsional stress, psi
M_i = Bending moment in plane of member (for members having significant orientation, such as elbows or tees; for the latter the moments in the header and branch portions are to be considered separately), in.-lbs
M_o = Bending moment out of, or transverse to, plane of member, in.-lbs
M_t = Torsional moment, in.-lbs
i_i = Stress intensification factor under bending in plane

Allowable Shear Stress

The allowable stress value in shear is computed in accordance with the ANSI Code B31.4, Section 402.3.1 (e):

$$S_{sh}\ (allow) = (.45)\,(SMYS)$$

Allowable Internal Pressure Stress

The allowed internal pressure stress is S, where S = (0.72) (E) (SMYS), psi

DOT/B31.8 Gas Transmission and Distribution Piping Systems Stress Compliances (1982)

Pressure Stress

The design pressure for steel gas piping systems or the nominal wall thickness for a given pressure is determined by:

$$P = \frac{2St}{D}\,(F)\,(E)\,(T)$$

(For limitations see Section 841.121)

where
P = Design pressure, psig
S = Specified minimum yield strength, psi (see Table 1-3). For special limitations on S see Section 841.121 (e) and (f).
D = Nominal outside diameter of pipe, in.
t = Nominal wall thickness, in.
F = Construction-type design factor obtained from Table 1-4
E = Longitudinal joint factor obtained from Table 1-5 (see also Section 811.253 (d))
T = Temperature derating factor obtained from Table 1-6

Table 1-3
Specified Minimum Yield Strength for Steel and Iron Pipe Commonly Used in Piping Systems*

Specification	Grade	Type (1)	SMYS (psi)
API 5L	A25	BW, ERW, S	25,000
API 5L	A	ERW, FW, S, DSA	30,000
API 5L	B	ERW, FW, S, DSA	35,000
API 5LS (2)	A	ERW, DSA	30,000
API 5LS	B	ERW, DSA	35,000
API 5LS	X42	ERW, DSA	42,000
API 5LS	X46	ERW, DSA	46,000
API 5LS	X52	ERW, DSA	52,000
API 5LS	X56	ERW, DSA	56,000
API 5LS	X60	ERW, DSA	60,000
API 5LS	X65	ERW, DSA	65,000
API 5LS	X70 (Tentative)	ERW, DSA	70,000
API 5LX (2)	X42	ERW, FW, S, DSA	42,000
API 5LX	X46	ERW, FW, S, DSA	46,000
API 5LX	X52	ERW, FW, S, DSA	52,000
API 5LX	X56	ERW, FW, S, DSA	56,000
API 5LX	X60	ERW, FW, S, DSA	60,000
API 5LX	X65	ERW, FW, S, DSA	65,000
API 5LX	X70 (Tentative)	ERW, FW, S, DSA	70,000
ASTM A53	Open Hearth, Basic Oxygen, Elect. Furnace	BW	25,000
ASTM A53	Bessemer	BW	30,000
ASTM A53	A	ERW, S	30,000
ASTM A53	B	ERW, S	35,000
ASTM A106	A	S	30,000
ASTM A106	B	S	35,000
ASTM A106	C	S	40,000
ASTM A135	A	ERW	30,000
ASTM A135	B	ERW	35,000
ASTM A139	A	EFW	30,000
ASTM A139	B	EFW	35,000
ASTM A381	Class Y-35	DSA	35,000
ASTM A381	Class Y-42	DSA	42,000
ASTM A381	Class Y-46	DSA	46,000
ASTM A381	Class Y-48	DSA	48,000
ASTM A381	Class Y-50	DSA	50,000
ASTM A381	Class Y-52	DSA	52,000
ASTM A381	Class Y-56	DSA	56,000
ASTM A381	Class Y-60	DSA	60,000
ASTM A381	Class Y-65	DSA	65,000
ASTM A134	–	EFW	(3)
ASTM A155	–	EFW	(3)
ASTM A333	1	S, ERW	30,000
ASTM A333	3	S, ERW	35,000
ASTM A333	4	S	35,000
ASTM A333	6	S, ERW	35,000
ASTM A333	7	S, ERW	35,000
ASTM A333	8	S, ERW	75,000
ASTM A333	9	S, ERW	46,000
ASTM A559	–	ERW	35,000

(1) Abbreviations: BW – Furnace butt-welded; ERW – Electric resistance welded; S – Seamless; FW – Flash welded; EFW – Electric fusion welded; DSA – Double submerged-arc welded.
(2) Intermediate grades are available in API 5LS and 5LX.
(3) See applicable plate specification for SMYS.

Note: This table is not complete. For minimum specified yield strength of other grades and grades in approved specifications, refer to the particular specification.
Reproduced from ANSI/ASME Code B31.8-1982, Appendix D. Reprinted courtesy of The American Society of Mechanical Engineers.

Table 1-4
Values of Design Factor *F*

Construction Type (See 841.151)	Design Factor *F*
Type – A	0.72
Type – B	0.60
Type – C	0.50
Type – D	0.40

Reproduced from ANSI/ASME Code B31.8-1982, Table 841.1C. Reprinted courtesy of The American Society of Mechanical Engineers.

Table 1-5
Longitudinal Joint Factor *E*

Spec. Number	Pipe Class	*E* Factor
ASTM A53	Seamless	1.00
	Electric Resistance Welded	1.00
	Furnace Butt Welded	.60
ASTM A106	Seamless	1.00
ASTM A134	Electric Fusion Arc Welded	.80
ASTM A135	Electric Resistance Welded	1.00
ASTM A139	Electric Fusion Welded	.80
ASTM A155	Electric Fusion Arc Welded	1.00
ASTM A211	Spiral Welded Steel Pipe	.80
ASTM A381	Double Submerged-Arc-Welded	1.00
API 5L	Seamless	1.00
	Electric Resistance Welded	1.00
	Electric Flash Welded	1.00
	Furnace Butt Welded	.60
	*Furnace Lap-Welded	.80
API 5LX	Seamless	1.00
	Electric Resistance Welded	1.00
	Electric Flash Welded	1.00
	Submerged Arc Welded	1.00
API 5LS	Electric Resistance Welded	1.00
	Submerged Arc Welded	1.00

Note: Definitions for the various classes of welded pipe are given in 804.243.

*Manufacture was discontinued and process deleted from API 5L in 1962.

Reproduced from ANSI/ASME Code B31.8-1982, Table 841.1A. Reprinted courtesy of The American Society of Mechanical Engineers.

Table 1-6
Temperature Derating Factor *T* for Steel Pipe

Temperature Degrees Fahrenheit	Temperature Derating Factor *T*
250 F or less	1.000
300 F	0.967
350 F	0.933
400 F	0.900
450 F	0.867

Note: For intermediate temperatures interpolate for derating factor.

Reproduced from ANSI/ASME Code B31.8-1982, Table 841.1B. Reprinted courtesy of The American Society of Mechanical Engineers.

Expansion Stress

This is calculated by using the Code equation:

$$S_e = (S_b^2 + 4S_t^2)^{1/2}$$

where S_e = Computed expansion stress, psi
S_b = Resultant bending stress, psi = iM/Z
S_t = Torsional stress, psi = $M_t/2Z$
M = Resultant bending moment on cross section, in.-lbs
M_t = Torsional moment on cross section, in.-lbs
Z = Section modulus of pipe, $in.^3$
i = Stress intensification factor (see ANSI Code B31.8, Appendix E)

Allowable Expansion Stress Range

This is calculated by using:

$$S_a = 0.72\ (SMYS)$$

where SMYS = Specified minimum yield strength, psi (see Table 1-3)

Longitudinal Pressure Stress

This is computed by using:

$$S_{lp} = \frac{P\ D_o}{4t}$$

where P = Design pressure, psig
D_o = Outside diameter of pipe, in.
t = Pipe wall thickness, in.

The sum of the longitudinal pressure and longitudinal bending stresses due to external loads such as weight of pipe and contents, wind, etc., should not exceed 75% of the allowable stress in the hot condition. The allowable for the sum of the longitudinal stresses is given by:

$$S_l = (allow) = 0.75\ (S)\ (F)\ (T)$$

where S = Specified minimum yield strength, psi
F = Design factor obtained from Table 1-4
T = Temperature derating factor, Table 1-6

Standard Outline for ANSI B31 Codes

ANSI Code B31.1: Power Piping

Includes

1. Power and auxiliary service piping systems for electric generating plants.
2. Industrial and institutional plants (also see ANSI Code B31.9).
3. Central and district heating plants (also see ANSI Code B31.9).
4. All piping and component parts within or part of plants as previously specified, unless specifically excluded.
5. Boiler external piping which is covered under the ASME Code, Section I, stamping requirements.
6. Geothermal steam and hot water piping.
7. Oil or gas piping, downstream of meter, within plant identified in 1, 2, or 3, above.
8. Air and hydraulic distribution systems.

Excludes

1. Piping specifically covered by other ANSI/ASME sections.
2. Components covered by ASME B and PV Code.
3. Fuel gas in industrial and institutional plants.
4. Building heating and distribution steam piping for 15 psi (100 kPa) gauge or less or hot water systems for 30 psi (200 kPa) gauge or less.
5. Roof drains, floor drains, plumbing, sewer or fire protection systems.
6. Piping for hydraulic or pneumatic tools.
7. Piping for nuclear power plants.

ANSI Code B31.2: Fuel Gas Piping

Includes

1. Natural gas.
2. Manufactured gas.
3. LPG—air mixtures above the combustible limit.
4. LPG—in the gaseous state.

Excludes

1. Fuel gas piping where the metal temperature is above 450°F (232°C) or below −20°F (−29°C).
2. Fuel gas piping covered by the ANSI Codes B31.1, B31.3, B31.8, Z21.30, or Z106.1
3. Pressure vessels covered by the ASME B and PV Code.
4. Gas gathering, transmission, and distribution systems covered by ANSI Code B31.8.
5. LPG in the liquid state.
6. Fuel gas—air mixtures in the combustible or flammable range.

Note: This Code will be withdrawn when the new issue of ANSI Code Z223.1 (which does not reference ANSI Code B31.2) is released. This service will be covered by ANSI Codes B31.9 and Z223.1.

ANSI Code B31.3: Chemical Plant and Petroleum Refinery Piping

Includes

1. All piping within the property limits of facilities engaged in the processing or handling of chemical or petroleum or related products.

Excludes

1. Nonhazardous fluid piping with pressures between 0 and 15 psi (100 kPa) and temperatures ranging from −20°F (−29°C) to 366°F (186°C).
2. Piping covered by the ASME B and PV Code, Section I or ANSI Code B31.1, which requires Section I, Inspection and Stamping (B.E.P. Piping).
3. Pressure vessels, heat exchangers, pumps, etc., including internal piping and connections for external piping.
4. Piping within the property limits which has been designated for design according to the ANSI Code B31.4 or B31.8 or to government regulation (pipeline rights-of-way).
5. Plumbing or sewers.
6. Piping for fire protection systems (covered by insurance underwriter's requirements).

ANSI Code B31.4: Liquid Petroleum Transportation Piping Systems

Includes

1. Piping transporting liquid petroleum and petroleum products between the producer's facilities and delivery and receiving points.

Excludes

1. Water, air, steam, lube oil, gas, and fuel piping.
2. Pressure vessels, heat exchangers, pumps, meters, etc., including internal piping and connections to external piping.
3. Piping systems designed for internal pressures less than 15 psi (100 kPa).
4. Piping systems designed for internal pressures greater than 15 psi (100 kPa) where the design temperature is below −20°F (−29°C) or above 250°F (120°C).
5. Casing, tubing, or pipe used in oil wells, wellhead assemblies, and piping connecting those assemblies.
6. Piping covered by the ANSI Code B31.3 or B31.8.
7. Ammonia refrigeration piping systems.

ANSI Code B31.5: Refrigeration Piping

Includes

1. Refrigeration and brine piping systems down to −350°F (−196°C) either erected on the premises or factory assembled, unless specifically excluded.

Excludes

1. Self-contained refrigeration systems covered by requirements of Underwriter's Laboratories or other nationally recognized testing laboratories.
2. Water piping systems.
3. Piping systems with internal or external pressure of 15 psi (100 kPa) or less.

ANSI Code B31.8: Gas Transmission and Distribution Piping

Includes

1. Gas transmission pipelines.
2. Gas compressor stations.
3. Gas metering and regulation stations.
4. Gas mains.
5. Service lines to outlet of customer's meter set.
6. Gas storage lines and storage equipment of the closed-pipe type.

Excludes

1. Pressure vessels and piping covered by the ASME B and PV Code.
2. Piping systems with metal temperatures above 450°F (232°C) or below −20°F (−29°C).
3. Piping in chemical plant or refinery property limits, natural gasoline extraction plants, etc., covered by ANSI Code B31.3.
4. Atmospheric vent piping for waste gases.
5. Low pressure gas which is covered by ANSI Code B31.4.
6. Wellhead assemblies.
7. Proprietary items of equipment.

ANSI Code B31.9: Building Services Piping

Includes*

1. Piping systems for building services for industrial, commercial, public, institutional, and multi-unit residential buildings.

Examples:

A. Dual-temperature water for heating and cooling.
B. Chilled water.
C. Condensing water.
D. Hot water.
E. Steam and condensate return.
F. Compressed air and other nonflammable gases.
G. Fuel gas over 60 psi (415 kPa) (fuel gas under 60 psi is covered by the new ANSI Code Z223.1)

Excludes

1. *Pressure limit exclusions:*

   A. Steam: 125 psi (860 kPa) Gauge
   B. Nonfuel gas: 125 (860 kPa) Gauge
   C. Liquids: 300 (2,070 kPa) Gauge
   D. Full vacuum for all fluids

---

* (as per latest draft.)

2. *Other exclusions:*

   A. Piping systems covered by ANSI Code B31.1
   B. Sanitary, potable water, and storm drain piping
   C. Fire protection systems
   D. Acetylene, hydrogen, oxygen and medical gas piping
   E. Fuel oil piping

ANSI Code B31.10: Cryogenic Piping*

Includes†

1. Liquid-solid mixtures (or slush), operating at temperatures ranging from 120K (−244°F, −153°C) to 0K (−459°F, −273°C), either erected on the premises or factory assembled.

Excludes

1. Vessels, heat exchangers, condensers, pumps, compressors, expanders, scrubbers, and other equipment.
2. Vacuum piping systems which supply insulating vacuum to vacuum jackets of cryogenic piping systems.
3. Piping systems specifically covered by ANSI Codes B31.5 or B31.3 (wording of draft).

ANSI Code B31.11: Slurry Piping Systems

Includes

1. Initial coverage will be coal transported in water.
2. Future coverages will include slurries of other solids transported in nonhazardous liquids.

---

* (To be included in future ANSI Code B31.3)

† (as per latest draft.)

2

Coefficients of Thermal Expansion

This chapter contains tables of the coefficients of thermal expansion (Table 2-1) and other tables relating to the physical properties of piping materials (Tables 2-2 through 2-4).

Table 2-1
Coefficients of Thermal Expansion
(in./100 ft)

Temp. (F)	Carbon Steel Carbon-moly Low-chrome (Thru 3 Cr Mo)	5 CR MO Thru 9 Cr Mo	Austenitic Stainless Steels 18 Cr 8 Ni	12 Cr 17 Cr 27 Cr	25 Cr 20 Ni	Monel 67 Ni 30 Cu	$3^1/_2$ Nickel
-325	-2.370	-2.220	-3.85	-2.040		-2.620	-2.250
-320	-2.344	-2.196	-3.806	-2.016		-2.596	-2.234
-315	-2.318	-2.172	-3.762	-1.992		-2.572	-2.218
-310	-2.292	-2.148	-3.718	-1.968		-2.548	-2.202
-305	-2.266	-2.124	-3.674	-1.944		-2.524	-2.186
-300	-2.240	-2.100	-3.630	-1.920		-2.500	-2.170
-295	-2.214	-2.076	-3.586	-1.896		-2.476	-2.150
-290	2.118	-2.052	-3.542	-1.872		-2.452	-2.130
-285	2.162	-2.028	-3.498	-1.848		-2.428	-2.110
-280	2.136	-2.004	-3.454	-1.824		-2.404	-2.090
-275	-2.110	-1.980	-3.410	-1.80		-2.380	-2.070
-270	-2.084	-1.956	-3.366	-1.776		-2.356	-2.048
-265	-2.058	-1.932	-3.322	-1.752		-2.332	-2.026
-260	-2.032	-1.908	-3.278	-1.728		-2.308	-2.004
-255	-2.006	-1.884	-3.234	-1.704		-2.284	-1.982
-250	-1.980	-1.860	-3.19	-1.68		-2.260	-1.960
-245	-1.954	-1.836	-3.146	-1.658		-2.236	-1.940
-240	-1.928	-1.812	-3.102	-1.636		-2.212	-1.920
-235	-1.902	-1.788	-3.058	-1.614		-2.188	-1.900
-230	-1.876	-1.764	-3.014	-1.592		-2.164	-1.880
-225	-1.850	-1.740	-2.960	-1.570		-2.140	-1.860
-220	-1.822	-1.716	-2.914	-1.548		-2.116	-1.840
-215	-1.794	-1.692	-2.870	-1.526		-2.092	-1.820
-210	-1.766	-1.668	-2.824	-1.504		-2.068	-1.800
-205	-1.738	-1.644	-2.778	-1.482		-2.044	-1.780
-200	-1.710	-1.620	-2.730	-1.46		-2.020	-1.760
-195	-1.689	-1.596	-2.685	-1.438		-1.996	-1.732
-190	-1.658	-1.572	-2.640	-1.416		-1.972	-1.704
-185	-1.632	-1.548	-2.595	-1.394		-1.948	-1.676
-180	-1.606	-1.524	-2.550	-1.372		-1.924	-1.648
-175	-1.580	-1.50	-2.500	-1.350		-1.90	-1.620
-170	-1.554	-1.474	-2.454	-1.328		-1.878	-1.592
-165	-1.528	-1.448	-2.408	-1.306		-1.856	-1.564
-160	-1.500	-1.422	-2.362	-1.284		-1.834	-1.536
-155	-1.474	-1.396	-2.316	-1.262		-1.812	-1.508
-150	-1.450	-1.370	-2.27	-1.240		-1.790	-1.480
-145	-1.420	-1.342	-2.218	-1.214		-1.750	-1.450
-140	-1.390	-1.314	-2.166	-1.188		-1.710	-1.420
-135	-1.360	-1.286	-2.114	-1.162		-1.670	-1.390
-130	-1.330	-1.258	-2.062	-1.136		-1.630	-1.360
-125	-1.300	-1.230	-2.01	-1.110		-1.590	-1.330
-120	-1.270	-1.200	-1.958	-1.084		-1.548	-1.298
-115	-1.240	-1.170	-1.906	-1.058		-1.506	-1.266
-110	-1.210	-1.140	-1.854	-1.032		-1.464	-1.234
-105	-1.180	-1.110	-1.802	-1.006		-1.422	-1.202
-100	-1.150	-1.080	-1.75	-0.98		-1.380	-1.170
- 95	-1.120	-1.052	-1.700	-0.954		-1.34	-1.138
- 90	-1.090	-1.024	-1.650	-0.928		-1.30	-1.106
- 85	-1.060	- .996	-1.600	-0.902		-1.26	-1.074
- 80	-1.030	- .968	-1.550	-0.876		-1.22	-1.042

Table 2-1
Continued

Temp. (F)	Carbon Steel Carbon-moly Low-chrome (Thru 3 Cr Mo)	5 CR MO Thru 9 Cr Mo	Austenitic Stainless Steels 18 Cr 8 Ni	12 Cr 17 Cr 27 Cr	25 Cr 20 Ni	Monel 67 Ni 30 Cu	3½ Nickel
- 75	-1.000	-0.940	-1.500	-0.85		-1.18	-1.010
- 70	-0.97	-0.910	-1.448	-0.824		-1.14	- .976
- 65	-0.94	-0.880	-1.396	-0.798		-1.10	- .942
- 60	-0.91	-0.850	-1.344	-0.772		-1.06	- .908
- 55	-0.88	-0.820	-1.292	-0.746		-1.02	- .874
- 50	-0.84	-0.790	-1.240	-0.72		-0.98	-0.840
- 45	-0.808	-0.758	-1.188	-0.690		-0.938	-0.806
- 40	-0.776	-0.726	-1.136	-0.630		-0.896	-0.772
- 35	-0.744	-0.694	-1.084	-0.600		-0.812	-0.704
- 30	-0.712	-0.662	-1.032				
- 25	-0.680	-0.630	-0.980	-0.57		-0.77	-0.670
- 20	-0.642	-.0596	-0.928	-0.54		-0.73	-0.636
- 15	-0.604	-0.562	-0.876	-0.51		-0.69	-0.602
- 10	-0.566	-0.528	-0.824	-0.48		-0.65	-0.568
- 5	-0.528	-0.494	-0.772	-0.45		-0.61	-0.534
- 0	-0.49	-0.460	-0.720	-0.42		-0.57	-0.50
5	-0.456	-0.428	-0.668	-0.39		-0.53	-0.464
10	-0.422	-0.396	-0.616	-0.36		-0.49	-0.428
15	-0.388	-0.364	-0.564	-0.33		-0.45	-0.392
20	-0.354	-0.332	-0.512	-0.30		-0.41	-0.356
25	-0.320	-0.300	-0.460	-0.27		-0.370	-0.320
30	-0.284	-0.266	-0.410	-0.24		-0.336	-0.286
35	-0.248	-0.232	-0.360	-0.21		-0.302	-0.252
40	-0.212	-0.198	-0.310	-0.18		-0.268	-0.218
45	-0.176	-0.164	-0.260	-0.15		-0.234	-0.184
50	-0.140	-0.13	-0.210	-0.12		-0.200	-0.15
55	-0.105	-0.098	-0.158	-0.09		-0.150	-0.113
60	-0.070	-0.066	-0.106	-0.06		-0.100	-0.076
65	-0.035	-0.034	-0.054	-0.03		-0.050	-0.038
70	0	0	0	0	0	0	0
75	0.038	0.037	0.056	0.033	0.053	0.047	0.038
80	0.076	0.074	0.112	0.066	0.106	0.094	0.076
85	0.114	0.111	0.168	0.099	0.159	0.140	0.114
90	0.152	0.148	0.225	0.137	0.212	0.186	0.152
95	0.190	0.185	0.282	0.166	0.265	0.233	0.190
100	0.230	0.22	0.340	0.200	0.320	0.28	0.23
105	0.268	0.258	0.396	0.232	0.372	0.328	0.268
110	0.306	0.294	0.452	0.264	0.424	0.376	0.306
115	0.344	0.332	0.508	0.296	0.476	0.424	0.344
120	0.382	0.370	0.564	0.328	0.528	0.472	0.382
125	0.420	0.40	0.620	0.360	0.58	0.52	0.42
130	0.458	0.436	0.876	0.394	0.632	0.568	0.458
135	0.496	0.472	0.732	0.428	0.684	0.616	0.496
140	0.534	0.508	0.788	0.462	0.736	0.664	0.534
145	0.572	0.544	0.844	0.496	0.783	0.712	0.572
150	0.610	0.580	0.90	0.530	0.84	0.75	0.61
155	0.648	0.616	0.956	0.562	0.892	0.798	0.648
160	0.686	0.652	1.012	0.594	0.944	0.846	0.686
165	0.724	0.688	1.068	0.626	0.996	0.894	0.724
170	0.762	0.724	1.124	0.658	1.048	0.942	0.762

Table 2-1
Continued

Temp. (F)	Carbon Steel Carbon-moly Low-chrome (Thru 3 Cr Mo)	5 CR MO Thru 9 Cr Mo	Austenitic Stainless Steels 18 Cr 8 Ni	12 Cr 17 Cr 27 Cr	25 Cr 20 Ni	Monel 67 Ni 30 Cu	3½ Nickel
175	0.80	0.76	1.180	0.69	1.10	0.99	0.81
180	0.838	0.796	1.236	0.724	1.152	1.038	0.85
185	0.876	0.832	1.292	0.758	1.204	1.086	0.89
190	0.914	0.868	1.348	0.792	1.256	1.134	0.93
195	0.952	0.904	1.404	0.826	1.308	1.182	0.97
200	0.990	.940	1.46	0.86	1.37	1.22	1.01
205	1.034	.978	1.518	0.894	1.424	1.268	1.05
210	1.078	1.016	1.576	0.928	1.478	1.316	1.09
215	1.122	1.054	1.634	0.962	1.532	1.364	1.13
220	1.166	1.092	1.692	0.996	1.586	1.412	1.17
225	1.210	1.130	1.750	1.03	1.64	1.460	1.210
230	1.248	1.170	1.806	1.066	1.694	1.508	1.252
235	1.286	1.210	1.862	1.102	1.748	1.556	1.294
240	1.324	1.250	1.918	1.138	1.802	1.604	1.336
245	1.362	1.290	1.974	1.174	1.866	1.652	1.378
250	1.400	1.330	2.030	1.210	1.910	1.710	1.420
255	1.442	1.368	2.088	1.244	1.964	1.760	1.462
260	1.484	1.406	2.146	1.278	2.018	1.810	1.504
265	1.526	1.444	2.204	1.312	2.072	1.860	1.546
270	1.568	1.482	2.262	1.346	2.126	1.910	1.588
275	1.610	1.520	2.320	1.380	2.180	1.960	1.630
280	1.652	1.558	2.378	1.416	2.234	2.010	1.672
285	1.694	1.596	2.436	1.454	2.288	2.060	1.714
290	1.736	1.634	2.444	1.490	2.342	2.110	1.756
295	1.778	1.672	2.552	1.526	2.396	2.160	1.798
300	1.82	1.710	2.610	1.56	2.450	2.210	1.84
305	1.864	1.748	2.668	1.596	2.504	2.256	1.882
310	1.908	1.786	2.726	1.632	2.558	2.302	1.924
315	1.952	1.824	2.784	1.668	2.612	2.348	1.966
320	1.996	1.862	2.842	1.704	2.666	2.394	
325	2.040	1.900	2.900	1.74	2.72	2.44	2.050
330	2.084	1.940	2.960	1.778	2.774	2.488	2.092
335	2.128	1.980	3.020	1.816	2.828	2.532	2.134
340	2.172	2.020	3.080	1.854	2.882	2.576	2.176
345	2.216	2.060	3.140	1.892	2.936	2.620	2.218
350	2.26	2.100	3.200	1.93	2.99	2.680	2.26
355	2.304	2.140	3.260	1.966	3.044	2.728	2.302
360	2.348	2.180	3.320	2.002	3.098	2.776	2.344
365	2.392	2.220	3.380	2.038	3.152	2.824	2.386
370	2.436	2.260	3.440	2.074	3.206	2.872	2.428
375	2.480	2.30	3.500	2.11	3.26	2.910	2.470
380	2.524	2.340	3.560	2.148	3.314	2.978	2.512
385	2.568	2.380	3.620	2.186	3.368	3.046	2.554
390	2.612	2.420	3.680	2.224	3.422	3.084	2.596
395	2.656	2.460	3.740	2.262	3.476	3.152	2.638
400	2.700	2.500	3.800	2.30	3.530	3.250	2.690
405	2.746	2.544	3.860	2.340	3.584	3.304	2.732
410	2.792	2.588	3.920	2.380	3.638	3.358	2.774
415	2.838	2.632	3.980	2.420	3.692	3.412	2.816
420	2.884	2.676	4.040	2.940	3.746	3.466	2.858

Table 2-1
Continued

Temp. (F)	Carbon Steel Carbon-moly Low-chrome (Thru 3 Cr Mo)	5 CR MO Thru 9 Cr Mo	Austenitic Stainless Steels 18 Cr 8 Ni	12 Cr 17 Cr 27 Cr	25 Cr 20 Ni	Monel 67 Ni 30 Cu	3½ Nickel
425	2.930	2.72	4.100	2.500	3.800	3.520	2.910
430	2.976	2.762	4.162	2.538	3.854	3.574	2.954
435	3.022	2.804	4.224	2.576	3.908	3.628	2.998
440	3.068	2.846	4.286	2.614	3.962	3.682	3.042
445	3.114	2.888	4.348	2.652	4.016	3.736	3.086
450	3.160	2.930	4.410	2.690	4.070	3.790	3.130
455	3.206	2.972	4.470	2.730	4.124	3.844	3.174
460	3.252	3.014	4.530	2.770	4.178	3.898	3.218
465	3.298	3.056	4.590	2.810	4.232	3.952	3.262
470	3.344	3.098	4.650	2.850	4.286	4.006	3.306
475	3.390	3.140	4.710	2.890	4.340	4.060	3.350
480	3.436	3.182	4.770	2.928	4.394	4.114	3.396
485	3.482	3.224	4.830	2.966	4.448	4.168	3.442
490	3.528	3.266	4.860	3.004	4.502	4.222	3.988
495	3.574	3.308	4.920	3.042	4.556	4.276	3.534
500	3.620	3.350	5.010	3.080	4.610	4.330	3.580
505	3.668	3.396	5.010	3.120	4.664	4.386	3.626
510	3.716	3.442	5.130	3.160	4.718	4.442	3.672
515	3.764	3.488	5.190	3.200	4.772	4.498	3.718
520	3.812	3.534	5.250	3.240	4.826	4.554	3.764
525	3.860	3.580	5.310	3.280	4.880	4.610	3.810
530	3.910	3.524	5.372	3.322	4.934	4.668	3.856
535	3.960	3.668	5.434	3.364	4.988	4.726	3.902
540	4.010	3.712	5.496	3.406	5.042	4.784	3.948
545	4.060	3.756	5.558	3.448	5.096	4.842	3.994
550	4.110	3.800	5.620	3.490	5.150	4.900	4.040
555	4.158	3.844	5.682	3.530	5.204	4.958	4.086
560	4.206	3.888	5.744	3.570	5.258	5.016	4.132
565	4.254	3.932	5.806	3.610	5.312	5.074	4.178
570	4.302	3.976	5.868	3.650	5.366	5.132	4.224
575	4.350	4.020	5.930	3.690	5.420	5.180	4.270
580	4.400	4.064	5.992	3.732	5.474	5.236	4.316
585	4.450	4.108	6.058	3.774	5.528	5.292	4.362
590	4.500	4.152	6.120	3.816	5.582	5.348	4.408
595	4.550	4.196	6.182	3.858	5.636	5.404	4.454
600	4.600	4.240	6.240	3.900	5.690	5.460	4.500
605	4.652	4.286	6.302	3.940	5.144	5.518	4.458
610	4.704	4.332	6.364	3.980	5.798	5.576	4.596
615	4.756	4.378	6.426	4.020	5.852	5.634	4.644
620	4.808	4.424	6.488	4.060	5.906	5.692	4.692
625	4.860	4.470	6.550	4.100	5.960	5.750	4.740
630	4.910	4.514	6.614	4.142	6.014	5.810	4.788
635	4.960	4.558	6.678	4.184	6.068	5.870	4.836
640	5.010	4.602	6.742	4.226	6.122	5.930	4.884
645	5.060	4.646	6.806	4.268	6.176	5.990	4.932
650	5.110	4.690	6.370	4.310	6.230	6.050	4.980
655	5.162	4.736	6.932	4.352	6.284	6.108	5.028
660	5.214	4.782	6.995	4.394	6.338	6.166	5.076
665	5.266	4.828	7.057	4.436	6.392	6.224	5.124
670	5.318	4.374	7.119	4.478	6.446	6.282	5.172

Table 2-1
Continued

Temp. (F)	Carbon Steel Carbon-moly Low-chrome (Thru 3 Cr Mo)	5 CR MO Thru 9 Cr Mo	Austenitic Stainless Steels 18 Cr 8 Ni	12 Cr 17 Cr 27 Cr	25 Cr 20 Ni	Monel 67 Ni 30 Cu	3½ Nickel
675	5.370	4.920	7.180	4.520	6.500	6.340	5.220
680	5.422	4.964	7.244	4.562	6.554	6.400	5.268
685	5.474	5.008	7.308	4.604	6.608	6.460	5.316
690	4.536	5.052	7.372	4.646	6.662	6.520	5.364
695	4.588	5.096	7.436	4.688	6.716	6.580	5.412
700	5.630	5.140	7.500	4.730	6.770	6.640	5.460
705	5.684	5.188	7.564	4.776	6.824	6.700	5.508
710	5.738	5.236	7.628	4.814	6.878	6.760	5.556
715	5.792	5.284	7.692	4.856	6.932	6.820	5.604
720	5.846	5.332	7.756	4.898	6.986	6.880	5.652
725	5.900	5.380	7.820	4.940	7.040	6.940	5.700
730	5.952	5.428	7.886	4.984	7.094	7.002	5.748
735	6.004	5.476	7.952	5.028	7.148	7.064	5.796
740	6.056	5.524	8.018	5.072	7.702	7.126	5.844
745	6.108	5.572	8.084	5.116	7.256	7.188	5.892
750	6.160	5.620	8.150	5.160	7.310	7.250	5.940
755	6.214	5.668	8.214	5.204	7.364	7.310	5.988
760	6.268	5.716	8.278	5.248	7.418	7.370	6.036
765	6.322	5.764	8.342	5.292	7.472	7.430	6.084
770	6.376	5.812	8.406	5.336	7.526	7.490	6.132
775	6.430	5.860	8.470	5.380	7.580	7.550	6.180
780	6.484	5.908	8.536	5.424	7.634	7.610	6.230
785	6.533	5.956	8.602	5.468	7.688	7.670	6.280
790	6.592	6.004	8.668	5.512	7.742	7.730	6.330
795	6.646	6.052	8.734	5.556	7.796	7.790	6.380
800	6.700	6.100	8.80	5.600	7.850	7.850	6.430
805	6.754	6.148	8.866	5.644	7.910	7.912	6.480
810	6.808	6.196	8.932	5.688	7.970	7.974	6.530
815	6.862	6.244	8.998	5.732	8.030	8.036	6.580
820	6.916	6.292	9.064	5.776	8.090	8.098	6.630
825	6.970	6.340	9.130	5.820	8.150	8.160	6.680
830	7.026	6.390	9.196	5.866	8.210	8.224	6.730
835	7.082	6.440	9.262	5.912	8.270	8.288	6.780
840	7.138	6.490	9.328	5.958	8.330	8.352	6.830
845	7.194	6.590	9.394	6.004	8.390	8.416	6.850
850	7.250	6.590	9.460	6.050	8.450	8.480	6.930
855	7.306	6.638	9.526	6.094	8.510	8.544	6.980
860	7.362	6.686	9.542	6.138	8.570	8.608	7.030
865	7.413	6.734	9.658	6.182	8.630	8.672	7.080
870	7.474	6.782	9.724	6.226	8.690	8.736	7.130
875	7.530	6.830	9.790	6.270	8.750	8.800	7.180
880	7.586	6.878	9.856	6.314	8.810	8.864	7.230
885	7.642	6.926	9.922	6.358	8.870	8.928	7.280
890	7.698	6.974	9.988	6.402	8.930	8.992	7.330
895	7.754	7.022	10.054	6.446	8.990	9.056	7.380
900	7.810	7.070	10.120	6.490	9.050	9.120	7.430
905	7.866	7.118	10.188	6.534	9.110	9.184	7.480
910	7.922	7.166	10.256	6.578	9.170	9.248	7.530
915	7.978	7.214	10.324	6.622	9.230	9.312	7.580
920	8.034	7.762	10.392	6.666	9.290	9.376	7.630

Table 2-1 Continued

Temp. (F)	Carbon Steel Carbon-moly Low-chrome (Thru 3 Cr Mo)	5 CR MO Thru 9 Cr Mo	Austenitic Stainless Steels 18 Cr 8 Ni	12 Cr 17 Cr 27 Cr	25 Cr 20 Ni	Monel 67 Ni 30 Cu	3½ Nickel
925	8.080	7.310	10.460	6.710	9.350	9.440	7.680
930	8.134	7.360	10.528	6.756	9.410	9.506	7.730
935	8.188	7.410	10.596	6.802	9.470	9.572	7.780
940	8.242	7.460	10.664	6.848	9.530	9.638	7.830
945	8.296	7.510	10.732	6.894	9.590	9.704	7.880
950	8.350	7.560	10.800	6.940	9.650	9.770	7.930
955	8.404	7.610	10.868	6.986	9.710	9.834	7.978
960	8.458	7.660	10.936	7.032	9.770	9.898	8.026
965	8.512	7.710	11.004	7.078	9.830	9.962	8.074
970	8.566	7.760	11.072	7.124	9.890	10.026	8.122
975	8.620	7.810	11.140	7.170	9.950	10.090	8.170
980	8.674	7.860	11.208	7.216	10.010	10.156	8.218
985	8.728	7.910	11.276	7.262	10.070	10.222	8.266
990	8.782	7.960	11.344	7.308	10.130	10.288	8.314
995	8.836	8.010	11.412	7.354	10.190	10.354	8.362
1000	8.890	8.060	11.480	7.400	10.250	10.420	8.410
1005	8.946	8.110	11.548	7.444	10.310	10.486	
1010	9.002	8.160	11.616	7.488	10.370	10.552	
1015	9.058	8.210	11.684	7.532	10.430	10.618	
1020	9.114	8.260	11.752	7.576	10.490	10.686	
1025	9.170	8.300	11.820	7.620	10.550	10.750	
1030	9.228	8.350	11.888	7.686	10.610	10.818	
1035	9.286	8.400	11.956	7.752	10.670	10.886	
1040	9.344	8.450	12.024	7.818	10.730	10.959	
1045	9.402	8.500	12.094	7.884	10.790	11.022	
1050	9.460	8.550	12.160	7.950	10.850	11.090	
1055	9.518	8.600	12.228	7.996	10.910	11.158	
1060	9.576	8.650	12.296	8.042	10.970	11.226	
1065	9.634	8.700	12.364	8.088	11.030	11.294	
1070	9.692	8.750	12.432	8.134	11.090	11.362	
1075	9.750	8.800	12.500	8.180	11.150	11.430	
1080	9.808	8.850	12.568	8.206	11.210	11.498	
1085	9.866	8.900	12.636	8.232	11.270	11.566	
1090	9.929	8.950	12.704	8.258	11.330	11.634	
1095	9.982	9.000	12.772	8.284	11.390	11.702	
1100	10.040	9.050	12.840	8.310	11.450	11.770	
1105	10.094	9.096	12.908	8.354	11.516	11.838	
1110	10.148	9.142	12.976	8.398	11.582	11.906	
1115	10.202	9.188	13.044	8.442	11.648	11.974	
1120	10.256	9.234	13.112	8.486	11.714	12.042	
1125	10.310	9.280	13.180	8.530	11.780	12.110	
1130	10.362	9.330	13.248	8.576	11.846	12.182	
1135	10.414	9.380	13.316	8.622	11.912	12.254	
1140	10.466	9.430	13.384	8.668	11.978	12.326	
1145	10.518	9.480	13.452	8.714	12.044	12.398	
1150	10.570	9.520	13.520	8.760	12.110	12.470	
1155	10.622	9.568	13.588	8.804	12.176	12.538	
1160	10.674	9.616	13.656	8.848	12.292	12.606	
1165	10.726	9.664	13.724	8.892	12.308	12.674	
1170	10.778	9.712	13.792	8.936	12.374	12.742	

Table 2-1
Continued

Temp. (F)	Carbon Steel Carbon-moly Low-chrome (Thru 3 Cr Mo)	5 CR MO Thru 9 Cr Mo	Austenitic Stainless Steels 18 Cr 8 Ni	12 Cr 17 Cr 27 Cr	25 Cr 20 Ni	Monel 67 Ni 30 Cu	3½ Nickel
1175	10.830	9.760	13.860	8.980	12.440	12.810	
1180	10.884	9.808	13.928	9.024	12.506	12.878	
1185	10.938	9.856	13.996	9.068	12.572	12.946	
1190	10.992	9.904	14.064	9.112	12.638	13.014	
1195	11.046	9.952	14.132	9.156	12.704	13.082	
1200	11.100	10.000	14.200	9.200	12.770	13.150	
1205	11.155	10.052	14.268	9.244	12.836	13.220	
1210	11.212	10.104	14.336	9.288	12.902	13.290	
1215	11.268	10.156	14.404	9.332	12.968	13.360	
1220	11.324	10.208	14.472	9.376	13.034	13.430	
1225	11.380	10.260	14.540	9.420	13.100	13.500	
1230	11.436	10 314	14.608	9.466	13.166	13.572	
1235	11.492	10.368	14.676	9.512	13.232	13.644	
1240	11.598	10.422	14.744	9.558	13.298	13.716	
1245	11.604	10.476	14.812	9.604	13.364	13.788	
1250	11.660	10.530	14.880	9.650	13.430	13.360	
1255	11.716	10.582	14.948	9.696	13.496	13.932	
1260	11.772	10.634	15.016	9.742	13.562	14.004	
1265	11.828	10.686	15.084	9.788	13.628	14.076	
1270	11.884	10.738	15.152	9.834	13.694	14.148	
1275	11.940	10.790	15.220	9.880	13.760	14.22	
1280	11.946	10.844	15.288	9.926	13.826	14.292	
1285	12.052	10.898	15.356	9.972	13.892	14.364	
1290	12.108	10.952	15.424	10.018	13.958	14.436	
1295	12.164	11.006	15.492	10.064	14.024	14.508	
1300	12.22	11.060	15.560	10.110	14.090	14.580	
1305	12.276	11.108	15.628	10.154	14.150	14.652	
1310	12.332	11.156	15.696	10.198	14.210	14.724	
1315	12.388	11.204	15.764	10.242	14.270	14.796	
1320	12.444	11.252	15.832	10.826	14.330	14.868	
1325	12.500	11.300	15.900	10.330	14.390	14.940	
1330	12.556	11.350	15.968	10.376	14.450	15.012	
1335	12.612	11.400	16.036	10.422	14.510	15.084	
1340	12.668	11.450	16.104	10.468	14.570	15.156	
1345	12.724	11.500	16.172	10.514	14.630	15.228	
1350	12.780	11.550	16.240	10.560	14.640	15.300	
1355	12.836	11.600	16.308	10.604	14.750	15.372	
1360	12.892	11.650	16.376	10.648	14.810	15.444	
1365	12.948	11.700	16.444	10.692	14.870	15.516	
1370	13.004	11.750	16.512	10.736	14.930	15.588	
1375	13.060	11.800	16.580	10.780	14.990	15.660	
1380	13.116	11.850	16.648	10.826	15.050	15.732	
1385	13.172	11.900	16.716	10.872	15.110	15.804	
1390	13.228	11.950	16.784	10.918	15.170	15.876	
1395	13.284	12.000	16.852	10.924	15.230	15.948	
1400	13.340	12.050	16.920	11.010	15.290	16.020	
1405			16.996				
1410			17.072				
1415			17.148				
1420			17.224				

Table 2-1
Continued

Temp. (F)	Carbon Steel Carbon-moly Low-chrome (Thru 3 Cr Mo)	5 CR MO Thru 9 Cr Mo	Austenitic Stainless Steels 18 Cr 8 Ni	12 Cr 17 Cr 27 Cr	25 Cr 20 Ni	Monel 67 Ni 30 Cu	3½ Nickel
1425			17.300				
1430			17.378				
1435			17.456				
1440			17.534				
1445			17.612				
1450			17.690				
1455			17.768				
1460			17.846				
1465			17.924				
1470			18.002				
1475			18.080				
1480			18.158				
1485			18.236				
1490			13.314				
1495			18.392				
1500			18.470				

Temp. (F)	Aluminum	Gray Cast Iron	Bronze	Brass	70 Cu 30 Ni	Ni-Fe-Cr	Ni-Cr-Fe	Ductile Iron
-325	-4.68		-3.98	-3.88	-3.15			
-320	-4.636		-3.932	-3.832	-3.094			
-315	-4.592		-3.884	-3.784	-3.038			
-310	-4.548		-3.836	-3.736	-2.982			
-305	-4.504		-3.788	-3.688	-2.926			
-300	-4.46		-3.74	-3.64	-2.87			
-295	-4.41		-3.692	-3.592	-2.836			
-290	-4.36		-3.644	-3.544	-2.802			
-285	-4.31		-3.596	-3.496	-2.768			
-280	-4.26		-3.548	-3.448	-2.734			
-275	-4.21		-3.5	-3.40	-2.70			
-270	-4.162		-3.452	-3.352	-2.666			
-265	-4.114		-3.404	-3.304	-2.632			
-260	-4.066		-3.356	-3.256	-2.598			
-255	-4.018		-3.308	-3.208	-2.564			
-250	-3.97		-3.26	-3.16	-2.53			
-245	-3.918		-3.212	-3.114	-2.496			
-240	-3.866		-3.164	-3.068	-2.462			
-235	-3.814		-3.116	-3.022	-2.428			
-230	-3.762		-3.068	-2.976	-2.394			
-225	-3.71		-3.02	-2.93	-2.36			
-220	-3.656		-2.972	-2.884	-2.326			
-215	-3.602		-2.924	-2.838	-2.292			
-210	-3.548		-2.876	-2.792	-2.258			
-205	-3.494		-2.828	-2.746	-2.224			

Table 2-1
Continued

Temp. (F)	Aluminum	Gray Cast Iron	Bronze	Brass	70 Cu 30 Ni	Ni-Fe-Cr	Ni-Cr-Fe	Ductile Iron
-200	-3.44		-2.78	-2.70	-2.19			-1.51
-195	-3.384		-2.732	-2.654	-2.176			-1.49
-190	-3.328		-2.684	-2.608	-2.162			-1.47
-185	-3.272		-2.636	-2.562	-2.148			-1.45
-180	-3.216		-2.588	-2.516	-2.134			-1.43
-175	-3.16		-2.54	-2.47	-2.12			-1.41
-170	-3.104		-2.494	-2.424	-2.086			-1.386
-165	-3.048		-2.448	-2.378	-2.052			-1.362
-160	-2.992		-2.402	-2.332	-2.018			-1.338
-155	-2.936		-2.356	-2.286	-1.984			-1.314
-150	-2.88		-2.31	-2.24	-1.95			-1.29
-145	-2.818		-2.26	-2.192	-1.908			-1.264
-140	-2.756		-2.21	-2.144	-1.866			-1.238
-135	-2.694		-2.16	-2.096	-1.824			-1.212
-130	-2.632		-2.11	-2.048	-1.782			-1.186
-125	-2.57		-2.06	-2.00	-1.74			-1.16
-120	-2.51		-2.01	-1.952	-1.698			-1.136
-115	-2.45		-1.96	-1.904	-1.656			-1.112
-110	-2.39		-1.91	-1.856	-1.614			-1.088
-105	-2.33		-1.86	-1.808	-1.572			-1.064
-100	-2.27		-1.81	-1.76	-1.53			-1.04
- 95	-2.21		-1.76	-1.712	-1.49			-1.014
- 90	-2.15		-1.71	-1.664	-1.45			-.988
- 85	-2.09		-1.66	-1.616	-1.41			-.962
- 80	-2.03		-1.61	-1.568	-1.37			-.936
- 75	-1.97		-1.56	-1.52	-1.33			-.91
- 70	-1.91		-1.512	-1.474	-1.29			-.882
- 65	-1.85		-1.464	-1.428	-1.25			-.854
- 60	-1.79		-1.416	-1.382	-1.21			-.826
- 55	-1.73		-1.368	-1.336	-1.17			-.798
- 50	-1.67		-1.32	-1.29	-1.13			-.77
- 45	-1.6		-1.306	-1.236	-1.082			-.74
- 40	-1.53		-1.292	-1.182	-1.034			-.71
- 35	-1.46		-1.278	-1.128	-0.986			-.68
- 30	-1.39		-1.264	-1.074	-0.938			-.65
- 25	-1.32		-1.25	-1.02	- .89			-.62
- 20	-1.25		-1.154	- .996	- .844			-.588
- 15	-1.18		-1.058	- .912	- .798			-.556
- 10	-1.11		- .962	- .858	- .752			-.524
- 5	-1.04		-0.866	- .804	- .706			-4.92
0	- .97		- .77	- .75	- .66			-.46
5	- .902		- .714	- .696	- .612			-.414
10	- .834		- .658	- .642	- .564			-.368
15	- .766		- .602	- .588	- .516			-.322
20	- .698		- .546	- .534	- .468			-.276
25	- .63		- .49	- .48	- .42			-.23
30	- .56		- .436	- .426	- .374			-.212
35	- .49		- .382	- .372	- .328			-.194
40	- .42		- .328	- .318	- .282			-.176
45	- .35		- .274	- .264	- .236			-.158

Table 2-1
Continued

Temp. (F)	Aluminum	Gray Cast Iron	Bronze	Brass	70 Cu 30 Ni	Ni-Fe-Cr	Ni-Cr-Fe	Ductile Iron
50	- .28		- .22	- .21				- .14
55	- .21		- .165	- .1575				- .105
60	- .14		- .11	- .105				- .07
65	- .07		- .055	- .525				- .035
70	0	0	0	0				0
75	.076	.035	.06	.0583	.0516	.0466	.0433	.035
80	.153	.07	.12	.1166	.1033	.0933	.0866	.07
85	.23	.105	.18	.175	.155	.14	.13	.105
90	.3066	.14	.24	.233	.206	.1866	.173	.14
95	.3833	.175	.3	.291	.258	.233	.216	.175
100	.46	.21	.36	.35	.31	.28	.26	.21
105	.538	.244	.42	.408	.36	.328	.304	.246
110	.616	.278	.48	.466	.41	.376	.348	.282
115	.694	.312	.54	.524	.46	.424	.392	.318
120	.772	.346	.6	.582	.51	.472	.436	.354
125	.85	.38	.66	.64	.56	.52	.48	.39
130	.926	.414	.72	.7	.612	.568	.524	.426
135	1.002	.448	.78	.76	.664	.616	.568	.462
140	1.078	.482	.84	.82	.716	.664	.612	.498
145	1.154	.516	.9	.88	.768	.712	.666	.534
150	1.23	.55	.96	.94	.82	.76	.7	.57
155	1.308	.586	1.02	.998	.87	.806	.744	.608
160	1.386	.622	1.08	1.056	.92	.852	.788	.646
165	1.464	.658	1.14	1.114	.97	.898	.832	.684
170	1.542	.694	1.2	1.172	1.02	.944	.876	.722
175	1.62	.73	1.26	1.23	1.07	.99	.92	.75
180	1.698	.764	1.32	1.288	1.122	1.038	.966	.788
185	1.776	.798	1.38	1.346	1.174	1.086	1.012	.826
190	1.854	.832	1.44	1.404	1.226	1.134	1.058	.864
195	1.932	.866	1.5	1.462	1.278	1.182	1.104	.902
200	2.00	.9	1.56	1.52	1.33	1.23	1.15	.94
205	2.082	.936	1.62	1.582	1.382	1.282	1.196	.976
210	2.164	.972	1.68	1.644	1.434	1.334	1.242	1.012
215	2.246	1.008	1.74	1.706	1.486	1.386	1.288	1.048
220	2.328	1.044	1.8	1.768	1.538	1.438	1.334	1.084
225	2.41	1.08	1.86	1.83	1.59	1.49	1.38	1.13
230	2.494	1.118	1.922	1.892	1.644	1.544	1.426	1.17
235	2.578	1.156	1.984	1.954	1.698	1.598	1.472	1.21
240	2.662	1.194	2.046	2.016	1.752	1.652	1.518	1.25
245	2.746	1.232	2.108	2.078	1.806	1.706	1.564	1.29
250	2.83	1.27	2.17	2.14	1.86	1.76	1.61	1.33
255	2.912	1.306	2.232	2.202	1.914	1.814	1.658	1.37
260	2.994	1.342	2.294	2.264	1.968	1.868	1.706	1.41
265	3.076	1.378	2.356	2.326	2.022	1.922	1.754	1.45
270	3.158	1.414	2.418	2.388	2.076	1.976	1.802	1.49
275	3.24	1.45	2.48	2.45	2.13	2.03	1.85	1.53
280	3.326	1.488	2.542	2.512	2.184	2.084	1.898	1.568
285	3.412	1.526	2.604	2.574	2.238	2.138	1.946	1.606
290	3.498	1.564	2.666	2.636	2.292	2.192	1.994	1.644
295	3.584	1.602	2.728	2.698	2.346	2.246	2.042	1.682

Table 2-1
Continued

Temp. (F)	Aluminum	Gray Cast Iron	Bronze	Brass	70 Cu 30 Ni	Ni-Fe-Cr	Ni-Cr-Fe	Ductile Iron
300	3.67	1.64	2.79	2.76	2.40	2.30	2.09	1.72
305	3.754	1.678	2.854	2.824	2.456	2.358	2.136	1.762
310	3.838	1.716	2.918	2.888	2.512	2.416	2.182	1.804
315	3.922	1.754	2.982	2.952	2.568	2.474	2.228	1.846
320	4.006	1.792	2.046	3.016	2.624	2.532	2.274	1.888
325	4.09	1.83	3.11	3.08	2.68	2.59	2.32	1.93
330	4.176	1.87	3.172	3.146	2.736	2.648	2.368	1.97
335	4.262	1.91	3.234	3.212	2.792	2.706	2.416	2.01
340	4.348	1.95	3.296	3.278	2.848	2.764	2.464	2.05
345	4.434	1.99	3.358	3.344	2.904	2.822	2.512	2.09
350	4.52	2.03	3.42	3.41	2.96	2.88	2.56	2.13
355	4.606	2.068	3.484	3.474	3.016	2.94	2.608	2.176
360	4.692	2.106	3.548	3.538	3.072	3.00	2.656	2.222
365	4.778	2.144	3.612	3.602	3.128	3.06	2.704	2.268
370	4.864	2.182	3.676	3.666	3.184	3.12	2.752	2.314
375	4.95	2.22	3.74	3.73	3.24	3.18	2.80	2.36
380	5.038	2.26	3.802	3.794	3.296	3.24	2.85	2.4
385	5.126	2.3	3.864	3.858	3.352	3.30	2.9	2.44
390	5.214	2.34	3.926	3.922	3.408	3.36	2.95	2.48
395	5.302	2.38	3.988	3.986	3.464	3.42	3.0	2.52
400	5.39	2.42	4.05	4.05	3.52	3.48	3.05	2.56
405	5.478	2.46	4.114	4.116		3.536	3.098	2.606
410	5.566	2.5	4.178	4.182		3.592	3.146	2.652
415	5.654	2.54	4.242	4.248		3.648	3.194	2.698
420	5.742	2.58	4.306	4.314		3.704	3.242	2.744
425	5.83	2.62	4.37	4.38		3.76	3.29	2.79
430	5.92	2.662	4.434	4.448		3.816	3.338	2.836
435	6.01	2.704	4.498	4.516		3.872	3.386	2.882
440	6.1	2.746	4.562	4.584		3,928	3.434	2.928
445	6.19	2.788	4.626	4.652		3.984	3.482	2.974
450	6.28	2.83	4.69	4.72		4.04	3.53	3.04
455	6.368	2.87	4.754	4.788		4.094	3.58	3.088
460	6.456	2.91	4.818	4.856		4.148	3.63	3.136
465	6.544	2.95	4.882	4.924		4.202	3.68	3.184
470	6.632	2.99	4.946	4.992		4.256	3.73	3.232
475	6.72	3.03	5.01	5.06		4.31	3.78	3.28
480	6.81	3.072	5.074	5.128		4.366	3.828	3.332
485	6.9	3.114	5.138	5.196		4.422	3.876	3.384
490	6.99	3.156	5.202	5.264		4.472	3.924	3.436
495	7.08	3.198	5.266	5.332		4.534	3.972	3.488
500	7.17	3.24	5.33	5.40		4.59	4.02	3.54
505	7.262	3.284	5.394	5.47		4.646	4.07	3.584
510	7.354	3.328	5.458	5.54		4.702	4.12	3.628
515	7.446	3.372	5.522	5.61		4.758	4.17	3.672
520	7.538	3.416	5.586	5.68		4.814	4.22	3.716
525	7.63	3.46	5.65	5.75		4.87	4.27	3.76
530	7.724	3.502	5.716	5.82		4.928	4.32	3.806
535	7.818	3.544	5.782	5.89		4.986	4.37	3.852
540	7.912	3.586	5.848	5.96		5.044	4.42	3.898
545	8.006	3.628	5.914	6.03		5.102	4.47	3.944

Table 2-1
Continued

Temp. (F)	Aluminum	Gray Cast Iron	Bronze	Brass	70 Cu 30 Ni	Ni-Fe-Cr	Ni-Cr-Fe	Ductile Iron
550	8.1	3.67	5.98	6.10		5.16	4.52	3.99
555	8.192	3.714	6.046	6.17		5.218	4.57	4.036
560	8.284	3.758	6.112	6.24		5.276	4.62	4.082
565	8.376	3.802	6.178	6.31		5.334	4.67	4.128
570	8.468	3.846	6.244	6.38		5.392	4.72	4.174
575	8.56	3.89	6.31	6.45		5.45	4.77	4.22
580	8.654	3.934	6.376	6.52		5.496	4.82	4.264
585	8.748	3.978	6.442	6.59		5.552	4.87	4.308
590	8.842	4.022	6.508	6.66		5.608	4.92	4.352
595	8.936	4.066	6.574	6.73		5.664	4.97	3.396
600	9.03	4.11	6.64	6.80		5.72	5.02	4.44
605		4.156	6.704	6.872		5.778	5.07	4.484
610		4.202	6.768	6.944		5.836	5.12	4.528
615		4.428	6.832	7.016		5.894	5.17	4.572
620		4.294	6.896	7.088		5.952	5.22	4.616
625		4.34	6.96	7.16		6.01	5.27	4.66
630		4.386	7.026	7.234		6.068	5.322	4.708
635		4.432	7.092	7.308		6.126	5.374	4.756
640		4.478	7.158	7.382		6.184	5.426	4.804
645		4.524	7.224	7.456		6.242	5.478	4.852
650		4.57	7.29	7.53		6.30	5.53	4.9
655		4.616	7.356	7.602		6.356	5.582	4.948
660		4.662	7.422	7.674		6.412	5.634	4.996
665		4.708	7.488	7.746		6.468	5.686	5.044
670		4.754	7.554	7.818		6.524	5.738	5.092
675		4.8	7.62	7.89		6.58	5.79	5.14
680		4.846	7.686	7.964		6.64	5.842	5.19
685		4.892	7.752	8.038		6.70	5.894	5.24
690		4.938	7.818	8.112		6.76	5.946	5.29
695		4.984	7.884	8.186		6.82	5.998	5.34
700		5.03	7.95	8.26		6.88	6.05	5.39
705		5.076	8.016	8.336		6.938	6.102	5.432
710		5.122	8.082	8.412		6.996	6.154	5.474
715		5.168	8.148	8.488		7.054	6.206	5.516
720		5.214	8.214	8.564		7.112	6.258	5.558
725		5.26	8.28	8.64		7.17	6.31	5.60
730		5.308	8.348	8.716		7.23	6.362	5.65
735		5.356	8.416	8.792		7.29	6.414	5.70
740		5.404	8.484	8.868		7.35	6.466	5.75
745		5.452	8.552	8.944		7.41	6.518	5.80
750		5.5	8.62	9.02		7.47	6.57	5.85
755		5.548	8.688	9.096		7.528	6.624	5.90
760		5.596	8.756	9.172		7.586	6.678	5.95
765		5.644	8.824	9.248		7.644	6.732	6.00
770		5.692	8.892	9.324		7.702	6.786	6.05
775		5.74	8.96	9.40		7.76	6.84	6.10
780		5.788	9.028	9.476		7.82	6.894	6.15
785		5.836	9.096	9.552		7.88	6.948	6.20
790		5.884	9.164	9.628		7.94	7.002	6.25
795		5.932	9.232	9.704		8.00	7.056	6.30

Table 2-1
Continued

Temp. (F)	Aluminum	Gray Cast Iron	Bronze	Brass	70 Cu 30 Ni	Ni-Fe-Cr	Ni-Cr-Fe	Ductile Iron
800		5.98	9.30	9.78		8.06	7.10	6.35
805		6.028	9.368	9.858		8.118		6.398
810		6.076	9.436	9.936		8.176		6.446
815		6.124	9.504	10.014		8.234		6.494
820		6.172	9.572	10.092		8.292		6.542
825		6.22	9.64	10.17		8.35		6.59
830		6.27	9.71	10.25		8.412		6.642
835		6.32	9.78	10.33		8.474		6.694
840		6.37	9.85	10.41		8.536		6.746
845		6.42	9.92	10.49		8.598		6.798
850		6.47	9.99	10.57		8.66		6.85
855		6.52	10.06	10.648		8.722		6.898
860		6.57	10.13	10.726		8.784		6.946
865		6.62	10.2	10.804		8.846		6.994
870		6.67	10.27	10.882		8.908		7.042
875		6.72	10.33	10.96		8.95		7.09
880		6.77	10.4	11.038		9.012		7.138
885		6.82	10.47	11.116		9.074		7.186
890		6.87	10.54	11.194		9.136		7.234
895		6.92	10.61	11.272		9.198		7.282
900		6.97	10.68	11.35		9.26		7.35
905		7.022	10.748	11.43		9.32		7.408
910		7.074	10.816	11.51		9.38		7.466
915		7.216	10.884	11.59		9.44		7.524
920		7.178	10.952	11.67		9.5		7.582
925		7.23	11.02	11.75		9.56		7.64
930		7.284	11.09	11.832		9.622		7.684
935		7.338	11.16	11.914		9.684		7.728
940		7.392	11.23	11.996		9.746		7.772
945		7.446	11.3	12.078		9.808		7.816
950		7.5	11.37	12.16		9.87		7.86
955		7.552	11.438	12.242		9.932		7.91
960		7.604	11.506	12.324		9.994		7.96
965		7.656	11.574	12.402		10.056		8.01
970		7.708	11.642	12.488		10.118		8.06
975		7.76	11.71	12.57		10.18		8.11
980		7.812	11.778	12.652		10.242		8.158
985		7.864	11.846	12.734		10.304		8.206
990		7.916	11.914	12.816		10.366		8.254
995		7.968	11.982	12.898		10.428		8.302
1000		8.02	12.05	12.98		10.49		8.35
1005			12.12	13.062		10.552		
1010			12.19	13.144		10.614		
1015			12.26	13.226		10.676		
1020			12.33	13.308		10.738		
1025			12.4	13.39		10.80		
1030			12.472	13.474		10.862		
1035			12.544	13.558		10.924		
1040			12.616	13.642		10.986		
1045			16.688	13.726		11.048		

Table 2-1
Continued

Temp. (F)	Aluminum	Gray Cast Iron	Bronze	Brass	70 Cu 30 Ni	Ni-Fe-Cr	Ni-Cr-Fe	Ductile Iron
1050			12.76	13.81		11.11		
1055			12.83	13.894		11.172		
1060			12.90	13.978		11.234		
1065			12.97	14.062		11.296		
1070			13.04	14.146		11.358		
1075			13.11	14.23		11.42		
1080			13.182	14.314		11.484		
1085			13.254	14.398		11.548		
1090			13.32	14.482		11.612		
1095			13.39	14.566		11.676		
			13.47	14.65				
1100						11.74		
1105						11.802		
1110						11.864		
1115						11.926		
1120						11.988		
1125						12.05		
1130						12.116		
1135						12.182		
1140						12.248		
1145						12.314		
1150						12.38		
1155						12.442		
1160						12.504		
1165						12.566		
1170						12.628		
1175						12.69		
1180						12.756		
1185						12.822		
1190						12.888		
1195						12.954		
1200						13.02		
1205						13.088		
1210						13.156		
1215						13.224		
1220						13.292		
1225						13.36		
1230						13.43		
1235						13.5		
1240						13.57		
1245						13.64		
1250						13.71		
1255						13.776		
1260						13.842		
1265						13.908		
1270						13.974		
1275						14.04		
1280						14.11		
1285						14.18		
1290						14.25		
1295						14.32		

Table 2-1
Continued

Temp. (F)	Aluminum	Gray Cast Iron	Bronze	Brass	70 Cu 30 Ni	Ni-Fe-Cr	Ni-Cr-Fe	Ductile Iron
1300						14.39		
1305						14.46		
1310						14.53		
1315						14.60		
1320						14.67		
1325						14.74		
1330						14.812		
1335						14.884		
1340						14.956		
1345						15.028		
1350						15.10		
1355						15.168		
1360						15.236		
1365						15.304		
1370						15.372		
1375						15.44		
1380						15.512		
1385						15.584		
1390						15.656		
1395						15.278		
1400						15.80		
1405						15.872		
1410						15.944		
1415						15.016		
1420						16.088		
1425						16.16		
1430						16.234		
1435						16.308		
1440						16.382		
1445						16.456		
1450						16.53		
1455						16.60		
1460						16.67		
1465						16.74		
1470						16.81		
1475						76.88		
1480						16.954		
1485						17.028		
1490						17.102		
1495						17.176		
1500						17.25		

Table 2-2
Modulus of Elasticity-Ferrous Material

E = Modulus of Elasticity, psi (Multiply Tabulated Values by 10^6)
Temperature, °F

Material	−325	−200	−100	70	200	300	400	500	600	700	800	900	1000	1100	1200	1300	1400	1500
Carbon steels with carbon content 0.3% or less, 3½ NI	30.0	29.5	29.0	27.9	27.7	27.4	27.0	26.4	25.7	24.8	23.4	18.5	15.4	13.0				
Carbon steels with carbon content above 0.30%	31.0	30.6	30.4	29.9	29.5	29.0	28.3	27.4	26.7	25.4	23.8	21.5	18.8	15.0	11.2			
Carbon-moly steels, low chrome steels through 3 Cr Mo	31.0	30.6	30.4	29.9	29.5	29.0	28.6	28.0	27.4	26.6	25.7	24.5	23.0	20.4	15.6			
Intermediate chrome steels (5 Cr Mo through 9 Cr Mo)	29.4	28.5	28.1	27.4	27.1	26.8	26.4	26.0	25.4	24.9	24.2	23.5	22.8	21.9	20.8	19.5	18.1	
Austenitic steels (Tp304, 310, 316, 321, 347)	30.4	29.9	29.4	28.3	27.7	27.1	26.6	26.1	25.4	24.8	24.1	23.4	22.7	22.0	21.3	20.7	19.3	17.9
Straight chromium steels (12 Cr, 17 Cr, 27 Cr)	30.8	30.3	29.8	29.2	28.7	28.3	27.7	27.0	26.0	24.8	23.1	21.1	18.6	15.6	12.2			
Gray cast iron				13.4	13.2	12.9	12.6	12.2	11.7	11.0	10.2							

These data are for information, and it is not implied that materials are suitable for all the temperatures shown.

Table 2-3
Modulus of Elasticity-Nonferrous Materials

E = Modulus of Elasticity, psi (Multiply Tabulated Values by 10^6)
Temperature, °F

Material	−325	−200	−100	70	100	200	300	400	500	600	700	800	900	1000	1100	1200
Monel (67 Ni-30 Cu) and (66 Ni-29 Cu-Al)	26.8	26.6	26.4	26.0	26.0	26.0	25.8	25.6	25.4	24.7	2.31	21.0	18.6	16.0	14.3	13.0
Copper-Nickel (70 Cu-30 Ni)				21.6	21.5	21.2	20.9	20.6	20.3	20.0	19.7	19.4				
Aluminum alloys	11.3	10.9	10.6	10.1	10.0	9.8	9.5	8.7	7.7							
Copper (99.98% Cu)	17.0	16.7	16.5	16.0	15.8	15.6	15.4	15.1	14.7	14.2	13.7					
Commercial brass (66 Cu-34 Zn)	15.0	14.7	14.5	14.0	13.9	13.7	13.5	13.0	12.7	12.2	11.8					
Leaded tin bronze (88 Cu-6 Sn-1.5 Pb-4.5 Zn)	14.2	13.8	13.5	13.0	12.9	12.7	12.4	12.0	11.7	11.3	10.9					

These data are for information, and it is not implied that materials are suitable for all the temperatures shown.

Table 2-4
Properties of Saturated Steam

Absolute Pressure		Vacuum Inches of Hg	Temperature	Heat of the Liquid	Latent Heat of Evaporation	Total Heat of Steam	Specific Volume
Lbs. per Sq. In. P'	Inches of Hg		t Degrees F	Btu/lb.	Btu/lb.	h_g Btu/lb.	$\overline{V}$ Cu. ft. per lb.
0.20	0.41	29.51	53.14	21.21	1063.8	1085.0	1526.0
0.25	0.51	29.41	59.30	27.36	1060.3	1087.7	1235.3
0.30	0.61	29.31	64.47	32.52	1057.4	1090.0	1039.5
0.35	0.71	29.21	68.93	36.97	1054.9	1091.9	898.5
0.40	0.81	29.11	72.86	40.89	1052.7	1093.6	791.9
0.45	0.92	29.00	76.38	44.41	1050.7	1095.1	708.5
0.50	1.02	28.90	79.58	47.60	1048.8	1096.4	641.4
0.60	1.22	28.70	85.21	53.21	1045.7	1098.9	540.0
0.70	1.43	28.49	90.08	58.07	1042.9	1101.0	466.9
0.80	1.63	28.29	94.38	62.36	1040.4	1102.8	411.7
0.90	1.83	28.09	98.24	66.21	1038.3	1104.5	368.4
1.0	2.04	27.88	101.74	69.70	1036.3	1106.0	333.6
1.2	2.44	27.48	107.92	75.87	1032.7	1108.6	280.9
1.4	2.85	27.07	113.26	81.20	1029.6	1110.8	243.0
1.6	3.26	26.66	117.99	85.91	1026.9	1112.8	214.3
1.8	3.66	26.26	122.23	90.14	1024.5	1114.6	191.8
2.0	4.07	25.85	126.08	93.99	1022.2	1116.2	173.73
2.2	4.48	25.44	129.62	97.52	1020.2	1117.7	158.85
2.4	4.89	25.03	132.89	100.79	1018.3	1119.1	146.38
2.6	5.29	24.63	135.94	103.83	1016.5	1120.3	135.78
2.8	5.70	24.22	138.79	106.68	1014.8	1121.5	126.65
3.0	6.11	23.81	141.48	109.37	1013.2	1122.6	118.71
3.5	7.13	22.79	147.57	115.46	1009.6	1125.1	102.72
4.0	8.14	21.78	152.97	120.86	1006.4	1127.3	90.63
4.5	9.16	20.76	157.83	125.71	1003.6	1129.3	81.16
5.0	10.18	19.74	162.24	130.13	1001.0	1131.1	73.52
5.5	11.20	18.72	166.30	134.19	998.5	1132.7	67.24
6.0	12.22	17.70	170.06	137.96	996.2	1134.2	61.98
6.5	13.23	16.69	173.56	141.47	994.1	1135.6	57.50
7.0	14.25	15.67	176.85	144.76	992.1	1136.9	53.64
7.5	15.27	14.65	179.94	147.86	990.2	1138.1	50.29
8.0	16.29	13.63	182.86	150.79	988.5	1139.3	47.34
8.5	17.31	12.61	185.64	153.57	986.8	1140.4	44.73
9.0	18.32	11.60	188.28	156.22	985.2	1141.4	42.40
9.5	19.34	10.58	190.80	158.75	983.6	1142.3	40.31
10.0	20.36	9.56	193.21	161.17	982.1	1143.3	38.42
11.0	22.40	7.52	197.75	165.73	979.3	1145.0	35.14
12.0	24.43	5.49	201.96	169.96	976.6	1146.6	32.40
13.0	26.47	3.45	205.88	173.91	974.2	1148.1	30.06
14.0	28.50	1.42	209.56	177.61	971.9	1149.5	28.04

Pressure Lbs. per Sq. In.		Temperature	Heat of the Liquid	Latent Heat of Evaporation	Total Heat of Steam	Specific Volume
Absolute P'	Gage P	t Degrees F	Btu/lb.	Btu/lb.	h_g Btu/lb.	$\overline{V}$ Cu. ft. per lb.
14.696	0.0	212.00	180.07	970.3	1150.4	26.80
15.0	0.3	213.03	181.11	969.7	1150.8	26.29
16.0	1.3	216.32	184.42	967.6	1152.0	24.75
17.0	2.3	219.44	187.56	965.5	1153.1	23.39
18.0	3.3	222.41	190.56	963.6	1154.2	22.17
19.0	4.3	225.24	193.42	961.9	1155.3	21.08
20.0	5.3	227.96	196.16	960.1	1156.3	20.089
21.0	6.3	230.57	198.79	958.4	1157.2	19.192
22.0	7.3	233.07	201.33	956.8	1158.1	18.375
23.0	8.3	235.49	203.78	955.2	1159.0	17.627
24.0	9.3	237.82	206.14	953.7	1159.8	16.938
25.0	10.3	240.07	208.42	952.1	1160.6	16.303
26.0	11.3	242.25	210.62	950.7	1161.3	15.715
27.0	12.3	244.36	212.75	949.3	1162.0	15.170
28.0	13.3	246.41	214.83	947.9	1162.7	14.663
29.0	14.3	248.40	216.86	946.5	1163.4	14.189
30.0	15.3	250.33	218.82	945.3	1164.1	13.746
31.0	16.3	252.22	220.73	944.0	1164.7	13.330
32.0	17.3	254.05	222.59	942.8	1165.4	12.940
33.0	18.3	255.84	224.41	941.6	1166.0	12.572
34.0	19.3	257.58	226.18	940.3	1166.5	12.226
35.0	20.3	259.28	227.91	939.2	1167.1	11.898
36.0	21.3	260.95	229.60	938.0	1167.6	11.588
37.0	22.3	262.57	231.26	936.9	1168.2	11.294
38.0	23.3	264.16	232.89	935.8	1168.7	11.015
39.0	24.3	265.72	234.48	934.7	1169.2	10.750
40.0	25.3	267.25	236.03	933.7	1169.7	10.498
41.0	26.3	268.74	237.55	932.6	1170.2	10.258
42.0	27.3	270.21	239.04	931.6	1170.7	10.029
43.0	28.3	271.64	240.51	930.6	1171.1	9.810
44.0	29.3	273.05	241.95	929.6	1171.6	9.601
45.0	30.3	274.44	243.36	928.6	1172.0	9.401
46.0	31.3	275.80	244.75	927.7	1172.4	9.209
47.0	32.3	277.13	246.12	926.7	1172.9	9.025
48.0	33.3	278.45	247.47	925.8	1173.3	8.848
49.0	34.3	279.74	248.79	924.9	1173.7	8.678
50.0	35.3	281.01	250.09	924.0	1174.1	8.515
51.0	36.3	282.26	251.37	923.0	1174.4	8.359
52.0	37.3	283.49	252.63	922.2	1174.8	8.208
53.0	38.3	284.70	253.87	921.3	1175.2	8.062
54.0	39.3	285.90	255.09	920.5	1175.6	7.922
55.0	40.3	287.07	256.30	919.6	1175.9	7.787
56.0	41.3	288.23	257.50	918.8	1176.3	7.656
57.0	42.3	289.37	258.67	917.9	1176.6	7.529
58.0	43.3	290.50	259.82	917.1	1176.9	7.407
59.0	44.3	291.61	260.96	916.3	1177.3	7.289

Table 2-4
Continued

Pressure Lbs. per Sq. In.		Temperature	Heat of the Liquid	Latent Heat of Evaporation	Total Heat of Steam	Specific Volume
Absolute P'	Gage P	t Degrees F	Btu/lb.	Btu/lb.	h_g Btu/lb.	$\bar{V}$ Cu. ft. per lb.
60.0	45.3	292.71	262.09	915.5	1177.6	7.175
61.0	46.3	293.79	263.20	914.7	1177.9	7.064
62.0	47.3	294.85	264.30	913.9	1178.2	6.957
63.0	48.3	295.90	265.38	913.1	1178.5	6.853
64.0	49.3	296.94	266.45	912.3	1178.8	6.752
65.0	50.3	297.97	267.50	911.6	1179.1	6.655
66.0	51.3	298.99	268.55	910.8	1179.4	6.560
67.0	52.3	299.99	269.58	910.1	1179.7	6.468
68.0	53.3	300.98	270.60	909.4	1180.0	6.378
69.0	54.3	301.96	271.61	908.7	1180.3	6.291
70.0	55.3	302.92	272.61	907.9	1180.6	6.206
71.0	56.3	303.88	273.60	907.2	1180.8	6.124
72.0	57.3	304.83	274.57	906.5	1181.1	6.044
73.0	58.3	305.76	275.54	905.8	1181.3	5.966
74.0	59.3	306.68	276.49	905.1	1181.6	5.890
75.0	60.3	307.60	277.43	904.5	1181.9	5.816
76.0	61.3	308.50	278.37	903.7	1182.1	5.743
77.0	62.3	309.40	279.30	903.1	1182.4	5.673
78.0	63.3	310.29	280.21	902.4	1182.6	5.604
79.0	64.3	311.16	281.12	901.7	1182.8	5.537
80.0	65.3	312.03	282.02	901.1	1183.1	5.472
81.0	66.3	312.89	282.91	900.4	1183.3	5.408
82.0	67.3	313.74	283.79	899.7	1183.5	5.346
83.0	68.3	314.59	284.66	899.1	1183.8	5.285
84.0	69.3	315.42	285.53	898.5	1184.0	5.226
85.0	70.3	316.25	286.39	897.8	1184.2	5.168
86.0	71.3	317.07	287.24	897.2	1184.4	5.111
87.0	72.3	317.88	288.08	896.5	1184.6	5.055
88.0	73.3	318.68	288.91	895.9	1184.8	5.001
89.0	74.3	319.48	289.74	895.3	1185.1	4.948
90.0	75.3	320.27	290.56	894.7	1185.3	4.896
91.0	76.3	321.06	291.38	894.1	1185.5	4.845
92.0	77.3	321.83	292.18	893.5	1185.7	4.796
93.0	78.3	322.60	292.98	892.9	1185.9	4.747
94.0	79.3	323.36	293.78	892.3	1186.1	4.699
95.0	80.3	324.12	294.56	891.7	1186.2	4.652
96.0	81.3	324.87	295.34	891.1	1186.4	4.606
97.0	82.3	325.61	296.12	890.5	1186.6	4.561
98.0	83.3	326.35	296.89	889.9	1186.8	4.517
99.0	84.3	327.08	297.65	889.4	1187.0	4.474
100.0	85.3	327.81	298.40	888.8	1187.2	4.432
101.0	86.3	328.53	299.15	888.2	1187.4	4.391
102.0	87.3	329.25	299.90	887.6	1187.5	4.350
103.0	88.3	329.96	300.64	887.1	1187.7	4.310
104.0	89.3	330.66	301.37	886.5	1187.9	4.271
105.0	90.3	331.36	302.10	886.0	1188.1	4.232
106.0	91.3	332.05	302.82	885.4	1188.2	4.194
107.0	92.3	332.74	303.54	884.9	1188.4	4.157
108.0	93.3	333.42	304.26	884.3	1188.6	4.120
109.0	94.3	334.10	304.97	883.7	1188.7	4.084
110.0	95.3	334.77	305.66	883.2	1188.9	4.049
111.0	96.3	335.44	306.37	882.6	1189.0	4.015
112.0	97.3	336.11	307.06	882.1	1189.2	3.981
113.0	98.3	336.77	307.75	881.6	1189.4	3.947
114.0	99.3	337.42	308.43	881.1	1189.5	3.914
115.0	100.3	338.07	309.11	880.6	1189.7	3.882
116.0	101.3	338.72	309.79	880.0	1189.8	3.850
117.0	102.3	339.36	310.46	879.5	1190.0	3.819
118.0	103.3	339.99	311.12	879.0	1190.1	3.788
119.0	104.3	340.62	311.78	878.4	1190.2	3.758
120.0	105.3	341.25	312.44	877.9	1190.4	3.728
121.0	106.3	341.88	313.10	877.4	1190.5	3.699
122.0	107.3	342.50	313.75	876.9	1190.7	3.670
123.0	108.3	343.11	314.40	876.4	1190.8	3.642
124.0	109.3	343.72	315.04	875.9	1190.9	3.614
125.0	110.3	344.33	315.68	875.4	1191.1	3.587
126.0	111.3	344.94	316.31	874.9	1191.2	3.560
127.0	112.3	345.54	316.94	874.4	1191.3	3.533
128.0	113.3	346.13	317.57	873.9	1191.5	3.507
129.0	114.3	346.73	318.19	873.4	1191.6	3.481
130.0	115.3	347.32	318.81	872.9	1191.7	3.455
131.0	116.3	347.90	319.43	872.5	1191.9	3.430
132.0	117.3	348.48	320.04	872.0	1192.0	3.405
133.0	118.3	349.06	320.65	871.5	1192.1	3.381
134.0	119.3	349.64	321.25	871.0	1192.2	3.357
135.0	120.3	350.21	321.85	870.6	1192.4	3.333
136.0	121.3	350.78	322.45	870.1	1192.5	3.310
137.0	122.3	351.35	323.05	869.6	1192.6	3.287
138.0	123.3	351.91	323.64	869.1	1192.7	3.264
139.0	124.3	352.47	324.23	868.7	1192.9	3.242
140.0	125.3	353.02	324.82	868.2	1193.0	3.220
141.0	126.3	353.57	325.40	867.7	1193.1	3.198
142.0	127.3	354.12	325.98	867.2	1193.2	3.177
143.0	128.3	354.67	326.56	866.7	1193.3	3.155
144.0	129.3	355.21	327.13	866.3	1193.4	3.134
145.0	130.3	355.76	327.70	865.8	1193.5	3.114
146.0	131.3	356.29	328.27	865.3	1193.6	3.094
147.0	132.3	356.83	328.83	864.9	1193.8	3.074
148.0	133.3	357.36	329.39	864.5	1193.9	3.054
149.0	134.3	357.89	329.95	864.0	1194.0	3.034
150.0	135.3	358.42	330.51	863.6	1194.1	3.015
152.0	137.3	359.46	331.61	862.7	1194.3	2.977
154.0	139.3	360.49	332.70	861.8	1194.5	2.940
156.0	141.3	361.52	333.79	860.9	1194.7	2.904
158.0	143.3	362.53	334.86	860.0	1194.9	2.869
160.0	145.3	363.53	335.93	859.2	1195.1	2.834
162.0	147.3	364.53	336.98	858.3	1195.3	2.801
164.0	149.3	365.51	338.02	857.5	1195.5	2.768
166.0	151.3	366.48	339.05	856.6	1195.7	2.736
168.0	153.3	367.45	340.07	855.7	1195.8	2.705

Table 2-4
Continued

Pressure Lbs. Per Sq. In. Absolute P'	Gage P	Temperature t Degrees F	Heat of the Liquid Btu/lb.	Latent Heat of Evaporation Btu/lb.	Total Heat of Steam h_g Btu/lb.	Specific Volume $\overline{V}$ Cu. ft. per lb.
170.0	155.3	368.41	341.09	854.9	1196.0	2.675
172.0	157.3	369.35	342.10	854.1	1196.2	2.645
174.0	159.3	370.29	343.10	853.3	1196.4	2.616
176.0	161.3	371.22	344.09	852.4	1196.5	2.587
178.0	163.3	372.14	345.06	851.6	1196.7	2.559
180.0	165.3	373.06	346.03	850.8	1196.9	2.532
182.0	167.3	373.96	347.00	850.0	1197.0	2.505
184.0	169.3	374.86	347.96	849.2	1197.2	2.479
186.0	171.3	375.75	348.92	848.4	1197.3	2.454
188.0	173.3	376.64	349.86	847.6	1197.5	2.429
190.0	175.3	377.51	350.79	846.8	1197.6	2.404
192.0	177.3	378.38	351.72	846.1	1197.8	2.380
194.0	179.3	379.24	352.64	845.3	1197.9	2.356
196.0	181.3	380.10	353.55	844.5	1198.1	2.333
198.0	183.3	380.95	354.46	843.7	1198.2	2.310
200.0	185.3	381.79	355.36	843.0	1198.4	2.288
205.0	190.3	383.86	357.58	841.1	1198.7	2.234
210.0	195.3	385.90	359.77	839.2	1199.0	2.183
215.0	200.3	387.89	361.91	837.4	1199.3	2.134
220.0	205.3	389.86	364.02	835.6	1199.6	2.087
225.0	210.3	391.79	366.09	833.8	1199.9	2.0422
230.0	215.3	393.68	368.13	832.0	1200.1	1.9992
235.0	220.3	395.54	370.14	830.3	1200.4	1.9579
240.0	225.3	397.37	372.12	828.5	1200.6	1.9183
245.0	230.3	399.18	374.08	826.8	1200.9	1.8803
250.0	235.3	400.95	376.00	825.1	1201.1	1.8438
255.0	240.3	402.70	377.89	823.4	1201.3	1.8086
260.0	245.3	404.42	379.76	821.8	1201.5	1.7748
265.0	250.3	406.11	381.60	820.1	1201.7	1.7422
270.0	255.3	407.78	383.42	818.5	1201.9	1.7107
275.0	260.3	409.43	385.21	816.9	1202.1	1.6804
280.0	265.3	411.05	386.98	815.3	1202.3	1.6511
285.0	270.3	412.65	388.73	813.7	1202.4	1.6228
290.0	275.3	414.23	390.46	812.1	1202.6	1.5954
295.0	280.3	415.79	392.16	810.5	1202.7	1.5689
300.0	285.3	417.33	393.84	809.0	1202.8	1.5433
320.0	305.3	423.29	400.39	803.0	1203.4	1.4485
340.0	325.3	428.97	406.66	797.1	1203.7	1.3645
360.0	345.3	434.40	412.67	791.4	1204.1	1.2895
380.0	365.3	439.60	418.45	785.8	1204.3	1.2222
400.0	385.3	444.59	424.0	780.5	1204.5	1.1613
420.0	405.3	449.39	429.4	775.2	1204.6	1.1061
440.0	425.3	454.02	434.6	770.0	1204.6	1.0556
460.0	445.3	458.50	439.7	764.9	1204.6	1.0094
480.0	465.3	462.82	444.6	759.9	1204.5	0.9670
500.0	485.3	467.01	449.4	755.0	1204.4	0.9278
520.0	505.3	471.07	454.1	750.1	1204.2	0.8915
540.0	525.3	475.01	458.6	745.4	1204.0	0.8578
560.0	545.3	478.85	463.0	740.8	1203.8	0.8265
580.0	565.3	482.58	467.4	736.1	1203.5	0.7973
600.0	585.3	486.21	471.6	731.6	1203.2	0.7698
620.0	605.3	489.75	475.7	727.2	1202.9	0.7440
640.0	625.3	493.21	479.8	722.7	1202.5	0.7198
660.0	645.3	496.58	483.8	718.3	1202.1	0.6971
680.0	665.3	499.88	487.7	714.0	1201.7	0.6757
700.0	685.3	503.10	491.5	709.7	1201.2	0.6554
720.0	705.3	506.25	495.3	705.4	1200.7	0.6362
740.0	725.3	509.34	499.0	701.2	1200.2	0.6180
760.0	745.3	512.36	502.6	697.1	1199.7	0.6007
780.0	765.3	515.33	506.2	692.9	1199.1	0.5843
800.0	785.3	518.23	509.7	688.9	1198.6	0.5687
820.0	805.3	521.08	513.2	684.8	1198.0	0.5538
840.0	825.3	523.88	516.6	680.8	1197.4	0.5396
860.0	845.3	526.63	520.0	676.8	1196.8	0.5260
880.0	865.3	529.33	523.3	672.8	1196.1	0.5130
900.0	885.3	531.98	526.6	668.8	1195.4	0.5006
920.0	905.3	534.59	529.8	664.9	1194.7	0.4886
940.0	925.3	537.16	533.0	661.0	1194.0	0.4772
960.0	945.3	539.68	536.2	657.1	1193.3	0.4663
980.0	965.3	542.17	539.3	653.3	1192.6	0.4557
1000.0	985.3	544.61	542.4	649.4	1191.8	0.4456
1050.0	1035.3	550.57	550.0	639.9	1189.9	0.4218
1100.0	1085.3	556.31	557.4	630.4	1187.8	0.4001
1150.0	1135.3	561.86	564.6	621.0	1185.6	0.3802
1200.0	1185.3	567.22	571.7	611.7	1183.4	0.3619
1250.0	1235.3	572.42	578.6	602.4	1181.0	0.3450
1300.0	1285.3	577.46	585.4	593.2	1178.6	0.3293
1350.0	1335.3	582.35	592.1	584.0	1176.1	0.3148
1400.0	1385.3	587.10	598.7	574.7	1173.4	0.3012
1450.0	1435.3	591.73	605.2	565.5	1170.7	0.2884
1500.0	1485.3	596.23	611.6	556.3	1167.9	0.2765
1600.0	1585.3	604.90	624.1	538.0	1162.1	0.2548
1700.0	1685.3	613.15	636.3	519.6	1155.9	0.2354
1800.0	1785.3	621.03	648.3	501.1	1149.4	0.2179
1900.0	1885.3	628.58	660.1	482.4	1142.4	0.2021
2000.0	1985.3	635.82	671.7	463.4	1135.1	0.1878
2100.0	2085.3	642.77	683.3	444.1	1127.4	0.1746
2200.0	2185.3	649.46	694.8	424.4	1119.2	0.1625
2300.0	2285.3	655.91	706.5	403.9	1110.4	0.1513
2400.0	2385.3	662.12	718.4	382.7	1101.1	0.1407
2500.0	2485.3	668.13	730.6	360.5	1091.1	0.1307
2600.0	2585.3	673.94	743.0	337.2	1080.2	0.1213
2700.0	2685.3	679.55	756.2	312.1	1068.3	0.1123
2800.0	2785.3	684.99	770.1	284.7	1054.8	0.1035
2900.0	2885.3	690.26	785.4	253.6	1039.0	0.0947
3000.0	2985.3	695.36	802.5	217.8	1020.3	0.0858
3100.0	3085.3	700.31	825.0	168.1	993.1	0.0753
3200.0	3185.3	705.11	872.4	62.0	934.4	0.0580
3206.2	3191.5	705.40	902.7	0.0	902.7	0.0503

Example Problem

Use Figure 2-1 to calculate the F factor for the following conditions:

T = 660°F
h = 10 ft–0 in.
t = 1 in.
K = 1 (skirt fully insulated)
70°F = Ambient temperature
T_{al} = Average temperature

Step 1. $\frac{Kh}{\sqrt{t}} = \frac{1 \times 10 \text{ ft}}{1} = 10$

Step 2. Enter the chart at the point along the bottom line where $kh/\sqrt{t}$. Then move up vertically to the point where the curve intersects. Then move horizontally to the left to find the temperature correction factor, F, which in this example is equal to 0.22.

Step 3. $T_1 = T - 70°F = 530°F.$

Step 4. $T_{al} = F \times T_1 = 0.22 \times 530°F = 116.6°F$ or 117°F.

Step 5. $T_a = T_{al} + 70°F = 117°F + 70°F = 187°F.$

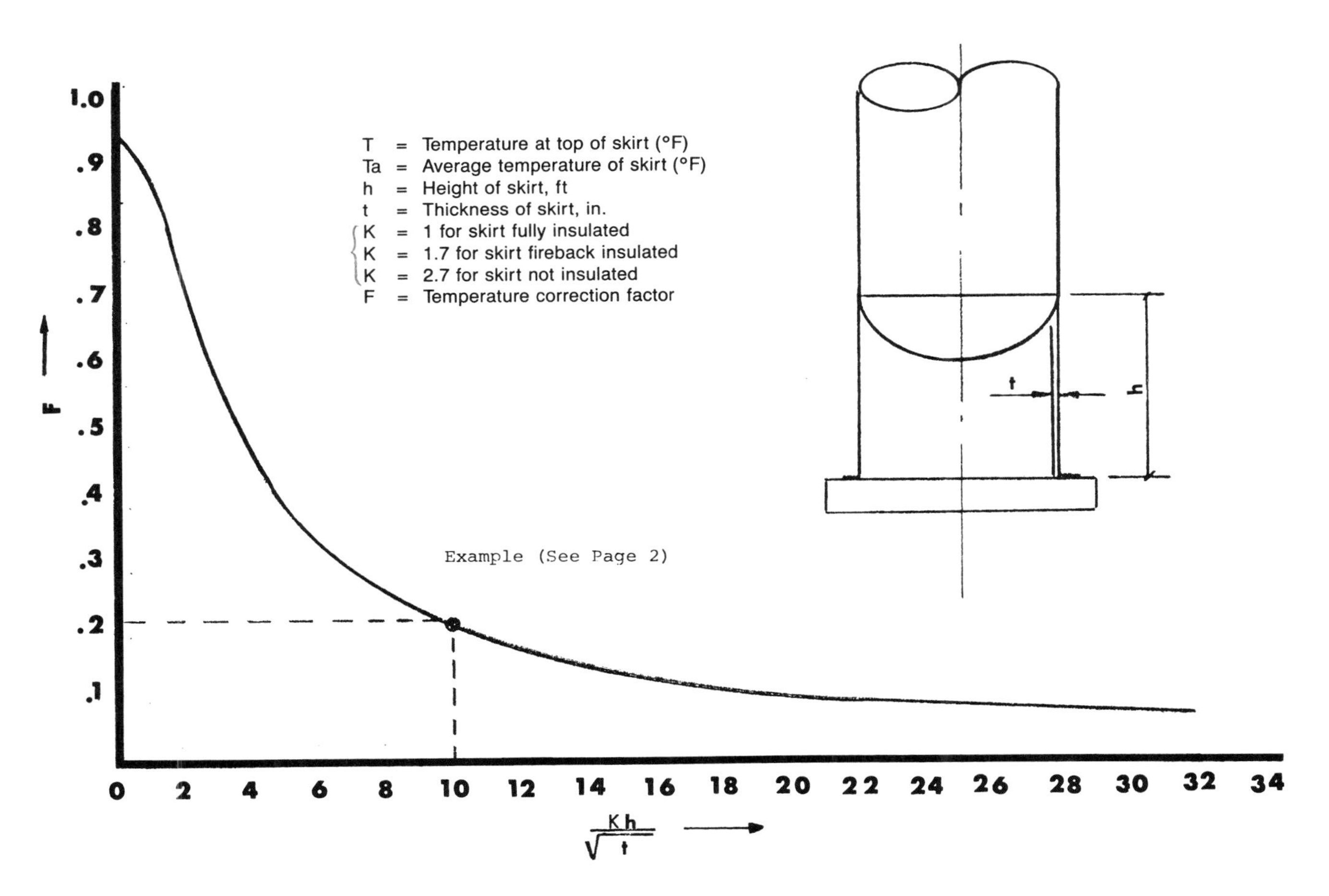

Figure 2-1. Curve for determination of average skirt temperature.

3

Allowable Stress Range for ANSI/ASME Power Piping Code B31.1 (1985)

This chapter contains allowable thermal stresses for petroleum piping. Values of Sh taken from ANSI/ASME Code B31.3-1980, Appendix A, Table 1. (Used courtesy of the American Society of Mechanical Engineers.)

HOT STRESS AND ALLOW. STRESS RANGE
BASED ON B31.1

S(A)=F*(1.25*S(C)+0.25*S(H)) F=1

MATERIAL	ASTM-A53-A		ASTM-A53-B		ASTM-A106-B		API-5L-GR-B		ASTM-A139-B	
TEMP(F)	HOT,S(H)	ALL,S(A)	HOT,S(H)	ALL,S(A)	HOT,S(H)	ALL,S(A)	HOT,S(H)	ALL,S(A)	HOT,S(H)	ALL,S(A)
100.00	12000.00	18000.00	15000.00	22500.00	15000.00	22500.00	15000.00	22500.00	12000.00	18000.00
110.00	12000.00	18000.00	15000.00	22500.00	15000.00	22500.00	15000.00	22500.00	12000.00	18000.00
120.00	12000.00	18000.00	15000.00	22500.00	15000.00	22500.00	15000.00	22500.00	12000.00	18000.00
130.00	12000.00	18000.00	15000.00	22500.00	15000.00	22500.00	15000.00	22500.00	12000.00	18000.00
140.00	12000.00	18000.00	15000.00	22500.00	15000.00	22500.00	15000.00	22500.00	12000.00	18000.00
150.00	12000.00	18000.00	15000.00	22500.00	15000.00	22500.00	15000.00	22500.00	12000.00	18000.00
160.00	12000.00	18000.00	15000.00	22500.00	15000.00	22500.00	15000.00	22500.00	12000.00	18000.00
170.00	12000.00	18000.00	15000.00	22500.00	15000.00	22500.00	15000.00	22500.00	12000.00	18000.00
180.00	12000.00	18000.00	15000.00	22500.00	15000.00	22500.00	15000.00	22500.00	12000.00	18000.00
190.00	12000.00	18000.00	15000.00	22500.00	15000.00	22500.00	15000.00	22500.00	12000.00	18000.00
200.00	12000.00	18000.00	15000.00	22500.00	15000.00	22500.00	15000.00	22500.00	12000.00	18000.00
210.00	12000.00	18000.00	15000.00	22500.00	15000.00	22500.00	15000.00	22500.00	12000.00	18000.00
220.00	12000.00	18000.00	15000.00	22500.00	15000.00	22500.00	15000.00	22500.00	12000.00	18000.00
230.00	12000.00	18000.00	15000.00	22500.00	15000.00	22500.00	15000.00	22500.00	12000.00	18000.00
240.00	12000.00	18000.00	15000.00	22500.00	15000.00	22500.00	15000.00	22500.00	12000.00	18000.00
250.00	12000.00	18000.00	15000.00	22500.00	15000.00	22500.00	15000.00	22500.00	12000.00	18000.00
260.00	12000.00	18000.00	15000.00	22500.00	15000.00	22500.00	15000.00	22500.00	12000.00	18000.00
270.00	12000.00	18000.00	15000.00	22500.00	15000.00	22500.00	15000.00	22500.00	12000.00	18000.00
280.00	12000.00	18000.00	15000.00	22500.00	15000.00	22500.00	15000.00	22500.00	12000.00	18000.00
290.00	12000.00	18000.00	15000.00	22500.00	15000.00	22500.00	15000.00	22500.00	12000.00	18000.00
300.00	12000.00	18000.00	15000.00	22500.00	15000.00	22500.00	15000.00	22500.00	12000.00	18000.00

NOTE ?- ALL ZERO STRESS VALUES INDICATE THAT THE CODE DOES NOT
**** RECOMMEND THE USE OF THE MATERIAL AT THAT TEMPERATURE

HOT STRESS AND ALLOW. STRESS RANGE
BASED ON B31.1

S(A)=F*(1.25*S(C)+0.25*S(H)) , F=1

MATERIAL	ASTM-A53-A		ASTM-A53-B		ASTM-A106-B		API-5L-GR-B		ASTM-A139-B	
TEMP(F)	HOT,S(H)	ALL,S(A)	HOT,S(H)	ALL,S(A)	HOT,S(H)	ALL,S(A)	HOT,S(H)	ALL,S(A)	HOT,S(H)	ALL,S(A)
310.00	12000.00	18000.00	15000.00	22500.00	15000.00	22500.00	15000.00	22500.00	12000.00	18000.00
320.00	12000.00	18000.00	15000.00	22500.00	15000.00	22500.00	15000.00	22500.00	12000.00	18000.00
330.00	12000.00	18000.00	15000.00	22500.00	15000.00	22500.00	15000.00	22500.00	12000.00	18000.00
340.00	12000.00	18000.00	15000.00	22500.00	15000.00	22500.00	15000.00	22500.00	12000.00	18000.00
350.00	12000.00	18000.00	15000.00	22500.00	15000.00	22500.00	15000.00	22500.00	12000.00	18000.00
360.00	12000.00	18000.00	15000.00	22500.00	15000.00	22500.00	15000.00	22500.00	12000.00	18000.00
370.00	12000.00	18000.00	15000.00	22500.00	15000.00	22500.00	15000.00	22500.00	12000.00	18000.00
380.00	12000.00	18000.00	15000.00	22500.00	15000.00	22500.00	15000.00	22500.00	12000.00	18000.00
390.00	12000.00	18000.00	15000.00	22500.00	15000.00	22500.00	15000.00	22500.00	12000.00	18000.00
400.00	12000.00	18000.00	15000.00	22500.00	15000.00	22500.00	15000.00	22500.00	12000.00	18000.00
410.00	12000.00	18000.00	15000.00	22500.00	15000.00	22500.00	15000.00	22500.00	12000.00	18000.00
420.00	12000.00	18000.00	15000.00	22500.00	15000.00	22500.00	15000.00	22500.00	12000.00	18000.00
430.00	12000.00	18000.00	15000.00	22500.00	15000.00	22500.00	15000.00	22500.00	12000.00	18000.00
440.00	12000.00	18000.00	15000.00	22500.00	15000.00	22500.00	15000.00	22500.00	12000.00	18000.00
450.00	12000.00	18000.00	15000.00	22500.00	15000.00	22500.00	15000.00	22500.00	12000.00	18000.00
460.00	12000.00	18000.00	15000.00	22500.00	15000.00	22500.00	15000.00	22500.00	12000.00	18000.00
470.00	12000.00	18000.00	15000.00	22500.00	15000.00	22500.00	15000.00	22500.00	12000.00	18000.00
480.00	12000.00	18000.00	15000.00	22500.00	15000.00	22500.00	15000.00	22500.00	12000.00	18000.00
490.00	12000.00	18000.00	15000.00	22500.00	15000.00	22500.00	15000.00	22500.00	12000.00	18000.00
500.00	12000.00	18000.00	15000.00	22500.00	15000.00	22500.00	15000.00	22500.00	12000.00	18000.00
510.00	12000.00	18000.00	15000.00	22500.00	15000.00	22500.00	15000.00	22500.00	12000.00	18000.00

NOTE ?- ALL ZERO STRESS VALUES INDICATE THAT THE CODE DOES NOT
**** RECOMMEND THE USE OF THE MATERIAL AT THAT TEMPERATURE

HOT STRESS AND ALLOW. STRESS RANGE
BASED ON B31.1

S(A)=F*(1.25*S(C)+0.25*S(H)) , F=1

MATERIAL	ASTM-A53-A		ASTM-A53-B		ASTM-A106-B		API-5L-GR-B		ASTM-A139-B	
TEMP(F)	HOT,S(H)	ALL,S(A)	HOT,S(H)	ALL,S(A)	HOT,S(H)	ALL,S(A)	HOT,S(H)	ALL,S(A)	HOT,S(H)	ALL,S(A)
520.00	12000.00	18000.00	15000.00	22500.00	15000.00	22500.00	15000.00	22500.00	12000.00	18000.00
530.00	12000.00	18000.00	15000.00	22500.00	15000.00	22500.00	15000.00	22500.00	12000.00	18000.00
540.00	12000.00	18000.00	15000.00	22500.00	15000.00	22500.00	15000.00	22500.00	12000.00	18000.00
550.00	12000.00	18000.00	15000.00	22500.00	15000.00	22500.00	15000.00	22500.00	12000.00	18000.00
560.00	12000.00	18000.00	15000.00	22500.00	15000.00	22500.00	15000.00	22500.00	12000.00	18000.00
570.00	12000.00	18000.00	15000.00	22500.00	15000.00	22500.00	15000.00	22500.00	12000.00	18000.00
580.00	12000.00	18000.00	15000.00	22500.00	15000.00	22500.00	15000.00	22500.00	12000.00	18000.00
590.00	12000.00	18000.00	15000.00	22500.00	15000.00	22500.00	15000.00	22500.00	12000.00	18000.00
600.00	12000.00	18000.00	15000.00	22500.00	15000.00	22500.00	15000.00	22500.00	12000.00	18000.00
610.00	12000.00	18000.00	15000.00	22500.00	15000.00	22500.00	15000.00	22500.00	12000.00	18000.00
620.00	12000.00	18000.00	15000.00	22500.00	15000.00	22500.00	15000.00	22500.00	12000.00	18000.00
630.00	12000.00	18000.00	15000.00	22500.00	15000.00	22500.00	15000.00	22500.00	12000.00	18000.00
640.00	12000.00	18000.00	15000.00	22500.00	15000.00	22500.00	15000.00	22500.00	12000.00	18000.00
650.00	12000.00	18000.00	15000.00	22500.00	15000.00	22500.00	15000.00	22500.00	12000.00	18000.00
660.00	11940.00	17985.00	14880.00	22470.00	14880.00	22470.00	14880.00	22470.00	11900.00	17975.00
670.00	11880.00	17970.00	14760.00	22440.00	14760.00	22440.00	14760.00	22440.00	11800.00	17950.00
680.00	11820.00	17955.00	14640.00	22410.00	14640.00	22410.00	14640.00	22410.00	11700.00	17925.00
690.00	11760.00	17940.00	14520.00	22380.00	14520.00	22380.00	14520.00	22380.00	11600.00	17900.00
700.00	11700.00	17925.00	14400.00	22350.00	14400.00	22350.00	14400.00	22350.00	11500.00	17875.00
710.00	11500.00	17875.00	14120.00	22280.00	14120.00	22280.00	14120.00	22280.00	11280.00	17820.00
720.00	11300.00	17825.00	13840.00	22210.00	13840.00	22210.00	13840.00	22210.00	11060.00	17765.00

NOTE ?- ALL ZERO STRESS VALUES INDICATE THAT THE CODE DOES NOT
**** RECOMMEND THE USE OF THE MATERIAL AT THAT TEMPERATURE

HOT STRESS AND ALLOW. STRESS RANGE
BASED ON B31.1

S(A)=F*(1.25*S(C)+0.25*S(H)) , F=1

MATERIAL	ASTM-A53-A		ASTM-A53-B		ASTM-A106-B		API-5L-GR-B		ASTM-A139-B	
TEMP(F)	HOT,S(H)	ALL,S(A)	HOT,S(H)	ALL,S(A)	HOT,S(H)	ALL,S(A)	HOT,S(H)	ALL,S(A)	HOT,S(H)	ALL,S(A)
730.00	11100.00	17775.00	13560.00	22140.00	13560.00	22140.00	13560.00	22140.00	10840.00	17710.00
740.00	10900.00	17725.00	13280.00	22070.00	13280.00	22070.00	13280.00	22070.00	10620.00	17655.00
750.00	10700.00	17675.00	13000.00	22000.00	13000.00	22000.00	13000.00	22000.00	10400.00	17600.00
760.00	10360.00	17590.00	12560.00	21890.00	12560.00	21890.00	12560.00	21890.00	10040.00	17510.00
770.00	10020.00	17505.00	12120.00	21780.00	12120.00	21780.00	12120.00	21780.00	9680.00	17420.00
780.00	9680.00	17420.00	11680.00	21670.00	11680.00	21670.00	11680.00	21670.00	9320.00	17330.00
790.00	9340.00	17335.00	11240.00	21560.00	11240.00	21560.00	11240.00	21560.00	8960.00	17240.00
800.00	9000.00	17250.00	10800.00	21450.00	10800.00	21450.00	10800.00	21450.00	8600.00	17150.00

NOTE ?- ALL ZERO STRESS VALUES INDICATE THAT THE CODE DOES NOT
**** RECOMMEND THE USE OF THE MATERIAL AT THAT TEMPERATURE

HOT STRESS AND ALLOW. STRESS RANGE
BASED ON B31.1

S(A)=F*(1.25*S(C)+0.25*S(H)) , F=1

MATERIAL	A335-P2		A335-P5,B,C		A335-GR-P9		A335-GR-P11		A335-GR-P22	
TEMP(F)	HOT,S(H)	ALL,S(A)	HOT,S(H)	ALL,S(A)	HOT,S(H)	ALL,S(A)	HOT,S(H)	ALL,S(A)	HOT,S(H)	ALL,S(A)
100.00	13800.00	20700.00	15000.00	22500.00	15000.00	22500.00	15000.00	22500.00	15000.00	22500.00
110.00	13800.00	20700.00	15000.00	22500.00	15000.00	22500.00	15000.00	22500.00	15000.00	22500.00
120.00	13800.00	20700.00	15000.00	22500.00	15000.00	22500.00	15000.00	22500.00	15000.00	22500.00
130.00	13800.00	20700.00	15000.00	22500.00	15000.00	22500.00	15000.00	22500.00	15000.00	22500.00
140.00	13800.00	20700.00	15000.00	22500.00	15000.00	22500.00	15000.00	22500.00	15000.00	22500.00
150.00	13800.00	20700.00	15000.00	22500.00	15000.00	22500.00	15000.00	22500.00	15000.00	22500.00
160.00	13800.00	20700.00	15000.00	22500.00	15000.00	22500.00	15000.00	22500.00	15000.00	22500.00
170.00	13800.00	20700.00	15000.00	22500.00	15000.00	22500.00	15000.00	22500.00	15000.00	22500.00
180.00	13800.00	20700.00	15000.00	22500.00	15000.00	22500.00	15000.00	22500.00	15000.00	22500.00
190.00	13800.00	20700.00	15000.00	22500.00	15000.00	22500.00	15000.00	22500.00	15000.00	22500.00
200.00	13800.00	20700.00	15000.00	22500.00	15000.00	22500.00	15000.00	22500.00	15000.00	22500.00
210.00	13800.00	20700.00	15000.00	22500.00	15000.00	22500.00	15000.00	22500.00	15000.00	22500.00
220.00	13800.00	20700.00	15000.00	22500.00	15000.00	22500.00	15000.00	22500.00	15000.00	22500.00
230.00	13800.00	20700.00	15000.00	22500.00	15000.00	22500.00	15000.00	22500.00	15000.00	22500.00
240.00	13800.00	20700.00	15000.00	22500.00	15000.00	22500.00	15000.00	22500.00	15000.00	22500.00
250.00	13800.00	20700.00	15000.00	22500.00	15000.00	22500.00	15000.00	22500.00	15000.00	22500.00
260.00	13800.00	20700.00	15000.00	22500.00	15000.00	22500.00	15000.00	22500.00	15000.00	22500.00
270.00	13800.00	20700.00	15000.00	22500.00	15000.00	22500.00	15000.00	22500.00	15000.00	22500.00
280.00	13800.00	20700.00	15000.00	22500.00	15000.00	22500.00	15000.00	22500.00	15000.00	22500.00
290.00	13800.00	20700.00	15000.00	22500.00	15000.00	22500.00	15000.00	22500.00	15000.00	22500.00
300.00	13800.00	20700.00	15000.00	22500.00	15000.00	22500.00	15000.00	22500.00	15000.00	22500.00

NOTE ?- ALL ZERO STRESS VALUES INDICATE THAT THE CODE DOES NOT
**** RECOMMEND THE USE OF THE MATERIAL AT THAT TEMPERATURE

HOT STRESS AND ALLOW. STRESS RANGE
BASED ON B31.1

S(A)=F*(1.25*S(C)+0.25*S(H)) , F=1

MATERIAL	A335-P2		A335-P5,B,C		A335-GR-P9		A335-GR-P11		A335-GR-P22	
TEMP(F)	HOT,S(H)	ALL,S(A)	HOT,S(H)	ALL,S(A)	HOT,S(H)	ALL,S(A)	HOT,S(H)	ALL,S(A)	HOT,S(H)	ALL,S(A)
310.00	13800.00	20700.00	15000.00	22500.00	15000.00	22500.00	15000.00	22500.00	15000.00	22500.00
320.00	13800.00	20700.00	15000.00	22500.00	15000.00	22500.00	15000.00	22500.00	15000.00	22500.00
330.00	13800.00	20700.00	15000.00	22500.00	15000.00	22500.00	15000.00	22500.00	15000.00	22500.00
340.00	13800.00	20700.00	15000.00	22500.00	15000.00	22500.00	15000.00	22500.00	15000.00	22500.00
350.00	13800.00	20700.00	15000.00	22500.00	15000.00	22500.00	15000.00	22500.00	15000.00	22500.00
360.00	13800.00	20700.00	15000.00	22500.00	15000.00	22500.00	15000.00	22500.00	15000.00	22500.00
370.00	13800.00	20700.00	15000.00	22500.00	15000.00	22500.00	15000.00	22500.00	15000.00	22500.00
380.00	13800.00	20700.00	15000.00	22500.00	15000.00	22500.00	15000.00	22500.00	15000.00	22500.00
390.00	13800.00	20700.00	15000.00	22500.00	15000.00	22500.00	15000.00	22500.00	15000.00	22500.00
400.00	13800.00	20700.00	15000.00	22500.00	15000.00	22500.00	15000.00	22500.00	15000.00	22500.00
410.00	13800.00	20700.00	14950.00	22487.50	14950.00	22487.50	15000.00	22500.00	15000.00	22500.00
420.00	13800.00	20700.00	14900.00	22475.00	14900.00	22475.00	15000.00	22500.00	15000.00	22500.00
430.00	13800.00	20700.00	14850.00	22462.50	14850.00	22462.50	15000.00	22500.00	15000.00	22500.00
440.00	13800.00	20700.00	14800.00	22450.00	14800.00	22450.00	15000.00	22500.00	15000.00	22500.00
450.00	13800.00	20700.00	14750.00	22437.50	14750.00	22437.50	15000.00	22500.00	15000.00	22500.00
460.00	13800.00	20700.00	14700.00	22425.00	14700.00	22425.00	15000.00	22500.00	15000.00	22500.00
470.00	13800.00	20700.00	14650.00	22412.50	14650.00	22412.50	15000.00	22500.00	15000.00	22500.00
480.00	13800.00	20700.00	14600.00	22400.00	14600.00	22400.00	15000.00	22500.00	15000.00	22500.00
490.00	13800.00	20700.00	14550.00	22387.50	14550.00	22387.50	15000.00	22500.00	15000.00	22500.00
500.00	13800.00	20700.00	14500.00	22375.00	14500.00	22375.00	15000.00	22500.00	15000.00	22500.00
510.00	13800.00	20700.00	14450.00	22362.50	14450.00	22362.50	15000.00	22500.00	15000.00	22500.00

NOTE ?- ALL ZERO STRESS VALUES INDICATE THAT THE CODE DOES NOT
**** RECOMMEND THE USE OF THE MATERIAL AT THAT TEMPERATURE

HOT STRESS AND ALLOW. STRESS RANGE
BASED ON B31.1

S(A)=F*(1.25*S(C)+0.25*S(H)) , F=1

MATERIAL	A335-P2		A335-P5,B,C		A335-GR-P9		A335-GR-P11		A335-GR-P22	
TEMP(F)	HOT,S(H)	ALL,S(A)	HOT,S(H)	ALL,S(A)	HOT,S(H)	ALL,S(A)	HOT,S(H)	ALL,S(A)	HOT,S(H)	ALL,S(A)
520.00	13800.00	20700.00	14400.00	22350.00	14400.00	22350.00	15000.00	22500.00	15000.00	22500.00
530.00	13800.00	20700.00	14350.00	22337.50	14350.00	22337.50	15000.00	22500.00	15000.00	22500.00
540.00	13800.00	20700.00	14300.00	22325.00	14300.00	22325.00	15000.00	22500.00	15000.00	22500.00
550.00	13800.00	20700.00	14250.00	22312.50	14250.00	22312.50	15000.00	22500.00	15000.00	22500.00
560.00	13800.00	20700.00	14200.00	22300.00	14200.00	22300.00	15000.00	22500.00	15000.00	22500.00
570.00	13800.00	20700.00	14150.00	22287.50	14150.00	22287.50	15000.00	22500.00	15000.00	22500.00
580.00	13800.00	20700.00	14100.00	22275.00	14100.00	22275.00	15000.00	22500.00	15000.00	22500.00
590.00	13800.00	20700.00	14050.00	22262.50	14050.00	22262.50	15000.00	22500.00	15000.00	22500.00
600.00	13800.00	20700.00	14000.00	22250.00	14000.00	22250.00	15000.00	22500.00	15000.00	22500.00
610.00	13800.00	20700.00	13940.00	22235.00	13940.00	22235.00	15000.00	22500.00	15000.00	22500.00
620.00	13800.00	20700.00	13880.00	22220.00	13880.00	22220.00	15000.00	22500.00	15000.00	22500.00
630.00	13800.00	20700.00	13820.00	22205.00	13820.00	22205.00	15000.00	22500.00	15000.00	22500.00
640.00	13800.00	20700.00	13760.00	22190.00	13760.00	22190.00	15000.00	22500.00	15000.00	22500.00
650.00	13800.00	20700.00	13700.00	22175.00	13700.00	22175.00	15000.00	22500.00	15000.00	22500.00
660.00	13800.00	20700.00	13640.00	22160.00	13640.00	22160.00	15000.00	22500.00	15000.00	22500.00
670.00	13800.00	20700.00	13580.00	22145.00	13580.00	22145.00	15000.00	22500.00	15000.00	22500.00
680.00	13800.00	20700.00	13520.00	22130.00	13520.00	22130.00	15000.00	22500.00	15000.00	22500.00
690.00	13800.00	20700.00	13460.00	22115.00	13460.00	22115.00	15000.00	22500.00	15000.00	22500.00
700.00	13800.00	20700.00	13400.00	22100.00	13400.00	22100.00	15000.00	22500.00	15000.00	22500.00
710.00	13800.00	20700.00	13340.00	22085.00	13340.00	22085.00	15000.00	22500.00	15000.00	22500.00
720.00	13800.00	20700.00	13280.00	22070.00	13280.00	22070.00	15000.00	22500.00	15000.00	22500.00

NOTE ?- ALL ZERO STRESS VALUES INDICATE THAT THE CODE DOES NOT
**** RECOMMEND THE USE OF THE MATERIAL AT THAT TEMPERATURE

HOT STRESS AND ALLOW. STRESS RANGE
BASED ON B31.1

S(A)=F*(1.25*S(C)+0.25*S(H)) , F=1

MATERIAL	A335-P2		A335-P5,B,C		A335-GR-P9		A335-GR-P11		A335-GR-P22	
TEMP(F)	HOT,S(H)	ALL,S(A)	HOT,S(H)	ALL,S(A)	HOT,S(H)	ALL,S(A)	HOT,S(H)	ALL,S(A)	HOT,S(H)	ALL,S(A)
730.00	13800.00	20700.00	13220.00	22055.00	13220.00	22055.00	15000.00	22500.00	15000.00	22500.00
740.00	13800.00	20700.00	13160.00	22040.00	13160.00	22040.00	15000.00	22500.00	15000.00	22500.00
750.00	13800.00	20700.00	13100.00	22025.00	13100.00	22025.00	15000.00	22500.00	15000.00	22500.00
760.00	13740.00	20685.00	13040.00	22010.00	13040.00	22010.00	15000.00	22500.00	15000.00	22500.00
770.00	13680.00	20670.00	12980.00	21995.00	12980.00	21995.00	15000.00	22500.00	15000.00	22500.00
780.00	13620.00	20655.00	12920.00	21980.00	12920.00	21980.00	15000.00	22500.00	15000.00	22500.00
790.00	13560.00	20640.00	12860.00	21965.00	12860.00	21965.00	15000.00	22500.00	15000.00	22500.00
800.00	13500.00	20625.00	12800.00	21950.00	12800.00	21950.00	15000.00	22500.00	15000.00	22500.00
810.00	13420.00	20605.00	12640.00	21910.00	12740.00	21935.00	14880.00	22470.00	14880.00	22470.00
820.00	13340.00	20585.00	12480.00	21870.00	12680.00	21920.00	14760.00	22440.00	14760.00	22440.00
830.00	13260.00	20565.00	12320.00	21830.00	12620.00	21905.00	14640.00	22410.00	14640.00	22410.00
840.00	13180.00	20545.00	12160.00	21790.00	12560.00	21890.00	14520.00	22380.00	14520.00	22380.00
850.00	13100.00	20525.00	12000.00	21750.00	12500.00	21875.00	14400.00	22350.00	14400.00	22350.00
860.00	13040.00	20510.00	11660.00	21665.00	12400.00	21850.00	14140.00	22285.00	14140.00	22285.00
870.00	12980.00	20495.00	11320.00	21580.00	12300.00	21825.00	13880.00	22220.00	13880.00	22220.00
880.00	12920.00	20480.00	10980.00	21495.00	12200.00	21800.00	13620.00	22155.00	13620.00	22155.00
890.00	12860.00	20465.00	10640.00	21410.00	12100.00	21775.00	13360.00	22090.00	13360.00	22090.00
900.00	12800.00	20450.00	10300.00	21325.00	12000.00	21750.00	13100.00	22025.00	13100.00	22025.00
910.00	12080.00	20270.00	9760.00	21190.00	11760.00	21690.00	12680.00	21920.00	12680.00	21920.00
920.00	11360.00	20090.00	9220.00	21055.00	11520.00	21630.00	12260.00	21815.00	12260.00	21815.00
930.00	10640.00	19910.00	8680.00	20920.00	11280.00	21570.00	11840.00	21710.00	11840.00	21710.00

NOTE ?- ALL ZERO STRESS VALUES INDICATE THAT THE CODE DOES NOT
**** RECOMMEND THE USE OF THE MATERIAL AT THAT TEMPERATURE

HOT STRESS AND ALLOW. STRESS RANGE
BASED ON B31.1

S(A)=F*(1.25*S(C)+0.25*S(H)) , F=1

MATERIAL	A335-P2		A335-P5,B,C		A335-GR-P9		A335-GR-P11		A335-GR-P22	
TEMP(F)	HOT,S(H)	ALL,S(A)	HOT,S(H)	ALL,S(A)	HOT,S(H)	ALL,S(A)	HOT,S(H)	ALL,S(A)	HOT,S(H)	ALL,S(A)
940.00	9920.00	19730.00	8140.00	20785.00	11040.00	21510.00	11420.00	21605.00	11420.00	21605.00
950.00	9200.00	19550.00	7600.00	20650.00	10800.00	21450.00	11000.00	21500.00	11000.00	21500.00
960.00	8540.00	19385.00	7200.00	20550.00	10340.00	21335.00	10120.00	21280.00	10360.00	21340.00
970.00	7880.00	19220.00	6800.00	20450.00	9880.00	21220.00	9240.00	21060.00	9720.00	21180.00
980.00	7220.00	19055.00	6400.00	20350.00	9420.00	21105.00	8360.00	20840.00	9080.00	21020.00
990.00	6560.00	18890.00	6000.00	20250.00	8960.00	20990.00	7480.00	20620.00	8440.00	20860.00
1000.00	5900.00	18725.00	5600.00	20150.00	8500.00	20875.00	6600.00	20400.00	7800.00	20700.00
1010.00	0.00	0.00	5300.00	20075.00	7900.00	20725.00	6100.00	20275.00	7400.00	20600.00
1020.00	0.00	0.00	5000.00	20000.00	7300.00	20575.00	5600.00	20150.00	7000.00	20500.00
1030.00	0.00	0.00	4700.00	19925.00	6700.00	20425.00	5100.00	20025.00	6600.00	20400.00
1040.00	0.00	0.00	4400.00	19850.00	6100.00	20275.00	4600.00	19900.00	6200.00	20300.00
1050.00	0.00	0.00	4100.00	19775.00	5500.00	20125.00	4100.00	19775.00	5800.00	20200.00
1060.00	0.00	0.00	3880.00	19720.00	5060.00	20015.00	3880.00	19720.00	5480.00	20120.00
1070.00	0.00	0.00	3660.00	19665.00	4620.00	19905.00	3660.00	19665.00	5160.00	20040.00
1080.00	0.00	0.00	3440.00	19610.00	4180.00	19795.00	3440.00	19610.00	4840.00	19960.00
1090.00	0.00	0.00	3220.00	19555.00	3740.00	19685.00	3220.00	19555.00	4520.00	19880.00
1100.00	0.00	0.00	3000.00	19500.00	3300.00	19575.00	3000.00	19500.00	4200.00	19800.00
1110.00	0.00	0.00	2800.00	19450.00	3080.00	19520.00	0.00	0.00	0.00	0.00
1120.00	0.00	0.00	2600.00	19400.00	2860.00	19465.00	0.00	0.00	0.00	0.00
1130.00	0.00	0.00	2400.00	19350.00	2640.00	19410.00	0.00	0.00	0.00	0.00
1140.00	0.00	0.00	2200.00	19300.00	2420.00	19355.00	0.00	0.00	0.00	0.00

NOTE ?- ALL ZERO STRESS VALUES INDICATE THAT THE CODE DOES NOT
**** RECOMMEND THE USE OF THE MATERIAL AT THAT TEMPERATURE

HOT STRESS AND ALLOW. STRESS RANGE
BASED ON B31.1

S(A)=F*(1.25*S(C)+0.25*S(H)) , F=1

MATERIAL	A335-P2		A335-P5,B,C		A335-GR-P9		A335-GR-P11		A335-GR-P22	
TEMP(F)	HOT,S(H)	ALL,S(A)	HOT,S(H)	ALL,S(A)	HOT,S(H)	ALL,S(A)	HOT,S(H)	ALL,S(A)	HOT,S(H)	ALL,S(A)
1150.00	0.00	0.00	2000.00	19250.00	2200.00	19300.00	0.00	0.00	0.00	0.00
1160.00	0.00	0.00	1860.00	19215.00	2060.00	19265.00	0.00	0.00	0.00	0.00
1170.00	0.00	0.00	1720.00	19180.00	1920.00	19230.00	0.00	0.00	0.00	0.00
1180.00	0.00	0.00	1580.00	19145.00	1780.00	19195.00	0.00	0.00	0.00	0.00
1190.00	0.00	0.00	1440.00	19110.00	1640.00	19160.00	0.00	0.00	0.00	0.00
1200.00	0.00	0.00	1300.00	19075.00	1500.00	19125.00	0.00	0.00	0.00	0.00

NOTE ?- ALL ZERO STRESS VALUES INDICATE THAT THE CODE DOES NOT
**** RECOMMEND THE USE OF THE MATERIAL AT THAT TEMPERATURE

HOT STRESS AND ALLOW. STRESS RANGE
BASED ON B31.1

S(A)=F*(1.25*S(C)+0.25*S(H)) , F=1

MATERIAL	A312-TP304		A312-TP304L		A312-TP316		A312-TP316L		A312-TP317	
TEMP(F)	HOT,S(H)	ALL,S(A)	HOT,S(H)	ALL,S(A)	HOT,S(H)	ALL,S(A)	HOT,S(H)	ALL,S(A)	HOT,S(H)	ALL,S(A)
100.00	18800.00	28200.00	15700.00	23550.00	18800.00	28200.00	15600.00	23400.00	18800.00	28200.00
110.00	18490.00	28122.50	15700.00	23550.00	18800.00	28200.00	15410.00	23352.50	18540.00	28135.00
120.00	18180.00	28045.00	15700.00	23550.00	18800.00	28200.00	15220.00	23305.00	18280.00	28070.00
130.00	17870.00	27967.50	15700.00	23550.00	18800.00	28200.00	15030.00	23257.50	18020.00	28005.00
140.00	17560.00	27890.00	15700.00	23550.00	18800.00	28200.00	14840.00	23210.00	17760.00	27940.00
150.00	17250.00	27812.50	15700.00	23550.00	18800.00	28200.00	14650.00	23162.50	17500.00	27875.00
160.00	16940.00	27735.00	15700.00	23550.00	18800.00	28200.00	14460.00	23115.00	17240.00	27810.00
170.00	16630.00	27657.50	15700.00	23550.00	18800.00	28200.00	14270.00	23067.50	16980.00	27745.00
180.00	16320.00	27580.00	15700.00	23550.00	18800.00	28200.00	14080.00	23020.00	16720.00	27680.00
190.00	16010.00	27502.50	15700.00	23550.00	18800.00	28200.00	13890.00	22972.50	16460.00	27615.00
200.00	15700.00	27425.00	15700.00	23550.00	18800.00	28200.00	13700.00	22925.00	16200.00	27550.00
210.00	15540.00	27385.00	15660.00	23540.00	18760.00	28190.00	13520.00	22880.00	16000.00	27500.00
220.00	15380.00	27345.00	15620.00	23530.00	18720.00	28180.00	13340.00	22835.00	15800.00	27450.00
230.00	15220.00	27305.00	15580.00	23520.00	18680.00	28170.00	13160.00	22790.00	15600.00	27400.00
240.00	15060.00	27265.00	15540.00	23510.00	18640.00	28160.00	12980.00	22745.00	15400.00	27350.00
250.00	14900.00	27225.00	15500.00	23500.00	18600.00	28150.00	12800.00	22700.00	15200.00	27300.00
260.00	14740.00	27185.00	15460.00	23490.00	18560.00	28140.00	12620.00	22655.00	15000.00	27250.00
270.00	14580.00	27145.00	15420.00	23480.00	18520.00	28130.00	12440.00	22610.00	14800.00	27200.00
280.00	14420.00	27105.00	15380.00	23470.00	18480.00	28120.00	12260.00	22565.00	14600.00	27150.00
290.00	14260.00	27065.00	15340.00	23460.00	18440.00	28110.00	12080.00	22520.00	14400.00	27100.00
300.00	14100.00	27025.00	15300.00	23450.00	18400.00	28100.00	11900.00	22475.00	14200.00	27050.00

NOTE ?- ALL ZERO STRESS VALUES INDICATE THAT THE CODE DOES NOT
**** RECOMMEND THE USE OF THE MATERIAL AT THAT TEMPERATURE

HOT STRESS AND ALLOW. STRESS RANGE
BASED ON B31.1

S(A)=F*(1.25*S(C)+0.25*S(H)) , F=1

MATERIAL	A312-TP304		A312-TP304L		A312-TP316		A312-TP316L		A312-TP317	
TEMP(F)	HOT,S(H)	ALL,S(A)	HOT,S(H)	ALL,S(A)	HOT,S(H)	ALL,S(A)	HOT,S(H)	ALL,S(A)	HOT,S(H)	ALL,S(A)
310.00	13990.00	26997.50	15240.00	23435.00	18370.00	28092.50	11790.00	22447.50	14120.00	27030.00
320.00	13880.00	26970.00	15180.00	23420.00	18340.00	28085.00	11680.00	22420.00	14040.00	27010.00
330.00	13770.00	26942.50	15120.00	23405.00	18310.00	28077.50	11570.00	22392.50	13960.00	26990.00
340.00	13660.00	26915.00	15060.00	23390.00	18280.00	28070.00	11460.00	22365.00	13880.00	26970.00
350.00	13550.00	26887.50	15000.00	23375.00	18250.00	28062.50	11350.00	22337.50	13800.00	26950.00
360.00	13440.00	26860.00	14940.00	23360.00	18220.00	28055.00	11240.00	22310.00	13720.00	26930.00
370.00	13330.00	26832.50	14880.00	23345.00	18190.00	28047.50	11130.00	22282.50	13640.00	26910.00
380.00	13220.00	26805.00	14820.00	23330.00	18160.00	28040.00	11020.00	22255.00	13560.00	26890.00
390.00	13110.00	26777.50	14760.00	23315.00	18130.00	28032.50	10910.00	22227.50	13480.00	26870.00
400.00	13000.00	26750.00	14700.00	23300.00	18100.00	28025.00	10800.00	22200.00	13400.00	26850.00
410.00	12920.00	26730.00	14670.00	23292.50	18090.00	28022.50	10720.00	22180.00	13310.00	26827.50
420.00	12840.00	26710.00	14640.00	23285.00	18080.00	28020.00	10640.00	22160.00	13220.00	26805.00
430.00	12760.00	26690.00	14610.00	23277.50	18070.00	28017.50	10560.00	22140.00	13130.00	26782.50
440.00	12680.00	26670.00	14580.00	23270.00	18060.00	28015.00	10480.00	22120.00	13040.00	26760.00
450.00	12600.00	26650.00	14550.00	23262.50	18050.00	28012.50	10400.00	22100.00	12950.00	26737.50
460.00	12520.00	26630.00	14520.00	23255.00	18040.00	28010.00	10320.00	22080.00	12860.00	26715.00
470.00	12440.00	26610.00	14490.00	23247.50	18030.00	28007.50	10240.00	22060.00	12770.00	26692.50
480.00	12360.00	26590.00	14460.00	23240.00	18020.00	28005.00	10160.00	22040.00	12680.00	26670.00
490.00	12280.00	26570.00	14430.00	23232.50	18010.00	28002.50	10080.00	22020.00	12590.00	26647.50
500.00	12200.00	26550.00	14400.00	23225.00	18000.00	28000.00	10000.00	22000.00	12500.00	26625.00
510.00	12120.00	26530.00	14360.00	23215.00	17900.00	27975.00	9940.00	21985.00	12430.00	26607.50

NOTE ?- ALL ZERO STRESS VALUES INDICATE THAT THE CODE DOES NOT
**** RECOMMEND THE USE OF THE MATERIAL AT THAT TEMPERATURE

HOT STRESS AND ALLOW. STRESS RANGE
BASED ON B31.1

S(A)=F*(1.25*S(C)+0.25*S(H)) , F=1

MATERIAL	A312-TP304		A312-TP304L		A312-TP316		A312-TP316L		A312-TP317	
TEMP(F)	HOT,S(H)	ALL,S(A)	HOT,S(H)	ALL,S(A)	HOT,S(H)	ALL,S(A)	HOT,S(H)	ALL,S(A)	HOT,S(H)	ALL,S(A)
520.00	12040.00	26510.00	14320.00	23205.00	17800.00	27950.00	9880.00	21970.00	12360.00	26590.00
530.00	11960.00	26490.00	14280.00	23195.00	17700.00	27925.00	9820.00	21955.00	12290.00	26572.50
540.00	11880.00	26470.00	14240.00	23185.00	17600.00	27900.00	9760.00	21940.00	12220.00	26555.00
550.00	11800.00	26450.00	14200.00	23175.00	17500.00	27875.00	9700.00	21925.00	12150.00	26537.50
560.00	11720.00	26430.00	14160.00	23165.00	17400.00	27850.00	9640.00	21910.00	12080.00	26520.00
570.00	11640.00	26410.00	14120.00	23155.00	17300.00	27825.00	9580.00	21895.00	12010.00	26502.50
580.00	11560.00	26390.00	14080.00	23145.00	17200.00	27800.00	9520.00	21880.00	11940.00	26485.00
590.00	11480.00	26370.00	14040.00	23135.00	17100.00	27775.00	9460.00	21865.00	11870.00	26467.50
600.00	11400.00	26350.00	14000.00	23125.00	17000.00	27750.00	9400.00	21850.00	11800.00	26450.00
610.00	11360.00	26340.00	13940.00	23110.00	16940.00	27735.00	9360.00	21840.00	11760.00	26440.00
620.00	11320.00	26330.00	13880.00	23095.00	16880.00	27720.00	9320.00	21830.00	11720.00	26430.00
630.00	11280.00	26320.00	13820.00	23080.00	16820.00	27705.00	9280.00	21820.00	11680.00	26420.00
640.00	11240.00	26310.00	13760.00	23065.00	16760.00	27690.00	9240.00	21810.00	11640.00	26410.00
650.00	11200.00	26300.00	13700.00	23050.00	16700.00	27675.00	9200.00	21800.00	11600.00	26400.00
660.00	11180.00	26295.00	13660.00	23040.00	16620.00	27655.00	9160.00	21790.00	11540.00	26385.00
670.00	11160.00	26290.00	13620.00	23030.00	16540.00	27635.00	9120.00	21780.00	11480.00	26370.00
680.00	11140.00	26285.00	13580.00	23020.00	16460.00	27615.00	9080.00	21770.00	11420.00	26355.00
690.00	11120.00	26280.00	13540.00	23010.00	16380.00	27595.00	9040.00	21760.00	11360.00	26340.00
700.00	11100.00	26275.00	13500.00	23000.00	16300.00	27575.00	9000.00	21750.00	11300.00	26325.00
710.00	11040.00	26260.00	13460.00	22990.00	16260.00	27565.00	8960.00	21740.00	11280.00	26320.00
720.00	10980.00	26245.00	13420.00	22980.00	16220.00	27555.00	8920.00	21730.00	11260.00	26315.00

NOTE ?- ALL ZERO STRESS VALUES INDICATE THAT THE CODE DOES NOT
**** RECOMMEND THE USE OF THE MATERIAL AT THAT TEMPERATURE

HOT STRESS AND ALLOW. STRESS RANGE
BASED ON B31.1

S(A)=F*(1.25*S(C)+0.25*S(H)) , F=1

MATERIAL	A312-TP304		A312-TP304L		A312-TP316		A312-TP316L		A312-TP317	
TEMP(F)	HOT,S(H)	ALL,S(A)	HOT,S(H)	ALL,S(A)	HOT,S(H)	ALL,S(A)	HOT,S(H)	ALL,S(A)	HOT,S(H)	ALL,S(A)
730.00	10920.00	26230.00	13380.00	22970.00	16180.00	27545.00	8880.00	21720.00	11240.00	26310.00
740.00	10860.00	26215.00	13340.00	22960.00	16140.00	27535.00	8840.00	21710.00	11220.00	26305.00
750.00	10800.00	26200.00	13300.00	22950.00	16100.00	27525.00	8800.00	21700.00	11200.00	26300.00
760.00	10760.00	26190.00	13240.00	22935.00	16060.00	27515.00	8760.00	21690.00	11160.00	26290.00
770.00	10720.00	26180.00	13180.00	22920.00	16020.00	27505.00	8720.00	21680.00	11120.00	26280.00
780.00	10680.00	26170.00	13120.00	22905.00	15980.00	27495.00	8680.00	21670.00	11080.00	26270.00
790.00	10640.00	26160.00	13060.00	22890.00	15940.00	27485.00	8640.00	21660.00	11040.00	26260.00
800.00	10600.00	26150.00	13000.00	22875.00	15900.00	27475.00	8600.00	21650.00	11000.00	26250.00
810.00	10560.00	26140.00	0.00	0.00	15860.00	27465.00	8560.00	21640.00	10980.00	26245.00
820.00	10520.00	26130.00	0.00	0.00	15820.00	27455.00	8520.00	21630.00	10960.00	26240.00
830.00	10480.00	26120.00	0.00	0.00	15780.00	27445.00	8480.00	21620.00	10940.00	26235.00
840.00	10440.00	26110.00	0.00	0.00	15740.00	27435.00	8440.00	21610.00	10920.00	26230.00
850.00	10400.00	26100.00	0.00	0.00	15700.00	27425.00	8400.00	21600.00	10900.00	26225.00
860.00	10360.00	26090.00	0.00	0.00	15680.00	27420.00	0.00	0.00	10880.00	26220.00
870.00	10320.00	26080.00	0.00	0.00	15660.00	27415.00	0.00	0.00	10860.00	26215.00
880.00	10280.00	26070.00	0.00	0.00	15640.00	27410.00	0.00	0.00	10840.00	26210.00
890.00	10240.00	26060.00	0.00	0.00	15620.00	27405.00	0.00	0.00	10820.00	26205.00
900.00	10200.00	26050.00	0.00	0.00	15600.00	27400.00	0.00	0.00	10800.00	26200.00
910.00	10160.00	26040.00	0.00	0.00	15560.00	27390.00	0.00	0.00	10780.00	26195.00
920.00	10120.00	26030.00	0.00	0.00	15520.00	27380.00	0.00	0.00	10760.00	26190.00
930.00	10080.00	26020.00	0.00	0.00	15480.00	27370.00	0.00	0.00	10740.00	26185.00

NOTE ?- ALL ZERO STRESS VALUES INDICATE THAT THE CODE DOES NOT
**** RECOMMEND THE USE OF THE MATERIAL AT THAT TEMPERATURE

HOT STRESS AND ALLOW. STRESS RANGE
BASED ON B31.1

S(A)=F*(1.25*S(C)+0.25*S(H)) , F=1

MATERIAL	A312-TP304		A312-TP304L		A312-TP316		A312-TP316L		A312-TP317	
TEMP(F)	HOT,S(H)	ALL,S(A)	HOT,S(H)	ALL,S(A)	HOT,S(H)	ALL,S(A)	HOT,S(H)	ALL,S(A)	HOT,S(H)	ALL,S(A)
940.00	10040.00	26010.00	0.00	0.00	15440.00	27360.00	0.00	0.00	10720.00	26180.00
950.00	10000.00	26000.00	0.00	0.00	15400.00	27350.00	0.00	0.00	10700.00	26175.00
960.00	9960.00	25990.00	0.00	0.00	15380.00	27345.00	0.00	0.00	10680.00	26170.00
970.00	9920.00	25980.00	0.00	0.00	15360.00	27340.00	0.00	0.00	10660.00	26165.00
980.00	9880.00	25970.00	0.00	0.00	15340.00	27335.00	0.00	0.00	10640.00	26160.00
990.00	9840.00	25960.00	0.00	0.00	15320.00	27330.00	0.00	0.00	10620.00	26155.00
1000.00	9800.00	25950.00	0.00	0.00	15300.00	27325.00	0.00	0.00	10600.00	26150.00
1010.00	9740.00	25935.00	0.00	0.00	15140.00	27285.00	0.00	0.00	10580.00	26145.00
1020.00	9680.00	25920.00	0.00	0.00	14980.00	27245.00	0.00	0.00	10560.00	26140.00
1030.00	9620.00	25905.00	0.00	0.00	14820.00	27205.00	0.00	0.00	10540.00	26135.00
1040.00	9560.00	25890.00	0.00	0.00	14660.00	27165.00	0.00	0.00	10520.00	26130.00
1050.00	9500.00	25875.00	0.00	0.00	14500.00	27125.00	0.00	0.00	10500.00	26125.00
1060.00	9380.00	25845.00	0.00	0.00	14080.00	27020.00	0.00	0.00	10460.00	26115.00
1070.00	9260.00	25815.00	0.00	0.00	13660.00	26915.00	0.00	0.00	10420.00	26105.00
1080.00	9140.00	25785.00	0.00	0.00	13240.00	26810.00	0.00	0.00	10380.00	26095.00
1090.00	9020.00	25755.00	0.00	0.00	12820.00	26705.00	0.00	0.00	10340.00	26085.00
1100.00	8900.00	25725.00	0.00	0.00	12400.00	26600.00	0.00	0.00	10300.00	26075.00
1110.00	8660.00	25665.00	0.00	0.00	11880.00	26470.00	0.00	0.00	10100.00	26025.00
1120.00	8420.00	25605.00	0.00	0.00	11360.00	26340.00	0.00	0.00	9900.00	25975.00
1130.00	8180.00	25545.00	0.00	0.00	10840.00	26210.00	0.00	0.00	9700.00	25925.00
1140.00	7940.00	25485.00	0.00	0.00	10320.00	26080.00	0.00	0.00	9500.00	25875.00

NOTE ?- ALL ZERO STRESS VALUES INDICATE THAT THE CODE DOES NOT
**** RECOMMEND THE USE OF THE MATERIAL AT THAT TEMPERATURE

HOT STRESS AND ALLOW. STRESS RANGE
BASED ON B31.1

S(A)=F*(1.25*S(C)+0.25*S(H)) , F=1

MATERIAL	A312-TP304		A312-TP304L		A312-TP316		A312-TP316L		A312-TP317	
TEMP(F)	HOT,S(H)	ALL,S(A)	HOT,S(H)	ALL,S(A)	HOT,S(H)	ALL,S(A)	HOT,S(H)	ALL,S(A)	HOT,S(H)	ALL,S(A)
1150.00	7700.00	25425.00	0.00	0.00	9800.00	25950.00	0.00	0.00	9300.00	25825.00
1160.00	7380.00	25345.00	0.00	0.00	9320.00	25830.00	0.00	0.00	8920.00	25730.00
1170.00	7060.00	25265.00	0.00	0.00	8840.00	25710.00	0.00	0.00	8540.00	25635.00
1180.00	6740.00	25185.00	0.00	0.00	8360.00	25590.00	0.00	0.00	8160.00	25540.00
1190.00	6420.00	25105.00	0.00	0.00	7880.00	25470.00	0.00	0.00	7780.00	25445.00
1200.00	6100.00	25025.00	0.00	0.00	7400.00	25350.00	0.00	0.00	7400.00	25350.00

NOTE ?- ALL ZERO STRESS VALUES INDICATE THAT THE CODE DOES NOT
**** RECOMMEND THE USE OF THE MATERIAL AT THAT TEMPERATURE

HOT STRESS AND ALLOW. STRESS RANGE
BASED ON B31.1

S(A)=F*(1.25*S(C)+0.25*S(H)) , F=1

MATERIAL	A312-TP321		A312-TP347		A376- TP304		A376- TP316		A376-TP321	
TEMP(F)	HOT,S(H)	ALL,S(A)	HOT,S(H)	ALL,S(A)	HOT,S(H)	ALL,S(A)	HOT,S(H)	ALL,S(A)	HOT,S(H)	ALL,S(A)
100.00	18800.00	28200.00	18800.00	28200.00	18700.00	28050.00	18800.00	28200.00	18800.00	28200.00
110.00	18760.00	28190.00	18710.00	28177.50	18390.00	27972.50	18800.00	28200.00	18760.00	28190.00
120.00	18720.00	28180.00	18620.00	28155.00	18080.00	27895.00	18800.00	28200.00	18720.00	28180.00
130.00	18680.00	28170.00	18530.00	28132.50	17770.00	27817.50	18800.00	28200.00	18680.00	28170.00
140.00	18640.00	28160.00	18440.00	28110.00	17460.00	27740.00	18800.00	28200.00	18640.00	28160.00
150.00	18600.00	28150.00	18350.00	28087.50	17150.00	27662.50	18800.00	28200.00	18600.00	28150.00
160.00	18560.00	28140.00	18260.00	28065.00	16840.00	27585.00	18800.00	28200.00	18560.00	28140.00
170.00	18520.00	28130.00	18170.00	28042.50	16530.00	27507.50	18800.00	28200.00	18520.00	28130.00
180.00	18480.00	28120.00	18080.00	28020.00	16220.00	27430.00	18800.00	28200.00	18480.00	28120.00
190.00	18440.00	28110.00	17990.00	27997.50	15910.00	27352.50	18800.00	28200.00	18440.00	28110.00
200.00	18400.00	28100.00	17900.00	27975.00	15600.00	27275.00	18800.00	28200.00	18400.00	28100.00
210.00	18290.00	28072.50	17750.00	27937.50	15440.00	27235.00	18760.00	28190.00	18290.00	28072.50
220.00	18180.00	28045.00	17600.00	27900.00	15280.00	27195.00	18720.00	28180.00	18180.00	28045.00
230.00	18070.00	28017.50	17450.00	27862.50	15120.00	27155.00	18680.00	28170.00	18070.00	28017.50
240.00	17960.00	27990.00	17300.00	27825.00	14960.00	27115.00	18640.00	28160.00	17960.00	27990.00
250.00	17850.00	27962.50	17150.00	27787.50	14800.00	27075.00	18600.00	28150.00	17850.00	27962.50
260.00	17740.00	27935.00	17000.00	27750.00	14640.00	27035.00	18560.00	28140.00	17740.00	27935.00
270.00	17630.00	27907.50	16850.00	27712.50	14480.00	26995.00	18520.00	28130.00	17630.00	27907.50
280.00	17520.00	27880.00	16700.00	27675.00	14320.00	26955.00	18480.00	28120.00	17520.00	27880.00
290.00	17410.00	27852.50	16550.00	27637.50	14160.00	26915.00	18440.00	28110.00	17410.00	27852.50
300.00	17300.00	27825.00	16400.00	27600.00	14000.00	26875.00	18400.00	28100.00	17300.00	27825.00

NOTE ?- ALL ZERO STRESS VALUES INDICATE THAT THE CODE DOES NOT
**** RECOMMEND THE USE OF THE MATERIAL AT THAT TEMPERATURE

HOT STRESS AND ALLOW. STRESS RANGE
BASED ON B31.1

S(A)=F*(1.25*S(C)+0.25*S(H)) , F=1

MATERIAL	A312-TP321		A312-TP347		A376- TP304		A376- TP316		A376-TP321	
TEMP(F)	HOT,S(H)	ALL,S(A)	HOT,S(H)	ALL,S(A)	HOT,S(H)	ALL,S(A)	HOT,S(H)	ALL,S(A)	HOT,S(H)	ALL,S(A)
310.00	17280.00	27820.00	16300.00	27575.00	13890.00	26847.50	18370.00	28092.50	17280.00	27820.00
320.00	17260.00	27815.00	16200.00	27550.00	13780.00	26820.00	18340.00	28085.00	17260.00	27815.00
330.00	17240.00	27810.00	16100.00	27525.00	13670.00	26792.50	18310.00	28077.50	17240.00	27810.00
340.00	17220.00	27805.00	16000.00	27500.00	13560.00	26765.00	18280.00	28070.00	17220.00	27805.00
350.00	17200.00	27800.00	15900.00	27475.00	13450.00	26737.50	18250.00	28062.50	17200.00	27800.00
360.00	17180.00	27795.00	15800.00	27450.00	13340.00	26710.00	18220.00	28055.00	17180.00	27795.00
370.00	17160.00	27790.00	15700.00	27425.00	13230.00	26682.50	18190.00	28047.50	17160.00	27790.00
380.00	17140.00	27785.00	15600.00	27400.00	13120.00	26655.00	18160.00	28040.00	17140.00	27785.00
390.00	17120.00	27780.00	15500.00	27375.00	13010.00	26627.50	18130.00	28032.50	17120.00	27780.00
400.00	17100.00	27775.00	15400.00	27350.00	12900.00	26600.00	18100.00	28025.00	17100.00	27775.00
410.00	17100.00	27775.00	15350.00	27337.50	12820.00	26580.00	18090.00	28022.50	17100.00	27775.00
420.00	17100.00	27775.00	15300.00	27325.00	12740.00	26560.00	18080.00	28020.00	17100.00	27775.00
430.00	17100.00	27775.00	15250.00	27312.50	12660.00	26540.00	18070.00	28017.50	17100.00	27775.00
440.00	17100.00	27775.00	15200.00	27300.00	12580.00	26520.00	18060.00	28015.00	17100.00	27775.00
450.00	17100.00	27775.00	15150.00	27287.50	12500.00	26500.00	18050.00	28012.50	17100.00	27775.00
460.00	17100.00	27775.00	15100.00	27275.00	12420.00	26480.00	18040.00	28010.00	17100.00	27775.00
470.00	17100.00	27775.00	15050.00	27262.50	12340.00	26460.00	18030.00	28007.50	17100.00	27775.00
480.00	17100.00	27775.00	15000.00	27250.00	12260.00	26440.00	18020.00	28005.00	17100.00	27775.00
490.00	17100.00	27775.00	14950.00	27237.50	12180.00	26420.00	18010.00	28002.50	17100.00	27775.00
500.00	17100.00	27775.00	14900.00	27225.00	12100.00	26400.00	18000.00	28000.00	17100.00	27775.00
510.00	17030.00	27757.50	14880.00	27220.00	12030.00	26382.50	17900.00	27975.00	17020.00	27755.00

NOTE ?- ALL ZERO STRESS VALUES INDICATE THAT THE CODE DOES NOT
**** RECOMMEND THE USE OF THE MATERIAL AT THAT TEMPERATURE

HOT STRESS AND ALLOW. STRESS RANGE
BASED ON B31.1

S(A)=F*(1.25*S(C)+0.25*S(H)) , F=1

MATERIAL	A312-TP321		A312-TP347		A376- TP304		A376- TP316		A376-TP321	
TEMP(F)	HOT,S(H)	ALL,S(A)	HOT,S(H)	ALL,S(A)	HOT,S(H)	ALL,S(A)	HOT,S(H)	ALL,S(A)	HOT,S(H)	ALL,S(A)
520.00	16960.00	27740.00	14860.00	27215.00	11960.00	26365.00	17800.00	27950.00	16940.00	27735.00
530.00	16890.00	27722.50	14840.00	27210.00	11890.00	26347.50	17700.00	27925.00	16860.00	27715.00
540.00	16820.00	27705.00	14820.00	27205.00	11820.00	26330.00	17600.00	27900.00	16780.00	27695.00
550.00	16750.00	27687.50	14800.00	27200.00	11750.00	26312.50	17500.00	27875.00	16700.00	27675.00
560.00	16680.00	27670.00	14780.00	27195.00	11680.00	26295.00	17400.00	27850.00	16620.00	27655.00
570.00	16610.00	27652.50	14760.00	27190.00	11610.00	26277.50	17300.00	27825.00	16540.00	27635.00
580.00	16540.00	27635.00	14740.00	27185.00	11540.00	26260.00	17200.00	27800.00	16460.00	27615.00
590.00	16470.00	27617.50	14720.00	27180.00	11470.00	26242.50	17100.00	27775.00	16380.00	27595.00
600.00	16400.00	27600.00	14700.00	27175.00	11400.00	26225.00	17000.00	27750.00	16300.00	27575.00
610.00	16340.00	27585.00	14700.00	27175.00	11360.00	26215.00	16940.00	27735.00	16260.00	27565.00
620.00	16280.00	27570.00	14700.00	27175.00	11320.00	26205.00	16880.00	27720.00	16220.00	27555.00
630.00	16220.00	27555.00	14700.00	27175.00	11280.00	26195.00	16820.00	27705.00	16180.00	27545.00
640.00	16160.00	27540.00	14700.00	27175.00	11240.00	26185.00	16760.00	27690.00	16140.00	27535.00
650.00	16100.00	27525.00	14700.00	27175.00	11200.00	26175.00	16700.00	27675.00	16100.00	27525.00
660.00	16040.00	27510.00	14680.00	27170.00	11160.00	26165.00	16620.00	27655.00	16040.00	27510.00
670.00	15980.00	27495.00	14660.00	27165.00	11120.00	26155.00	16540.00	27635.00	15980.00	27495.00
680.00	15920.00	27480.00	14640.00	27160.00	11080.00	26145.00	16460.00	27615.00	15920.00	27480.00
690.00	15860.00	27465.00	14620.00	27155.00	11040.00	26135.00	16380.00	27595.00	15860.00	27465.00
700.00	15800.00	27450.00	14600.00	27150.00	11000.00	26125.00	16300.00	27575.00	15800.00	27450.00
710.00	15780.00	27445.00	14620.00	27155.00	10960.00	26115.00	16260.00	27565.00	15780.00	27445.00
720.00	15760.00	27440.00	14640.00	27160.00	10920.00	26105.00	16220.00	27555.00	15760.00	27440.00

NOTE ?- ALL ZERO STRESS VALUES INDICATE THAT THE CODE DOES NOT
**** RECOMMEND THE USE OF THE MATERIAL AT THAT TEMPERATURE

HOT STRESS AND ALLOW. STRESS RANGE
BASED ON B31.1

S(A)=F*(1.25*S(C)+0.25*S(H)) , F=1

MATERIAL	A312-TP321		A312-TP347		A376- TP304		A376- TP316		A376-TP321	
TEMP(F)	HOT,S(H)	ALL,S(A)	HOT,S(H)	ALL,S(A)	HOT,S(H)	ALL,S(A)	HOT,S(H)	ALL,S(A)	HOT,S(H)	ALL,S(A)
730.00	15740.00	27435.00	14660.00	27165.00	10880.00	26095.00	16180.00	27545.00	15740.00	27435.00
740.00	15720.00	27430.00	14680.00	27170.00	10840.00	26085.00	16140.00	27535.00	15720.00	27430.00
750.00	15700.00	27425.00	14700.00	27175.00	10800.00	26075.00	16100.00	27525.00	15700.00	27425.00
760.00	15660.00	27415.00	14700.00	27175.00	10740.00	26060.00	16060.00	27515.00	15660.00	27415.00
770.00	15620.00	27405.00	14700.00	27175.00	10680.00	26045.00	16020.00	27505.00	15620.00	27405.00
780.00	15580.00	27395.00	14700.00	27175.00	10620.00	26030.00	15980.00	27495.00	15580.00	27395.00
790.00	15540.00	27385.00	14700.00	27175.00	10560.00	26015.00	15940.00	27485.00	15540.00	27385.00
800.00	15500.00	27375.00	14700.00	27175.00	10500.00	26000.00	15900.00	27475.00	15500.00	27375.00
810.00	15480.00	27370.00	14700.00	27175.00	10460.00	25990.00	15860.00	27465.00	15480.00	27370.00
820.00	15460.00	27365.00	14700.00	27175.00	10420.00	25980.00	15820.00	27455.00	15460.00	27365.00
830.00	15440.00	27360.00	14700.00	27175.00	10380.00	25970.00	15780.00	27445.00	15440.00	27360.00
840.00	15420.00	27355.00	14700.00	27175.00	10340.00	25960.00	15740.00	27435.00	15420.00	27355.00
850.00	15400.00	27350.00	14700.00	27175.00	10300.00	25950.00	15700.00	27425.00	15400.00	27350.00
860.00	15380.00	27345.00	14700.00	27175.00	10260.00	25940.00	15680.00	27420.00	15380.00	27345.00
870.00	15360.00	27340.00	14700.00	27175.00	10220.00	25930.00	15660.00	27415.00	15360.00	27340.00
880.00	15340.00	27335.00	14700.00	27175.00	10180.00	25920.00	15640.00	27410.00	15340.00	27335.00
890.00	15320.00	27330.00	14700.00	27175.00	10140.00	25910.00	15620.00	27405.00	15320.00	27330.00
900.00	15300.00	27325.00	14700.00	27175.00	10100.00	25900.00	15600.00	27400.00	15300.00	27325.00
910.00	15280.00	27320.00	14680.00	27170.00	10060.00	25890.00	15560.00	27390.00	15280.00	27320.00
920.00	15260.00	27315.00	14660.00	27165.00	10020.00	25880.00	15520.00	27380.00	15260.00	27315.00
930.00	15240.00	27310.00	14640.00	27160.00	9980.00	25870.00	15480.00	27370.00	15240.00	27310.00

NOTE ?- ALL ZERO STRESS VALUES INDICATE THAT THE CODE DOES NOT
**** RECOMMEND THE USE OF THE MATERIAL AT THAT TEMPERATURE

HOT STRESS AND ALLOW. STRESS RANGE
BASED ON B31.1

S(A)=F*(1.25*S(C)+0.25*S(H)) , F=1

MATERIAL	A312-TP321		A312-TP347		A376- TP304		A376- TP316		A376-TP321	
TEMP(F)	HOT,S(H)	ALL,S(A)	HOT,S(H)	ALL,S(A)	HOT,S(H)	ALL,S(A)	HOT,S(H)	ALL,S(A)	HOT,S(H)	ALL,S(A)
940.00	15220.00	27305.00	14620.00	27155.00	9940.00	25860.00	15440.00	27360.00	15220.00	27305.00
950.00	15200.00	27300.00	14600.00	27150.00	9900.00	25850.00	15400.00	27350.00	15200.00	27300.00
960.00	14920.00	27230.00	14480.00	27120.00	9860.00	25840.00	15380.00	27345.00	14920.00	27230.00
970.00	14640.00	27160.00	14360.00	27090.00	9820.00	25830.00	15360.00	27340.00	14640.00	27160.00
980.00	14360.00	27090.00	14240.00	27060.00	9780.00	25820.00	15340.00	27335.00	14360.00	27090.00
990.00	14080.00	27020.00	14120.00	27030.00	9740.00	25810.00	15320.00	27330.00	14080.00	27020.00
1000.00	13800.00	26950.00	14000.00	27000.00	9700.00	25800.00	15300.00	27325.00	13800.00	26950.00
1010.00	12960.00	26740.00	13620.00	26905.00	9660.00	25790.00	15140.00	27285.00	12960.00	26740.00
1020.00	12120.00	26530.00	13240.00	26810.00	9620.00	25780.00	14980.00	27245.00	12120.00	26530.00
1030.00	11280.00	26320.00	12860.00	26715.00	9580.00	25770.00	14820.00	27205.00	11280.00	26320.00
1040.00	10440.00	26110.00	12480.00	26620.00	9540.00	25760.00	14660.00	27165.00	10440.00	26110.00
1050.00	9600.00	25900.00	12100.00	26525.00	9500.00	25750.00	14500.00	27125.00	9600.00	25900.00
1060.00	9060.00	25765.00	11500.00	26375.00	9360.00	25715.00	14080.00	27020.00	9060.00	25765.00
1070.00	8520.00	25630.00	10900.00	26225.00	9220.00	25680.00	13660.00	26915.00	8520.00	25630.00
1080.00	7980.00	25495.00	10300.00	26075.00	9080.00	25645.00	13240.00	26810.00	7980.00	25495.00
1090.00	7440.00	25360.00	9700.00	25925.00	8940.00	25610.00	12820.00	26705.00	7440.00	25360.00
1100.00	6900.00	25225.00	9100.00	25775.00	8800.00	25575.00	12400.00	26600.00	6900.00	25225.00
1110.00	6520.00	25130.00	8500.00	25625.00	8580.00	25520.00	11880.00	26470.00	6520.00	25130.00
1120.00	6140.00	25035.00	7900.00	25475.00	8360.00	25465.00	11360.00	26340.00	6140.00	25035.00
1130.00	5760.00	24940.00	7300.00	25325.00	8140.00	25410.00	10840.00	26210.00	5760.00	24940.00
1140.00	5380.00	24845.00	6700.00	25175.00	7920.00	25355.00	10320.00	26080.00	5380.00	24845.00

NOTE ?- ALL ZERO STRESS VALUES INDICATE THAT THE CODE DOES NOT
**** RECOMMEND THE USE OF THE MATERIAL AT THAT TEMPERATURE

HOT STRESS AND ALLOW. STRESS RANGE
BASED ON B31.1

S(A)=F*(1.25*S(C)+0.25*S(H)) , F=1

MATERIAL	A312-TP321		A312-TP347		A376- TP304		A376- TP316		A376-TP321	
TEMP(F)	HOT,S(H)	ALL,S(A)	HOT,S(H)	ALL,S(A)	HOT,S(H)	ALL,S(A)	HOT,S(H)	ALL,S(A)	HOT,S(H)	ALL,S(A)
1150.00	5000.00	24750.00	6100.00	25025.00	7700.00	25300.00	9800.00	25950.00	5000.00	24750.00
1160.00	4720.00	24680.00	5760.00	24940.00	7360.00	25215.00	9320.00	25830.00	4720.00	24680.00
1170.00	4440.00	24610.00	5420.00	24855.00	7020.00	25130.00	8840.00	25710.00	4440.00	24610.00
1180.00	4160.00	24540.00	5080.00	24770.00	6680.00	25045.00	8360.00	25590.00	4160.00	24540.00
1190.00	3880.00	24470.00	4740.00	24685.00	6340.00	24960.00	7880.00	25470.00	3880.00	24470.00
1200.00	3600.00	24400.00	4400.00	24600.00	6000.00	24875.00	7400.00	25350.00	3600.00	24400.00

NOTE ?- ALL ZERO STRESS VALUES INDICATE THAT THE CODE DOES NOT
**** RECOMMEND THE USE OF THE MATERIAL AT THAT TEMPERATURE

HOT STRESS AND ALLOW. STRESS RANGE
BASED ON B31.1

S(A)=F*(1.25*S(C)+0.25*S(H)) , F=1

MATERIAL	A358---304		COPPER-B42-3		RED-BRASS-B1		NICKELB161#5		NICKELB161)5	
TEMP(F)	HOT,S(H)	ALL,S(A)	HOT,S(H)	ALL,S(A)	HOT,S(H)	ALL,S(A)	HOT,S(H)	ALL,S(A)	HOT,S(H)	ALL,S(A)
100.00	16900.00	25350.00	6000.00	9000.00	8000.00	12000.00	8000.00	12000.00	6700.00	10050.00
110.00	16620.00	25280.00	5880.00	8970.00	8000.00	12000.00	7970.00	11992.50	6670.00	10042.50
120.00	16340.00	25210.00	5760.00	8940.00	8000.00	12000.00	7940.00	11985.00	6640.00	10035.00
130.00	16060.00	25140.00	5640.00	8910.00	8000.00	12000.00	7910.00	11977.50	6610.00	10027.50
140.00	15780.00	25070.00	5520.00	8880.00	8000.00	12000.00	7880.00	11970.00	6580.00	10020.00
150.00	15500.00	25000.00	5400.00	8850.00	8000.00	12000.00	7850.00	11962.50	6550.00	10012.50
160.00	15220.00	24930.00	5280.00	8820.00	8000.00	12000.00	7820.00	11955.00	6520.00	10005.00
170.00	14940.00	24860.00	5160.00	8790.00	8000.00	12000.00	7790.00	11947.50	6490.00	9997.50
180.00	14660.00	24790.00	5040.00	8760.00	8000.00	12000.00	7760.00	11940.00	6460.00	9990.00
190.00	14380.00	24720.00	4920.00	8730.00	8000.00	12000.00	7730.00	11932.50	6430.00	9982.50
200.00	14100.00	24650.00	4800.00	8700.00	8000.00	12000.00	7700.00	11925.00	6400.00	9975.00
210.00	13960.00	24615.00	4790.00	8697.50	8000.00	12000.00	7680.00	11920.00	6390.00	9972.50
220.00	13820.00	24580.00	4780.00	8695.00	8000.00	12000.00	7660.00	11915.00	6380.00	9970.00
230.00	13680.00	24545.00	4770.00	8692.50	8000.00	12000.00	7640.00	11910.00	6370.00	9967.50
240.00	13540.00	24510.00	4760.00	8690.00	8000.00	12000.00	7620.00	11905.00	6360.00	9965.00
250.00	13400.00	24475.00	4750.00	8687.50	8000.00	12000.00	7600.00	11900.00	6350.00	9962.50
260.00	13260.00	24440.00	4740.00	8685.00	8000.00	12000.00	7580.00	11895.00	6340.00	9960.00
270.00	13120.00	24405.00	4730.00	8682.50	8000.00	12000.00	7560.00	11890.00	6330.00	9957.50
280.00	12980.00	24370.00	4720.00	8680.00	8000.00	12000.00	7540.00	11885.00	6320.00	9955.00
290.00	12840.00	24335.00	4710.00	8677.50	8000.00	12000.00	7520.00	11880.00	6310.00	9952.50
300.00	12700.00	24300.00	4700.00	8675.00	8000.00	12000.00	7500.00	11875.00	6300.00	9950.00

NOTE ?- ALL ZERO STRESS VALUES INDICATE THAT THE CODE DOES NOT
**** RECOMMEND THE USE OF THE MATERIAL AT THAT TEMPERATURE

HOT STRESS AND ALLOW. STRESS RANGE
BASED ON B31.1

S(A)=F*(1.25*S(C)+0.25*S(H)) , F=1

MATERIAL	A358---304		COPPER-B42-3		RED-BRASS-B1		NICKELB161#5		NICKELB161)5	
TEMP(F)	HOT,S(H)	ALL,S(A)	HOT,S(H)	ALL,S(A)	HOT,S(H)	ALL,S(A)	HOT,S(H)	ALL,S(A)	HOT,S(H)	ALL,S(A)
310.00	12600.00	24275.00	4530.00	8632.50	7700.00	11925.00	7500.00	11875.00	6290.00	9947.50
320.00	12500.00	24250.00	4360.00	8590.00	7400.00	11850.00	7500.00	11875.00	6280.00	9945.00
330.00	12400.00	24225.00	4190.00	8547.50	7100.00	11775.00	7500.00	11875.00	6270.00	9942.50
340.00	12300.00	24200.00	4020.00	8505.00	6800.00	11700.00	7500.00	11875.00	6260.00	9940.00
350.00	12200.00	24175.00	3850.00	8462.50	6500.00	11625.00	7500.00	11875.00	6250.00	9937.50
360.00	12100.00	24150.00	3680.00	8420.00	6200.00	11550.00	7500.00	11875.00	6240.00	9935.00
370.00	12000.00	24125.00	3510.00	8377.50	5900.00	11475.00	7500.00	11875.00	6230.00	9932.50
380.00	11900.00	24100.00	3340.00	8335.00	5600.00	11400.00	7500.00	11875.00	6220.00	9930.00
390.00	11800.00	24075.00	3170.00	8292.50	5300.00	11325.00	7500.00	11875.00	6210.00	9927.50
400.00	11700.00	24050.00	3000.00	8250.00	5000.00	11250.00	7500.00	11875.00	6200.00	9925.00
410.00	11630.00	24032.50	0.00	0.00	0.00	0.00	7500.00	11875.00	6200.00	9925.00
420.00	11560.00	24015.00	0.00	0.00	0.00	0.00	7500.00	11875.00	6200.00	9925.00
430.00	11490.00	23997.50	0.00	0.00	0.00	0.00	7500.00	11875.00	6200.00	9925.00
440.00	11420.00	23980.00	0.00	0.00	0.00	0.00	7500.00	11875.00	6200.00	9925.00
450.00	11350.00	23962.50	0.00	0.00	0.00	0.00	7500.00	11875.00	6200.00	9925.00
460.00	11280.00	23945.00	0.00	0.00	0.00	0.00	7500.00	11875.00	6200.00	9925.00
470.00	11210.00	23927.50	0.00	0.00	0.00	0.00	7500.00	11875.00	6200.00	9925.00
480.00	11140.00	23910.00	0.00	0.00	0.00	0.00	7500.00	11875.00	6200.00	9925.00
490.00	11070.00	23892.50	0.00	0.00	0.00	0.00	7500.00	11875.00	6200.00	9925.00
500.00	11000.00	23875.00	0.00	0.00	0.00	0.00	7500.00	11875.00	6200.00	9925.00
510.00	10930.00	23857.50	0.00	0.00	0.00	0.00	7500.00	11875.00	6200.00	9925.00

NOTE ?- ALL ZERO STRESS VALUES INDICATE THAT THE CODE DOES NOT
**** RECOMMEND THE USE OF THE MATERIAL AT THAT TEMPERATURE

HOT STRESS AND ALLOW. STRESS RANGE
BASED ON B31.1

S(A)=F*(1.25*S(C)+0.25*S(H)) , F=1

MATERIAL	A358---304		COPPER-B42-3		RED-BRASS-B1		NICKELB161#5		NICKELB161)5	
TEMP(F)	HOT,S(H)	ALL,S(A)	HOT,S(H)	ALL,S(A)	HOT,S(H)	ALL,S(A)	HOT,S(H)	ALL,S(A)	HOT,S(H)	ALL,S(A)
520.00	10860.00	23840.00	0.00	0.00	0.00	0.00	7500.00	11875.00	6200.00	9925.00
530.00	10790.00	23822.50	0.00	0.00	0.00	0.00	7500.00	11875.00	6200.00	9925.00
540.00	10720.00	23805.00	0.00	0.00	0.00	0.00	7500.00	11875.00	6200.00	9925.00
550.00	10650.00	23787.50	0.00	0.00	0.00	0.00	7500.00	11875.00	6200.00	9925.00
560.00	10580.00	23770.00	0.00	0.00	0.00	0.00	7500.00	11875.00	6200.00	9925.00
570.00	10510.00	23752.50	0.00	0.00	0.00	0.00	7500.00	11875.00	6200.00	9925.00
580.00	10440.00	23735.00	0.00	0.00	0.00	0.00	7500.00	11875.00	6200.00	9925.00
590.00	10370.00	23717.50	0.00	0.00	0.00	0.00	7500.00	11875.00	6200.00	9925.00
600.00	10300.00	23700.00	0.00	0.00	0.00	0.00	7500.00	11875.00	6200.00	9925.00
610.00	10280.00	23695.00	0.00	0.00	0.00	0.00	7500.00	11875.00	6200.00	9925.00
620.00	10260.00	23690.00	0.00	0.00	0.00	0.00	7500.00	11875.00	6200.00	9925.00
630.00	10240.00	23685.00	0.00	0.00	0.00	0.00	7500.00	11875.00	6200.00	9925.00
640.00	10220.00	23680.00	0.00	0.00	0.00	0.00	7500.00	11875.00	6200.00	9925.00
650.00	10200.00	23675.00	0.00	0.00	0.00	0.00	7500.00	11875.00	6200.00	9925.00
660.00	10160.00	23665.00	0.00	0.00	0.00	0.00	7480.00	11870.00	6200.00	9925.00
670.00	10120.00	23655.00	0.00	0.00	0.00	0.00	7460.00	11865.00	6200.00	9925.00
680.00	10080.00	23645.00	0.00	0.00	0.00	0.00	7440.00	11860.00	6200.00	9925.00
690.00	10040.00	23635.00	0.00	0.00	0.00	0.00	7420.00	11855.00	6200.00	9925.00
700.00	10000.00	23625.00	0.00	0.00	0.00	0.00	7400.00	11850.00	6200.00	9925.00
710.00	9940.00	23610.00	0.00	0.00	0.00	0.00	7380.00	11845.00	6160.00	9915.00
720.00	9880.00	23595.00	0.00	0.00	0.00	0.00	7360.00	11840.00	6120.00	9905.00

NOTE ?- ALL ZERO STRESS VALUES INDICATE THAT THE CODE DOES NOT
**** RECOMMEND THE USE OF THE MATERIAL AT THAT TEMPERATURE

HOT STRESS AND ALLOW. STRESS RANGE
BASED ON B31.1

S(A)=F*(1.25*S(C)+0.25*S(H)) , F=1

MATERIAL	A358---304		COPPER-B42-3		RED-BRASS-B1		NICKELB161#5		NICKELB161)5	
TEMP(F)	HOT,S(H)	ALL,S(A)	HOT,S(H)	ALL,S(A)	HOT,S(H)	ALL,S(A)	HOT,S(H)	ALL,S(A)	HOT,S(H)	ALL,S(A)
730.00	9820.00	23580.00	0.00	0.00	0.00	0.00	7340.00	11835.00	6080.00	9895.00
740.00	9760.00	23565.00	0.00	0.00	0.00	0.00	7320.00	11830.00	6040.00	9885.00
750.00	9700.00	23550.00	0.00	0.00	0.00	0.00	7300.00	11825.00	6000.00	9875.00
760.00	9660.00	23540.00	0.00	0.00	0.00	0.00	7280.00	11820.00	5980.00	9870.00
770.00	9620.00	23530.00	0.00	0.00	0.00	0.00	7260.00	11815.00	5960.00	9865.00
780.00	9580.00	23520.00	0.00	0.00	0.00	0.00	7240.00	11810.00	5940.00	9860.00
790.00	9540.00	23510.00	0.00	0.00	0.00	0.00	7220.00	11805.00	5920.00	9855.00
800.00	9500.00	23500.00	0.00	0.00	0.00	0.00	7200.00	11800.00	5900.00	9850.00
810.00	9480.00	23495.00	0.00	0.00	0.00	0.00	6920.00	11730.00	5880.00	9845.00
820.00	9460.00	23490.00	0.00	0.00	0.00	0.00	6640.00	11660.00	5860.00	9840.00
830.00	9440.00	23485.00	0.00	0.00	0.00	0.00	6360.00	11590.00	5840.00	9835.00
840.00	9420.00	23480.00	0.00	0.00	0.00	0.00	6080.00	11520.00	5820.00	9830.00
850.00	9400.00	23475.00	0.00	0.00	0.00	0.00	5800.00	11450.00	5800.00	9825.00
860.00	9360.00	23465.00	0.00	0.00	0.00	0.00	5540.00	11385.00	5540.00	9760.00
870.00	9320.00	23455.00	0.00	0.00	0.00	0.00	5280.00	11320.00	5280.00	9695.00
880.00	9280.00	23445.00	0.00	0.00	0.00	0.00	5020.00	11255.00	5020.00	9630.00
890.00	9240.00	23435.00	0.00	0.00	0.00	0.00	4760.00	11190.00	4760.00	9565.00
900.00	9200.00	23425.00	0.00	0.00	0.00	0.00	4500.00	11125.00	4500.00	9500.00
910.00	9140.00	23410.00	0.00	0.00	0.00	0.00	4340.00	11085.00	4340.00	9460.00
920.00	9080.00	23395.00	0.00	0.00	0.00	0.00	4180.00	11045.00	4180.00	9420.00
930.00	9020.00	23380.00	0.00	0.00	0.00	0.00	4020.00	11005.00	4020.00	9380.00

NOTE ?- ALL ZERO STRESS VALUES INDICATE THAT THE CODE DOES NOT
**** RECOMMEND THE USE OF THE MATERIAL AT THAT TEMPERATURE

HOT STRESS AND ALLOW. STRESS RANGE
BASED ON B31.1

S(A)=F*(1.25*S(C)+0.25*S(H)) , F=1

MATERIAL	A358---304		COPPER-B42-3		RED-BRASS-B1		NICKELB161#5		NICKELB161)5	
TEMP(F)	HOT,S(H)	ALL,S(A)	HOT,S(H)	ALL,S(A)	HOT,S(H)	ALL,S(A)	HOT,S(H)	ALL,S(A)	HOT,S(H)	ALL,S(A)
940.00	8960.00	23365.00	0.00	0.00	0.00	0.00	3860.00	10965.00	3860.00	9340.00
950.00	8900.00	23350.00	0.00	0.00	0.00	0.00	3700.00	10925.00	3700.00	9300.00
960.00	8880.00	23345.00	0.00	0.00	0.00	0.00	3560.00	10890.00	3560.00	9265.00
970.00	8860.00	23340.00	0.00	0.00	0.00	0.00	3420.00	10855.00	3420.00	9230.00
980.00	8840.00	23335.00	0.00	0.00	0.00	0.00	3280.00	10820.00	3280.00	9195.00
990.00	8820.00	23330.00	0.00	0.00	0.00	0.00	3140.00	10785.00	3140.00	9160.00
1000.00	8800.00	23325.00	0.00	0.00	0.00	0.00	3000.00	10750.00	3000.00	9125.00
1010.00	8760.00	23315.00	0.00	0.00	0.00	0.00	2880.00	10720.00	2880.00	9095.00
1020.00	8720.00	23305.00	0.00	0.00	0.00	0.00	2760.00	10690.00	2760.00	9065.00
1030.00	8680.00	23295.00	0.00	0.00	0.00	0.00	2640.00	10660.00	2640.00	9035.00
1040.00	8640.00	23285.00	0.00	0.00	0.00	0.00	2520.00	10630.00	2520.00	9005.00
1050.00	8600.00	23275.00	0.00	0.00	0.00	0.00	2400.00	10600.00	2400.00	8975.00
1060.00	8480.00	23245.00	0.00	0.00	0.00	0.00	2320.00	10580.00	2320.00	8955.00
1070.00	8360.00	23215.00	0.00	0.00	0.00	0.00	2240.00	10560.00	2240.00	8935.00
1080.00	8240.00	23185.00	0.00	0.00	0.00	0.00	2160.00	10540.00	2160.00	8915.00
1090.00	8120.00	23155.00	0.00	0.00	0.00	0.00	2080.00	10520.00	2080.00	8895.00
1100.00	8000.00	23125.00	0.00	0.00	0.00	0.00	2000.00	10500.00	2000.00	8875.00
1110.00	7780.00	23070.00	0.00	0.00	0.00	0.00	1900.00	10475.00	1900.00	8850.00
1120.00	7560.00	23015.00	0.00	0.00	0.00	0.00	1800.00	10450.00	1800.00	8825.00
1130.00	7340.00	22960.00	0.00	0.00	0.00	0.00	1700.00	10425.00	1700.00	8800.00
1140.00	7120.00	22905.00	0.00	0.00	0.00	0.00	1600.00	10400.00	1600.00	8775.00

NOTE ?- ALL ZERO STRESS VALUES INDICATE THAT THE CODE DOES NOT
**** RECOMMEND THE USE OF THE MATERIAL AT THAT TEMPERATURE

HOT STRESS AND ALLOW. STRESS RANGE
BASED ON B31.1

S(A)=F*(1.25*S(C)+0.25*S(H)) , F=1

MATERIAL	A358---304		COPPER-B42-3		RED-BRASS-B1		NICKELB161#5		NICKELB161)5	
TEMP(F)	HOT,S(H)	ALL,S(A)	HOT,S(H)	ALL,S(A)	HOT,S(H)	ALL,S(A)	HOT,S(H)	ALL,S(A)	HOT,S(H)	ALL,S(A)
1150.00	6900.00	22850.00	0.00	0.00	0.00	0.00	1500.00	10375.00	1500.00	8750.00
1160.00	6620.00	22780.00	0.00	0.00	0.00	0.00	1440.00	10360.00	1440.00	8735.00
1170.00	6340.00	22710.00	0.00	0.00	0.00	0.00	1380.00	10345.00	1380.00	8720.00
1180.00	6060.00	22640.00	0.00	0.00	0.00	0.00	1320.00	10330.00	1320.00	8705.00
1190.00	5780.00	22570.00	0.00	0.00	0.00	0.00	1260.00	10315.00	1260.00	8690.00
1200.00	5500.00	22500.00	0.00	0.00	0.00	0.00	1200.00	10300.00	1200.00	8675.00

NOTE ?- ALL ZERO STRESS VALUES INDICATE THAT THE CODE DOES NOT
**** RECOMMEND THE USE OF THE MATERIAL AT THAT TEMPERATURE

HOT STRESS AND ALLOW. STRESS RANGE
BASED ON B31.1

S(A)=F*(1.25*S(C)+0.25*S(H)) , F=1

MATERIAL	B165 MONEL-N		ASTM-B167-#5		ASTM-B167-)5		AL-B241-6061		AL-B241-6063	
TEMP(F)	HOT,S(H)	ALL,S(A)	HOT,S(H)	ALL,S(A)	HOT,S(H)	ALL,S(A)	HOT,S(H)	ALL,S(A)	HOT,S(H)	ALL,S(A)
100.00	16600.00	24900.00	20000.00	30000.00	16700.00	25050.00	9500.00	14250.00	7500.00	11250.00
110.00	16400.00	24850.00	20000.00	30000.00	16560.00	25015.00	9500.00	14250.00	7490.00	11247.50
120.00	16200.00	24800.00	20000.00	30000.00	16420.00	24980.00	9500.00	14250.00	7480.00	11245.00
130.00	16000.00	24750.00	20000.00	30000.00	16280.00	24945.00	9500.00	14250.00	7470.00	11242.50
140.00	15800.00	24700.00	20000.00	30000.00	16140.00	24910.00	9500.00	14250.00	7460.00	11240.00
150.00	15600.00	24650.00	20000.00	30000.00	16000.00	24875.00	9500.00	14250.00	7450.00	11237.50
160.00	15400.00	24600.00	20000.00	30000.00	15860.00	24840.00	9500.00	14250.00	7440.00	11235.00
170.00	15200.00	24550.00	20000.00	30000.00	15720.00	24805.00	9500.00	14250.00	7430.00	11232.50
180.00	15000.00	24500.00	20000.00	30000.00	15580.00	24770.00	9500.00	14250.00	7420.00	11230.00
190.00	14800.00	24450.00	20000.00	30000.00	15440.00	24735.00	9500.00	14250.00	7410.00	11227.50
200.00	14600.00	24400.00	20000.00	30000.00	15300.00	24700.00	9500.00	14250.00	7400.00	11225.00
210.00	14500.00	24375.00	20000.00	30000.00	15220.00	24680.00	9340.00	14210.00	7160.00	11165.00
220.00	14400.00	24350.00	20000.00	30000.00	15140.00	24660.00	9180.00	14170.00	6920.00	11105.00
230.00	14300.00	24325.00	20000.00	30000.00	15060.00	24640.00	9020.00	14130.00	6680.00	11045.00
240.00	14200.00	24300.00	20000.00	30000.00	14980.00	24620.00	8860.00	14090.00	6440.00	10985.00
250.00	14100.00	24275.00	20000.00	30000.00	14900.00	24600.00	8700.00	14050.00	6200.00	10925.00
260.00	14000.00	24250.00	20000.00	30000.00	14820.00	24580.00	8540.00	14010.00	5960.00	10865.00
270.00	13900.00	24225.00	20000.00	30000.00	14740.00	24560.00	8380.00	13970.00	5720.00	10805.00
280.00	13800.00	24200.00	20000.00	30000.00	14660.00	24540.00	8220.00	13930.00	5480.00	10745.00
290.00	13700.00	24175.00	20000.00	30000.00	14580.00	24520.00	8060.00	13890.00	5240.00	10685.00
300.00	13600.00	24150.00	20000.00	30000.00	14500.00	24500.00	7900.00	13850.00	5000.00	10625.00

NOTE ?- ALL ZERO STRESS VALUES INDICATE THAT THE CODE DOES NOT
**** RECOMMEND THE USE OF THE MATERIAL AT THAT TEMPERATURE

HOT STRESS AND ALLOW. STRESS RANGE
BASED ON B31.1

S(A)=F*(1.25*S(C)+0.25*S(H)) , F=1

MATERIAL	B165 MONEL-N		ASTM-B167-#5		ASTM-B167-)5		AL-B241-6061		AL-B241-6063	
TEMP(F)	HOT,S(H)	ALL,S(A)	HOT,S(H)	ALL,S(A)	HOT,S(H)	ALL,S(A)	HOT,S(H)	ALL,S(A)	HOT,S(H)	ALL,S(A)
310.00	13560.00	24140.00	20000.00	30000.00	14450.00	24487.50	7560.00	13765.00	4700.00	10550.00
320.00	13520.00	24130.00	20000.00	30000.00	14400.00	24475.00	7220.00	13680.00	4400.00	10475.00
330.00	13480.00	24120.00	20000.00	30000.00	14350.00	24462.50	6880.00	13595.00	4100.00	10400.00
340.00	13440.00	24110.00	20000.00	30000.00	14300.00	24450.00	6540.00	13510.00	3800.00	10325.00
350.00	13400.00	24100.00	20000.00	30000.00	14250.00	24437.50	6200.00	13425.00	3500.00	10250.00
360.00	13360.00	24090.00	20000.00	30000.00	14200.00	24425.00	5860.00	13340.00	3200.00	10175.00
370.00	13320.00	24080.00	20000.00	30000.00	14150.00	24412.50	5520.00	13255.00	2900.00	10100.00
380.00	13280.00	24070.00	20000.00	30000.00	14100.00	24400.00	5180.00	13170.00	2600.00	10025.00
390.00	13240.00	24060.00	20000.00	30000.00	14050.00	24387.50	4840.00	13085.00	2300.00	9950.00
400.00	13200.00	24050.00	20000.00	30000.00	14000.00	24375.00	4500.00	13000.00	2000.00	9875.00
410.00	13190.00	24047.50	20000.00	30000.00	13960.00	24365.00	0.00	0.00	0.00	0.00
420.00	13180.00	24045.00	20000.00	30000.00	13920.00	24355.00	0.00	0.00	0.00	0.00
430.00	13170.00	24042.50	20000.00	30000.00	13880.00	24345.00	0.00	0.00	0.00	0.00
440.00	13160.00	24040.00	20000.00	30000.00	13840.00	24335.00	0.00	0.00	0.00	0.00
450.00	13150.00	24037.50	20000.00	30000.00	13800.00	24325.00	0.00	0.00	0.00	0.00
460.00	13140.00	24035.00	20000.00	30000.00	13760.00	24315.00	0.00	0.00	0.00	0.00
470.00	13130.00	24032.50	20000.00	30000.00	13720.00	24305.00	0.00	0.00	0.00	0.00
480.00	13120.00	24030.00	20000.00	30000.00	13680.00	24295.00	0.00	0.00	0.00	0.00
490.00	13110.00	24027.50	20000.00	30000.00	13640.00	24285.00	0.00	0.00	0.00	0.00
500.00	13100.00	24025.00	20000.00	30000.00	13600.00	24275.00	0.00	0.00	0.00	0.00
510.00	13100.00	24025.00	20000.00	30000.00	13560.00	24265.00	0.00	0.00	0.00	0.00

NOTE ?- ALL ZERO STRESS VALUES INDICATE THAT THE CODE DOES NOT
**** RECOMMEND THE USE OF THE MATERIAL AT THAT TEMPERATURE

HOT STRESS AND ALLOW. STRESS RANGE
BASED ON B31.1

S(A)=F*(1.25*S(C)+0.25*S(H)) , F=1

MATERIAL	B165 MONEL-N		ASTM-B167-#5		ASTM-B167-)5		AL-B241-6061		AL-B241-6063	
TEMP(F)	HOT,S(H)	ALL,S(A)	HOT,S(H)	ALL,S(A)	HOT,S(H)	ALL,S(A)	HOT,S(H)	ALL,S(A)	HOT,S(H)	ALL,S(A)
520.00	13100.00	24025.00	20000.00	30000.00	13520.00	24255.00	0.00	0.00	0.00	0.00
530.00	13100.00	24025.00	20000.00	30000.00	13480.00	24245.00	0.00	0.00	0.00	0.00
540.00	13100.00	24025.00	20000.00	30000.00	13440.00	24235.00	0.00	0.00	0.00	0.00
550.00	13100.00	24025.00	20000.00	30000.00	13400.00	24225.00	0.00	0.00	0.00	0.00
560.00	13100.00	24025.00	20000.00	30000.00	13360.00	24215.00	0.00	0.00	0.00	0.00
570.00	13100.00	24025.00	20000.00	30000.00	13320.00	24205.00	0.00	0.00	0.00	0.00
580.00	13100.00	24025.00	20000.00	30000.00	13280.00	24195.00	0.00	0.00	0.00	0.00
590.00	13100.00	24025.00	20000.00	30000.00	13240.00	24185.00	0.00	0.00	0.00	0.00
600.00	13100.00	24025.00	20000.00	30000.00	13200.00	24175.00	0.00	0.00	0.00	0.00
610.00	13100.00	24025.00	20000.00	30000.00	13180.00	24170.00	0.00	0.00	0.00	0.00
620.00	13100.00	24025.00	20000.00	30000.00	13160.00	24165.00	0.00	0.00	0.00	0.00
630.00	13100.00	24025.00	20000.00	30000.00	13140.00	24160.00	0.00	0.00	0.00	0.00
640.00	13100.00	24025.00	20000.00	30000.00	13120.00	24155.00	0.00	0.00	0.00	0.00
650.00	13100.00	24025.00	20000.00	30000.00	13100.00	24150.00	0.00	0.00	0.00	0.00
660.00	13100.00	24025.00	20000.00	30000.00	13080.00	24145.00	0.00	0.00	0.00	0.00
670.00	13100.00	24025.00	20000.00	30000.00	13060.00	24140.00	0.00	0.00	0.00	0.00
680.00	13100.00	24025.00	20000.00	30000.00	13040.00	24135.00	0.00	0.00	0.00	0.00
690.00	13100.00	24025.00	20000.00	30000.00	13020.00	24130.00	0.00	0.00	0.00	0.00
700.00	13100.00	24025.00	20000.00	30000.00	13000.00	24125.00	0.00	0.00	0.00	0.00
710.00	13080.00	24020.00	20000.00	30000.00	12980.00	24120.00	0.00	0.00	0.00	0.00
720.00	13060.00	24015.00	20000.00	30000.00	12960.00	24115.00	0.00	0.00	0.00	0.00

NOTE ?- ALL ZERO STRESS VALUES INDICATE THAT THE CODE DOES NOT
**** RECOMMEND THE USE OF THE MATERIAL AT THAT TEMPERATURE

HOT STRESS AND ALLOW. STRESS RANGE
BASED ON B31.1

S(A)=F*(1.25*S(C)+0.25*S(H)) , F=1

MATERIAL	B165 MONEL-N		ASTM-B167-#5		ASTM-B167-)5		AL-B241-6061		AL-B241-6063	
TEMP(F)	HOT,S(H)	ALL,S(A)	HOT,S(H)	ALL,S(A)	HOT,S(H)	ALL,S(A)	HOT,S(H)	ALL,S(A)	HOT,S(H)	ALL,S(A)
730.00	13040.00	24010.00	20000.00	30000.00	12940.00	24110.00	0.00	0.00	0.00	0.00
740.00	13020.00	24005.00	20000.00	30000.00	12920.00	24105.00	0.00	0.00	0.00	0.00
750.00	13000.00	24000.00	20000.00	30000.00	12900.00	24100.00	0.00	0.00	0.00	0.00
760.00	12940.00	23985.00	20000.00	30000.00	12860.00	24090.00	0.00	0.00	0.00	0.00
770.00	12880.00	23970.00	20000.00	30000.00	12820.00	24080.00	0.00	0.00	0.00	0.00
780.00	12820.00	23955.00	20000.00	30000.00	12780.00	24070.00	0.00	0.00	0.00	0.00
790.00	12760.00	23940.00	20000.00	30000.00	12740.00	24060.00	0.00	0.00	0.00	0.00
800.00	12700.00	23925.00	20000.00	30000.00	12700.00	24050.00	0.00	0.00	0.00	0.00
810.00	12360.00	23840.00	19920.00	29980.00	12620.00	24030.00	0.00	0.00	0.00	0.00
820.00	12020.00	23755.00	19840.00	29960.00	12540.00	24010.00	0.00	0.00	0.00	0.00
830.00	11680.00	23670.00	19760.00	29940.00	12460.00	23990.00	0.00	0.00	0.00	0.00
840.00	11340.00	23585.00	19680.00	29920.00	12380.00	23970.00	0.00	0.00	0.00	0.00
850.00	11000.00	23500.00	19600.00	29900.00	12300.00	23950.00	0.00	0.00	0.00	0.00
860.00	10400.00	23350.00	18880.00	29720.00	12200.00	23925.00	0.00	0.00	0.00	0.00
870.00	9800.00	23200.00	18160.00	29540.00	12100.00	23900.00	0.00	0.00	0.00	0.00
880.00	9200.00	23050.00	17440.00	29360.00	12000.00	23875.00	0.00	0.00	0.00	0.00
890.00	8600.00	22900.00	16720.00	29180.00	11900.00	23850.00	0.00	0.00	0.00	0.00
900.00	8000.00	22750.00	16000.00	29000.00	11800.00	23825.00	0.00	0.00	0.00	0.00
910.00	0.00	0.00	14920.00	28730.00	11560.00	23765.00	0.00	0.00	0.00	0.00
920.00	0.00	0.00	13840.00	28460.00	11320.00	23705.00	0.00	0.00	0.00	0.00
930.00	0.00	0.00	12760.00	28190.00	11080.00	23645.00	0.00	0.00	0.00	0.00

NOTE ?- ALL ZERO STRESS VALUES INDICATE THAT THE CODE DOES NOT
**** RECOMMEND THE USE OF THE MATERIAL AT THAT TEMPERATURE

HOT STRESS AND ALLOW. STRESS RANGE
BASED ON B31.1

S(A)=F*(1.25*S(C)+0.25*S(H)) , F=1

MATERIAL	B165 MONEL-N		ASTM-B167-#5		ASTM-B167-)5		AL-B241-6061		AL-B241-6063	
TEMP(F)	HOT,S(H)	ALL,S(A)	HOT,S(H)	ALL,S(A)	HOT,S(H)	ALL,S(A)	HOT,S(H)	ALL,S(A)	HOT,S(H)	ALL,S(A)
940.00	0.00	0.00	11680.00	27920.00	10840.00	23585.00	0.00	0.00	0.00	0.00
950.00	0.00	0.00	10600.00	27650.00	10600.00	23525.00	0.00	0.00	0.00	0.00
960.00	0.00	0.00	9880.00	27470.00	9880.00	23345.00	0.00	0.00	0.00	0.00
970.00	0.00	0.00	9160.00	27290.00	9160.00	23165.00	0.00	0.00	0.00	0.00
980.00	0.00	0.00	8440.00	27110.00	8440.00	22985.00	0.00	0.00	0.00	0.00
990.00	0.00	0.00	7720.00	26930.00	7720.00	22805.00	0.00	0.00	0.00	0.00
1000.00	0.00	0.00	7000.00	26750.00	7000.00	22625.00	0.00	0.00	0.00	0.00
1010.00	0.00	0.00	6500.00	26625.00	6500.00	22500.00	0.00	0.00	0.00	0.00
1020.00	0.00	0.00	6000.00	26500.00	6000.00	22375.00	0.00	0.00	0.00	0.00
1030.00	0.00	0.00	5500.00	26375.00	5500.00	22250.00	0.00	0.00	0.00	0.00
1040.00	0.00	0.00	5000.00	26250.00	5000.00	22125.00	0.00	0.00	0.00	0.00
1050.00	0.00	0.00	4500.00	26125.00	4500.00	22000.00	0.00	0.00	0.00	0.00
1060.00	0.00	0.00	4200.00	26050.00	4200.00	21925.00	0.00	0.00	0.00	0.00
1070.00	0.00	0.00	3900.00	25975.00	3900.00	21850.00	0.00	0.00	0.00	0.00
1080.00	0.00	0.00	3600.00	25900.00	3600.00	21775.00	0.00	0.00	0.00	0.00
1090.00	0.00	0.00	3300.00	25825.00	3300.00	21700.00	0.00	0.00	0.00	0.00
1100.00	0.00	0.00	3000.00	25750.00	3000.00	21625.00	0.00	0.00	0.00	0.00
1110.00	0.00	0.00	2840.00	25710.00	2840.00	21585.00	0.00	0.00	0.00	0.00
1120.00	0.00	0.00	2680.00	25670.00	2680.00	21545.00	0.00	0.00	0.00	0.00
1130.00	0.00	0.00	2520.00	25630.00	2520.00	21505.00	0.00	0.00	0.00	0.00
1140.00	0.00	0.00	2360.00	25590.00	2360.00	21465.00	0.00	0.00	0.00	0.00

NOTE ?- ALL ZERO STRESS VALUES INDICATE THAT THE CODE DOES NOT
**** RECOMMEND THE USE OF THE MATERIAL AT THAT TEMPERATURE

HOT STRESS AND ALLOW. STRESS RANGE
BASED ON B31.1

S(A)=F*(1.25*S(C)+0.25*S(H)) , F=1

MATERIAL	B165 MONEL-N		ASTM-B167-#5		ASTM-B167-)5		AL-B241-6061		AL-B241-6063	
TEMP(F)	HOT,S(H)	ALL,S(A)	HOT,S(H)	ALL,S(A)	HOT,S(H)	ALL,S(A)	HOT,S(H)	ALL,S(A)	HOT,S(H)	ALL,S(A)
1150.00	0.00	0.00	2200.00	25550.00	2200.00	21425.00	0.00	0.00	0.00	0.00
1160.00	0.00	0.00	2160.00	25540.00	2160.00	21415.00	0.00	0.00	0.00	0.00
1170.00	0.00	0.00	2120.00	25530.00	2120.00	21405.00	0.00	0.00	0.00	0.00
1180.00	0.00	0.00	2080.00	25520.00	2080.00	21395.00	0.00	0.00	0.00	0.00
1190.00	0.00	0.00	2040.00	25510.00	2040.00	21385.00	0.00	0.00	0.00	0.00
1200.00	0.00	0.00	2000.00	25500.00	2000.00	21375.00	0.00	0.00	0.00	0.00

NOTE ?- ALL ZERO STRESS VALUES INDICATE THAT THE CODE DOES NOT
**** RECOMMEND THE USE OF THE MATERIAL AT THAT TEMPERATURE

4

Allowable Stress Range for ANSI/ASME Petroleum Piping Code B31.3 (1984)

This chapter contains allowable thermal stresses for power piping.

HOT STRESS AND ALLOW. STRESS RANGE
BASED ON B31.3

S(A)=F*(1.25*S(C)+0.25*S(H)) , F=1

MATERIAL	ASTM-A53-A		ASTM-A53-B		ASTM-A106-B		API-5L-GR-B		ASTM-A139-B	
TEMP(F)	HOT,S(H)	ALL,S(A)	HOT,S(H)	ALL,S(A)	HOT,S(H)	ALL,S(A)	HOT,S(H)	ALL,S(A)	HOT,S(H)	ALL,S(A)
100.00	16000.00	24000.00	20000.00	30000.00	20000.00	30000.00	20000.00	30000.00	16000.00	24000.00
110.00	16000.00	24000.00	20000.00	30000.00	20000.00	30000.00	20000.00	30000.00	16000.00	24000.00
120.00	16000.00	24000.00	20000.00	30000.00	20000.00	30000.00	20000.00	30000.00	16000.00	24000.00
130.00	16000.00	24000.00	20000.00	30000.00	20000.00	30000.00	20000.00	30000.00	16000.00	24000.00
140.00	16000.00	24000.00	20000.00	30000.00	20000.00	30000.00	20000.00	30000.00	16000.00	24000.00
150.00	16000.00	24000.00	20000.00	30000.00	20000.00	30000.00	20000.00	30000.00	16000.00	24000.00
160.00	16000.00	24000.00	20000.00	30000.00	20000.00	30000.00	20000.00	30000.00	16000.00	24000.00
170.00	16000.00	24000.00	20000.00	30000.00	20000.00	30000.00	20000.00	30000.00	16000.00	24000.00
180.00	16000.00	24000.00	20000.00	30000.00	20000.00	30000.00	20000.00	30000.00	16000.00	24000.00
190.00	16000.00	24000.00	20000.00	30000.00	20000.00	30000.00	20000.00	30000.00	16000.00	24000.00
200.00	16000.00	24000.00	20000.00	30000.00	20000.00	30000.00	20000.00	30000.00	16000.00	24000.00
210.00	16000.00	24000.00	20000.00	30000.00	20000.00	30000.00	20000.00	30000.00	16000.00	24000.00
220.00	16000.00	24000.00	20000.00	30000.00	20000.00	30000.00	20000.00	30000.00	16000.00	24000.00
230.00	16000.00	24000.00	20000.00	30000.00	20000.00	30000.00	20000.00	30000.00	16000.00	24000.00
240.00	16000.00	24000.00	20000.00	30000.00	20000.00	30000.00	20000.00	30000.00	16000.00	24000.00
250.00	16000.00	24000.00	20000.00	30000.00	20000.00	30000.00	20000.00	30000.00	16000.00	24000.00
260.00	16000.00	24000.00	20000.00	30000.00	20000.00	30000.00	20000.00	30000.00	16000.00	24000.00
270.00	16000.00	24000.00	20000.00	30000.00	20000.00	30000.00	20000.00	30000.00	16000.00	24000.00
280.00	16000.00	24000.00	20000.00	30000.00	20000.00	30000.00	20000.00	30000.00	16000.00	24000.00
290.00	16000.00	24000.00	20000.00	30000.00	20000.00	30000.00	20000.00	30000.00	16000.00	24000.00
300.00	16000.00	24000.00	20000.00	30000.00	20000.00	30000.00	20000.00	30000.00	16000.00	24000.00

NOTE ?- ALL ZERO STRESS VALUES INDICATE THAT THE CODE DOES NOT
**** RECOMMEND THE USE OF THE MATERIAL AT THAT TEMPERATURE

HOT STRESS AND ALLOW. STRESS RANGE
BASED ON B31.3

S(A)=F*(1.25*S(C)+0.25*S(H)) , F=1

MATERIAL	ASTM-A53-A		ASTM-A53-B		ASTM-A106-B		API-5L-GR-B		ASTM-A139-B	
TEMP(F)	HOT,S(H)	ALL,S(A)	HOT,S(H)	ALL,S(A)	HOT,S(H)	ALL,S(A)	HOT,S(H)	ALL,S(A)	HOT,S(H)	ALL,S(A)
310.00	16000.00	24000.00	20000.00	30000.00	20000.00	30000.00	20000.00	30000.00	0.00	0.00
320.00	16000.00	24000.00	20000.00	30000.00	20000.00	30000.00	20000.00	30000.00	0.00	0.00
330.00	16000.00	24000.00	20000.00	30000.00	20000.00	30000.00	20000.00	30000.00	0.00	0.00
340.00	16000.00	24000.00	20000.00	30000.00	20000.00	30000.00	20000.00	30000.00	0.00	0.00
350.00	16000.00	24000.00	20000.00	30000.00	20000.00	30000.00	20000.00	30000.00	0.00	0.00
360.00	16000.00	24000.00	20000.00	30000.00	20000.00	30000.00	20000.00	30000.00	0.00	0.00
370.00	16000.00	24000.00	20000.00	30000.00	20000.00	30000.00	20000.00	30000.00	0.00	0.00
380.00	16000.00	24000.00	20000.00	30000.00	20000.00	30000.00	20000.00	30000.00	0.00	0.00
390.00	16000.00	24000.00	20000.00	30000.00	20000.00	30000.00	20000.00	30000.00	0.00	0.00
400.00	16000.00	24000.00	20000.00	30000.00	20000.00	30000.00	20000.00	30000.00	0.00	0.00
410.00	16000.00	24000.00	19890.00	29972.50	19890.00	29972.50	19890.00	29972.50	0.00	0.00
420.00	16000.00	24000.00	19780.00	29945.00	19780.00	29945.00	19780.00	29945.00	0.00	0.00
430.00	16000.00	24000.00	19670.00	29917.50	19670.00	29917.50	19670.00	29917.50	0.00	0.00
440.00	16000.00	24000.00	19560.00	29890.00	19560.00	29890.00	19560.00	29890.00	0.00	0.00
450.00	16000.00	24000.00	19450.00	29862.50	19450.00	29862.50	19450.00	29862.50	0.00	0.00
460.00	16000.00	24000.00	19340.00	29835.00	19340.00	29835.00	19340.00	29835.00	0.00	0.00
470.00	16000.00	24000.00	19230.00	29807.50	19230.00	29807.50	19230.00	29807.50	0.00	0.00
480.00	16000.00	24000.00	19120.00	29780.00	19120.00	29780.00	19120.00	29780.00	0.00	0.00
490.00	16000.00	24000.00	19010.00	29752.50	19010.00	29752.50	19010.00	29752.50	0.00	0.00
500.00	16000.00	24000.00	18900.00	29725.00	18900.00	29725.00	18900.00	29725.00	0.00	0.00
510.00	15880.00	23970.00	18740.00	29685.00	18740.00	29685.00	18740.00	29685.00	0.00	0.00

NOTE ?- ALL ZERO STRESS VALUES INDICATE THAT THE CODE DOES NOT
**** RECOMMEND THE USE OF THE MATERIAL AT THAT TEMPERATURE

HOT STRESS AND ALLOW. STRESS RANGE
BASED ON B31.3

S(A)=F*(1.25*S(C)+0.25*S(H)) , F=1

MATERIAL	ASTM-A53-A		ASTM-A53-B		ASTM-A106-B		API-5L-GR-B		ASTM-A139-B	
TEMP(F)	HOT,S(H)	ALL,S(A)	HOT,S(H)	ALL,S(A)	HOT,S(H)	ALL,S(A)	HOT,S(H)	ALL,S(A)	HOT,S(H)	ALL,S(A)
520.00	15760.00	23940.00	18580.00	29645.00	18580.00	29645.00	18580.00	29645.00	0.00	0.00
530.00	15640.00	23910.00	18420.00	29605.00	18420.00	29605.00	18420.00	29605.00	0.00	0.00
540.00	15520.00	23880.00	18260.00	29565.00	18260.00	29565.00	18260.00	29565.00	0.00	0.00
550.00	15400.00	23850.00	18100.00	29525.00	18100.00	29525.00	18100.00	29525.00	0.00	0.00
560.00	15280.00	23820.00	17940.00	29485.00	17940.00	29485.00	17940.00	29485.00	0.00	0.00
570.00	15160.00	23790.00	17780.00	29445.00	17780.00	29445.00	17780.00	29445.00	0.00	0.00
580.00	15040.00	23760.00	17620.00	29405.00	17620.00	29405.00	17620.00	29405.00	0.00	0.00
590.00	14920.00	23730.00	17460.00	29365.00	17460.00	29365.00	17460.00	29365.00	0.00	0.00
600.00	14800.00	23700.00	17300.00	29325.00	17300.00	29325.00	17300.00	29325.00	0.00	0.00
610.00	14740.00	23685.00	17240.00	29310.00	17240.00	29310.00	17240.00	29310.00	0.00	0.00
620.00	14680.00	23670.00	17180.00	29295.00	17180.00	29295.00	17180.00	29295.00	0.00	0.00
630.00	14620.00	23655.00	17120.00	29280.00	17120.00	29280.00	17120.00	29280.00	0.00	0.00
640.00	14560.00	23640.00	17060.00	29265.00	17060.00	29265.00	17060.00	29265.00	0.00	0.00
650.00	14500.00	23625.00	17000.00	29250.00	17000.00	29250.00	17000.00	29250.00	0.00	0.00
660.00	14480.00	23620.00	16960.00	29240.00	16960.00	29240.00	16960.00	29240.00	0.00	0.00
670.00	14460.00	23615.00	16920.00	29230.00	16920.00	29230.00	16920.00	29230.00	0.00	0.00
680.00	14440.00	23610.00	16880.00	29220.00	16880.00	29220.00	16880.00	29220.00	0.00	0.00
690.00	14420.00	23605.00	16840.00	29210.00	16840.00	29210.00	16840.00	29210.00	0.00	0.00
700.00	14400.00	23600.00	16800.00	29200.00	16800.00	29200.00	16800.00	29200.00	0.00	0.00
710.00	13660.00	23415.00	16040.00	29010.00	16040.00	29010.00	16040.00	29010.00	0.00	0.00
720.00	12920.00	23230.00	15280.00	28820.00	15280.00	28820.00	15280.00	28820.00	0.00	0.00

NOTE ?- ALL ZERO STRESS VALUES INDICATE THAT THE CODE DOES NOT
**** RECOMMEND THE USE OF THE MATERIAL AT THAT TEMPERATURE

HOT STRESS AND ALLOW. STRESS RANGE
BASED ON B31.3

S(A)=F*(1.25*S(C)+0.25*S(H)) , F=1

MATERIAL	ASTM-A53-A		ASTM-A53-B		ASTM-A106-B		API-5L-GR-B		ASTM-A139-B	
TEMP(F)	HOT,S(H)	ALL,S(A)	HOT,S(H)	ALL,S(A)	HOT,S(H)	ALL,S(A)	HOT,S(H)	ALL,S(A)	HOT,S(H)	ALL,S(A)
730.00	12180.00	23045.00	14520.00	28630.00	14520.00	28630.00	14520.00	28630.00	0.00	0.00
740.00	11440.00	22860.00	13760.00	28440.00	13760.00	28440.00	13760.00	28440.00	0.00	0.00
750.00	10700.00	22675.00	13000.00	28250.00	13000.00	28250.00	13000.00	28250.00	0.00	0.00
760.00	10420.00	22605.00	12560.00	28140.00	12560.00	28140.00	12560.00	28140.00	0.00	0.00
770.00	10140.00	22535.00	12120.00	28030.00	12120.00	28030.00	12120.00	28030.00	0.00	0.00
780.00	9860.00	22465.00	11680.00	27920.00	11680.00	27920.00	11680.00	27920.00	0.00	0.00
790.00	9580.00	22395.00	11240.00	27810.00	11240.00	27810.00	11240.00	27810.00	0.00	0.00
800.00	9300.00	22325.00	10800.00	27700.00	10800.00	27700.00	10800.00	27700.00	0.00	0.00
810.00	9020.00	22255.00	10380.00	27595.00	10380.00	27595.00	10380.00	27595.00	0.00	0.00
820.00	8740.00	22185.00	9960.00	27490.00	9960.00	27490.00	9960.00	27490.00	0.00	0.00
830.00	8460.00	22115.00	9540.00	27385.00	9540.00	27385.00	9540.00	27385.00	0.00	0.00
840.00	8180.00	22045.00	9120.00	27280.00	9120.00	27280.00	9120.00	27280.00	0.00	0.00
850.00	7900.00	21975.00	8700.00	27175.00	8700.00	27175.00	8700.00	27175.00	0.00	0.00
860.00	7620.00	21905.00	8260.00	27065.00	8260.00	27065.00	8260.00	27065.00	0.00	0.00
870.00	7340.00	21835.00	7820.00	26955.00	7820.00	26955.00	7820.00	26955.00	0.00	0.00
880.00	7060.00	21765.00	7380.00	26845.00	7380.00	26845.00	7380.00	26845.00	0.00	0.00
890.00	6780.00	21695.00	6940.00	26735.00	6940.00	26735.00	6940.00	26735.00	0.00	0.00
900.00	6500.00	21625.00	6500.00	26625.00	6500.00	26625.00	6500.00	26625.00	0.00	0.00
910.00	6100.00	21525.00	6100.00	26525.00	6100.00	26525.00	6100.00	26525.00	0.00	0.00
920.00	5700.00	21425.00	5700.00	26425.00	5700.00	26425.00	5700.00	26425.00	0.00	0.00
930.00	5300.00	21325.00	5300.00	26325.00	5300.00	26325.00	5300.00	26325.00	0.00	0.00

NOTE ?- ALL ZERO STRESS VALUES INDICATE THAT THE CODE DOES NOT
**** RECOMMEND THE USE OF THE MATERIAL AT THAT TEMPERATURE

HOT STRESS AND ALLOW. STRESS RANGE
BASED ON B31.3

S(A)=F*(1.25*S(C)+0.25*S(H)) , F=1

MATERIAL	ASTM-A53-A		ASTM-A53-B		ASTM-A106-B		API-5L-GR-B		ASTM-A139-B	
TEMP(F)	HOT,S(H)	ALL,S(A)	HOT,S(H)	ALL,S(A)	HOT,S(H)	ALL,S(A)	HOT,S(H)	ALL,S(A)	HOT,S(H)	ALL,S(A)
940.00	4900.00	21225.00	4900.00	26225.00	4900.00	26225.00	4900.00	26225.00	0.00	0.00
950.00	4500.00	21125.00	4500.00	26125.00	4500.00	26125.00	4500.00	26125.00	0.00	0.00
960.00	4100.00	21025.00	4100.00	26025.00	4100.00	26025.00	4100.00	26025.00	0.00	0.00
970.00	3700.00	20925.00	3700.00	25925.00	3700.00	25925.00	3700.00	25925.00	0.00	0.00
980.00	3300.00	20825.00	3300.00	25825.00	3300.00	25825.00	3300.00	25825.00	0.00	0.00
990.00	2900.00	20725.00	2900.00	25725.00	2900.00	25725.00	2900.00	25725.00	0.00	0.00
1000.00	2500.00	20625.00	2500.00	25625.00	2500.00	25625.00	2500.00	25625.00	0.00	0.00
1010.00	2320.00	20580.00	2320.00	25580.00	2320.00	25580.00	2320.00	25580.00	0.00	0.00
1020.00	2140.00	20535.00	2140.00	25535.00	2140.00	25535.00	2140.00	25535.00	0.00	0.00
1030.00	1960.00	20490.00	1960.00	25490.00	1960.00	25490.00	1960.00	25490.00	0.00	0.00
1040.00	1780.00	20445.00	1780.00	25445.00	1780.00	25445.00	1780.00	25445.00	0.00	0.00
1050.00	1600.00	20400.00	1600.00	25400.00	1600.00	25400.00	1600.00	25400.00	0.00	0.00
1060.00	1480.00	20370.00	1480.00	25370.00	1480.00	25370.00	1480.00	25370.00	0.00	0.00
1070.00	1360.00	20340.00	1360.00	25340.00	1360.00	25340.00	1360.00	25340.00	0.00	0.00
1080.00	1240.00	20310.00	1240.00	25310.00	1240.00	25310.00	1240.00	25310.00	0.00	0.00
1090.00	1120.00	20280.00	1120.00	25280.00	1120.00	25280.00	1120.00	25280.00	0.00	0.00
1100.00	1000.00	20250.00	1000.00	25250.00	1000.00	25250.00	1000.00	25250.00	0.00	0.00

NOTE ?- ALL ZERO STRESS VALUES INDICATE THAT THE CODE DOES NOT
**** RECOMMEND THE USE OF THE MATERIAL AT THAT TEMPERATURE

HOT STRESS AND ALLOW. STRESS RANGE
BASED ON B31.3

S(A)=F*(1.25*S(C)+0.25*S(H)) , F=1

MATERIAL	A335-P2		A335-P5,B,C		A335-GR-P9		A335-GR-P11		A335-GR-P22	
TEMP(F)	HOT,S(H)	ALL,S(A)	HOT,S(H)	ALL,S(A)	HOT,S(H)	ALL,S(A)	HOT,S(H)	ALL,S(A)	HOT,S(H)	ALL,S(A)
100.00	18300.00	27450.00	20000.00	30000.00	20000.00	30000.00	20000.00	30000.00	20000.00	30000.00
110.00	18300.00	27450.00	19810.00	29952.50	19810.00	29952.50	19870.00	29967.50	19850.00	29962.50
120.00	18300.00	27450.00	19620.00	29905.00	19620.00	29905.00	19740.00	29935.00	19700.00	29925.00
130.00	18300.00	27450.00	19430.00	29857.50	19430.00	29857.50	19610.00	29902.50	19550.00	29887.50
140.00	18300.00	27450.00	19240.00	29810.00	19240.00	29810.00	19480.00	29870.00	19400.00	29850.00
150.00	18300.00	27450.00	19050.00	29762.50	19050.00	29762.50	19350.00	29837.50	19250.00	29812.50
160.00	18300.00	27450.00	18860.00	29715.00	18860.00	29715.00	19220.00	29805.00	19100.00	29775.00
170.00	18300.00	27450.00	18670.00	29667.50	18670.00	29667.50	19090.00	29772.50	18950.00	29737.50
180.00	18300.00	27450.00	18480.00	29620.00	18480.00	29620.00	18960.00	29740.00	18800.00	29700.00
190.00	18300.00	27450.00	18290.00	29572.50	18290.00	29572.50	18830.00	29707.50	18650.00	29662.50
200.00	18300.00	27450.00	18100.00	29525.00	18100.00	29525.00	18700.00	29675.00	18500.00	29625.00
210.00	18220.00	27430.00	18030.00	29507.50	18030.00	29507.50	18630.00	29657.50	18450.00	29612.50
220.00	18140.00	27410.00	17960.00	29490.00	17960.00	29490.00	18560.00	29640.00	18400.00	29600.00
230.00	18060.00	27390.00	17890.00	29472.50	17890.00	29472.50	18490.00	29622.50	18350.00	29587.50
240.00	17980.00	27370.00	17820.00	29455.00	17820.00	29455.00	18420.00	29605.00	18300.00	29575.00
250.00	17900.00	27350.00	17750.00	29437.50	17750.00	29437.50	18350.00	29587.50	18250.00	29562.50
260.00	17820.00	27330.00	17680.00	29420.00	17680.00	29420.00	18280.00	29570.00	18200.00	29550.00
270.00	17740.00	27310.00	17610.00	29402.50	17610.00	29402.50	18210.00	29552.50	18150.00	29537.50
280.00	17660.00	27290.00	17540.00	29385.00	17540.00	29385.00	18140.00	29535.00	18100.00	29525.00
290.00	17580.00	27270.00	17470.00	29367.50	17470.00	29367.50	18070.00	29517.50	18050.00	29512.50
300.00	17500.00	27250.00	17400.00	29350.00	17400.00	29350.00	18000.00	29500.00	18000.00	29500.00

NOTE ?- ALL ZERO STRESS VALUES INDICATE THAT THE CODE DOES NOT
**** RECOMMEND THE USE OF THE MATERIAL AT THAT TEMPERATURE

HOT STRESS AND ALLOW. STRESS RANGE
BASED ON B31.3

S(A)=F*(1.25*S(C)+0.25*S(H)) , F=1

MATERIAL	A335-P2		A335-P5,B,C		A335-GR-P9		A335-GR-P11		A335-GR-P22	
TEMP(F)	HOT,S(H)	ALL,S(A)	HOT,S(H)	ALL,S(A)	HOT,S(H)	ALL,S(A)	HOT,S(H)	ALL,S(A)	HOT,S(H)	ALL,S(A)
310.00	17440.00	27235.00	17380.00	29345.00	17380.00	29345.00	17950.00	29487.50	17990.00	29497.50
320.00	17380.00	27220.00	17360.00	29340.00	17360.00	29340.00	17900.00	29475.00	17980.00	29495.00
330.00	17320.00	27205.00	17340.00	29335.00	17340.00	29335.00	17850.00	29462.50	17970.00	29492.50
340.00	17260.00	27190.00	17320.00	29330.00	17320.00	29330.00	17800.00	29450.00	17960.00	29490.00
350.00	17200.00	27175.00	17300.00	29325.00	17300.00	29325.00	17750.00	29437.50	17950.00	29487.50
360.00	17140.00	27160.00	17280.00	29320.00	17280.00	29320.00	17700.00	29425.00	17940.00	29485.00
370.00	17080.00	27145.00	17260.00	29315.00	17260.00	29315.00	17650.00	29412.50	17930.00	29482.50
380.00	17020.00	27130.00	17240.00	29310.00	17240.00	29310.00	17600.00	29400.00	17920.00	29480.00
390.00	16960.00	27115.00	17220.00	29305.00	17220.00	29305.00	17550.00	29387.50	17910.00	29477.50
400.00	16900.00	27100.00	17200.00	29300.00	17200.00	29300.00	17500.00	29375.00	17900.00	29475.00
410.00	16840.00	27085.00	17190.00	29297.50	17190.00	29297.50	17470.00	29367.50	17900.00	29475.00
420.00	16780.00	27070.00	17180.00	29295.00	17180.00	29295.00	17440.00	29360.00	17900.00	29475.00
430.00	16720.00	27055.00	17170.00	29292.50	17170.00	29292.50	17410.00	29352.50	17900.00	29475.00
440.00	16660.00	27040.00	17160.00	29290.00	17160.00	29290.00	17380.00	29345.00	17900.00	29475.00
450.00	16600.00	27025.00	17150.00	29287.50	17150.00	29287.50	17350.00	29337.50	17900.00	29475.00
460.00	16540.00	27010.00	17140.00	29285.00	17140.00	29285.00	17320.00	29330.00	17900.00	29475.00
470.00	16480.00	26995.00	17130.00	29282.50	17130.00	29282.50	17290.00	29322.50	17900.00	29475.00
480.00	16420.00	26980.00	17120.00	29280.00	17120.00	29280.00	17260.00	29315.00	17900.00	29475.00
490.00	16360.00	26965.00	17110.00	29277.50	17110.00	29277.50	17230.00	29307.50	17900.00	29475.00
500.00	16300.00	26950.00	17100.00	29275.00	17100.00	29275.00	17200.00	29300.00	17900.00	29475.00
510.00	16240.00	26935.00	17070.00	29267.50	17070.00	29267.50	17150.00	29287.50	17900.00	29475.00

NOTE ?- ALL ZERO STRESS VALUES INDICATE THAT THE CODE DOES NOT
**** RECOMMEND THE USE OF THE MATERIAL AT THAT TEMPERATURE

HOT STRESS AND ALLOW. STRESS RANGE
BASED ON B31.3

S(A)=F*(1.25*S(C)+0.25*S(H)) , F=1

MATERIAL	A335-P2		A335-P5,B,C		A335-GR-P9		A335-GR-P11		A335-GR-P22	
TEMP(F)	HOT,S(H)	ALL,S(A)	HOT,S(H)	ALL,S(A)	HOT,S(H)	ALL,S(A)	HOT,S(H)	ALL,S(A)	HOT,S(H)	ALL,S(A)
520.00	16180.00	26920.00	17040.00	29260.00	17040.00	29260.00	17100.00	29275.00	17900.00	29475.00
530.00	16120.00	26905.00	17010.00	29252.50	17010.00	29252.50	17050.00	29262.50	17900.00	29475.00
540.00	16060.00	26890.00	16980.00	29245.00	16980.00	29245.00	17000.00	29250.00	17900.00	29475.00
550.00	16000.00	26875.00	16950.00	29237.50	16950.00	29237.50	16950.00	29237.50	17900.00	29475.00
560.00	15940.00	26860.00	16920.00	29230.00	16920.00	29230.00	16900.00	29225.00	17900.00	29475.00
570.00	15880.00	26845.00	16890.00	29222.50	16890.00	29222.50	16850.00	29212.50	17900.00	29475.00
580.00	15820.00	26830.00	16860.00	29215.00	16860.00	29215.00	16800.00	29200.00	17900.00	29475.00
590.00	15760.00	26815.00	16830.00	29207.50	16830.00	29207.50	16750.00	29187.50	17900.00	29475.00
600.00	15700.00	26800.00	16800.00	29200.00	16800.00	29200.00	16700.00	29175.00	17900.00	29475.00
610.00	15640.00	26785.00	16760.00	29190.00	16760.00	29190.00	16600.00	29150.00	17900.00	29475.00
620.00	15580.00	26770.00	16720.00	29180.00	16720.00	29180.00	16500.00	29125.00	17900.00	29475.00
630.00	15520.00	26755.00	16680.00	29170.00	16680.00	29170.00	16400.00	29100.00	17900.00	29475.00
640.00	15460.00	26740.00	16640.00	29160.00	16640.00	29160.00	16300.00	29075.00	17900.00	29475.00
650.00	15400.00	26725.00	16600.00	29150.00	16600.00	29150.00	16200.00	29050.00	17900.00	29475.00
660.00	15340.00	26710.00	16540.00	29135.00	16540.00	29135.00	16080.00	29020.00	17900.00	29475.00
670.00	15280.00	26695.00	16480.00	29120.00	16480.00	29120.00	15960.00	28990.00	17900.00	29475.00
680.00	15220.00	26680.00	16420.00	29105.00	16420.00	29105.00	15840.00	28960.00	17900.00	29475.00
690.00	15160.00	26665.00	16360.00	29090.00	16360.00	29090.00	15720.00	28930.00	17900.00	29475.00
700.00	15100.00	26650.00	16300.00	29075.00	16300.00	29075.00	15600.00	28900.00	17900.00	29475.00
710.00	14840.00	26585.00	15680.00	28920.00	15680.00	28920.00	15520.00	28880.00	17900.00	29475.00
720.00	14580.00	26520.00	15060.00	28765.00	15060.00	28765.00	15440.00	28860.00	17900.00	29475.00

NOTE ?- ALL ZERO STRESS VALUES INDICATE THAT THE CODE DOES NOT
**** RECOMMEND THE USE OF THE MATERIAL AT THAT TEMPERATURE

HOT STRESS AND ALLOW. STRESS RANGE
BASED ON B31.3

S(A)=F*(1.25*S(C)+0.25*S(H)) , F=1

MATERIAL	A335-P2		A335-P5,B,C		A335-GR-P9		A335-GR-P11		A335-GR-P22	
TEMP(F)	HOT,S(H)	ALL,S(A)	HOT,S(H)	ALL,S(A)	HOT,S(H)	ALL,S(A)	HOT,S(H)	ALL,S(A)	HOT,S(H)	ALL,S(A)
730.00	14320.00	26455.00	14440.00	28610.00	14440.00	28610.00	15360.00	28840.00	17900.00	29475.00
740.00	14060.00	26390.00	13820.00	28455.00	13820.00	28455.00	15280.00	28820.00	17900.00	29475.00
750.00	13800.00	26325.00	13200.00	28300.00	13200.00	28300.00	15200.00	28800.00	17900.00	29475.00
760.00	13740.00	26310.00	13120.00	28280.00	13120.00	28280.00	15160.00	28790.00	17360.00	29340.00
770.00	13680.00	26295.00	13040.00	28260.00	13040.00	28260.00	15120.00	28780.00	16820.00	29205.00
780.00	13620.00	26280.00	12960.00	28240.00	12960.00	28240.00	15080.00	28770.00	16280.00	29070.00
790.00	13560.00	26265.00	12880.00	28220.00	12880.00	28220.00	15040.00	28760.00	15740.00	28935.00
800.00	13500.00	26250.00	12800.00	28200.00	12800.00	28200.00	15000.00	28750.00	15200.00	28800.00
810.00	13440.00	26235.00	12660.00	28165.00	12660.00	28165.00	14900.00	28725.00	15060.00	28765.00
820.00	13380.00	26220.00	12520.00	28130.00	12520.00	28130.00	14800.00	28700.00	14920.00	28730.00
830.00	13320.00	26205.00	12380.00	28095.00	12380.00	28095.00	14700.00	28675.00	14780.00	28695.00
840.00	13260.00	26190.00	12240.00	28060.00	12240.00	28060.00	14600.00	28650.00	14640.00	28660.00
850.00	13200.00	26175.00	12100.00	28025.00	12100.00	28025.00	14500.00	28625.00	14500.00	28625.00
860.00	13120.00	26155.00	11860.00	27965.00	11960.00	27990.00	14160.00	28540.00	14160.00	28540.00
870.00	13040.00	26135.00	11620.00	27905.00	11820.00	27955.00	13820.00	28455.00	13820.00	28455.00
880.00	12960.00	26115.00	11380.00	27845.00	11680.00	27920.00	13480.00	28370.00	13480.00	28370.00
890.00	12880.00	26095.00	11140.00	27785.00	11540.00	27885.00	13140.00	28285.00	13140.00	28285.00
900.00	12800.00	26075.00	10900.00	27725.00	11400.00	27850.00	12800.00	28200.00	12800.00	28200.00
910.00	12080.00	25895.00	10320.00	27580.00	11240.00	27810.00	12440.00	28110.00	12440.00	28110.00
920.00	11360.00	25715.00	9740.00	27435.00	11080.00	27770.00	12080.00	28020.00	12080.00	28020.00
930.00	10640.00	25535.00	9160.00	27290.00	10920.00	27730.00	11720.00	27930.00	11720.00	27930.00

NOTE ?- ALL ZERO STRESS VALUES INDICATE THAT THE CODE DOES NOT
**** RECOMMEND THE USE OF THE MATERIAL AT THAT TEMPERATURE

HOT STRESS AND ALLOW. STRESS RANGE
BASED ON B31.3

S(A)=F*(1.25*S(C)+0.25*S(H)) , F=1

MATERIAL	A335-P2		A335-P5,B,C		A335-GR-P9		A335-GR-P11		A335-GR-P22	
TEMP(F)	HOT,S(H)	ALL,S(A)	HOT,S(H)	ALL,S(A)	HOT,S(H)	ALL,S(A)	HOT,S(H)	ALL,S(A)	HOT,S(H)	ALL,S(A)
940.00	9920.00	25355.00	8580.00	27145.00	10760.00	27690.00	11360.00	27840.00	11360.00	27840.00
950.00	9200.00	25175.00	8000.00	27000.00	10600.00	27650.00	11000.00	27750.00	11000.00	27750.00
960.00	8540.00	25010.00	7560.00	26890.00	9960.00	27490.00	10360.00	27590.00	10360.00	27590.00
970.00	7880.00	24845.00	7120.00	26780.00	9320.00	27330.00	9720.00	27430.00	9720.00	27430.00
980.00	7220.00	24680.00	6680.00	26670.00	8680.00	27170.00	9080.00	27270.00	9080.00	27270.00
990.00	6560.00	24515.00	6240.00	26560.00	8040.00	27010.00	8440.00	27110.00	8440.00	27110.00
1000.00	5900.00	24350.00	5800.00	26450.00	7400.00	26850.00	7800.00	26950.00	7800.00	26950.00
1010.00	0.00	0.00	5480.00	26370.00	6920.00	26730.00	7340.00	26835.00	7400.00	26850.00
1020.00	0.00	0.00	5160.00	26290.00	6440.00	26610.00	6880.00	26720.00	7000.00	26750.00
1030.00	0.00	0.00	4840.00	26210.00	5960.00	26490.00	6420.00	26605.00	6600.00	26650.00
1040.00	0.00	0.00	4520.00	26130.00	5480.00	26370.00	5960.00	26490.00	6200.00	26550.00
1050.00	0.00	0.00	4200.00	26050.00	5000.00	26250.00	5500.00	26375.00	5800.00	26450.00
1060.00	0.00	0.00	3940.00	25985.00	4660.00	26165.00	5200.00	26300.00	5480.00	26370.00
1070.00	0.00	0.00	3680.00	25920.00	4320.00	26080.00	4900.00	26225.00	5160.00	26290.00
1080.00	0.00	0.00	3420.00	25855.00	3980.00	25995.00	4600.00	26150.00	4840.00	26210.00
1090.00	0.00	0.00	3160.00	25790.00	3640.00	25910.00	4300.00	26075.00	4520.00	26130.00
1100.00	0.00	0.00	2900.00	25725.00	3300.00	25825.00	4000.00	26000.00	4200.00	26050.00
1110.00	0.00	0.00	2720.00	25680.00	3080.00	25770.00	3700.00	25925.00	3960.00	25990.00
1120.00	0.00	0.00	2540.00	25635.00	2860.00	25715.00	3400.00	25850.00	3720.00	25930.00
1130.00	0.00	0.00	2360.00	25590.00	2640.00	25660.00	3100.00	25775.00	3480.00	25870.00
1140.00	0.00	0.00	2180.00	25545.00	2420.00	25605.00	2800.00	25700.00	3240.00	25810.00

NOTE ?- ALL ZERO STRESS VALUES INDICATE THAT THE CODE DOES NOT
**** RECOMMEND THE USE OF THE MATERIAL AT THAT TEMPERATURE

HOT STRESS AND ALLOW. STRESS RANGE
BASED ON B31.3

S(A)=F*(1.25*S(C)+0.25*S(H)) , F=1

MATERIAL	A335-P2		A335-P5,B,C		A335-GR-P9		A335-GR-P11		A335-GR-P22	
TEMP(F)	HOT,S(H)	ALL,S(A)	HOT,S(H)	ALL,S(A)	HOT,S(H)	ALL,S(A)	HOT,S(H)	ALL,S(A)	HOT,S(H)	ALL,S(A)
1150.00	0.00	0.00	2000.00	25500.00	2200.00	25550.00	2500.00	25625.00	3000.00	25750.00
1160.00	0.00	0.00	1860.00	25465.00	2060.00	25515.00	2240.00	25560.00	2800.00	25700.00
1170.00	0.00	0.00	1720.00	25430.00	1920.00	25480.00	1980.00	25495.00	2600.00	25650.00
1180.00	0.00	0.00	1580.00	25395.00	1780.00	25445.00	1720.00	25430.00	2400.00	25600.00
1190.00	0.00	0.00	1440.00	25360.00	1640.00	25410.00	1460.00	25365.00	2200.00	25550.00
1200.00	0.00	0.00	1300.00	25325.00	1500.00	25375.00	1200.00	25300.00	2000.00	25500.00

NOTE ?- ALL ZERO STRESS VALUES INDICATE THAT THE CODE DOES NOT
**** RECOMMEND THE USE OF THE MATERIAL AT THAT TEMPERATURE

HOT STRESS AND ALLOW. STRESS RANGE
BASED ON B31.3

S(A)=F*(1.25*S(C)+0.25*S(H)) , F=1

MATERIAL	A312-TP304		A312-TP304L		A312-TP316		A312-TP316L		A312-TP317	
TEMP(F)	HOT,S(H)	ALL,S(A)	HOT,S(H)	ALL,S(A)	HOT,S(H)	ALL,S(A)	HOT,S(H)	ALL,S(A)	HOT,S(H)	ALL,S(A)
100.00	20000.00	30000.00	16700.00	25050.00	20000.00	30000.00	16700.00	25050.00	20000.00	30000.00
110.00	20000.00	30000.00	16700.00	25050.00	20000.00	30000.00	16700.00	25050.00	20000.00	30000.00
120.00	20000.00	30000.00	16700.00	25050.00	20000.00	30000.00	16700.00	25050.00	20000.00	30000.00
130.00	20000.00	30000.00	16700.00	25050.00	20000.00	30000.00	16700.00	25050.00	20000.00	30000.00
140.00	20000.00	30000.00	16700.00	25050.00	20000.00	30000.00	16700.00	25050.00	20000.00	30000.00
150.00	20000.00	30000.00	16700.00	25050.00	20000.00	30000.00	16700.00	25050.00	20000.00	30000.00
160.00	20000.00	30000.00	16700.00	25050.00	20000.00	30000.00	16700.00	25050.00	20000.00	30000.00
170.00	20000.00	30000.00	16700.00	25050.00	20000.00	30000.00	16700.00	25050.00	20000.00	30000.00
180.00	20000.00	30000.00	16700.00	25050.00	20000.00	30000.00	16700.00	25050.00	20000.00	30000.00
190.00	20000.00	30000.00	16700.00	25050.00	20000.00	30000.00	16700.00	25050.00	20000.00	30000.00
200.00	20000.00	30000.00	16700.00	25050.00	20000.00	30000.00	16700.00	25050.00	20000.00	30000.00
210.00	20000.00	30000.00	16700.00	25050.00	20000.00	30000.00	16700.00	25050.00	20000.00	30000.00
220.00	20000.00	30000.00	16700.00	25050.00	20000.00	30000.00	16700.00	25050.00	20000.00	30000.00
230.00	20000.00	30000.00	16700.00	25050.00	20000.00	30000.00	16700.00	25050.00	20000.00	30000.00
240.00	20000.00	30000.00	16700.00	25050.00	20000.00	30000.00	16700.00	25050.00	20000.00	30000.00
250.00	20000.00	30000.00	16700.00	25050.00	20000.00	30000.00	16700.00	25050.00	20000.00	30000.00
260.00	20000.00	30000.00	16700.00	25050.00	20000.00	30000.00	16700.00	25050.00	20000.00	30000.00
270.00	20000.00	30000.00	16700.00	25050.00	20000.00	30000.00	16700.00	25050.00	20000.00	30000.00
280.00	20000.00	30000.00	16700.00	25050.00	20000.00	30000.00	16700.00	25050.00	20000.00	30000.00
290.00	20000.00	30000.00	16700.00	25050.00	20000.00	30000.00	16700.00	25050.00	20000.00	30000.00
300.00	20000.00	30000.00	16700.00	25050.00	20000.00	30000.00	16700.00	25050.00	20000.00	30000.00

NOTE ?- ALL ZERO STRESS VALUES INDICATE THAT THE CODE DOES NOT
**** RECOMMEND THE USE OF THE MATERIAL AT THAT TEMPERATURE

HOT STRESS AND ALLOW. STRESS RANGE
BASED ON B31.3

S(A)=F*(1.25*S(C)+0.25*S(H)) , F=1

MATERIAL	A312-TP304		A312-TP304L		A312-TP316		A312-TP316L		A312-TP317	
TEMP(F)	HOT,S(H)	ALL,S(A)	HOT,S(H)	ALL,S(A)	HOT,S(H)	ALL,S(A)	HOT,S(H)	ALL,S(A)	HOT,S(H)	ALL,S(A)
310.00	19870.00	29967.50	16610.00	25027.50	19930.00	29982.50	16580.00	25020.00	19930.00	29982.50
320.00	19740.00	29935.00	16520.00	25005.00	19860.00	29965.00	16460.00	24990.00	19860.00	29965.00
330.00	19610.00	29902.50	16430.00	24982.50	19790.00	29947.50	16340.00	24960.00	19790.00	29947.50
340.00	19480.00	29870.00	16340.00	24960.00	19720.00	29930.00	16220.00	24930.00	19720.00	29930.00
350.00	19350.00	29837.50	16250.00	24937.50	19650.00	29912.50	16100.00	24900.00	19650.00	29912.50
360.00	19220.00	29805.00	16160.00	24915.00	19580.00	29895.00	15980.00	24870.00	19580.00	29895.00
370.00	19090.00	29772.50	16070.00	24892.50	19510.00	29877.50	15860.00	24840.00	19510.00	29877.50
380.00	18960.00	29740.00	15980.00	24870.00	19440.00	29860.00	15740.00	24810.00	19440.00	29860.00
390.00	18830.00	29707.50	15890.00	24847.50	19370.00	29842.50	15620.00	24780.00	19370.00	29842.50
400.00	18700.00	29675.00	15800.00	24825.00	19300.00	29825.00	15500.00	24750.00	19300.00	29825.00
410.00	18580.00	29645.00	15700.00	24800.00	19160.00	29790.00	15390.00	24722.50	19160.00	29790.00
420.00	18460.00	29615.00	15600.00	24775.00	19020.00	29755.00	15280.00	24695.00	19020.00	29755.00
430.00	18340.00	29585.00	15500.00	24750.00	18880.00	29720.00	15170.00	24667.50	18880.00	29720.00
440.00	18220.00	29555.00	15400.00	24725.00	18740.00	29685.00	15060.00	24640.00	18740.00	29685.00
450.00	18100.00	29525.00	15300.00	24700.00	18600.00	29650.00	14950.00	24612.50	18600.00	29650.00
460.00	17980.00	29495.00	15200.00	24675.00	18460.00	29615.00	14840.00	24585.00	18460.00	29615.00
470.00	17860.00	29465.00	15100.00	24650.00	18320.00	29580.00	14730.00	24557.50	18320.00	29580.00
480.00	17740.00	29435.00	15000.00	24625.00	18180.00	29545.00	14620.00	24530.00	18180.00	29545.00
490.00	17620.00	29405.00	14900.00	24600.00	18040.00	29510.00	14510.00	24502.50	18040.00	29510.00
500.00	17500.00	29375.00	14800.00	24575.00	17900.00	29475.00	14400.00	24475.00	17900.00	29475.00
510.00	17390.00	29347.50	14720.00	24555.00	17810.00	29452.50	14310.00	24452.50	17810.00	29452.50

NOTE ?- ALL ZERO STRESS VALUES INDICATE THAT THE CODE DOES NOT
**** RECOMMEND THE USE OF THE MATERIAL AT THAT TEMPERATURE

HOT STRESS AND ALLOW. STRESS RANGE
BASED ON B31.3

S(A)=F*(1.25*S(C)+0.25*S(H)) , F=1

MATERIAL	A312-TP304		A312-TP304L		A312-TP316		A312-TP316L		A312-TP317	
TEMP(F)	HOT,S(H)	ALL,S(A)	HOT,S(H)	ALL,S(A)	HOT,S(H)	ALL,S(A)	HOT,S(H)	ALL,S(A)	HOT,S(H)	ALL,S(A)
520.00	17280.00	29320.00	14640.00	24535.00	17720.00	29430.00	14220.00	24430.00	17720.00	29430.00
530.00	17170.00	29292.50	14560.00	24515.00	17630.00	29407.50	14130.00	24407.50	17630.00	29407.50
540.00	17060.00	29265.00	14480.00	24495.00	17540.00	29385.00	14040.00	24385.00	17540.00	29385.00
550.00	16950.00	29237.50	14400.00	24475.00	17450.00	29362.50	13950.00	24362.50	17450.00	29362.50
560.00	16840.00	29210.00	14320.00	24455.00	17360.00	29340.00	13860.00	24340.00	17360.00	29340.00
570.00	16730.00	29182.50	14240.00	24435.00	17270.00	29317.50	13770.00	24317.50	17270.00	29317.50
580.00	16620.00	29155.00	14160.00	24415.00	17180.00	29295.00	13680.00	24295.00	17180.00	29295.00
590.00	16510.00	29127.50	14080.00	24395.00	17090.00	29272.50	13590.00	24272.50	17090.00	29272.50
600.00	16400.00	29100.00	14000.00	24375.00	17000.00	29250.00	13500.00	24250.00	17000.00	29250.00
610.00	16360.00	29090.00	13940.00	24360.00	16940.00	29235.00	13440.00	24235.00	16940.00	29235.00
620.00	16320.00	29080.00	13880.00	24345.00	16880.00	29220.00	13380.00	24220.00	16880.00	29220.00
630.00	16280.00	29070.00	13820.00	24330.00	16820.00	29205.00	13320.00	24205.00	16820.00	29205.00
640.00	16240.00	29060.00	13760.00	24315.00	16760.00	29190.00	13260.00	24190.00	16760.00	29190.00
650.00	16200.00	29050.00	13700.00	24300.00	16700.00	29175.00	13200.00	24175.00	16700.00	29175.00
660.00	16160.00	29040.00	13660.00	24290.00	16620.00	29155.00	13140.00	24160.00	16620.00	29155.00
670.00	16120.00	29030.00	13620.00	24280.00	16540.00	29135.00	13080.00	24145.00	16540.00	29135.00
680.00	16080.00	29020.00	13580.00	24270.00	16460.00	29115.00	13020.00	24130.00	16460.00	29115.00
690.00	16040.00	29010.00	13540.00	24260.00	16380.00	29095.00	12960.00	24115.00	16380.00	29095.00
700.00	16000.00	29000.00	13500.00	24250.00	16300.00	29075.00	12900.00	24100.00	16300.00	29075.00
710.00	15920.00	28980.00	13460.00	24240.00	16260.00	29065.00	12840.00	24085.00	16260.00	29065.00
720.00	15840.00	28960.00	13420.00	24230.00	16220.00	29055.00	12780.00	24070.00	16220.00	29055.00

NOTE ?- ALL ZERO STRESS VALUES INDICATE THAT THE CODE DOES NOT
**** RECOMMEND THE USE OF THE MATERIAL AT THAT TEMPERATURE

HOT STRESS AND ALLOW. STRESS RANGE
BASED ON B31.3

S(A)=F*(1.25*S(C)+0.25*S(H)) , F=1

MATERIAL	A312-TP304		A312-TP304L		A312-TP316		A312-TP316L		A312-TP317	
TEMP(F)	HOT,S(H)	ALL,S(A)	HOT,S(H)	ALL,S(A)	HOT,S(H)	ALL,S(A)	HOT,S(H)	ALL,S(A)	HOT,S(H)	ALL,S(A)
730.00	15760.00	28940.00	13380.00	24220.00	16180.00	29045.00	12720.00	24055.00	16180.00	29045.00
740.00	15680.00	28920.00	13340.00	24210.00	16140.00	29035.00	12660.00	24040.00	16140.00	29035.00
750.00	15600.00	28900.00	13300.00	24200.00	16100.00	29025.00	12600.00	24025.00	16100.00	29025.00
760.00	15520.00	28880.00	13240.00	24185.00	16060.00	29015.00	12560.00	24015.00	16060.00	29015.00
770.00	15440.00	28860.00	13180.00	24170.00	16020.00	29005.00	12520.00	24005.00	16020.00	29005.00
780.00	15360.00	28840.00	13120.00	24155.00	15980.00	28995.00	12480.00	23995.00	15980.00	28995.00
790.00	15280.00	28820.00	13060.00	24140.00	15940.00	28985.00	12440.00	23985.00	15940.00	28985.00
800.00	15200.00	28800.00	13000.00	24125.00	15900.00	28975.00	12400.00	23975.00	15900.00	28975.00
810.00	15140.00	28785.00	12960.00	24115.00	15860.00	28965.00	12340.00	23960.00	15860.00	28965.00
820.00	15080.00	28770.00	12920.00	24105.00	15820.00	28955.00	12280.00	23945.00	15820.00	28955.00
830.00	15020.00	28755.00	12880.00	24095.00	15780.00	28945.00	12220.00	23930.00	15780.00	28945.00
840.00	14960.00	28740.00	12840.00	24085.00	15740.00	28935.00	12160.00	23915.00	15740.00	28935.00
850.00	14900.00	28725.00	12800.00	24075.00	15700.00	28925.00	12100.00	23900.00	15700.00	28925.00
860.00	14840.00	28710.00	12620.00	24030.00	15660.00	28915.00	12040.00	23885.00	15660.00	28915.00
870.00	14780.00	28695.00	12440.00	23985.00	15620.00	28905.00	11980.00	23870.00	15620.00	28905.00
880.00	14720.00	28680.00	12260.00	23940.00	15580.00	28895.00	11920.00	23855.00	15580.00	28895.00
890.00	14660.00	28665.00	12080.00	23895.00	15540.00	28885.00	11860.00	23840.00	15540.00	28885.00
900.00	14600.00	28650.00	11900.00	23850.00	15500.00	28875.00	11800.00	23825.00	15500.00	28875.00
910.00	14560.00	28640.00	11500.00	23750.00	15480.00	28870.00	11740.00	23810.00	15480.00	28870.00
920.00	14520.00	28630.00	11100.00	23650.00	15460.00	28865.00	11680.00	23795.00	15460.00	28865.00
930.00	14480.00	28620.00	10700.00	23550.00	15440.00	28860.00	11620.00	23780.00	15440.00	28860.00

NOTE ?- ALL ZERO STRESS VALUES INDICATE THAT THE CODE DOES NOT
**** RECOMMEND THE USE OF THE MATERIAL AT THAT TEMPERATURE

HOT STRESS AND ALLOW. STRESS RANGE
BASED ON B31.3

S(A)=F*(1.25*S(C)+0.25*S(H)) , F=1

MATERIAL	A312-TP304		A312-TP304L		A312-TP316		A312-TP316L		A312-TP317	
TEMP(F)	HOT,S(H)	ALL,S(A)	HOT,S(H)	ALL,S(A)	HOT,S(H)	ALL,S(A)	HOT,S(H)	ALL,S(A)	HOT,S(H)	ALL,S(A)
940.00	14440.00	28610.00	10300.00	23450.00	15420.00	28855.00	11560.00	23765.00	15420.00	28855.00
950.00	14400.00	28600.00	9900.00	23350.00	15400.00	28850.00	11500.00	23750.00	15400.00	28850.00
960.00	14280.00	28570.00	9480.00	23245.00	15380.00	28845.00	11440.00	23735.00	15380.00	28845.00
970.00	14160.00	28540.00	9060.00	23140.00	15360.00	28840.00	11380.00	23720.00	15360.00	28840.00
980.00	14040.00	28510.00	8640.00	23035.00	15340.00	28835.00	11320.00	23705.00	15340.00	28835.00
990.00	13920.00	28480.00	8220.00	22930.00	15320.00	28830.00	11260.00	23690.00	15320.00	28830.00
1000.00	13800.00	28450.00	7800.00	22825.00	15300.00	28825.00	11200.00	23675.00	15300.00	28825.00
1010.00	13480.00	28370.00	7500.00	22750.00	15140.00	28785.00	11120.00	23655.00	15140.00	28785.00
1020.00	13160.00	28290.00	7200.00	22675.00	14980.00	28745.00	11040.00	23635.00	14980.00	28745.00
1030.00	12840.00	28210.00	6900.00	22600.00	14820.00	28705.00	10960.00	23615.00	14820.00	28705.00
1040.00	12520.00	28130.00	6600.00	22525.00	14660.00	28665.00	10880.00	23595.00	14660.00	28665.00
1050.00	12200.00	28050.00	6300.00	22450.00	14500.00	28625.00	10800.00	23575.00	14500.00	28625.00
1060.00	11700.00	27925.00	6060.00	22390.00	14080.00	28520.00	10680.00	23545.00	14080.00	28520.00
1070.00	11200.00	27800.00	5820.00	22330.00	13660.00	28415.00	10560.00	23515.00	13660.00	28415.00
1080.00	10700.00	27675.00	5580.00	22270.00	13240.00	28310.00	10440.00	23485.00	13240.00	28310.00
1090.00	10200.00	27550.00	5340.00	22210.00	12820.00	28205.00	10320.00	23455.00	12820.00	28205.00
1100.00	9700.00	27425.00	5100.00	22150.00	12400.00	28100.00	10200.00	23425.00	12400.00	28100.00
1110.00	9300.00	27325.00	4880.00	22095.00	11880.00	27970.00	9920.00	23355.00	11880.00	27970.00
1120.00	8900.00	27225.00	4660.00	22040.00	11360.00	27840.00	9640.00	23285.00	11360.00	27840.00
1130.00	8500.00	27125.00	4440.00	21985.00	10840.00	27710.00	9360.00	23215.00	10840.00	27710.00
1140.00	8100.00	27025.00	4220.00	21930.00	10320.00	27580.00	9080.00	23145.00	10320.00	27580.00

NOTE ?- ALL ZERO STRESS VALUES INDICATE THAT THE CODE DOES NOT
**** RECOMMEND THE USE OF THE MATERIAL AT THAT TEMPERATURE

HOT STRESS AND ALLOW. STRESS RANGE
BASED ON B31.3

S(A)=F*(1.25*S(C)+0.25*S(H)) , F=1

MATERIAL	A312-TP304		A312-TP304L		A312-TP316		A312-TP316L		A312-TP317	
TEMP(F)	HOT,S(H)	ALL,S(A)	HOT,S(H)	ALL,S(A)	HOT,S(H)	ALL,S(A)	HOT,S(H)	ALL,S(A)	HOT,S(H)	ALL,S(A)
1150.00	7700.00	26925.00	4000.00	21875.00	9800.00	27450.00	8800.00	23075.00	9800.00	27450.00
1160.00	7360.00	26840.00	3840.00	21835.00	9320.00	27330.00	8320.00	22955.00	9320.00	27330.00
1170.00	7020.00	26755.00	3680.00	21795.00	8840.00	27210.00	7840.00	22835.00	8840.00	27210.00
1180.00	6680.00	26670.00	3520.00	21755.00	8360.00	27090.00	7360.00	22715.00	8360.00	27090.00
1190.00	6340.00	26585.00	3360.00	21715.00	7880.00	26970.00	6880.00	22595.00	7880.00	26970.00
1200.00	6000.00	26500.00	3200.00	21675.00	7400.00	26850.00	6400.00	22475.00	7400.00	26850.00
1210.00	5740.00	26435.00	3080.00	21645.00	7020.00	26755.00	6060.00	22390.00	7020.00	26755.00
1220.00	5480.00	26370.00	2960.00	21615.00	6640.00	26660.00	5720.00	22305.00	6640.00	26660.00
1230.00	5220.00	26305.00	2840.00	21585.00	6260.00	26565.00	5380.00	22220.00	6260.00	26565.00
1240.00	4960.00	26240.00	2720.00	21555.00	5880.00	26470.00	5040.00	22135.00	5880.00	26470.00
1250.00	4700.00	26175.00	2600.00	21525.00	5500.00	26375.00	4700.00	22050.00	5500.00	26375.00
1260.00	4500.00	26125.00	2500.00	21500.00	5220.00	26305.00	4460.00	21990.00	5220.00	26305.00
1270.00	4300.00	26075.00	2400.00	21475.00	4940.00	26235.00	4220.00	21930.00	4940.00	26235.00
1280.00	4100.00	26025.00	2300.00	21450.00	4660.00	26165.00	3980.00	21870.00	4660.00	26165.00
1290.00	3900.00	25975.00	2200.00	21425.00	4380.00	26095.00	3740.00	21810.00	4380.00	26095.00
1300.00	3700.00	25925.00	2100.00	21400.00	4100.00	26025.00	3500.00	21750.00	4100.00	26025.00
1310.00	3540.00	25885.00	2020.00	21380.00	3900.00	25975.00	3300.00	21700.00	3900.00	25975.00
1320.00	3380.00	25845.00	1940.00	21360.00	3700.00	25925.00	3100.00	21650.00	3700.00	25925.00
1330.00	3220.00	25805.00	1860.00	21340.00	3500.00	25875.00	2900.00	21600.00	3500.00	25875.00
1340.00	3060.00	25765.00	1780.00	21320.00	3300.00	25825.00	2700.00	21550.00	3300.00	25825.00
1350.00	2900.00	25725.00	1700.00	21300.00	3100.00	25775.00	2500.00	21500.00	3100.00	25775.00

NOTE ?- ALL ZERO STRESS VALUES INDICATE THAT THE CODE DOES NOT
**** RECOMMEND THE USE OF THE MATERIAL AT THAT TEMPERATURE

HOT STRESS AND ALLOW. STRESS RANGE
BASED ON B31.3

S(A)=F*(1.25*S(C)+0.25*S(H)) , F=1

MATERIAL	A312-TP304		A312-TP304L		A312-TP316		A312-TP316L		A312-TP317	
TEMP(F)	HOT,S(H)	ALL,S(A)	HOT,S(H)	ALL,S(A)	HOT,S(H)	ALL,S(A)	HOT,S(H)	ALL,S(A)	HOT,S(H)	ALL,S(A)
1360.00	2780.00	25695.00	1580.00	21270.00	2940.00	25735.00	2360.00	21465.00	2940.00	25735.00
1370.00	2660.00	25665.00	1460.00	21240.00	2780.00	25695.00	2220.00	21430.00	2780.00	25695.00
1380.00	2540.00	25635.00	1340.00	21210.00	2620.00	25655.00	2080.00	21395.00	2620.00	25655.00
1390.00	2420.00	25605.00	1220.00	21180.00	2460.00	25615.00	1940.00	21360.00	2460.00	25615.00
1400.00	2300.00	25575.00	1100.00	21150.00	2300.00	25575.00	1800.00	21325.00	2300.00	25575.00
1410.00	2200.00	25550.00	1080.00	21145.00	2180.00	25545.00	1700.00	21300.00	2180.00	25545.00
1420.00	2100.00	25525.00	1060.00	21140.00	2060.00	25515.00	1600.00	21275.00	2060.00	25515.00
1430.00	2000.00	25500.00	1040.00	21135.00	1940.00	25485.00	1500.00	21250.00	1940.00	25485.00
1440.00	1900.00	25475.00	1020.00	21130.00	1820.00	25455.00	1400.00	21225.00	1820.00	25455.00
1450.00	1800.00	25450.00	1000.00	21125.00	1700.00	25425.00	1300.00	21200.00	1700.00	25425.00
1460.00	1720.00	25430.00	980.00	21120.00	1620.00	25405.00	1240.00	21185.00	1620.00	25405.00
1470.00	1640.00	25410.00	960.00	21115.00	1540.00	25385.00	1180.00	21170.00	1540.00	25385.00
1480.00	1560.00	25390.00	940.00	21110.00	1460.00	25365.00	1120.00	21155.00	1460.00	25365.00
1490.00	1480.00	25370.00	920.00	21105.00	1380.00	25345.00	1060.00	21140.00	1380.00	25345.00
1500.00	1400.00	25350.00	900.00	21100.00	1300.00	25325.00	1000.00	21125.00	1300.00	25325.00

NOTE ?- ALL ZERO STRESS VALUES INDICATE THAT THE CODE DOES NOT
**** RECOMMEND THE USE OF THE MATERIAL AT THAT TEMPERATURE

HOT STRESS AND ALLOW. STRESS RANGE
BASED ON B31.3

S(A)=F*(1.25*S(C)+0.25*S(H)) , F=1

MATERIAL	A312-TP321		A312-TP347		A376- TP304		A376- TP316		A376-TP321	
TEMP(F)	HOT,S(H)	ALL,S(A)	HOT,S(H)	ALL,S(A)	HOT,S(H)	ALL,S(A)	HOT,S(H)	ALL,S(A)	HOT,S(H)	ALL,S(A)
100.00	20000.00	30000.00	20000.00	30000.00	20000.00	30000.00	20000.00	30000.00	20000.00	30000.00
110.00	20000.00	30000.00	20000.00	30000.00	20000.00	30000.00	20000.00	30000.00	20000.00	30000.00
120.00	20000.00	30000.00	20000.00	30000.00	20000.00	30000.00	20000.00	30000.00	20000.00	30000.00
130.00	20000.00	30000.00	20000.00	30000.00	20000.00	30000.00	20000.00	30000.00	20000.00	30000.00
140.00	20000.00	30000.00	20000.00	30000.00	20000.00	30000.00	20000.00	30000.00	20000.00	30000.00
150.00	20000.00	30000.00	20000.00	30000.00	20000.00	30000.00	20000.00	30000.00	20000.00	30000.00
160.00	20000.00	30000.00	20000.00	30000.00	20000.00	30000.00	20000.00	30000.00	20000.00	30000.00
170.00	20000.00	30000.00	20000.00	30000.00	20000.00	30000.00	20000.00	30000.00	20000.00	30000.00
180.00	20000.00	30000.00	20000.00	30000.00	20000.00	30000.00	20000.00	30000.00	20000.00	30000.00
190.00	20000.00	30000.00	20000.00	30000.00	20000.00	30000.00	20000.00	30000.00	20000.00	30000.00
200.00	20000.00	30000.00	20000.00	30000.00	20000.00	30000.00	20000.00	30000.00	20000.00	30000.00
210.00	20000.00	30000.00	20000.00	30000.00	20000.00	30000.00	20000.00	30000.00	20000.00	30000.00
220.00	20000.00	30000.00	20000.00	30000.00	20000.00	30000.00	20000.00	30000.00	20000.00	30000.00
230.00	20000.00	30000.00	20000.00	30000.00	20000.00	30000.00	20000.00	30000.00	20000.00	30000.00
240.00	20000.00	30000.00	20000.00	30000.00	20000.00	30000.00	20000.00	30000.00	20000.00	30000.00
250.00	20000.00	30000.00	20000.00	30000.00	20000.00	30000.00	20000.00	30000.00	20000.00	30000.00
260.00	20000.00	30000.00	20000.00	30000.00	20000.00	30000.00	20000.00	30000.00	20000.00	30000.00
270.00	20000.00	30000.00	20000.00	30000.00	20000.00	30000.00	20000.00	30000.00	20000.00	30000.00
280.00	20000.00	30000.00	20000.00	30000.00	20000.00	30000.00	20000.00	30000.00	20000.00	30000.00
290.00	20000.00	30000.00	20000.00	30000.00	20000.00	30000.00	20000.00	30000.00	20000.00	30000.00
300.00	20000.00	30000.00	20000.00	30000.00	20000.00	30000.00	20000.00	30000.00	20000.00	30000.00

NOTE ?- ALL ZERO STRESS VALUES INDICATE THAT THE CODE DOES NOT
**** RECOMMEND THE USE OF THE MATERIAL AT THAT TEMPERATURE

HOT STRESS AND ALLOW. STRESS RANGE
BASED ON B31.3

S(A)=F*(1.25*S(C)+0.25*S(H)) , F=1

MATERIAL	A312-TP321		A312-TP347		A376- TP304		A376- TP316		A376-TP321	
TEMP(F)	HOT,S(H)	ALL,S(A)	HOT,S(H)	ALL,S(A)	HOT,S(H)	ALL,S(A)	HOT,S(H)	ALL,S(A)	HOT,S(H)	ALL,S(A)
310.00	19860.00	29965.00	20000.00	30000.00	19870.00	29967.50	19930.00	29982.50	19860.00	29965.00
320.00	19720.00	29930.00	20000.00	30000.00	19740.00	29935.00	19860.00	29965.00	19720.00	29930.00
330.00	19580.00	29895.00	20000.00	30000.00	19610.00	29902.50	19790.00	29947.50	19580.00	29895.00
340.00	19440.00	29860.00	20000.00	30000.00	19480.00	29870.00	19720.00	29930.00	19440.00	29860.00
350.00	19300.00	29825.00	20000.00	30000.00	19350.00	29837.50	19650.00	29912.50	19300.00	29825.00
360.00	19160.00	29790.00	20000.00	30000.00	19220.00	29805.00	19580.00	29895.00	19160.00	29790.00
370.00	19020.00	29755.00	20000.00	30000.00	19090.00	29772.50	19510.00	29877.50	19020.00	29755.00
380.00	18880.00	29720.00	20000.00	30000.00	18960.00	29740.00	19440.00	29860.00	18880.00	29720.00
390.00	18740.00	29685.00	20000.00	30000.00	18830.00	29707.50	19370.00	29842.50	18740.00	29685.00
400.00	18600.00	29650.00	20000.00	30000.00	18700.00	29675.00	19300.00	29825.00	18600.00	29650.00
410.00	18470.00	29617.50	19990.00	29997.50	18580.00	29645.00	19160.00	29790.00	18470.00	29617.50
420.00	18340.00	29585.00	19980.00	29995.00	18460.00	29615.00	19020.00	29755.00	18340.00	29585.00
430.00	18210.00	29552.50	19970.00	29992.50	18340.00	29585.00	18880.00	29720.00	18210.00	29552.50
440.00	18080.00	29520.00	19960.00	29990.00	18220.00	29555.00	18740.00	29685.00	18080.00	29520.00
450.00	17950.00	29487.50	19950.00	29987.50	18100.00	29525.00	18600.00	29650.00	17950.00	29487.50
460.00	17820.00	29455.00	19940.00	29985.00	17980.00	29495.00	18460.00	29615.00	17820.00	29455.00
470.00	17690.00	29422.50	19930.00	29982.50	17860.00	29465.00	18320.00	29580.00	17690.00	29422.50
480.00	17560.00	29390.00	19920.00	29980.00	17740.00	29435.00	18180.00	29545.00	17560.00	29390.00
490.00	17430.00	29357.50	19910.00	29977.50	17620.00	29405.00	18040.00	29510.00	17430.00	29357.50
500.00	17300.00	29325.00	19900.00	29975.00	17500.00	29375.00	17900.00	29475.00	17300.00	29325.00
510.00	17210.00	29302.50	19840.00	29960.00	17390.00	29347.50	17810.00	29452.50	17210.00	29302.50

NOTE ?- ALL ZERO STRESS VALUES INDICATE THAT THE CODE DOES NOT
**** RECOMMEND THE USE OF THE MATERIAL AT THAT TEMPERATURE

HOT STRESS AND ALLOW. STRESS RANGE
BASED ON B31.3

S(A)=F*(1.25*S(C)+0.25*S(H)) , F=1

MATERIAL	A312-TP321		A312-TP347		A376- TP304		A376- TP316		A376-TP321	
TEMP(F)	HOT,S(H)	ALL,S(A)	HOT,S(H)	ALL,S(A)	HOT,S(H)	ALL,S(A)	HOT,S(H)	ALL,S(A)	HOT,S(H)	ALL,S(A)
520.00	17120.00	29280.00	19780.00	29945.00	17280.00	29320.00	17720.00	29430.00	17120.00	29280.00
530.00	17030.00	29257.50	19720.00	29930.00	17170.00	29292.50	17630.00	29407.50	17030.00	29257.50
540.00	16940.00	29235.00	19660.00	29915.00	17060.00	29265.00	17540.00	29385.00	16940.00	29235.00
550.00	16850.00	29212.50	19600.00	29900.00	16950.00	29237.50	17450.00	29362.50	16850.00	29212.50
560.00	16760.00	29190.00	19540.00	29885.00	16840.00	29210.00	17360.00	29340.00	16760.00	29190.00
570.00	16670.00	29167.50	19480.00	29870.00	16730.00	29182.50	17270.00	29317.50	16670.00	29167.50
580.00	16580.00	29145.00	19420.00	29855.00	16620.00	29155.00	17180.00	29295.00	16580.00	29145.00
590.00	16490.00	29122.50	19360.00	29840.00	16510.00	29127.50	17090.00	29272.50	16490.00	29122.50
600.00	16400.00	29100.00	19300.00	29825.00	16400.00	29100.00	17000.00	29250.00	16400.00	29100.00
610.00	16340.00	29085.00	19240.00	29810.00	16360.00	29090.00	16940.00	29235.00	16340.00	29085.00
620.00	16280.00	29070.00	19180.00	29795.00	16320.00	29080.00	16880.00	29220.00	16280.00	29070.00
630.00	16220.00	29055.00	19120.00	29780.00	16280.00	29070.00	16820.00	29205.00	16220.00	29055.00
640.00	16160.00	29040.00	19060.00	29765.00	16240.00	29060.00	16760.00	29190.00	16160.00	29040.00
650.00	16100.00	29025.00	19000.00	29750.00	16200.00	29050.00	16700.00	29175.00	16100.00	29025.00
660.00	16040.00	29010.00	18920.00	29730.00	16160.00	29040.00	16620.00	29155.00	16040.00	29010.00
670.00	15980.00	28995.00	18840.00	29710.00	16120.00	29030.00	16540.00	29135.00	15980.00	28995.00
680.00	15920.00	28980.00	18760.00	29690.00	16080.00	29020.00	16460.00	29115.00	15920.00	28980.00
690.00	15860.00	28965.00	18680.00	29670.00	16040.00	29010.00	16380.00	29095.00	15860.00	28965.00
700.00	15800.00	28950.00	18600.00	29650.00	16000.00	29000.00	16300.00	29075.00	15800.00	28950.00
710.00	15780.00	28945.00	18580.00	29645.00	15920.00	28980.00	16250.00	29062.50	15780.00	28945.00
720.00	15760.00	28940.00	18560.00	29640.00	15840.00	28960.00	16200.00	29050.00	15760.00	28940.00

NOTE ?- ALL ZERO STRESS VALUES INDICATE THAT THE CODE DOES NOT
***** RECOMMEND THE USE OF THE MATERIAL AT THAT TEMPERATURE

HOT STRESS AND ALLOW. STRESS RANGE
BASED ON B31.3

S(A)=F*(1.25*S(C)+0.25*S(H)) , F=1

MATERIAL	A312-TP321		A312-TP347		A376- TP304		A376- TP316		A376-TP321	
TEMP(F)	HOT,S(H)	ALL,S(A)	HOT,S(H)	ALL,S(A)	HOT,S(H)	ALL,S(A)	HOT,S(H)	ALL,S(A)	HOT,S(H)	ALL,S(A)
730.00	15740.00	28935.00	18540.00	29635.00	15760.00	28940.00	16150.00	29037.50	15740.00	28935.00
740.00	15720.00	28930.00	18520.00	29630.00	15680.00	28920.00	16100.00	29025.00	15720.00	28930.00
750.00	15700.00	28925.00	18500.00	29625.00	15600.00	28900.00	16050.00	29012.50	15700.00	28925.00
760.00	15660.00	28915.00	18460.00	29615.00	15520.00	28880.00	16020.00	29005.00	15660.00	28915.00
770.00	15620.00	28905.00	18420.00	29605.00	15440.00	28860.00	15990.00	28997.50	15620.00	28905.00
780.00	15580.00	28895.00	18380.00	29595.00	15360.00	28840.00	15960.00	28990.00	15580.00	28895.00
790.00	15540.00	28885.00	18340.00	29585.00	15280.00	28820.00	15930.00	28982.50	15540.00	28885.00
800.00	15500.00	28875.00	18300.00	29575.00	15200.00	28800.00	15900.00	28975.00	15500.00	28875.00
810.00	15470.00	28867.50	17720.00	29430.00	15140.00	28785.00	15860.00	28965.00	15460.00	28865.00
820.00	15440.00	28860.00	17140.00	29285.00	15080.00	28770.00	15820.00	28955.00	15420.00	28855.00
830.00	15410.00	28852.50	16560.00	29140.00	15020.00	28755.00	15780.00	28945.00	15380.00	28845.00
840.00	15380.00	28845.00	15980.00	28995.00	14960.00	28740.00	15740.00	28935.00	15340.00	28835.00
850.00	15350.00	28837.50	15400.00	28850.00	14900.00	28725.00	15700.00	28925.00	15300.00	28825.00
860.00	15340.00	28835.00	15300.00	28825.00	14840.00	28710.00	15660.00	28915.00	15280.00	28820.00
870.00	15330.00	28832.50	15200.00	28800.00	14780.00	28695.00	15620.00	28905.00	15260.00	28815.00
880.00	15320.00	28830.00	15100.00	28775.00	14720.00	28680.00	15580.00	28895.00	15240.00	28810.00
890.00	15310.00	28827.50	15000.00	28750.00	14660.00	28665.00	15540.00	28885.00	15220.00	28805.00
900.00	15300.00	28825.00	14900.00	28725.00	14600.00	28650.00	15500.00	28875.00	15200.00	28800.00
910.00	15270.00	28817.50	14880.00	28720.00	14560.00	28640.00	15480.00	28870.00	15180.00	28795.00
920.00	15240.00	28810.00	14860.00	28715.00	14520.00	28630.00	15460.00	28865.00	15160.00	28790.00
930.00	15210.00	28802.50	14840.00	28710.00	14480.00	28620.00	15440.00	28860.00	15140.00	28785.00

NOTE ?- ALL ZERO STRESS VALUES INDICATE THAT THE CODE DOES NOT
**** RECOMMEND THE USE OF THE MATERIAL AT THAT TEMPERATURE

HOT STRESS AND ALLOW. STRESS RANGE
BASED ON B31.3

S(A)=F*(1.25*S(C)+0.25*S(H)) , F=1

MATERIAL	A312-TP321		A312-TP347		A376- TP304		A376- TP316		A376-TP321	
TEMP(F)	HOT,S(H)	ALL,S(A)	HOT,S(H)	ALL,S(A)	HOT,S(H)	ALL,S(A)	HOT,S(H)	ALL,S(A)	HOT,S(H)	ALL,S(A)
940.00	15180.00	28795.00	14820.00	28705.00	14440.00	28610.00	15420.00	28855.00	15120.00	28780.00
950.00	15150.00	28787.50	14800.00	28700.00	14400.00	28600.00	15400.00	28850.00	15100.00	28775.00
960.00	14880.00	28720.00	14640.00	28660.00	14280.00	28570.00	15380.00	28845.00	14840.00	28710.00
970.00	14610.00	28652.50	14480.00	28620.00	14160.00	28540.00	15360.00	28840.00	14580.00	28645.00
980.00	14340.00	28585.00	14320.00	28580.00	14040.00	28510.00	15340.00	28835.00	14320.00	28580.00
990.00	14070.00	28517.50	14160.00	28540.00	13920.00	28480.00	15320.00	28830.00	14060.00	28515.00
1000.00	13800.00	28450.00	14000.00	28500.00	13800.00	28450.00	15300.00	28825.00	13800.00	28450.00
1010.00	12960.00	28240.00	13620.00	28405.00	13480.00	28370.00	15140.00	28785.00	12960.00	28240.00
1020.00	12120.00	28030.00	13240.00	28310.00	13160.00	28290.00	14980.00	28745.00	12120.00	28030.00
1030.00	11280.00	27820.00	12860.00	28215.00	12840.00	28210.00	14820.00	28705.00	11280.00	27820.00
1040.00	10440.00	27610.00	12480.00	28120.00	12520.00	28130.00	14660.00	28665.00	10440.00	27610.00
1050.00	9600.00	27400.00	12100.00	28025.00	12200.00	28050.00	14500.00	28625.00	9600.00	27400.00
1060.00	9060.00	27265.00	11500.00	27875.00	11700.00	27925.00	14080.00	28520.00	9060.00	27265.00
1070.00	8520.00	27130.00	10900.00	27725.00	11200.00	27800.00	13660.00	28415.00	8520.00	27130.00
1080.00	7980.00	26995.00	10300.00	27575.00	10700.00	27675.00	13240.00	28310.00	7980.00	26995.00
1090.00	7440.00	26860.00	9700.00	27425.00	10200.00	27550.00	12820.00	28205.00	7440.00	26860.00
1100.00	6900.00	26725.00	9100.00	27275.00	9700.00	27425.00	12400.00	28100.00	6900.00	26725.00
1110.00	6520.00	26630.00	8500.00	27125.00	9300.00	27325.00	11880.00	27970.00	6520.00	26630.00
1120.00	6140.00	26535.00	7900.00	26975.00	8900.00	27225.00	11360.00	27840.00	6140.00	26535.00
1130.00	5760.00	26440.00	7300.00	26825.00	8500.00	27125.00	10840.00	27710.00	5760.00	26440.00
1140.00	5380.00	26345.00	6700.00	26675.00	8100.00	27025.00	10320.00	27580.00	5380.00	26345.00

NOTE ?- ALL ZERO STRESS VALUES INDICATE THAT THE CODE DOES NOT
**** RECOMMEND THE USE OF THE MATERIAL AT THAT TEMPERATURE

HOT STRESS AND ALLOW. STRESS RANGE
BASED ON B31.3

S(A)=F*(1.25*S(C)+0.25*S(H)) , F=1

MATERIAL	A312-TP321		A312-TP347		A376- TP304		A376- TP316		A376-TP321	
TEMP(F)	HOT,S(H)	ALL,S(A)	HOT,S(H)	ALL,S(A)	HOT,S(H)	ALL,S(A)	HOT,S(H)	ALL,S(A)	HOT,S(H)	ALL,S(A)
1150.00	5000.00	26250.00	6100.00	26525.00	7700.00	26925.00	9800.00	27450.00	5000.00	26250.00
1160.00	4720.00	26180.00	5760.00	26440.00	7360.00	26840.00	9320.00	27330.00	4720.00	26180.00
1170.00	4440.00	26110.00	5420.00	26355.00	7020.00	26755.00	8840.00	27210.00	4440.00	26110.00
1180.00	4160.00	26040.00	5080.00	26270.00	6680.00	26670.00	8360.00	27090.00	4160.00	26040.00
1190.00	3880.00	25970.00	4740.00	26185.00	6340.00	26585.00	7880.00	26970.00	3880.00	25970.00
1200.00	3600.00	25900.00	4400.00	26100.00	6000.00	26500.00	7400.00	26850.00	3600.00	25900.00
1210.00	3400.00	25850.00	4180.00	26045.00	5740.00	26435.00	7020.00	26755.00	3340.00	25835.00
1220.00	3200.00	25800.00	3960.00	25990.00	5480.00	26370.00	6640.00	26660.00	3080.00	25770.00
1230.00	3000.00	25750.00	3740.00	25935.00	5220.00	26305.00	6260.00	26565.00	2820.00	25705.00
1240.00	2800.00	25700.00	3520.00	25880.00	4960.00	26240.00	5880.00	26470.00	2560.00	25640.00
1250.00	2600.00	25650.00	3300.00	25825.00	4700.00	26175.00	5500.00	26375.00	2300.00	25575.00
1260.00	2420.00	25605.00	3080.00	25770.00	4500.00	26125.00	5220.00	26305.00	2180.00	25545.00
1270.00	2240.00	25560.00	2860.00	25715.00	4300.00	26075.00	4940.00	26235.00	2060.00	25515.00
1280.00	2060.00	25515.00	2640.00	25660.00	4100.00	26025.00	4660.00	26165.00	1940.00	25485.00
1290.00	1880.00	25470.00	2420.00	25605.00	3900.00	25975.00	4380.00	26095.00	1820.00	25455.00
1300.00	1700.00	25425.00	2200.00	25550.00	3700.00	25925.00	4100.00	26025.00	1700.00	25425.00
1310.00	1580.00	25395.00	2060.00	25515.00	3540.00	25885.00	3900.00	25975.00	1580.00	25395.00
1320.00	1460.00	25365.00	1920.00	25480.00	3380.00	25845.00	3700.00	25925.00	1460.00	25365.00
1330.00	1340.00	25335.00	1780.00	25445.00	3220.00	25805.00	3500.00	25875.00	1340.00	25335.00
1340.00	1220.00	25305.00	1640.00	25410.00	3060.00	25765.00	3300.00	25825.00	1220.00	25305.00
1350.00	1100.00	25275.00	1500.00	25375.00	2900.00	25725.00	3100.00	25775.00	1100.00	25275.00

NOTE ?- ALL ZERO STRESS VALUES INDICATE THAT THE CODE DOES NOT
**** RECOMMEND THE USE OF THE MATERIAL AT THAT TEMPERATURE

HOT STRESS AND ALLOW. STRESS RANGE
BASED ON B31.3

S(A)=F*(1.25*S(C)+0.25*S(H)) , F=1

MATERIAL	A312-TP321		A312-TP347		A376- TP304		A376- TP316		A376-TP321	
TEMP(F)	HOT,S(H)	ALL,S(A)	HOT,S(H)	ALL,S(A)	HOT,S(H)	ALL,S(A)	HOT,S(H)	ALL,S(A)	HOT,S(H)	ALL,S(A)
1360.00	1040.00	25260.00	1440.00	25360.00	2780.00	25695.00	2940.00	25735.00	1040.00	25260.00
1370.00	980.00	25245.00	1380.00	25345.00	2660.00	25665.00	2780.00	25695.00	980.00	25245.00
1380.00	920.00	25230.00	1320.00	25330.00	2540.00	25635.00	2620.00	25655.00	920.00	25230.00
1390.00	860.00	25215.00	1260.00	25315.00	2420.00	25605.00	2460.00	25615.00	860.00	25215.00
1400.00	800.00	25200.00	1200.00	25300.00	2300.00	25575.00	2300.00	25575.00	800.00	25200.00
1410.00	740.00	25185.00	1140.00	25285.00	2200.00	25550.00	2180.00	25545.00	740.00	25185.00
1420.00	680.00	25170.00	1080.00	25270.00	2100.00	25525.00	2060.00	25515.00	680.00	25170.00
1430.00	620.00	25155.00	1020.00	25255.00	2000.00	25500.00	1940.00	25485.00	620.00	25155.00
1440.00	560.00	25140.00	960.00	25240.00	1900.00	25475.00	1820.00	25455.00	560.00	25140.00
1450.00	500.00	25125.00	900.00	25225.00	1800.00	25450.00	1700.00	25425.00	500.00	25125.00
1460.00	460.00	25115.00	880.00	25220.00	1720.00	25430.00	1620.00	25405.00	460.00	25115.00
1470.00	420.00	25105.00	860.00	25215.00	1640.00	25410.00	1540.00	25385.00	420.00	25105.00
1480.00	380.00	25095.00	840.00	25210.00	1560.00	25390.00	1460.00	25365.00	380.00	25095.00
1490.00	340.00	25085.00	820.00	25205.00	1480.00	25370.00	1380.00	25345.00	340.00	25085.00
1500.00	300.00	25075.00	800.00	25200.00	1400.00	25350.00	1300.00	25325.00	300.00	25075.00

NOTE ?- ALL ZERO STRESS VALUES INDICATE THAT THE CODE DOES NOT
**** RECOMMEND THE USE OF THE MATERIAL AT THAT TEMPERATURE

HOT STRESS AND ALLOW. STRESS RANGE
BASED ON B31.3

S(A)=F*(1.25*S(C)+0.25*S(H)) , F=1

MATERIAL	A358---304		COPPER-B42-D		RED-BRAS-B43		NICKELB161#5		NICKELB161)5	
TEMP(F)	HOT,S(H)	ALL,S(A)	HOT,S(H)	ALL,S(A)	HOT,S(H)	ALL,S(A)	HOT,S(H)	ALL,S(A)	HOT,S(H)	ALL,S(A)
100.00	17000.00	25500.00	15000.00	22500.00	8000.00	12000.00	8000.00	12000.00	6700.00	10050.00
110.00	17000.00	25500.00	14620.00	22405.00	8000.00	12000.00	7970.00	11992.50	6670.00	10042.50
120.00	17000.00	25500.00	14240.00	22310.00	8000.00	12000.00	7940.00	11985.00	6640.00	10035.00
130.00	17000.00	25500.00	13860.00	22215.00	8000.00	12000.00	7910.00	11977.50	6610.00	10027.50
140.00	17000.00	25500.00	13480.00	22120.00	8000.00	12000.00	7880.00	11970.00	6580.00	10020.00
150.00	17000.00	25500.00	13100.00	22025.00	8000.00	12000.00	7850.00	11962.50	6550.00	10012.50
160.00	17000.00	25500.00	12720.00	21930.00	8000.00	12000.00	7820.00	11955.00	6520.00	10005.00
170.00	17000.00	25500.00	12340.00	21835.00	8000.00	12000.00	7790.00	11947.50	6490.00	9997.50
180.00	17000.00	25500.00	11960.00	21740.00	8000.00	12000.00	7760.00	11940.00	6460.00	9990.00
190.00	17000.00	25500.00	11580.00	21645.00	8000.00	12000.00	7730.00	11932.50	6430.00	9982.50
200.00	17000.00	25500.00	11200.00	21550.00	8000.00	12000.00	7700.00	11925.00	6400.00	9975.00
210.00	17000.00	25500.00	11180.00	21545.00	8000.00	12000.00	7680.00	11920.00	6390.00	9972.50
220.00	17000.00	25500.00	11160.00	21540.00	8000.00	12000.00	7660.00	11915.00	6380.00	9970.00
230.00	17000.00	25500.00	11140.00	21535.00	8000.00	12000.00	7640.00	11910.00	6370.00	9967.50
240.00	17000.00	25500.00	11120.00	21530.00	8000.00	12000.00	7620.00	11905.00	6360.00	9965.00
250.00	17000.00	25500.00	11100.00	21525.00	8000.00	12000.00	7600.00	11900.00	6350.00	9962.50
260.00	17000.00	25500.00	11080.00	21520.00	8000.00	12000.00	7580.00	11895.00	6340.00	9960.00
270.00	17000.00	25500.00	11060.00	21515.00	8000.00	12000.00	7560.00	11890.00	6330.00	9957.50
280.00	17000.00	25500.00	11040.00	21510.00	8000.00	12000.00	7540.00	11885.00	6320.00	9955.00
290.00	17000.00	25500.00	11020.00	21505.00	8000.00	12000.00	7520.00	11880.00	6310.00	9952.50
300.00	17000.00	25500.00	11000.00	21500.00	8000.00	12000.00	7500.00	11875.00	6300.00	9950.00

NOTE ?- ALL ZERO STRESS VALUES INDICATE THAT THE CODE DOES NOT
**** RECOMMEND THE USE OF THE MATERIAL AT THAT TEMPERATURE

HOT STRESS AND ALLOW. STRESS RANGE
BASED ON B31.3

S(A)=F*(1.25*S(C)+0.25*S(H)) , F=1

MATERIAL	A358---304		COPPER-B42-D		RED-BRAS-B43		NICKELB161#5		NICKELB161)5	
TEMP(F)	HOT,S(H)	ALL,S(A)	HOT,S(H)	ALL,S(A)	HOT,S(H)	ALL,S(A)	HOT,S(H)	ALL,S(A)	HOT,S(H)	ALL,S(A)
310.00	16890.00	25472.50	10320.00	21330.00	7700.00	11925.00	7500.00	11875.00	6290.00	9947.50
320.00	16780.00	25445.00	9640.00	21160.00	7400.00	11850.00	7500.00	11875.00	6280.00	9945.00
330.00	16670.00	25417.50	8960.00	20990.00	7100.00	11775.00	7500.00	11875.00	6270.00	9942.50
340.00	16560.00	25390.00	8280.00	20820.00	6800.00	11700.00	7500.00	11875.00	6260.00	9940.00
350.00	16450.00	25362.50	7600.00	20650.00	6500.00	11625.00	7500.00	11875.00	6250.00	9937.50
360.00	16340.00	25335.00	6920.00	20480.00	6200.00	11550.00	7500.00	11875.00	6240.00	9935.00
370.00	16230.00	25307.50	6240.00	20310.00	5900.00	11475.00	7500.00	11875.00	6230.00	9932.50
380.00	16120.00	25280.00	5560.00	20140.00	5600.00	11400.00	7500.00	11875.00	6220.00	9930.00
390.00	16010.00	25252.50	4880.00	19970.00	5300.00	11325.00	7500.00	11875.00	6210.00	9927.50
400.00	15900.00	25225.00	4200.00	19800.00	5000.00	11250.00	7500.00	11875.00	6200.00	9925.00
410.00	15790.00	25197.50	0.00	0.00	0.00	0.00	7500.00	11875.00	6200.00	9925.00
420.00	15680.00	25170.00	0.00	0.00	0.00	0.00	7500.00	11875.00	6200.00	9925.00
430.00	15570.00	25142.50	0.00	0.00	0.00	0.00	7500.00	11875.00	6200.00	9925.00
440.00	15460.00	25115.00	0.00	0.00	0.00	0.00	7500.00	11875.00	6200.00	9925.00
450.00	15350.00	25087.50	0.00	0.00	0.00	0.00	7500.00	11875.00	6200.00	9925.00
460.00	15240.00	25060.00	0.00	0.00	0.00	0.00	7500.00	11875.00	6200.00	9925.00
470.00	15130.00	25032.50	0.00	0.00	0.00	0.00	7500.00	11875.00	6200.00	9925.00
480.00	15020.00	25005.00	0.00	0.00	0.00	0.00	7500.00	11875.00	6200.00	9925.00
490.00	14910.00	24977.50	0.00	0.00	0.00	0.00	7500.00	11875.00	6200.00	9925.00
500.00	14800.00	24950.00	0.00	0.00	0.00	0.00	7500.00	11875.00	6200.00	9925.00
510.00	14720.00	24930.00	0.00	0.00	0.00	0.00	7500.00	11875.00	6200.00	9925.00

NOTE ?- ALL ZERO STRESS VALUES INDICATE THAT THE CODE DOES NOT
**** RECOMMEND THE USE OF THE MATERIAL AT THAT TEMPERATURE

HOT STRESS AND ALLOW. STRESS RANGE
BASED ON B31.3

S(A)=F*(1.25*S(C)+0.25*S(H)) , F=1

MATERIAL	A358---304		COPPER-B42-D		RED-BRAS-B43		NICKELB161#5		NICKELB161)5	
TEMP(F)	HOT,S(H)	ALL,S(A)	HOT,S(H)	ALL,S(A)	HOT,S(H)	ALL,S(A)	HOT,S(H)	ALL,S(A)	HOT,S(H)	ALL,S(A)
520.00	14640.00	24910.00	0.00	0.00	0.00	0.00	7500.00	11875.00	6200.00	9925.00
530.00	14560.00	24890.00	0.00	0.00	0.00	0.00	7500.00	11875.00	6200.00	9925.00
540.00	14480.00	24870.00	0.00	0.00	0.00	0.00	7500.00	11875.00	6200.00	9925.00
550.00	14400.00	24850.00	0.00	0.00	0.00	0.00	7500.00	11875.00	6200.00	9925.00
560.00	14320.00	24830.00	0.00	0.00	0.00	0.00	7500.00	11875.00	6200.00	9925.00
570.00	14240.00	24810.00	0.00	0.00	0.00	0.00	7500.00	11875.00	6200.00	9925.00
580.00	14160.00	24790.00	0.00	0.00	0.00	0.00	7500.00	11875.00	6200.00	9925.00
590.00	14080.00	24770.00	0.00	0.00	0.00	0.00	7500.00	11875.00	6200.00	9925.00
600.00	14000.00	24750.00	0.00	0.00	0.00	0.00	7500.00	11875.00	6200.00	9925.00
610.00	13940.00	24735.00	0.00	0.00	0.00	0.00	7500.00	11875.00	6200.00	9925.00
620.00	13880.00	24720.00	0.00	0.00	0.00	0.00	7500.00	11875.00	6200.00	9925.00
630.00	13820.00	24705.00	0.00	0.00	0.00	0.00	7500.00	11875.00	6200.00	9925.00
640.00	13760.00	24690.00	0.00	0.00	0.00	0.00	7500.00	11875.00	6200.00	9925.00
650.00	13700.00	24675.00	0.00	0.00	0.00	0.00	7500.00	11875.00	6200.00	9925.00
660.00	13680.00	24670.00	0.00	0.00	0.00	0.00	7480.00	11870.00	6200.00	9925.00
670.00	13660.00	24665.00	0.00	0.00	0.00	0.00	7460.00	11865.00	6200.00	9925.00
680.00	13640.00	24660.00	0.00	0.00	0.00	0.00	7440.00	11860.00	6200.00	9925.00
690.00	13620.00	24655.00	0.00	0.00	0.00	0.00	7420.00	11855.00	6200.00	9925.00
700.00	13600.00	24650.00	0.00	0.00	0.00	0.00	7400.00	11850.00	6200.00	9925.00
710.00	13520.00	24630.00	0.00	0.00	0.00	0.00	7380.00	11845.00	6180.00	9920.00
720.00	13440.00	24610.00	0.00	0.00	0.00	0.00	7360.00	11840.00	6160.00	9915.00

NOTE ?- ALL ZERO STRESS VALUES INDICATE THAT THE CODE DOES NOT
**** RECOMMEND THE USE OF THE MATERIAL AT THAT TEMPERATURE

HOT STRESS AND ALLOW. STRESS RANGE
BASED ON B31.3

S(A)=F*(1.25*S(C)+0.25*S(H)) , F=1

MATERIAL	A358---304		COPPER-B42-D		RED-BRAS-B43		NICKELB161#5		NICKELB161)5	
TEMP(F)	HOT,S(H)	ALL,S(A)	HOT,S(H)	ALL,S(A)	HOT,S(H)	ALL,S(A)	HOT,S(H)	ALL,S(A)	HOT,S(H)	ALL,S(A)
730.00	13360.00	24590.00	0.00	0.00	0.00	0.00	7340.00	11835.00	6140.00	9910.00
740.00	13280.00	24570.00	0.00	0.00	0.00	0.00	7320.00	11830.00	6120.00	9905.00
750.00	13200.00	24550.00	0.00	0.00	0.00	0.00	7300.00	11825.00	6100.00	9900.00
760.00	13140.00	24535.00	0.00	0.00	0.00	0.00	7280.00	11820.00	6060.00	9890.00
770.00	13080.00	24520.00	0.00	0.00	0.00	0.00	7260.00	11815.00	6020.00	9880.00
780.00	13020.00	24505.00	0.00	0.00	0.00	0.00	7240.00	11810.00	5980.00	9870.00
790.00	12960.00	24490.00	0.00	0.00	0.00	0.00	7220.00	11805.00	5940.00	9860.00
800.00	12900.00	24475.00	0.00	0.00	0.00	0.00	7200.00	11800.00	5900.00	9850.00
810.00	12860.00	24465.00	0.00	0.00	0.00	0.00	6920.00	11730.00	5880.00	9845.00
820.00	12820.00	24455.00	0.00	0.00	0.00	0.00	6640.00	11660.00	5860.00	9840.00
830.00	12780.00	24445.00	0.00	0.00	0.00	0.00	6360.00	11590.00	5840.00	9835.00
840.00	12740.00	24435.00	0.00	0.00	0.00	0.00	6080.00	11520.00	5820.00	9830.00
850.00	12700.00	24425.00	0.00	0.00	0.00	0.00	5800.00	11450.00	5800.00	9825.00
860.00	12660.00	24415.00	0.00	0.00	0.00	0.00	0.00	0.00	0.00	0.00
870.00	12620.00	24405.00	0.00	0.00	0.00	0.00	0.00	0.00	0.00	0.00
880.00	12580.00	24395.00	0.00	0.00	0.00	0.00	0.00	0.00	0.00	0.00
890.00	12540.00	24385.00	0.00	0.00	0.00	0.00	0.00	0.00	0.00	0.00
900.00	12500.00	24375.00	0.00	0.00	0.00	0.00	0.00	0.00	0.00	0.00
910.00	12440.00	24360.00	0.00	0.00	0.00	0.00	0.00	0.00	0.00	0.00
920.00	12380.00	24345.00	0.00	0.00	0.00	0.00	0.00	0.00	0.00	0.00
930.00	12320.00	24330.00	0.00	0.00	0.00	0.00	0.00	0.00	0.00	0.00

NOTE ?- ALL ZERO STRESS VALUES INDICATE THAT THE CODE DOES NOT
**** RECOMMEND THE USE OF THE MATERIAL AT THAT TEMPERATURE

HOT STRESS AND ALLOW. STRESS RANGE
BASED ON B31.3

S(A)=F*(1.25*S(C)+0.25*S(H)) , F=1

MATERIAL	A358---304		COPPER-B42-D		RED-BRAS-B43		NICKELB161#5		NICKELB161)5	
TEMP(F)	HOT,S(H)	ALL,S(A)	HOT,S(H)	ALL,S(A)	HOT,S(H)	ALL,S(A)	HOT,S(H)	ALL,S(A)	HOT,S(H)	ALL,S(A)
940.00	12260.00	24315.00	0.00	0.00	0.00	0.00	0.00	0.00	0.00	0.00
950.00	12200.00	24300.00	0.00	0.00	0.00	0.00	0.00	0.00	0.00	0.00
960.00	12100.00	24275.00	0.00	0.00	0.00	0.00	0.00	0.00	0.00	0.00
970.00	12000.00	24250.00	0.00	0.00	0.00	0.00	0.00	0.00	0.00	0.00
980.00	11900.00	24225.00	0.00	0.00	0.00	0.00	0.00	0.00	0.00	0.00
990.00	11800.00	24200.00	0.00	0.00	0.00	0.00	0.00	0.00	0.00	0.00
1000.00	11700.00	24175.00	0.00	0.00	0.00	0.00	0.00	0.00	0.00	0.00
1010.00	11420.00	24105.00	0.00	0.00	0.00	0.00	0.00	0.00	0.00	0.00
1020.00	11140.00	24035.00	0.00	0.00	0.00	0.00	0.00	0.00	0.00	0.00
1030.00	10860.00	23965.00	0.00	0.00	0.00	0.00	0.00	0.00	0.00	0.00
1040.00	10580.00	23895.00	0.00	0.00	0.00	0.00	0.00	0.00	0.00	0.00
1050.00	10300.00	23825.00	0.00	0.00	0.00	0.00	0.00	0.00	0.00	0.00
1060.00	9900.00	23725.00	0.00	0.00	0.00	0.00	0.00	0.00	0.00	0.00
1070.00	9500.00	23625.00	0.00	0.00	0.00	0.00	0.00	0.00	0.00	0.00
1080.00	9100.00	23525.00	0.00	0.00	0.00	0.00	0.00	0.00	0.00	0.00
1090.00	8700.00	23425.00	0.00	0.00	0.00	0.00	0.00	0.00	0.00	0.00
1100.00	8300.00	23325.00	0.00	0.00	0.00	0.00	0.00	0.00	0.00	0.00
1110.00	7940.00	23235.00	0.00	0.00	0.00	0.00	0.00	0.00	0.00	0.00
1120.00	7580.00	23145.00	0.00	0.00	0.00	0.00	0.00	0.00	0.00	0.00
1130.00	7220.00	23055.00	0.00	0.00	0.00	0.00	0.00	0.00	0.00	0.00
1140.00	6860.00	22965.00	0.00	0.00	0.00	0.00	0.00	0.00	0.00	0.00

NOTE ?- ALL ZERO STRESS VALUES INDICATE THAT THE CODE DOES NOT
**** RECOMMEND THE USE OF THE MATERIAL AT THAT TEMPERATURE

HOT STRESS AND ALLOW. STRESS RANGE
BASED ON B31.3

S(A)=F*(1.25*S(C)+0.25*S(H)) , F=1

MATERIAL	A358---304		COPPER-B42-D		RED-BRAS-B43		NICKELB161#5		NICKELB161)5	
TEMP(F)	HOT,S(H)	ALL,S(A)	HOT,S(H)	ALL,S(A)	HOT,S(H)	ALL,S(A)	HOT,S(H)	ALL,S(A)	HOT,S(H)	ALL,S(A)
1150.00	6500.00	22875.00	0.00	0.00	0.00	0.00	0.00	0.00	0.00	0.00
1160.00	6220.00	22805.00	0.00	0.00	0.00	0.00	0.00	0.00	0.00	0.00
1170.00	5940.00	22735.00	0.00	0.00	0.00	0.00	0.00	0.00	0.00	0.00
1180.00	5660.00	22665.00	0.00	0.00	0.00	0.00	0.00	0.00	0.00	0.00
1190.00	5380.00	22595.00	0.00	0.00	0.00	0.00	0.00	0.00	0.00	0.00
1200.00	5100.00	22525.00	0.00	0.00	0.00	0.00	0.00	0.00	0.00	0.00
1210.00	4880.00	22470.00	0.00	0.00	0.00	0.00	0.00	0.00	0.00	0.00
1220.00	4660.00	22415.00	0.00	0.00	0.00	0.00	0.00	0.00	0.00	0.00
1230.00	4440.00	22360.00	0.00	0.00	0.00	0.00	0.00	0.00	0.00	0.00
1240.00	4220.00	22305.00	0.00	0.00	0.00	0.00	0.00	0.00	0.00	0.00
1250.00	4000.00	22250.00	0.00	0.00	0.00	0.00	0.00	0.00	0.00	0.00
1260.00	3820.00	22205.00	0.00	0.00	0.00	0.00	0.00	0.00	0.00	0.00
1270.00	3640.00	22160.00	0.00	0.00	0.00	0.00	0.00	0.00	0.00	0.00
1280.00	3460.00	22115.00	0.00	0.00	0.00	0.00	0.00	0.00	0.00	0.00
1290.00	3280.00	22070.00	0.00	0.00	0.00	0.00	0.00	0.00	0.00	0.00
1300.00	3100.00	22025.00	0.00	0.00	0.00	0.00	0.00	0.00	0.00	0.00
1310.00	2980.00	21995.00	0.00	0.00	0.00	0.00	0.00	0.00	0.00	0.00
1320.00	2860.00	21965.00	0.00	0.00	0.00	0.00	0.00	0.00	0.00	0.00
1330.00	2740.00	21935.00	0.00	0.00	0.00	0.00	0.00	0.00	0.00	0.00
1340.00	2620.00	21905.00	0.00	0.00	0.00	0.00	0.00	0.00	0.00	0.00
1350.00	2500.00	21875.00	0.00	0.00	0.00	0.00	0.00	0.00	0.00	0.00

NOTE ?- ALL ZERO STRESS VALUES INDICATE THAT THE CODE DOES NOT
**** RECOMMEND THE USE OF THE MATERIAL AT THAT TEMPERATURE

HOT STRESS AND ALLOW. STRESS RANGE
BASED ON B31.3

S(A)=F*(1.25*S(C)+0.25*S(H)) , F=1

MATERIAL	A358---304		COPPER-B42-D		RED-BRAS-B43		NICKELB161#5		NICKELB161)5	
TEMP(F)	HOT,S(H)	ALL,S(A)	HOT,S(H)	ALL,S(A)	HOT,S(H)	ALL,S(A)	HOT,S(H)	ALL,S(A)	HOT,S(H)	ALL,S(A)
1360.00	2400.00	21850.00	0.00	0.00	0.00	0.00	0.00	0.00	0.00	0.00
1370.00	2300.00	21825.00	0.00	0.00	0.00	0.00	0.00	0.00	0.00	0.00
1380.00	2200.00	21800.00	0.00	0.00	0.00	0.00	0.00	0.00	0.00	0.00
1390.00	2100.00	21775.00	0.00	0.00	0.00	0.00	0.00	0.00	0.00	0.00
1400.00	2000.00	21750.00	0.00	0.00	0.00	0.00	0.00	0.00	0.00	0.00
1410.00	1900.00	21725.00	0.00	0.00	0.00	0.00	0.00	0.00	0.00	0.00
1420.00	1800.00	21700.00	0.00	0.00	0.00	0.00	0.00	0.00	0.00	0.00
1430.00	1700.00	21675.00	0.00	0.00	0.00	0.00	0.00	0.00	0.00	0.00
1440.00	1600.00	21650.00	0.00	0.00	0.00	0.00	0.00	0.00	0.00	0.00
1450.00	1500.00	21625.00	0.00	0.00	0.00	0.00	0.00	0.00	0.00	0.00
1460.00	1440.00	21610.00	0.00	0.00	0.00	0.00	0.00	0.00	0.00	0.00
1470.00	1380.00	21595.00	0.00	0.00	0.00	0.00	0.00	0.00	0.00	0.00
1480.00	1320.00	21580.00	0.00	0.00	0.00	0.00	0.00	0.00	0.00	0.00
1490.00	1260.00	21565.00	0.00	0.00	0.00	0.00	0.00	0.00	0.00	0.00
1500.00	1200.00	21550.00	0.00	0.00	0.00	0.00	0.00	0.00	0.00	0.00

NOTE ?- ALL ZERO STRESS VALUES INDICATE THAT THE CODE DOES NOT
**** RECOMMEND THE USE OF THE MATERIAL AT THAT TEMPERATURE

HOT STRESS AND ALLOW. STRESS RANGE
BASED ON B31.3

S(A)=F*(1.25*S(C)+0.25*S(H)) , F=1

MATERIAL	B165MONEL-NC		ASTM-B167-#5		ASTM-B167-)5		AL-B241-6061		AL-B241-6063	
TEMP(F)	HOT,S(H)	ALL,S(A)	HOT,S(H)	ALL,S(A)	HOT,S(H)	ALL,S(A)	HOT,S(H)	ALL,S(A)	HOT,S(H)	ALL,S(A)
100.00	18200.00	27300.00	16700.00	25050.00	20000.00	30000.00	12700.00	19050.00	10000.00	15000.00
110.00	18020.00	27255.00	16700.00	25050.00	20000.00	30000.00	12700.00	19050.00	9980.00	14995.00
120.00	17840.00	27210.00	16700.00	25050.00	20000.00	30000.00	12700.00	19050.00	9960.00	14990.00
130.00	17660.00	27165.00	16700.00	25050.00	20000.00	30000.00	12700.00	19050.00	9940.00	14985.00
140.00	17480.00	27120.00	16700.00	25050.00	20000.00	30000.00	12700.00	19050.00	9920.00	14980.00
150.00	17300.00	27075.00	16700.00	25050.00	20000.00	30000.00	12700.00	19050.00	9900.00	14975.00
160.00	17120.00	27030.00	16700.00	25050.00	20000.00	30000.00	12700.00	19050.00	9880.00	14970.00
170.00	16940.00	26985.00	16700.00	25050.00	20000.00	30000.00	12700.00	19050.00	9860.00	14965.00
180.00	16760.00	26940.00	16700.00	25050.00	20000.00	30000.00	12700.00	19050.00	9840.00	14960.00
190.00	16580.00	26895.00	16700.00	25050.00	20000.00	30000.00	12700.00	19050.00	9820.00	14955.00
200.00	16400.00	26850.00	16700.00	25050.00	20000.00	30000.00	12700.00	19050.00	9800.00	14950.00
210.00	16300.00	26825.00	16700.00	25050.00	20000.00	30000.00	12490.00	18997.50	9480.00	14870.00
220.00	16200.00	26800.00	16700.00	25050.00	20000.00	30000.00	12280.00	18945.00	9160.00	14790.00
230.00	16100.00	26775.00	16700.00	25050.00	20000.00	30000.00	12070.00	18892.50	8840.00	14710.00
240.00	16000.00	26750.00	16700.00	25050.00	20000.00	30000.00	11860.00	18840.00	8520.00	14630.00
250.00	15900.00	26725.00	16700.00	25050.00	20000.00	30000.00	11650.00	18787.50	8200.00	14550.00
260.00	15800.00	26700.00	16700.00	25050.00	20000.00	30000.00	11440.00	18735.00	7880.00	14470.00
270.00	15700.00	26675.00	16700.00	25050.00	20000.00	30000.00	11230.00	18682.50	7560.00	14390.00
280.00	15600.00	26650.00	16700.00	25050.00	20000.00	30000.00	11020.00	18630.00	7240.00	14310.00
290.00	15500.00	26625.00	16700.00	25050.00	20000.00	30000.00	10810.00	18577.50	6920.00	14230.00
300.00	15400.00	26600.00	16700.00	25050.00	20000.00	30000.00	10600.00	18525.00	6600.00	14150.00

NOTE ?- ALL ZERO STRESS VALUES INDICATE THAT THE CODE DOES NOT
**** RECOMMEND THE USE OF THE MATERIAL AT THAT TEMPERATURE

HOT STRESS AND ALLOW. STRESS RANGE
BASED ON B31.3

S(A)=F*(1.25*S(C)+0.25*S(H)) , F=1

MATERIAL	B165MONEL-NC		ASTM-B167-#5		ASTM-B167-)5		AL-B241-6061		AL-B241-6063	
TEMP(F)	HOT,S(H)	ALL,S(A)	HOT,S(H)	ALL,S(A)	HOT,S(H)	ALL,S(A)	HOT,S(H)	ALL,S(A)	HOT,S(H)	ALL,S(A)
310.00	15340.00	26585.00	16700.00	25050.00	20000.00	30000.00	10100.00	18400.00	6140.00	14035.00
320.00	15280.00	26570.00	16700.00	25050.00	20000.00	30000.00	9600.00	18275.00	5680.00	13920.00
330.00	15220.00	26555.00	16700.00	25050.00	20000.00	30000.00	9100.00	18150.00	5220.00	13805.00
340.00	15160.00	26540.00	16700.00	25050.00	20000.00	30000.00	8600.00	18025.00	4760.00	13690.00
350.00	15100.00	26525.00	16700.00	25050.00	20000.00	30000.00	8100.00	17900.00	4300.00	13575.00
360.00	15040.00	26510.00	16700.00	25050.00	20000.00	30000.00	7600.00	17775.00	3840.00	13460.00
370.00	14980.00	26495.00	16700.00	25050.00	20000.00	30000.00	7100.00	17650.00	3380.00	13345.00
380.00	14920.00	26480.00	16700.00	25050.00	20000.00	30000.00	6600.00	17525.00	2920.00	13230.00
390.00	14860.00	26465.00	16700.00	25050.00	20000.00	30000.00	6100.00	17400.00	2460.00	13115.00
400.00	14800.00	26450.00	16700.00	25050.00	20000.00	30000.00	5600.00	17275.00	2000.00	13000.00
410.00	14800.00	26450.00	16700.00	25050.00	20000.00	30000.00	0.00	0.00	0.00	0.00
420.00	14800.00	26450.00	16700.00	25050.00	20000.00	30000.00	0.00	0.00	0.00	0.00
430.00	14800.00	26450.00	16700.00	25050.00	20000.00	30000.00	0.00	0.00	0.00	0.00
440.00	14800.00	26450.00	16700.00	25050.00	20000.00	30000.00	0.00	0.00	0.00	0.00
450.00	14800.00	26450.00	16700.00	25050.00	20000.00	30000.00	0.00	0.00	0.00	0.00
460.00	14800.00	26450.00	16700.00	25050.00	20000.00	30000.00	0.00	0.00	0.00	0.00
470.00	14800.00	26450.00	16700.00	25050.00	20000.00	30000.00	0.00	0.00	0.00	0.00
480.00	14800.00	26450.00	16700.00	25050.00	20000.00	30000.00	0.00	0.00	0.00	0.00
490.00	14800.00	26450.00	16700.00	25050.00	20000.00	30000.00	0.00	0.00	0.00	0.00
500.00	14800.00	26450.00	16700.00	25050.00	20000.00	30000.00	0.00	0.00	0.00	0.00
510.00	14800.00	26450.00	16700.00	25050.00	20000.00	30000.00	0.00	0.00	0.00	0.00

NOTE ?- ALL ZERO STRESS VALUES INDICATE THAT THE CODE DOES NOT
**** RECOMMEND THE USE OF THE MATERIAL AT THAT TEMPERATURE

HOT STRESS AND ALLOW. STRESS RANGE
BASED ON B31.3

S(A)=F*(1.25*S(C)+0.25*S(H)) , F=1

MATERIAL	B165MONEL-NC		ASTM-B167-#5		ASTM-B167-)5		AL-B241-6061		AL-B241-6063	
TEMP(F)	HOT,S(H)	ALL,S(A)	HOT,S(H)	ALL,S(A)	HOT,S(H)	ALL,S(A)	HOT,S(H)	ALL,S(A)	HOT,S(H)	ALL,S(A)
520.00	14800.00	26450.00	16700.00	25050.00	20000.00	30000.00	0.00	0.00	0.00	0.00
530.00	14800.00	26450.00	16700.00	25050.00	20000.00	30000.00	0.00	0.00	0.00	0.00
540.00	14800.00	26450.00	16700.00	25050.00	20000.00	30000.00	0.00	0.00	0.00	0.00
550.00	14800.00	26450.00	16700.00	25050.00	20000.00	30000.00	0.00	0.00	0.00	0.00
560.00	14800.00	26450.00	16700.00	25050.00	20000.00	30000.00	0.00	0.00	0.00	0.00
570.00	14800.00	26450.00	16700.00	25050.00	20000.00	30000.00	0.00	0.00	0.00	0.00
580.00	14800.00	26450.00	16700.00	25050.00	20000.00	30000.00	0.00	0.00	0.00	0.00
590.00	14800.00	26450.00	16700.00	25050.00	20000.00	30000.00	0.00	0.00	0.00	0.00
600.00	14800.00	26450.00	16700.00	25050.00	20000.00	30000.00	0.00	0.00	0.00	0.00
610.00	14800.00	26450.00	16700.00	25050.00	20000.00	30000.00	0.00	0.00	0.00	0.00
620.00	14800.00	26450.00	16700.00	25050.00	20000.00	30000.00	0.00	0.00	0.00	0.00
630.00	14800.00	26450.00	16700.00	25050.00	20000.00	30000.00	0.00	0.00	0.00	0.00
640.00	14800.00	26450.00	16700.00	25050.00	20000.00	30000.00	0.00	0.00	0.00	0.00
650.00	14800.00	26450.00	16700.00	25050.00	20000.00	30000.00	0.00	0.00	0.00	0.00
660.00	14800.00	26450.00	16700.00	25050.00	20000.00	30000.00	0.00	0.00	0.00	0.00
670.00	14800.00	26450.00	16700.00	25050.00	20000.00	30000.00	0.00	0.00	0.00	0.00
680.00	14800.00	26450.00	16700.00	25050.00	20000.00	30000.00	0.00	0.00	0.00	0.00
690.00	14800.00	26450.00	16700.00	25050.00	20000.00	30000.00	0.00	0.00	0.00	0.00
700.00	14800.00	26450.00	16700.00	25050.00	20000.00	30000.00	0.00	0.00	0.00	0.00
710.00	14760.00	26440.00	16700.00	25050.00	20000.00	30000.00	0.00	0.00	0.00	0.00
720.00	14720.00	26430.00	16700.00	25050.00	20000.00	30000.00	0.00	0.00	0.00	0.00

NOTE ?- ALL ZERO STRESS VALUES INDICATE THAT THE CODE DOES NOT
**** RECOMMEND THE USE OF THE MATERIAL AT THAT TEMPERATURE

HOT STRESS AND ALLOW. STRESS RANGE
BASED ON B31.3

S(A)=F*(1.25*S(C)+0.25*S(H)) , F=1

MATERIAL	B165MONEL-NC		ASTM-B167-#5		ASTM-B167-)5		AL-B241-6061		AL-B241-6063	
TEMP(F)	HOT,S(H)	ALL,S(A)	HOT,S(H)	ALL,S(A)	HOT,S(H)	ALL,S(A)	HOT,S(H)	ALL,S(A)	HOT,S(H)	ALL,S(A)
730.00	14680.00	26420.00	16700.00	25050.00	20000.00	30000.00	0.00	0.00	0.00	0.00
740.00	14640.00	26410.00	16700.00	25050.00	20000.00	30000.00	0.00	0.00	0.00	0.00
750.00	14600.00	26400.00	16700.00	25050.00	20000.00	30000.00	0.00	0.00	0.00	0.00
760.00	14520.00	26380.00	16700.00	25050.00	20000.00	30000.00	0.00	0.00	0.00	0.00
770.00	14440.00	26360.00	16700.00	25050.00	20000.00	30000.00	0.00	0.00	0.00	0.00
780.00	14360.00	26340.00	16700.00	25050.00	20000.00	30000.00	0.00	0.00	0.00	0.00
790.00	14280.00	26320.00	16700.00	25050.00	20000.00	30000.00	0.00	0.00	0.00	0.00
800.00	14200.00	26300.00	16700.00	25050.00	20000.00	30000.00	0.00	0.00	0.00	0.00
810.00	0.00	0.00	16660.00	25040.00	19920.00	29980.00	0.00	0.00	0.00	0.00
820.00	0.00	0.00	16620.00	25030.00	19840.00	29960.00	0.00	0.00	0.00	0.00
830.00	0.00	0.00	16580.00	25020.00	19760.00	29940.00	0.00	0.00	0.00	0.00
840.00	0.00	0.00	16540.00	25010.00	19680.00	29920.00	0.00	0.00	0.00	0.00
850.00	0.00	0.00	16500.00	25000.00	19600.00	29900.00	0.00	0.00	0.00	0.00
860.00	0.00	0.00	16380.00	24970.00	18880.00	29720.00	0.00	0.00	0.00	0.00
870.00	0.00	0.00	16260.00	24940.00	18160.00	29540.00	0.00	0.00	0.00	0.00
880.00	0.00	0.00	16140.00	24910.00	17440.00	29360.00	0.00	0.00	0.00	0.00
890.00	0.00	0.00	16020.00	24880.00	16720.00	29180.00	0.00	0.00	0.00	0.00
900.00	0.00	0.00	15900.00	24850.00	16000.00	29000.00	0.00	0.00	0.00	0.00
910.00	0.00	0.00	14840.00	24585.00	14920.00	28730.00	0.00	0.00	0.00	0.00
920.00	0.00	0.00	13780.00	24320.00	13840.00	28460.00	0.00	0.00	0.00	0.00
930.00	0.00	0.00	12720.00	24055.00	12760.00	28190.00	0.00	0.00	0.00	0.00

NOTE ?- ALL ZERO STRESS VALUES INDICATE THAT THE CODE DOES NOT
**** RECOMMEND THE USE OF THE MATERIAL AT THAT TEMPERATURE

HOT STRESS AND ALLOW. STRESS RANGE
BASED ON B31.3

S(A)=F*(1.25*S(C)+0.25*S(H)) , F=1

MATERIAL	B165MONEL-NC		ASTM-B167-#5		ASTM-B167-)5		AL-B241-6061		AL-B241-6063	
TEMP(F)	HOT,S(H)	ALL,S(A)	HOT,S(H)	ALL,S(A)	HOT,S(H)	ALL,S(A)	HOT,S(H)	ALL,S(A)	HOT,S(H)	ALL,S(A)
940.00	0.00	0.00	11660.00	23790.00	11680.00	27920.00	0.00	0.00	0.00	0.00
950.00	0.00	0.00	10600.00	23525.00	10600.00	27650.00	0.00	0.00	0.00	0.00
960.00	0.00	0.00	9880.00	23345.00	9880.00	27470.00	0.00	0.00	0.00	0.00
970.00	0.00	0.00	9160.00	23165.00	9160.00	27290.00	0.00	0.00	0.00	0.00
980.00	0.00	0.00	8440.00	22985.00	8440.00	27110.00	0.00	0.00	0.00	0.00
990.00	0.00	0.00	7720.00	22805.00	7720.00	26930.00	0.00	0.00	0.00	0.00
1000.00	0.00	0.00	7000.00	22625.00	7000.00	26750.00	0.00	0.00	0.00	0.00
1010.00	0.00	0.00	6500.00	22500.00	6500.00	26625.00	0.00	0.00	0.00	0.00
1020.00	0.00	0.00	6000.00	22375.00	6000.00	26500.00	0.00	0.00	0.00	0.00
1030.00	0.00	0.00	5500.00	22250.00	5500.00	26375.00	0.00	0.00	0.00	0.00
1040.00	0.00	0.00	5000.00	22125.00	5000.00	26250.00	0.00	0.00	0.00	0.00
1050.00	0.00	0.00	4500.00	22000.00	4500.00	26125.00	0.00	0.00	0.00	0.00
1060.00	0.00	0.00	4200.00	21925.00	4200.00	26050.00	0.00	0.00	0.00	0.00
1070.00	0.00	0.00	3900.00	21850.00	3900.00	25975.00	0.00	0.00	0.00	0.00
1080.00	0.00	0.00	3600.00	21775.00	3600.00	25900.00	0.00	0.00	0.00	0.00
1090.00	0.00	0.00	3300.00	21700.00	3300.00	25825.00	0.00	0.00	0.00	0.00
1100.00	0.00	0.00	3000.00	21625.00	3000.00	25750.00	0.00	0.00	0.00	0.00
1110.00	0.00	0.00	6800.00	22575.00	2840.00	25710.00	0.00	0.00	0.00	0.00
1120.00	0.00	0.00	10600.00	23525.00	2680.00	25670.00	0.00	0.00	0.00	0.00
1130.00	0.00	0.00	14400.00	24475.00	2520.00	25630.00	0.00	0.00	0.00	0.00
1140.00	0.00	0.00	18200.00	25425.00	2360.00	25590.00	0.00	0.00	0.00	0.00

NOTE ?- ALL ZERO STRESS VALUES INDICATE THAT THE CODE DOES NOT
**** RECOMMEND THE USE OF THE MATERIAL AT THAT TEMPERATURE

HOT STRESS AND ALLOW. STRESS RANGE
BASED ON B31.3

S(A)=F*(1.25*S(C)+0.25*S(H)) , F=1

MATERIAL	B165MONEL-NC		ASTM-B167-#5		ASTM-B167-)5		AL-B241-6061		AL-R241-6063	
TEMP(F)	HOT,S(H)	ALL,S(A)	HOT,S(H)	ALL,S(A)	HOT,S(H)	ALL,S(A)	HOT,S(H)	ALL,S(A)	HOT,S(H)	ALL,S(A)
1150.00	0.00	0.00	22000.00	26375.00	2200.00	25550.00	0.00	0.00	0.00	0.00
1160.00	0.00	0.00	18000.00	25375.00	2160.00	25540.00	0.00	0.00	0.00	0.00
1170.00	0.00	0.00	14000.00	24375.00	2120.00	25530.00	0.00	0.00	0.00	0.00
1180.CC	0.00	0.00	10000.00	23375.00	2080.00	25520.00	0.00	0.00	0.00	0.00
1190.00	0.00	0.00	6000.00	22375.00	2040.00	25510.00	0.00	0.00	0.00	0.00
1200.00	0.00	0.00	2000.00	21375.00	2000.00	25500.00	0.00	0.00	0.00	0.00

NOTE ?- ALL ZERO STRESS VALUES INDICATE THAT THE CODE DOES NOT
**** RECOMMEND THE USE OF THE MATERIAL AT THAT TEMPERATURE

5

Stress Intensification and Flexibility Factors

The following is an explanation of the terms used in figuring flexibility and stress intensification factors. Refer to Tables 5-1 through 5-3 for a tabular listing of the factors for different piping configurations. Figures 5-1 and 5-2 illustrate these factors for widely spaced, two-weld and three-weld miter elbows, respectively.

Definitions

h = Flexibility characteristic
k = Flexibility factor (never less than unity, factor for torsion equal to unity)
i = Stress intensification factor (never less than unity, factor for torsion equal to unity)
$\overline{T}$ = Nominal wall thickness of the fitting for elbows, and miter bends, in.
$\overline{T}$ = Nominal wall thickness of the matching pipe for tees, in.
T_o = Crotch thickness of tee, in.
T_r = Pad or saddle thickness, when t_r is 1.5T, use $h = 4T/r^2$, in.
$\emptyset$ = One-half angle between adjacent miter axes, deg
r_2 = Mean radius of matching pipe, in.
R_1 = Bend radius of welding elbow or pipe bend, in.

- For closely spaced miters $R_1 = S \cot \emptyset /2$
- For widely spaced miters $R_1 = [r_2 (1 + \cot \emptyset)]/2$

r_x = Radius of curvature of the external contoured portion of the outlet measured in the plane containing the axis of the run and branch in inches. This is subjected to the following limitations:

- *Minimum radius.* This dimension must not be less than .05 D_{ob} except with a branch diameter larger than 30 in. It need not exceed 1.50 inches.
- *Maximum radius.* For outlet pipe sizes 8 inches nominal and larger, this dimension must not exceed 0.10 D_{ob} + 0.50 in. For outlet pipe sizes less than 8 in. nominal, this dimension shall not be greater than 1.25 in.
- When the external contour contains more than one radius, the radius of any arc sector of approximately 45° must meet the requirements for maximum and minimum of radii.
- Machining must not be employed in order to meet the preceding requirements.

S = Miter spacing at centerline, in.

- Closely spaced miter bend: $S < r_2 (1 + \tan \emptyset)$
- Widely spaced miter bend: $S \geq r_2 (1 + \tan \emptyset)$

D_{ob} = O.D. of branch, in.
C_1 = Correction factor for curves with one end flanged, $C_1 = h^{1/6}$
C_2 = Correction factor for curves with both ends flanged, $C_2 = h^{1/3}$

The piping code does not specify any particular distance from the end of the elbows arc or the centerline or a miter weld in which a flange will be effective in modifying the K and i factors on these items. Until a better definition is published, the following rules can be applied:

- Weld elbows—Modify the k and i factor when the butt weld of the flange is within one pipe diameter of the butt of the elbow.

(Text continued on page 120.)

Table 5-1
Flexibility and Stress Intensification Factors

Description	Flexibility Factor k	Stress Int. Factor[1,8] Outplane i_o	Stress Int. Factor[1,8] Inplane i_i	Flexibility Characteristic h	Sketch
Welding elbow or pipe bend	$\frac{1.65}{h}$	$\frac{0.75}{h^{2/3}}$	$\frac{0.9}{h^{2/3}}$	$\frac{\bar{T} R_1}{(r_2)^2}$	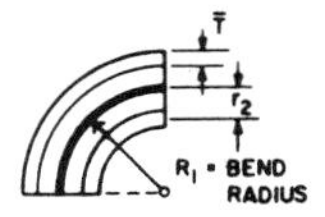 R_1 = BEND RADIUS
Closely spaced miter bend $s < r_2\ (1 + \tan\theta)$	$\frac{1.52}{h^{5/6}}$	$\frac{0.9}{h^{2/3}}$	$\frac{0.9}{h^{2/3}}$	$\frac{\cot\theta}{2}\ \frac{\bar{T}s}{(r_2)^2}$	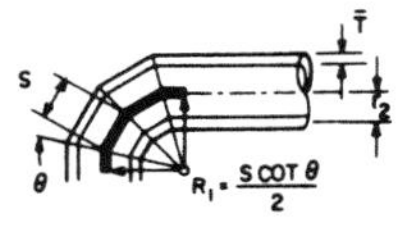 $R_1 = \frac{s \cot\theta}{2}$
Single miter bend or widely spaced miter bend $s \geqslant r_2\ (1 + \tan\theta)$	$\frac{1.52}{h^{5/6}}$	$\frac{0.9}{h^{2/3}}$	$\frac{0.9}{h^{2/3}}$	$\frac{1+\cot\theta}{2}\ \frac{\bar{T}}{r_2}$	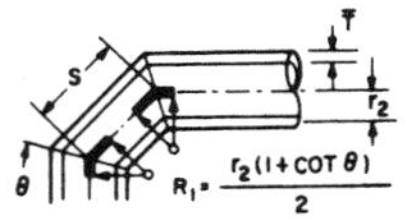 $R_1 = \frac{r_2(1+\cot\theta)}{2}$
Welding tee per ANSI B16.9 with $r_x \geqslant 1/8\ D_b$ $T_c \geqslant 1.5\ \bar{T}$	1	$\frac{0.9}{h^{2/3}}$	$3/4\ i_o + 1/4$	$4.4\ \frac{\bar{T}}{r_2}$	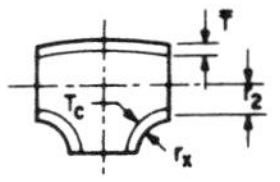
Reinforced fabricated tee with pad or saddle	1	$\frac{0.9}{h^{2/3}}$	$3/4\ i_o + 1/4$	$\frac{(\bar{T} + \frac{1}{2} t_r)^{5/2}}{\bar{T}^{3/2}\ r_2}$	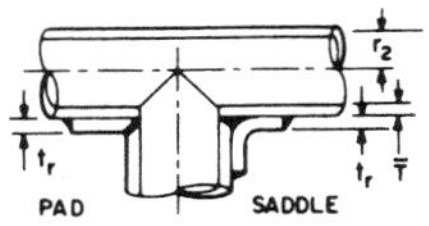 PAD SADDLE
Unreinforced fabricated tee	1	$\frac{0.9}{h^{2/3}}$	$3/4\ i_o + 1/4$	$\frac{\bar{T}}{r_2}$	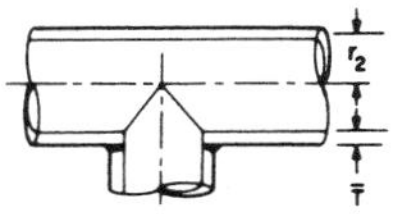
Extruded welding tee $T_c < 1.5\ \bar{T}$	1	$\frac{0.9}{h^{2/3}}$	$3/4\ i_o + 1/4$	$\left(1 + \frac{r_x}{r_2}\right)\frac{\bar{T}}{r_2}$	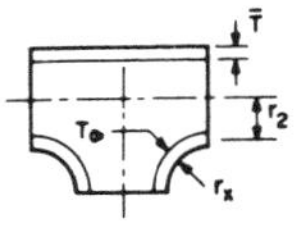
Welded-in contour insert $r_x \geqslant 1/8\ D_b$ $T_c \geqslant 1.5\ \bar{T}$	1	$\frac{0.9}{h^{2/3}}$	$3/4\ i_o + 1/4$	$4.4\ \frac{\bar{T}}{r_2}$	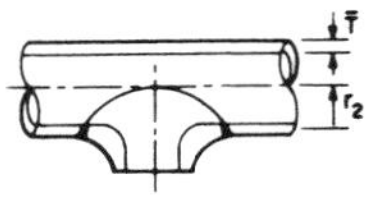
Branch welded-on fitting (integrally reinforced)	1	$\frac{0.9}{h^{2/3}}$	$\frac{0.9}{h^{2/3}}$	$3.3\ \frac{\bar{T}}{r_2}$	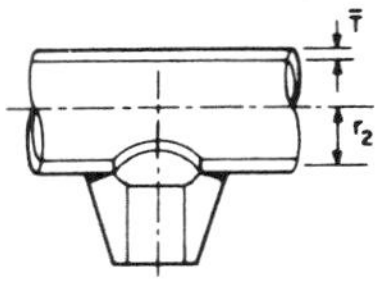

ANSI/ASME B31.3d–1984

Reproduced from ANSI/ASME Code B31.3-1980, Appendix D Table 1. Reprinted courtesy of The American Society of Mechanical Engineers.

Table 5-2
Stress Intensification Factors for Branch Connections

PIPE SIZE	SCH	WELDING TEE, WELDED CONTOUR INSERT	
		i_i INPLANE	i_o OUTPLANE
2"	40	1.19	1.25
	80	1.00	1.00
	160	1.00	1.00
3"	40	1.22	1.29
	80	1.01	1.02
	160	1.00	1.00
4"	40	1.34	1.45
	80	1.10	1.13
	120	1.00	1.00
	160	1.00	1.00
	XXS	1.00	1.00
6"	40	1.52	1.69
	80	1.18	1.24
	120	1.02	1.03
	160	1.00	1.00
	XXS	1.00	1.00
8"	20	1.89	2.19
	30	1.78	2.04
	40	1.63	1.84
	60	1.45	1.60
	80	1.27	1.36
	100	1.15	1.20
	120	1.03	1.04
	140	1.00	1.00
	XXS	1.00	1.00
	160	1.00	1.00
10"	20	2.16	2.55
	30	1.92	2.22
	40	1.73	1.97
	60	1.44	1.58
	80	1.30	1.40
	100	1.17	1.23
	120	1.07	1.09
	140	1.00	1.00
	160	1.00	1.00
12"	20	2.40	2.87
	30	2.03	2.37
	Std	1.88	2.17
	40	1.80	2.06
	XS	1.59	1.78
	60	1.48	1.64
	80	1.32	1.43
	100	1.17	1.23
	120	1.07	1.09
	140	1.00	1.00
	160	1.00	1.00
14"	10	2.54	3.05
	20	2.22	2.63
	30	1.99	2.32
	40	1.81	2.08
	XS	1.68	1.90
	60	1.52	1.69
	80	1.32	1.43
	100	1.17	1.23
	120	1.08	1.10
	140	1.00	1.00
	160	1.00	1.00
16"	10	2.70	4.07
	20	2.41	3.49
	30	2.16	3.09
	40	1.81	2.53
	60	1.55	2.09
	80	1.34	1.76
	100	1.20	1.52
16"	120	1.08	1.35
	140	1.00	1.19
	160	1.00	1.13
18"	10	2.97	3.62
	20	2.59	3.12
	ST	2.31	2.75
	30	2.10	2.47
	XS	1.95	2.26
	40	1.82	2.09
	60	1.53	1.71
	80	1.35	1.46
	100	1.20	1.26
	120	1.08	1.11
	140	1.01	1.01
	160	1.00	1.00
20"	10	3.17	3.89
	20	2.46	2.95
	30	2.07	2.43
	40	1.87	2.16
	60	1.56	1.74
	80	1.35	1.47
	100	1.20	1.26
	120	1.10	1.13
	140	1.01	1.01
	160	1.00	1.00
24"	10	3.54	4.39
	20	2.76	3.35
	XS	2.31	2.75
	30	2.16	2.54
	40	1.91	2.21
	60	1.56	1.75
	80	1.37	1.49
	100	1.20	1.27
	120	1.09	1.12
	140	1.01	1.02
	160	1.00	1.00
26"	.250	3.73	4.64
	10	3.25	4.00
	Std	2.90	3.53
	20	2.43	2.90
30"	.250	4.08	5.11
	10	3.55	4.40
	Std	3.17	3.89
	20	2.65	3.20
	30	2.31	2.75
34"	.250	4.42	5.56
	10	3.84	4.79
	Std	3.42	4.23
	20	2.86	3.48
	30	2.49	2.99
	40	2.35	2.80
36"	.250	4.59	5.78
	10	3.99	4.98
	Std	3.55	4.40
	20	2.97	3.62
	30	2.58	3.11
	40	2.31	2.75
42"	.250	5.06	6.40
	.312	4.39	5.52
	Std	3.91	4.88
	20	3.27	4.02
	30	2.85	3.46
	40	2.54	3.05

Table 5-2
Continued

PIPE SIZE	SCH	BRANCH WELDED - ON FITTING
		$i_i = i_o$ INPLANE OUTPLANE
2"	40	1.51
	80	1.18
	160	1.00
3"	40	1.57
	80	1.29
	160	1.00
4"	40	1.76
	80	1.36
	120	1.13
	160	1.0
	XXS	1.0
6"	40	2.27
	80	1.51
	120	1.25
	160	1.04
	XXS	1.00
8"	20	2.66
	30	2.47
	40	2.24
	60	1.90
	80	1.64
	100	1.45
	120	1.28
	140	1.16
	XXS	1.10
	160	1.06
10"	20	3.10
	30	2.68
	40	2.35
	60	2.36
	80	1.70
	100	1.48
	120	1.32
	140	1.18
	160	1.08
12"	20	3.47
	30	2.98
	Std.	2.64
	40	2.50
	XS	2.16
	60	1.99
	80	1.73
	100	1.49
	120	1.32
	140	1.22
	160	1.08
14"	10	3.70
	20	2.88
	30	2.64
	40	2.50
	XS	2.16
	60	1.99
	80	1.73
	100	1.49
	120	1.32
	140	1.22
	160	1.08
16"	10	4.07
	20	3.49
	30	3.09
	40	2.53
	60	2.09
	80	1.76
	100	1.52
16"	120	1.35
	140	1.19
	160	1.13
18"	10	4.39
	20	3.79
	ST	3.34
	30	3.01
	XS	2.75
	40	2.53
	60	2.07
	80	1.77
	100	1.53
	120	1.35
	140	1.23
	160	1.11
20"	10	4.73
	20	3.58
	30	2.95
	40	2.62
	60	2.10
	80	1.72
	100	1.53
	120	1.36
	140	1.22
	160	1.12
24"	10	5.36
	20	4.09
	XS	3.34
	30	3.08
	40	2.69
	60	2.12
	80	1.80
	100	1.53
	120	1.36
	140	1.24
	160	1.13
26"	.250	5.66
	10	4.86
	Std	4.39
	20	3.53
30"	.250	6.25
	10	5.36
	Std	4.74
	20	3.91
	30	3.34
34"	.250	6.56
	10	5.80
	Std	5.17
	20	4.24
	30	3.64
	40	3.41
36"	.250	7.03
	10	6.08
	Std	5.36
	20	4.39
	30	3.79
	40	3.34
42"	.250	7.82
	.312	7.75
	Std	5.96
	20	4.89
	30	4.20
	40	3.70

Table 5-2
Continued

PIPE SIZE	SCH	*REINFORCED FABRICATED TEE	
		i_i INPLANE	i_o OUTPLANE
2"	40	1.53	1.70
	80	1.25	1.33
	160	1.00	1.00
3"	40	1.58	1.77
	80	1.30	1.40
	160	1.04	1.05
4"	40	1.74	1.99
	80	1.41	1.54
	120	1.20	1.27
	160	1.08	1.10
	XXS	1.00	1.00
6"	40	1.62	1.83
	80	1.53	1.70
	120	1.31	1.41
	160	1.14	1.18
	XXS	1.01	1.02
8"	20	2.50	3.00
	30	2.34	2.79
	40	2.14	2.52
	60	1.86	2.14
	80	1.64	1.85
	100	1.48	1.64
	120	1.32	1.43
	140	1.23	1.30
	XXS	1.17	1.23
	160	1.15	1.20
10"	20	2.87	3.49
	30	2.52	3.03
	40	2.27	2.69
	60	1.87	2.16
	80	1.68	1.91
	100	1.50	1.67
	120	1.37	1.49
	140	1.24	1.32
	160	1.16	1.21
12"	20	3.18	3.91
	30	2.68	3.24
	Std	2.48	2.97
	40	2.36	2.81
	XS	2.07	2.43
	60	1.94	2.25
	80	1.71	1.94
	100	1.51	1.68
	120	1.37	1.49
	140	1.28	1.37
	160	1.17	1.22
14"	10	3.38	4.17
	20	2.94	3.59
	30	2.63	3.17
	40	2.38	2.84
	XS	2.20	2.60
	60	1.98	2.31
	80	1.72	1.96
	100	1.50	1.67
	120	1.38	1.50
	140	1.27	1.36
	160	1.19	1.25
16"	10	3.68	4.57
	20	3.20	3.93
	30	2.85	3.47
	40	2.39	2.85
	60	2.02	2.36
	80	1.74	1.98
	100	1.53	1.71

PIPE SIZE	SCH	*REINFORCED FABRICATED TEE	
		i_i INPLANE	i_o OUTPLANE
16"	120	1.39	1.52
	140	1.26	1.35
	160	1.19	1.25
18"	10	3.96	4.94
	20	3.45	4.26
	ST	3.06	3.75
	30	2.79	3.38
	XS	2.57	3.09
	40	2.39	2.85
	60	2.00	2.33
	80	1.74	1.99
	100	1.54	1.72
	120	1.39	1.52
	140	1.29	1.39
	160	1.20	1.26
20"	10	4.23	5.31
	20	3.28	4.04
	30	2.71	3.28
	40	2.46	2.95
	60	2.04	2.38
	80	1.74	1.99
	100	1.54	1.72
	120	1.41	1.54
	140	1.29	1.38
	160	1.20	1.26
24"	10	4.74	5.99
	20	3.67	4.56
	XS	3.06	3.75
	30	2.85	3.47
	40	2.55	3.07
	60	2.04	2.39
	80	1.77	2.03
	100	1.55	1.73
	120	1.40	1.53
	140	1.30	1.40
	160	1.20	1.27
26"	.250	5.00	6.34
	10	4.35	5.46
	Std	3.87	4.82
	20	3.23	3.97
30"	.250	5.49	6.98
	10	4.76	6.01
	Std	4.23	5.31
	20	3.77	4.69
	30	3.07	3.76
34"	.250	5.94	7.59
	10	5.16	6.54
	Std	4.59	5.78
	20	3.82	4.76
	30	3.32	4.09
	40	3.12	3.82
36"	.250	6.17	7.89
	10	5.35	6.80
	Std	4.75	6.00
	20	3.96	4.95
	30	3.44	4.25
	40	3.07	3.76
42"	.250	6.81	8.75
	.312	5.90	7.53
	Std	5.24	6.66
	20	4.36	5.48
	30	3.79	4.72
	40	3.38	4.17

*REINFORCED FABRICATED TEE PAD THICKNESS EQUAL TO NOMINAL THICKNESS OF PIPE HEADER

Table 5-2
Continued

PIPE SIZE	SCH	UNREINFORCED FABRICATED TEE	
		i_i INPLANE	i_o OUTPLANE
2"	40	2.76	3.35
	80	2.22	2.63
	160	1.64	1.85
3"	40	2.85	3.47
	80	2.30	2.74
	160	1.80	2.07
4"	40	3.18	3.90
	80	2.52	3.03
	120	2.13	2.50
	160	1.88	2.17
	XXS	1.61	1.81
6"	40	3.68	4.57
	80	2.76	3.34
	120	2.33	2.77
	160	1.98	2.31
	XXS	1.76	2.01
8"	20	4.67	5.89
	30	4.37	5.49
	40	3.96	4.95
	60	3.41	4.21
	80	2.98	3.64
	100	2.67	3.22
	120	2.35	2.80
	140	2.17	2.56
	XXS	2.07	2.43
	160	2.02	2.36
10"	20	5.39	6.85
	30	4.71	5.95
	40	4.21	5.28
	60	3.44	4.25
	80	3.07	3.76
	100	2.72	3.29
	120	2.45	2.93
	140	2.19	2.59
	160	2.03	2.37
12"	20	6.02	7.69
	30	5.03	6.37
	Std	4.62	5.83
	40	4.39	5.52
	XS	3.84	4.78
	60	3.55	4.40
	80	3.12	3.83
	100	2.73	3.30
	120	2.45	2.93
	140	2.27	2.69
	160	2.05	2.40
14"	10	6.40	8.20
	20	5.54	7.05
	30	4.92	6.22
	40	4.44	5.59
	XS	4.08	5.10
	60	3.65	4.53
	80	3.14	3.85
	100	2.72	3.29
	120	2.46	2.94
	140	2.25	2.67
	160	2.09	2.45
16"	10	6.92	8.89
	20	6.04	7.72
	30	5.36	6.81
	40	4.45	5.60
	60	3.73	4.64
	80	3.18	3.90
	100	2.78	3.37
16"	120	2.49	2.99
	140	2.23	2.64
	160	2.10	2.46
18"	10	7.53	9.71
	20	6.52	8.36
	ST	5.79	7.38
	30	5.23	6.64
	XS	4.80	6.07
	40	4.45	5.60
	60	3.69	4.58
	80	3.19	3.92
	100	2.79	3.39
	120	2.49	2.99
	140	2.29	2.72
	160	2.10	2.47
20"	10	8.08	10.44
	20	6.21	7.94
	30	5.14	6.52
	40	4.60	5.80
	60	3.75	4.67
	80	3.21	3.94
	100	2.79	3.39
	120	2.52	3.03
	140	2.28	2.70
	160	2.11	2.48
24"	10	9.09	11.79
	20	6.99	8.98
	XS	5.79	7.38
	30	5.36	6.81
	40	4.71	5.94
	60	3.77	4.69
	80	3.24	3.99
	100	2.79	3.39
	120	2.52	3.02
	140	2.31	2.74
	160	2.13	2.50
26"	.250	9.60	12.46
	10	8.30	10.73
	Std	7.56	9.75
	20	6.10	7.80
30"	.250	10.54	13.72
	10	9.12	11.82
	Std	8.08	10.44
	20	6.68	8.57
	30	5.79	7.38
34"	.250	11.44	14.92
	10	9.90	12.86
	Std	8.77	11.36
	20	7.26	9.35
	30	6.26	8.01
	40	5.90	7.53
36"	.250	11.88	15.50
	10	10.27	13.36
	Std	9.12	11.82
	20	7.54	9.72
	30	6.54	8.38
	40	5.79	7.38
42"	.250	13.14	17.19
	.312	11.37	14.82
	Std	10.30	13.40
	20	8.35	10.80
	30	7.21	9.28
	40	6.40	8.20

Table 5-3
Flanged Elbows—Flexibility Factors and Stress Intensification Factors

SIZE	WALL THICK	NOT FLANGED		BOTH END FLANGED		ONE END FLANGED	
		i	i_o	i_2	i_o2	i_1	i_o1
2"	.065	3.25	2.71	1.71	1.43	2.35	1.97
2"	.109	2.24	1.74	1.42	1.10	1.78	1.39
2"	.154	1.73	1.44	1.25	1.04	1.47	1.22
2"	.218	1.32	1.03	1.09	1.00	1.20	1.00
2"	.343	1.00	1.00	1.00	1.00	1.00	1.00
2"	.436	1.00	1.00	1.00	1.00	1.00	1.00
2 ½"	.083	3.06	2.55	1.66	1.38	2.26	1.88
2 ½"	.120	2.36	1.83	1.46	1.13	1.86	1.44
2 ½"	.203	1.59	1.24	1.20	1.00	1.38	1.08
2 ½"	.276	1.25	1.00	1.06	1.00	1.15	1.00
2 ½"	.375	1.00	1.00	1.00	1.00	1.00	1.00
2 ½"	.552	1.00	1.00	1.00	1.00	1.00	1.00
3"	.083	3.54	2.95	1.78	1.49	2.52	2.09
3"	.120	2.74	2.28	1.57	1.31	2.08	1.73
3"	.216	2.78	1.48	1.28	1.06	1.50	1.25
3"	.300	1.38	1.15	1.12	1.00	1.24	1.03
3"	.438	1.01	1.00	1.00	1.00	1.00	1.00
3"	.600	1.00	1.00	1.00	1.00	1.00	1.00
3 ½"	.083	3.85	3.21	1.87	1.55	2.68	2.23
3 ½"	.120	2.97	2.47	1.64	1.36	2.20	1.83
3 ½"	.226	1.88	1.56	1.30	1.08	1.56	1.30
3 ½"	.318	1.44	1.20	1.14	1.00	1.28	1.07
3 ½"	.636	1.00	1.00	1.00	1.00	1.00	1.00
4"	.083	4.13	3.44	1.93	1.61	2.83	2.35
4"	.120	3.19	2.66	1.70	1.41	2.33	1.94
4"	.237	1.96	1.63	1.33	1.11	1.61	1.34
4"	.337	1.50	1.25	1.16	1.00	1.32	1.10
4"	.438	1.22	1.01	1.05	1.00	1.13	1.00
4"	.531	1.04	1.00	1.00	1.00	1.00	1.00
4"	.674	1.00	1.00	1.00	1.00	1.00	1.00
5"	.109	3.93	3.28	1.88	1.57	2.72	2.27
5"	.134	3.41	2.84	1.76	1.46	2.45	2.04
5"	.258	2.13	1.78	1.38	1.16	1.72	1.44
5"	.375	1.61	1.34	1.20	1.00	1.39	1.16
5"	.500	1.29	1.00	1.09	1.00	1.18	1.00
5"	.625	1.07	1.00	1.00	1.00	1.02	1.00
5"	.750	1.00	1.00	1.00	1.00	1.00	1.00
6"	.109	4.41	3.68	1.99	1.66	2.96	2.47
6"	.134	3.81	3.18	1.85	1.54	2.66	2.22
6"	.280	2.27	1.89	1.43	1.19	1.80	1.50
6"	.432	1.65	1.37	1.22	1.01	1.42	1.18
6"	.562	1.34	1.12	1.10	1.00	1.21	1.01
6"	.718	1.10	1.00	1.00	1.00	1.05	1.00
6"	.864	1.00	1.00	1.00	1.00	1.00	1.00
8"	.109	5.20	4.34	2.16	1.81	3.35	2.80
8"	.148	4.23	3.52	1.96	1.63	2.88	2.39
8"	.250	2.92	2.44	1.63	1.35	2.18	1.82
8"	.277	2.72	2.27	1.57	1.31	2.06	1.72
8"	.322	2.45	2.04	1.49	1.24	1.91	1.59
8"	.406	2.06	1.72	1.36	1.14	1.68	1.40
8"	.500	1.77	1.47	1.27	1.06	1.50	1.24
8"	.593	1.55	1.30	1.18	1.00	1.35	1.13
8"	.718	1.34	1.11	1.11	1.00	1.21	1.00
8"	.812	1.23	1.02	1.06	1.00	1.14	1.00
8"	.875	1.14	1.00	1.01	1.00	1.07	1.00
8"	.906	1.11	1.00	1.00	1.00	1.05	1.00

Note: i_o, i_o1, i_o2 are out-of-plane intensification factors
i, i_1, i_2 are in plane intensification factors

Table 5-3
Continued

SIZE	WALL THICK	NOT FLANGED i	NOT FLANGED i_o	BOTH END FLANGED i_2	BOTH END FLANGED i_o2	ONE END FLANGED i_1	ONE END FLANGED i_o1
10"	.134	5.23	4.36	2.17	1.81	3.37	2.81
10"	.165	4.55	3.79	2.03	1.69	3.03	2.53
10"	.250	3.41	2.84	1.75	1.46	2.44	2.04
10"	.307	2.94	2.45	1.63	1.35	2.18	1.82
10"	.365	2.61	2.17	1.53	1.28	2.00	1.66
10"	.500	2.08	1.73	1.37	1.14	1.69	1.40
10"	.593	1.83	1.52	1.28	1.07	1.53	1.27
10"	.718	1.58	1.32	1.19	1.00	1.37	1.14
10"	.843	1.40	1.17	1.12	1.00	1.25	1.05
10"	1.00	1.22	1.00	1.05	1.00	1.13	1.00
10"	1.125	1.11	1.00	1.00	1.00	1.05	1.00
12"	.156	5.26	4.39	2.18	1.82	3.39	2.83
12"	.180	4.79	3.99	2.08	1.73	3.16	2.63
12"	.250	3.81	3.18	1.85	1.54	2.66	2.22
12"	.330	3.14	2.61	1.69	1.41	2.30	1.91
12"	.375	2.87	2.39	1.61	1.34	2.15	1.79
12"	.406	2.71	2.26	1.56	1.30	2.06	1.72
12"	.500	2.33	1.94	1.45	1.21	1.84	1.53
12"	.562	2.15	1.79	1.41	1.17	1.73	1.44
12"	.687	1.85	1.54	1.29	1.08	1.55	1.29
12"	.843	1.58	1.32	1.19	1.00	1.37	1.15
12"	1.000	1.39	1.16	1.12	1.00	1.25	1.04
12"	1.125	1.27	1.06	1.07	1.00	1.17	1.00
12"	1.312	1.12	1.00	1.00	1.00	1.06	1.00
14"	.250	3.90	3.25	1.87	1.56	2.70	2.25
14"	.312	2.35	2.79	1.74	1.45	2.41	2.00
14"	.375	2.92	2.44	1.62	1.35	2.17	1.82
14"	.438	2.68	2.23	1.57	1.31	2.05	1.71
14"	.500	2.33	1.94	1.45	1.21	1.84	1.53
14"	.593	2.12	1.77	1.38	1.15	1.73	1.44
14"	.750	1.79	1.49	1.27	1.06	1.51	1.26
14"	.937	1.51	1.26	1.17	1.00	1.33	1.10
14"	1.093	1.34	1.12	1.10	0.92	1.21	1.01
14"	1.250	1.21	1.01	1.05	1.00	1.13	1.00
14"	1.406	1.09	1.00	1.00	1.00	1.04	1.00
16"	.250	4.27	3.55	1.96	1.64	2.90	2.41
16"	.312	3.81	3.18	1.83	1.52	2.60	2.16
16"	.375	3.23	2.70	1.71	1.42	2.34	1.96
16"	.500	2.63	2.19	1.54	1.28	2.01	1.68
16"	.656	2.17	1.81	1.40	1.17	1.74	1.45
16"	.843	1.81	1.51	1.28	1.06	1.52	1.27
16"	1.031	1.55	1.29	1.18	1.00	1.35	1.13
16"	1.218	1.37	1.14	1.11	1.00	1.23	1.03
16"	1.438	1.20	1.00	1.04	1.00	1.12	1.00
16"	1.593	1.10	1.00	1.03	1.00	1.05	1.00
18"	.25	4.62	3.85	2.04	1.70	3.07	2.56
18"	.312	3.98	3.32	1.90	1.58	2.75	2.29
18"	.475	3.52	2.93	1.78	1.49	2.51	2.09
18"	.438	3.16	2.63	1.69	1.41	2.31	1.93
18"	.500	2.87	2.39	1.61	1.34	2.15	1.79
18"	.562	2.63	2.19	1.54	1.28	2.01	1.68
18"	.750	2.15	1.79	1.39	1.16	1.73	1.44
18"	.937	1.82	1.52	1.28	1.07	1.53	1.27
18"	1.156	1.56	1.30	1.18	0.99	1.36	1.14
18"	1.375	1.36	1.13	1.11	1.00	1.23	1.02
18"	1.562	1.23	1.00	1.05	1.00	1.14	1.00
18"	1.781	1.11	1.00	1.00	1.00	1.05	1.00

Note: i_o, i_o1, i_o2 are out-of-plane intensification factors
i, i_1, i_2 are in plane intensification factors

Table 5-3
Continued

SIZE	WALL THICK	NOT FLANGED i	i_o	BOTH END FLANGED i_2	i_o2	ONE END FLANGED i_1	i_o1
20"	.250	4.97	4.14	2.12	1.77	3.24	2.70
20"	.375	3.77	3.14	1.84	1.53	2.64	2.20
20"	.500	3.08	2.57	1.67	1.39	2.26	1.89
20"	.593	2.74	2.28	1.57	1.31	2.08	1.73
20"	.812	2.18	1.82	1.38	1.15	1.75	1.46
20"	1.031	1.84	1.53	1.29	1.07	1.54	1.28
20"	1.281	1.56	1.30	1.19	1.00	1.36	1.13
20"	1.500	1.38	1.15	1.11	1.00	1.24	1.03
20"	1.750	1.22	1.02	1.05	1.00	1.13	1.00
20"	1.968	1.11	1.00	1.00	1.00	1.05	1.00
24"	.250	5.63	4.69	2.25	1.88	3.55	2.96
24"	.375	4.29	3.57	1.97	1.64	2.91	2.42
24"	.500	3.52	2.93	1.78	1.48	2.51	2.09
24"	.562	3.24	2.70	1.71	1.42	2.35	1.96
24"	.687	2.80	2.34	1.59	1.32	2.11	1.76
24"	.968	2.20	1.83	1.39	1.15	1.76	1.46
24"	1.218	1.86	1.55	1.30	1.08	1.55	1.29
24"	1.531	1.56	1.30	1.19	1.00	1.36	1.13
24"	1.812	1.37	1.15	1.13	1.00	1.23	1.04
24"	2.062	1.24	1.03	1.06	1.00	1.15	1.00
24"	2.343	1.12	1.00	1.00	1.00	1.06	1.00
30"	.250	6.57	5.47	2.43	2.03	3.99	3.33
30"	.312	5.63	4.69	2.25	1.88	3.56	2.96
30"	.375	4.97	4.14	2.12	1.77	3.24	2.70
30"	.500	4.11	3.42	1.93	1.61	2.82	2.34
30"	.625	3.52	2.93	1.78	1.49	2.51	2.09
30"	.750	3.08	2.57	1.67	1.39	2.27	1.89

- Miter bends—Modify the K and i factor when the butt weld of the flange is located within one and one half pipe diameters of the nearest miter weld measured from the centerline of the pipe.

Although not specified by the Code, this will apply to both closely and widely spaced miters.

Note: Large-diameter thin-wall piping elbows and miters are affected by internal line pressure. According to a "Batelle" report to the AGA, the flexibility factors on these items are seriously impaired by internal pressure. To correct the values from Table 5-1:

Divide K by:

$$(1 + 6) \frac{(P)}{E_c} \frac{(r)^{7/3}}{t^2} \frac{(R_1)^{1/3}}{r_2}$$

Divide i by:

$$(1 + 3.25) \frac{(P)}{E_c} \frac{(r)^{5/2}}{t^2} \frac{(R_1)^{2/3}}{r^2}$$

Factors and Characteristics h, k, and i

	h	k	I
Butt-weld joint	—	1	1.0
Reducer	—	1	1.0
Weld-neck flange	—	1	1.0
Double-welded slip-on flange	—	1	1.2
Fillet-welded joint—single weld	—	1	1.3
Socket-welded flange	—	1	1.3
Single-welded slip-on flange	—	1	1.3
Lap-joint flange (with ANSI Code B16.9 lap-joint stub)	—	1	1.6
Screwed pipe joint or screwed flange	—	1	2.3
Corrugated straight pipe or corrugated or creased bend.	—	5	2.5

Note: Factors shown apply to bending flexibility factor for torsion equal to 0.9.

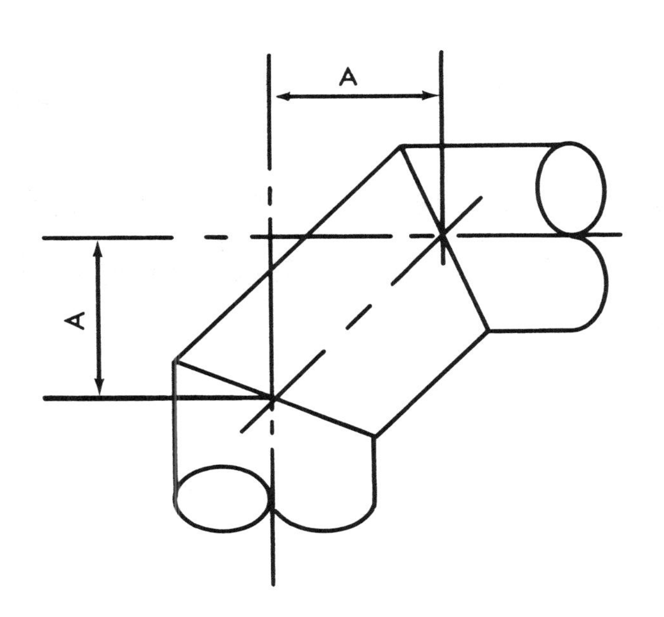

Widely Spaced Miters

D = Pipe Size (in.)	0.250 Wall 2-Weld Miter		0.375 Wall 2-Weld Miter		Dimensions (in decimals of feet)
	K	$i_i = i_o$	K	$i_i = i_o$	A
12	14.2	5.4	10.1	4.1	0.878
14	15.4	5.7	10.9	4.4	1.025
16	17.3	6.3	12.2	4.8	1.171
18	19.1	6.8	13.5	5.2	1.318
20	20.8	7.3	14.8	5.6	1.464
24	24.3	8.3	17.3	6.3	1.757
26	26.0	8.7	18.5	6.6	1.903
30	29.3	9.6	20.8	7.3	2.196
32	30.9	10.0	22.0	7.6	2.343
32	32.6	10.4	23.2	8.0	2.489
36	34.2	10.9	24.3	8.3	2.636
40	37.3	11.7	26.6	8.9	2.938
42	38.9	12.0	27.7	9.2	3.075
48	43.5	13.2	31.0	10.0	3.514
54	48.0	14.2	34.2	10.9	3.954
60	52.4	15.3	37.3	11.9	4.393
72	61.0	17.3	43.5	13.2	5.272

K = *flexibility factor*
i_o = *out-of-plane stress intensification factor*
i_i = *in-plane stress intensification factor*

Figure 5-1. Flexibility and stress intensification factors of two-weld miter elbows.

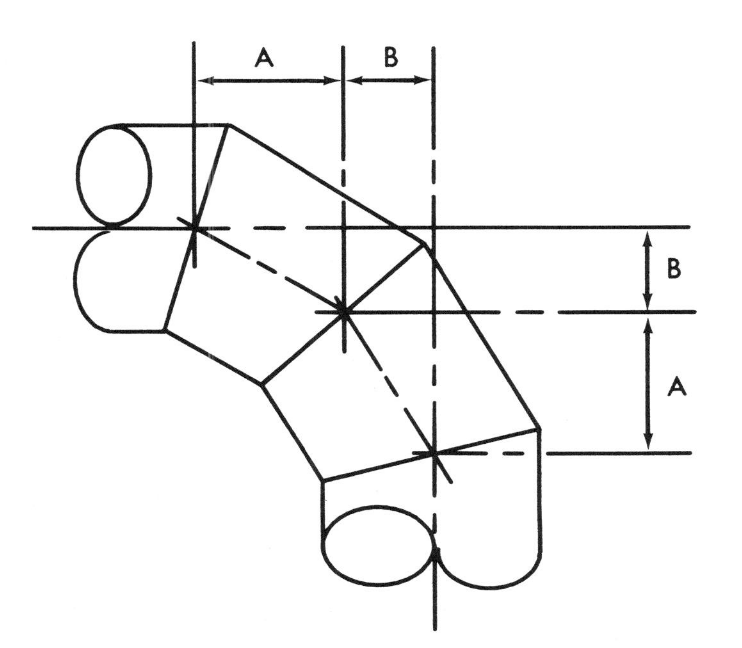

Widely Spaced Miters

D = Pipe Size (in.)	0.250 Wall 3-Weld Miter		0.375 Wall 3-Weld Miter		Dimensions (in decimals of feet)	
	K	$i_i = i_o$	K	$i_i = i_o$		B
12	10.8	4.3	7.7	3.3	0.696	0.401
14	11.7	4.6	8.3	3.5	0.812	0.468
16	13.1	5.1	9.3	3.8	0.928	0.535
18	14.5	5.5	10.3	4.2	1.044	0.602
20	15.9	5.9	11.3	4.5	1.160	0.669
24	18.5	6.7	13.1	5.1	1.392	0.803
26	19.8	7.0	14.1	5.3	1.508	0.870
30	22.3	7.7	15.9	5.9	1.740	1.004
32	23.6	8.1	16.8	6.1	1.856	1.071
34	24.8	8.4	17.6	6.4	1.972	1.138
36	26.0	8.7	18.5	6.6	2.088	1.205
40	28.4	9.4	20.2	7.1	2.320	1.339
42	29.6	9.7	21.1	7.4	2.436	1.406
48	33.1	10.6	23.6	8.1	2.784	1.607
54	36.6	11.5	26.0	8.7	3.132	1.808
60	39.9	12.3	28.4	9.4	3.480	2.009
72	46.5	13.9	33.1	10.6	4.176	2.411

K = *flexibility factor*
i_o = *out-of-plane stress intensification factor*
i_i = *in-plane stress intensification factor*

Figure 5-2. Flexibility and stress intensification factors of three-weld miter elbows.

6

Rotational Nozzle Flexibilities for Cylindrical Vessels

It is customary for piping stress analysts to model a piping system with rigid ends or anchors at the equipment nozzles. This assumption is acceptable when the system is flexible and the anchor loads are low. But anytime the system shows high loads and stresses, the analyst must determine how reasonable the assumption in modeling the nozzles as rigid anchors was.

The author has developed tables of rotational nozzle flexibilities for cylindrical vessels ranging in diameters from 2 ft to 20 ft and connecting nozzles ranging in diameters from 2 in. to 48 in. STD. thickness.*

To demonstrate how these flexibility factors really affect the accuracy of stress calculations for a simple piping system, an example where a 14-in. O.D. pipe from an exchanger E-1 ties to a tower T-1 is shown in Figure 6-1.

The computer stress calculation with rigid ends or anchors show a high stress of 33, 616 psi in the system and forces and moments at the nozzles as:

O.D.	F_x (lb)	F_y (lb)	M_z (ft-lb)
5	−11,113	−28,182	85,749
30	11,113	28,182	149,174

To reduce these high forces and moments, we will have to modify the piping configuration with more elbows or an additional expansion joint. But before we spend more time and money on these changes, let's model the nozzle data points 5 and 30 with flexible end conditions using the flexibility factors from Table 6-1. The table shows that for exchanger E-1 the in-plane rotational flexibility (R.F.) is $.626 \times 10^6$ in.-lbs/deg, and the out-of-plane R.F. is $.209 \times 10^6$ in.-lbs/deg. For the tower T-1 the in-plane R.F. is 1.22×10^6 in.-lbs/deg, and the out-of-plane R.F. is $.407 \times 10^6$ in.-lbs/deg. The new computer calculations show that the highest stress is 12,015 psi and the new forces at anchor are:

D.P.	F_x (lb)	F_y (lb)	M_z (ft-lbs)
5	−2,100	−6,082	3,369
30	2,100	6,082	−20,741

These forces are obviously much lower than the first assumption with rigid ends. Now we know that the piping system is not overstressed. The shell of the exchanger E-1 or the tower T-1 needs to be checked for local stresses with the new loads. It is quite possible that they are acceptable to the exchanger and vessel designer and manufacturers.

The following is a method for determining the spring rate of nozzles attached to vessels or stubbed into larger piping. Only in- and out-of-plane rotational spring rates are included, since the radial flexibility is normally ignored. Nozzle flexibilities should not be used if the nozzle or pad diameter is greater than one third of the run or vessel diameter.

Nozzle flexibilities were calculated in accordance with the phase report ORNL 115-3, Equation 8, page 6.

$$K = \frac{C\ W_B\ D_B\ (-D/W)^{3/2}}{WD} \quad (6\text{-}1)$$

$$\theta = \frac{M\ D_B\ K}{EI} \quad (6\text{-}2)$$

$$\text{Spring Rate} = \frac{E\ I\ PI}{2160 D_B K} \quad (6\text{-}3)$$

Solving Equation 6-2 for (M/θ) and converting units to ft-lbs/deg we have Equation 6-3.

where
- C = .09 for in-plane bending
- C = .27 for out-of-plane bending
- D = Diameter of vessel or run, in.
- D_B = Diameter of branch, in.
- E = Modulus of elasticity, psi
- I = Moment of inertia of branch, $in.^4$
- K = Flexibility factor
- M = Moment, in.-lbs
- PI = Circumference of a circle divided by the diameter
- θ = Angle of rotation, radians
- W = Wall thickness of vessel or run, in.
- W_B = Wall thickness of branch, in.

In-plane bending refers to *longitudinal* bending in the run or vessel in the plane formed by the intersection of the branch and vessel or run centerlines. *Out-of-plane* bending refers to *circumferential* bending in a plane perpendicular to the vessel or run diameter.

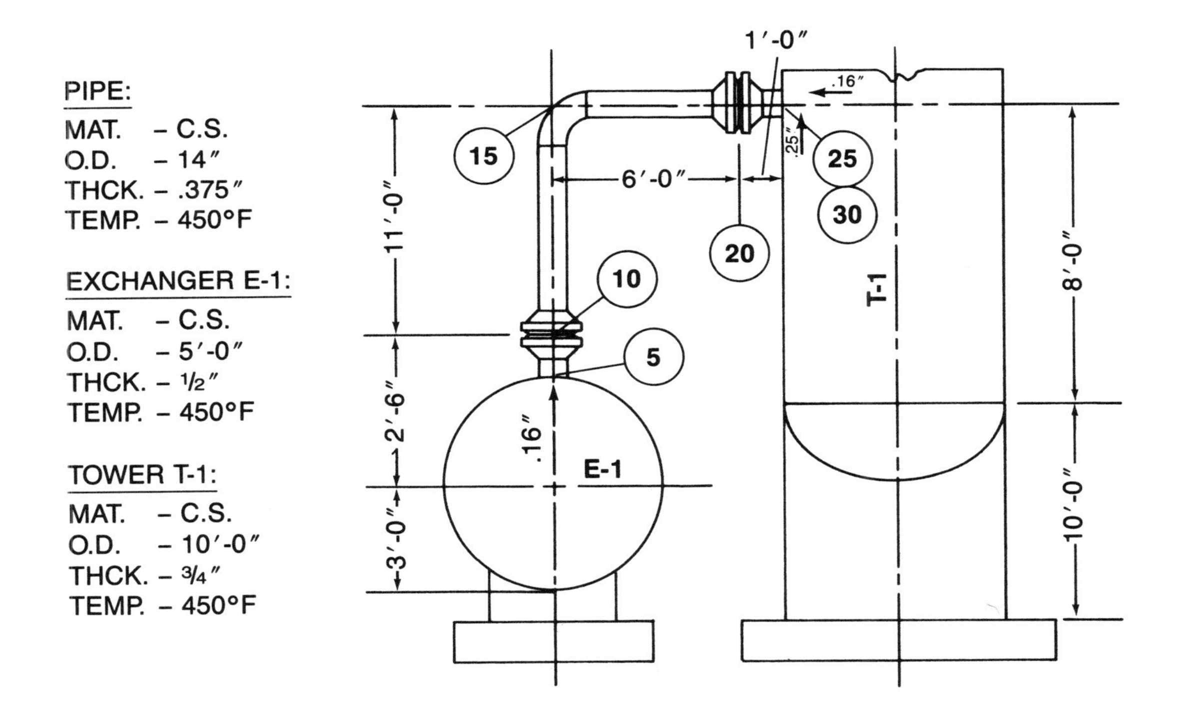

Figure 6-1. An example diagram of a piping system where 14-in. O.D. pipe from an exchanger ties to a tower.

Table 6-1
Rota Stiff Calculation, Cyl. Vessel

ROTA STIFF CALCULATION, CYL. VESSEL

VESSEL OD,FT	VESSEL TCK,IN	NOZZLE OD,IN	NOZZLE TCK,IN STD	ROT STIF IN.LB/DEG INPLANE LONGI	OUTPLANE CIRCU
2.000	.250	2.375	.154	.265E+05	.882E+04
2.000	.375	2.375	.154	.729E+05	.243E+05
2.000	.500	2.375	.154	.150E+06	.499E+05
2.000	.625	2.375	.154	.261E+06	.871E+05
2.000	.750	2.375	.154	.412E+06	.137E+06
2.000	1.000	2.375	.154	.847E+06	.282E+06
2.000	1.250	2.375	.154	.148E+07	.493E+06
2.000	1.500	2.375	.154	.233E+07	.778E+06
2.000	1.750	2.375	.154	.343E+07	.114E+07
2.000	2.000	2.375	.154	.479E+07	.160E+07
2.000	.250	3.500	.216	.394E+05	.131E+05
2.000	.375	3.500	.216	.108E+06	.362E+05
2.000	.500	3.500	.216	.223E+06	.742E+05
2.000	.625	3.500	.216	.389E+06	.130E+06
2.000	.750	3.500	.216	.614E+06	.205E+06
2.000	1.000	3.500	.216	.126E+07	.420E+06
2.000	1.250	3.500	.216	.220E+07	.733E+06
2.000	1.500	3.500	.216	.347E+07	.116E+07
2.000	1.750	3.500	.216	.510E+07	.170E+07
2.000	2.000	3.500	.216	.712E+07	.237E+07
2.000	.250	4.500	.237	.520E+05	.173E+05
2.000	.375	4.500	.237	.143E+06	.478E+05
2.000	.500	4.500	.237	.294E+06	.981E+05
2.000	.625	4.500	.237	.514E+06	.171E+06
2.000	.750	4.500	.237	.811E+06	.270E+06
2.000	1.000	4.500	.237	.166E+07	.555E+06
2.000	1.250	4.500	.237	.291E+07	.969E+06
2.000	1.500	4.500	.237	.459E+07	.153E+07
2.000	1.750	4.500	.237	.674E+07	.225E+07
2.000	2.000	4.500	.237	.942E+07	.314E+07
2.000	.250	6.625	.280	.790E+05	.263E+05
2.000	.375	6.625	.280	.218E+06	.726E+05
2.000	.500	6.625	.280	.447E+06	.149E+06
2.000	.625	6.625	.280	.781E+06	.260E+06
2.000	.750	6.625	.280	.123E+07	.411E+06
2.000	1.000	6.625	.280	.253E+07	.843E+06
2.000	1.250	6.625	.280	.442E+07	.147E+07
2.000	1.500	6.625	.280	.697E+07	.232E+07
2.000	1.750	6.625	.280	.102E+08	.342E+07
2.000	2.000	6.625	.280	.143E+08	.477E+07
2.500	.250	2.375	.154	.237E+05	.789E+04
2.500	.375	2.375	.154	.652E+05	.217E+05
2.500	.500	2.375	.154	.134E+06	.446E+05
2.500	.625	2.375	.154	.234E+06	.779E+05
2.500	.750	2.375	.154	.369E+06	.123E+06
2.500	1.000	2.375	.154	.757E+06	.252E+06
2.500	1.250	2.375	.154	.132E+07	.441E+06
2.500	1.500	2.375	.154	.209E+07	.695E+06
2.500	1.750	2.375	.154	.307E+07	.102E+07
2.500	2.000	2.375	.154	.428E+07	.143E+07
2.500	.250	3.500	.216	.352E+05	.117E+05
2.500	.375	3.500	.216	.970E+05	.323E+05
2.500	.500	3.500	.216	.199E+06	.664E+05
2.500	.625	3.500	.216	.348E+06	.116E+06
2.500	.750	3.500	.216	.549E+06	.183E+06
2.500	1.000	3.500	.216	.113E+07	.376E+06
2.500	1.250	3.500	.216	.197E+07	.656E+06
2.500	1.500	3.500	.216	.310E+07	.103E+07
2.500	1.750	3.500	.216	.456E+07	.152E+07

Table 6-1
Continued

ROTA STIFF CALCULATION, CYL. VESSEL

VESSEL OD,FT	VESSEL TCK,IN	NOZZLE OD,IN	NOZZLE TCK,IN STD	ROT STIF IN.LB/DEG INPLANE LONGI	OUTPLANE CIRCU
2.500	2.000	3.500	.216	.637E+07	.212E+07
2.500	.250	4.500	.237	.465E+05	.155E+05
2.500	.375	4.500	.237	.128E+06	.427E+05
2.500	.500	4.500	.237	.263E+06	.877E+05
2.500	.625	4.500	.237	.460E+06	.153E+06
2.500	.750	4.500	.237	.725E+06	.242E+06
2.500	1.000	4.500	.237	.149E+07	.496E+06
2.500	1.250	4.500	.237	.260E+07	.867E+06
2.500	1.500	4.500	.237	.410E+07	.137E+07
2.500	1.750	4.500	.237	.603E+07	.201E+07
2.500	2.000	4.500	.237	.842E+07	.281E+07
2.500	.250	6.625	.280	.707E+05	.236E+05
2.500	.375	6.625	.280	.195E+06	.649E+05
2.500	.500	6.625	.280	.400E+06	.133E+06
2.500	.625	6.625	.280	.699E+06	.233E+06
2.500	.750	6.625	.280	.110E+07	.367E+06
2.500	1.000	6.625	.280	.226E+07	.754E+06
2.500	1.250	6.625	.280	.395E+07	.132E+07
2.500	1.500	6.625	.280	.623E+07	.208E+07
2.500	1.750	6.625	.280	.917E+07	.306E+07
2.500	2.000	6.625	.280	.128E+08	.427E+07
2.500	.250	8.625	.322	.934E+05	.311E+05
2.500	.375	8.625	.322	.257E+06	.858E+05
2.500	.500	8.625	.322	.529E+06	.176E+06
2.500	.625	8.625	.322	.923E+06	.308E+06
2.500	.750	8.625	.322	.146E+07	.485E+06
2.500	1.000	8.625	.322	.299E+07	.997E+06
2.500	1.250	8.625	.322	.522E+07	.174E+07
2.500	1.500	8.625	.322	.824E+07	.275E+07
2.500	1.750	8.625	.322	.121E+08	.404E+07
2.500	2.000	8.625	.322	.169E+08	.564E+07
3.000	.250	2.375	.154	.216E+05	.720E+04
3.000	.375	2.375	.154	.595E+05	.198E+05
3.000	.500	2.375	.154	.122E+06	.407E+05
3.000	.625	2.375	.154	.213E+06	.711E+05
3.000	.750	2.375	.154	.337E+06	.112E+06
3.000	1.000	2.375	.154	.691E+06	.230E+06
3.000	1.250	2.375	.154	.121E+07	.402E+06
3.000	1.500	2.375	.154	.190E+07	.635E+06
3.000	1.750	2.375	.154	.280E+07	.933E+06
3.000	2.000	2.375	.154	.391E+07	.130E+07
3.000	.250	3.500	.216	.321E+05	.107E+05
3.000	.375	3.500	.216	.886E+05	.295E+05
3.000	.500	3.500	.216	.182E+06	.606E+05
3.000	.625	3.500	.216	.318E+06	.106E+06
3.000	.750	3.500	.216	.501E+06	.167E+06
3.000	1.000	3.500	.216	.103E+07	.343E+06
3.000	1.250	3.500	.216	.180E+07	.599E+06
3.000	1.500	3.500	.216	.283E+07	.945E+06
3.000	1.750	3.500	.216	.417E+07	.139E+07
3.000	2.000	3.500	.216	.582E+07	.194E+07
3.000	.250	4.500	.237	.425E+05	.142E+05
3.000	.375	4.500	.237	.117E+06	.390E+05
3.000	.500	4.500	.237	.240E+06	.801E+05
3.000	.625	4.500	.237	.420E+06	.140E+06
3.000	.750	4.500	.237	.662E+06	.221E+06
3.000	1.000	4.500	.237	.136E+07	.453E+06
3.000	1.250	4.500	.237	.237E+07	.791E+06
3.000	1.500	4.500	.237	.375E+07	.125E+07

Table 6-1
Continued

ROTA STIFF CALCULATION, CYL. VESSEL

VESSEL OD,FT	VESSEL TCK,IN	NOZZLE OD,IN	NOZZLE TCK,IN STD	ROT STIF IN.LB/DEG INPLANE LONGI	OUTPLANE CIRCU
3.000	1.750	4.500	.237	.551E+07	.184E+07
3.000	2.000	4.500	.237	.769E+07	.256E+07
3.000	.250	6.625	.280	.645E+05	.215E+05
3.000	.375	6.625	.280	.178E+06	.593E+05
3.000	.500	6.625	.280	.365E+06	.122E+06
3.000	.625	6.625	.280	.638E+06	.213E+06
3.000	.750	6.625	.280	.101E+07	.335E+06
3.000	1.000	6.625	.280	.207E+07	.688E+06
3.000	1.250	6.625	.280	.361E+07	.120E+07
3.000	1.500	6.625	.280	.569E+07	.190E+07
3.000	1.750	6.625	.280	.837E+07	.279E+07
3.000	2.000	6.625	.280	.117E+08	.389E+07
3.000	.250	8.625	.322	.853E+05	.284E+05
3.000	.375	8.625	.322	.235E+06	.783E+05
3.000	.500	8.625	.322	.482E+06	.161E+06
3.000	.625	8.625	.322	.843E+06	.281E+06
3.000	.750	8.625	.322	.133E+07	.443E+06
3.000	1.000	8.625	.322	.273E+07	.910E+06
3.000	1.250	8.625	.322	.477E+07	.159E+07
3.000	1.500	8.625	.322	.752E+07	.251E+07
3.000	1.750	8.625	.322	.111E+08	.369E+07
3.000	2.000	8.625	.322	.154E+08	.515E+07
3.000	.250	10.750	.365	.107E+06	.358E+05
3.000	.375	10.750	.365	.296E+06	.986E+05
3.000	.500	10.750	.365	.608E+06	.203E+06
3.000	.625	10.750	.365	.106E+07	.354E+06
3.000	.750	10.750	.365	.167E+07	.558E+06
3.000	1.000	10.750	.365	.344E+07	.115E+07
3.000	1.250	10.750	.365	.600E+07	.200E+07
3.000	1.500	10.750	.365	.947E+07	.316E+07
3.000	1.750	10.750	.365	.139E+08	.464E+07
3.000	2.000	10.750	.365	.194E+08	.648E+07
3.500	.250	2.375	.154	.200E+05	.667E+04
3.500	.375	2.375	.154	.551E+05	.184E+05
3.500	.500	2.375	.154	.113E+06	.377E+05
3.500	.625	2.375	.154	.198E+06	.659E+05
3.500	.750	2.375	.154	.312E+06	.104E+06
3.500	1.000	2.375	.154	.640E+06	.213E+06
3.500	1.250	2.375	.154	.112E+07	.373E+06
3.500	1.500	2.375	.154	.176E+07	.588E+06
3.500	1.750	2.375	.154	.259E+07	.864E+06
3.500	2.000	2.375	.154	.362E+07	.121E+07
3.500	.250	3.500	.216	.298E+05	.992E+04
3.500	.375	3.500	.216	.820E+05	.273E+05
3.500	.500	3.500	.216	.168E+06	.561E+05
3.500	.625	3.500	.216	.294E+06	.980E+05
3.500	.750	3.500	.216	.464E+06	.155E+06
3.500	1.000	3.500	.216	.952E+06	.317E+06
3.500	1.250	3.500	.216	.166E+07	.554E+06
3.500	1.500	3.500	.216	.262E+07	.875E+06
3.500	1.750	3.500	.216	.386E+07	.129E+07
3.500	2.000	3.500	.216	.539E+07	.180E+07
3.500	.250	4.500	.237	.393E+05	.131E+05
3.500	.375	4.500	.237	.108E+06	.361E+05
3.500	.500	4.500	.237	.222E+06	.741E+05
3.500	.625	4.500	.237	.389E+06	.130E+06
3.500	.750	4.500	.237	.613E+06	.204E+06
3.500	1.000	4.500	.237	.126E+07	.419E+06
3.500	1.250	4.500	.237	.220E+07	.733E+06

Table 6-1
Continued

ROTA STIFF CALCULATION, CYL. VESSEL

VESSEL OD,FT	VESSEL TCK,IN	NOZZLE OD,IN	NOZZLE TCK,IN STD	ROT STIF IN.LB/DEG INPLANE LONGI	OUTPLANE CIRCU
3.500	1.500	4.500	.237	.347E+07	.116E+07
3.500	1.750	4.500	.237	.510E+07	.170E+07
3.500	2.000	4.500	.237	.712E+07	.237E+07
3.500	.250	6.625	.280	.597E+05	.199E+05
3.500	.375	6.625	.280	.165E+06	.549E+05
3.500	.500	6.625	.280	.338E+06	.113E+06
3.500	.625	6.625	.280	.590E+06	.197E+06
3.500	.750	6.625	.280	.931E+06	.310E+06
3.500	1.000	6.625	.280	.191E+07	.637E+06
3.500	1.250	6.625	.280	.334E+07	.111E+07
3.500	1.500	6.625	.280	.527E+07	.176E+07
3.500	1.750	6.625	.280	.775E+07	.258E+07
3.500	2.000	6.625	.280	.108E+08	.361E+07
3.500	.250	8.625	.322	.790E+05	.263E+05
3.500	.375	8.625	.322	.218E+06	.725E+05
3.500	.500	8.625	.322	.447E+06	.149E+06
3.500	.625	8.625	.322	.780E+06	.260E+06
3.500	.750	8.625	.322	.123E+07	.410E+06
3.500	1.000	8.625	.322	.253E+07	.842E+06
3.500	1.250	8.625	.322	.441E+07	.147E+07
3.500	1.500	8.625	.322	.696E+07	.232E+07
3.500	1.750	8.625	.322	.102E+08	.341E+07
3.500	2.000	8.625	.322	.143E+08	.476E+07
3.500	.250	10.750	.365	.994E+05	.331E+05
3.500	.375	10.750	.365	.274E+06	.913E+05
3.500	.500	10.750	.365	.562E+06	.187E+06
3.500	.625	10.750	.365	.983E+06	.328E+06
3.500	.750	10.750	.365	.155E+07	.517E+06
3.500	1.000	10.750	.365	.318E+07	.106E+07
3.500	1.250	10.750	.365	.556E+07	.185E+07
3.500	1.500	10.750	.365	.877E+07	.292E+07
3.500	1.750	10.750	.365	.129E+08	.430E+07
3.500	2.000	10.750	.365	.180E+08	.600E+07
3.500	.250	12.750	.375	.120E+06	.399E+05
3.500	.375	12.750	.375	.329E+06	.110E+06
3.500	.500	12.750	.375	.676E+06	.225E+06
3.500	.625	12.750	.375	.118E+07	.394E+06
3.500	.750	12.750	.375	.186E+07	.621E+06
3.500	1.000	12.750	.375	.383E+07	.128E+07
3.500	1.250	12.750	.375	.668E+07	.223E+07
3.500	1.500	12.750	.375	.105E+08	.351E+07
3.500	1.750	12.750	.375	.155E+08	.517E+07
3.500	2.000	12.750	.375	.216E+08	.721E+07
4.000	.250	2.375	.154	.187E+05	.624E+04
4.000	.375	2.375	.154	.515E+05	.172E+05
4.000	.500	2.375	.154	.106E+06	.353E+05
4.000	.625	2.375	.154	.185E+06	.616E+05
4.000	.750	2.375	.154	.292E+06	.972E+05
4.000	1.000	2.375	.154	.599E+06	.200E+06
4.000	1.250	2.375	.154	.105E+07	.349E+06
4.000	1.500	2.375	.154	.165E+07	.550E+06
4.000	1.750	2.375	.154	.243E+07	.808E+06
4.000	2.000	2.375	.154	.339E+07	.113E+07
4.000	.250	3.500	.216	.278E+05	.928E+04
4.000	.375	3.500	.216	.767E+05	.256E+05
4.000	.500	3.500	.216	.157E+06	.525E+05
4.000	.625	3.500	.216	.275E+06	.917E+05
4.000	.750	3.500	.216	.434E+06	.145E+06
4.000	1.000	3.500	.216	.891E+06	.297E+06

Table 6-1
Continued

ROTA STIFF CALCULATION, CYL. VESSEL

VESSEL OD,FT	VESSEL TCK,IN	NOZZLE OD,IN	NOZZLE TCK,IN STD	ROT STIF IN.LB/DEG INPLANE LONGI	OUTPLANE CIRCU
4.000	1.250	3.500	.216	.156E+07	.519E+06
4.000	1.500	3.500	.216	.245E+07	.818E+06
4.000	1.750	3.500	.216	.361E+07	.120E+07
4.000	2.000	3.500	.216	.504E+07	.168E+07
4.000	.250	4.500	.237	.368E+05	.123E+05
4.000	.375	4.500	.237	.101E+06	.338E+05
4.000	.500	4.500	.237	.208E+06	.694E+05
4.000	.625	4.500	.237	.363E+06	.121E+06
4.000	.750	4.500	.237	.573E+06	.191E+06
4.000	1.000	4.500	.237	.118E+07	.392E+06
4.000	1.250	4.500	.237	.206E+07	.685E+06
4.000	1.500	4.500	.237	.324E+07	.108E+07
4.000	1.750	4.500	.237	.477E+07	.159E+07
4.000	2.000	4.500	.237	.666E+07	.222E+07
4.000	.250	6.625	.280	.559E+05	.186E+05
4.000	.375	6.625	.280	.154E+06	.513E+05
4.000	.500	6.625	.280	.316E+06	.105E+06
4.000	.625	6.625	.280	.552E+06	.184E+06
4.000	.750	6.625	.280	.871E+06	.290E+06
4.000	1.000	6.625	.280	.179E+07	.596E+06
4.000	1.250	6.625	.280	.312E+07	.104E+07
4.000	1.500	6.625	.280	.493E+07	.164E+07
4.000	1.750	6.625	.280	.725E+07	.242E+07
4.000	2.000	6.625	.280	.101E+08	.337E+07
4.000	.250	8.625	.322	.739E+05	.246E+05
4.000	.375	8.625	.322	.204E+06	.678E+05
4.000	.500	8.625	.322	.418E+06	.139E+06
4.000	.625	8.625	.322	.730E+06	.243E+06
4.000	.750	8.625	.322	.115E+07	.384E+06
4.000	1.000	8.625	.322	.236E+07	.788E+06
4.000	1.250	8.625	.322	.413E+07	.138E+07
4.000	1.500	8.625	.322	.651E+07	.217E+07
4.000	1.750	8.625	.322	.958E+07	.319E+07
4.000	2.000	8.625	.322	.134E+08	.446E+07
4.000	.250	10.750	.365	.930E+05	.310E+05
4.000	.375	10.750	.365	.256E+06	.854E+05
4.000	.500	10.750	.365	.526E+06	.175E+06
4.000	.625	10.750	.365	.919E+06	.306E+06
4.000	.750	10.750	.365	.145E+07	.483E+06
4.000	1.000	10.750	.365	.298E+07	.992E+06
4.000	1.250	10.750	.365	.520E+07	.173E+07
4.000	1.500	10.750	.365	.820E+07	.273E+07
4.000	1.750	10.750	.365	.121E+08	.402E+07
4.000	2.000	10.750	.365	.168E+08	.561E+07
4.000	.250	12.750	.375	.112E+06	.373E+05
4.000	.375	12.750	.375	.308E+06	.103E+06
4.000	.500	12.750	.375	.633E+06	.211E+06
4.000	.625	12.750	.375	.111E+07	.368E+06
4.000	.750	12.750	.375	.174E+07	.581E+06
4.000	1.000	12.750	.375	.358E+07	.119E+07
4.000	1.250	12.750	.375	.625E+07	.208E+07
4.000	1.500	12.750	.375	.986E+07	.329E+07
4.000	1.750	12.750	.375	.145E+08	.483E+07
4.000	2.000	12.750	.375	.202E+08	.675E+07
4.000	.250	14.000	.375	.124E+06	.413E+05
4.000	.375	14.000	.375	.341E+06	.114E+06
4.000	.500	14.000	.375	.700E+06	.233E+06
4.000	.625	14.000	.375	.122E+07	.408E+06
4.000	.750	14.000	.375	.193E+07	.643E+06
4.000	1.000	14.000	.375	.396E+07	.132E+07
4.000	1.250	14.000	.375	.692E+07	.231E+07

Table 6-1
Continued

ROTA STIFF CALCULATION, CYL. VESSEL

VESSEL OD,FT	VESSEL TCK,IN	NOZZLE OD,IN	NOZZLE TCK,IN STD	ROT STIF IN.LB/DEG INPLANE LONGI	OUTPLANE CIRCU
4.000	1.500	14.000	.375	.109E+08	.364E+07
4.000	1.750	14.000	.375	.160E+08	.535E+07
4.000	2.000	14.000	.375	.224E+08	.747E+07
5.000	.250	2.375	.154	.167E+05	.558E+04
5.000	.375	2.375	.154	.461E+05	.154E+05
5.000	.500	2.375	.154	.946E+05	.315E+05
5.000	.625	2.375	.154	.165E+06	.551E+05
5.000	.750	2.375	.154	.261E+06	.869E+05
5.000	1.000	2.375	.154	.535E+06	.178E+06
5.000	1.250	2.375	.154	.935E+06	.312E+06
5.000	1.500	2.375	.154	.148E+07	.492E+06
5.000	1.750	2.375	.154	.217E+07	.723E+06
5.000	2.000	2.375	.154	.303E+07	.101E+07
5.000	.250	3.500	.216	.249E+05	.830E+04
5.000	.375	3.500	.216	.686E+05	.229E+05
5.000	.500	3.500	.216	.141E+06	.469E+05
5.000	.625	3.500	.216	.246E+06	.820E+05
5.000	.750	3.500	.216	.388E+06	.129E+06
5.000	1.000	3.500	.216	.797E+06	.266E+06
5.000	1.250	3.500	.216	.139E+07	.464E+06
5.000	1.500	3.500	.216	.220E+07	.732E+06
5.000	1.750	3.500	.216	.323E+07	.108E+07
5.000	2.000	3.500	.216	.451E+07	.150E+07
5.000	.250	4.500	.237	.329E+05	.110E+05
5.000	.375	4.500	.237	.907E+05	.302E+05
5.000	.500	4.500	.237	.186E+06	.620E+05
5.000	.625	4.500	.237	.325E+06	.108E+06
5.000	.750	4.500	.237	.513E+06	.171E+06
5.000	1.000	4.500	.237	.105E+07	.351E+06
5.000	1.250	4.500	.237	.184E+07	.613E+06
5.000	1.500	4.500	.237	.290E+07	.967E+06
5.000	1.750	4.500	.237	.427E+07	.142E+07
5.000	2.000	4.500	.237	.596E+07	.199E+07
5.000	.250	6.625	.280	.500E+05	.167E+05
5.000	.375	6.625	.280	.138E+06	.459E+05
5.000	.500	6.625	.280	.283E+06	.943E+05
5.000	.625	6.625	.280	.494E+06	.165E+06
5.000	.750	6.625	.280	.779E+06	.260E+06
5.000	1.000	6.625	.280	.160E+07	.533E+06
5.000	1.250	6.625	.280	.279E+07	.932E+06
5.000	1.500	6.625	.280	.441E+07	.147E+07
5.000	1.750	6.625	.280	.648E+07	.216E+07
5.000	2.000	6.625	.280	.905E+07	.302E+07
5.000	.250	8.625	.322	.661E+05	.220E+05
5.000	.375	8.625	.322	.182E+06	.607E+05
5.000	.500	8.625	.322	.374E+06	.125E+06
5.000	.625	8.625	.322	.653E+06	.218E+06
5.000	.750	8.625	.322	.103E+07	.343E+06
5.000	1.000	8.625	.322	.211E+07	.705E+06
5.000	1.250	8.625	.322	.369E+07	.123E+07
5.000	1.500	8.625	.322	.583E+07	.194E+07
5.000	1.750	8.625	.322	.856E+07	.285E+07
5.000	2.000	8.625	.322	.120E+08	.399E+07
5.000	.250	10.750	.365	.832E+05	.277E+05
5.000	.375	10.750	.365	.229E+06	.764E+05
5.000	.500	10.750	.365	.471E+06	.157E+06
5.000	.625	10.750	.365	.822E+06	.274E+06
5.000	.750	10.750	.365	.130E+07	.432E+06
5.000	1.000	10.750	.365	.266E+07	.887E+06
5.000	1.250	10.750	.365	.465E+07	.155E+07

Table 6-1
Continued

ROTA STIFF CALCULATION, CYL. VESSEL

VESSEL OD,FT	VESSEL TCK,IN	NOZZLE OD,IN	NOZZLE TCK,IN STD	ROT STIF IN.LB/DEG INPLANE LONGI	OUTPLANE CIRCU
5.000	1.500	10.750	.365	.734E+07	.245E+07
5.000	1.750	10.750	.365	.108E+08	.359E+07
5.000	2.000	10.750	.365	.151E+08	.502E+07
5.000	.250	12.750	.375	.100E+06	.333E+05
5.000	.375	12.750	.375	.276E+06	.919E+05
5.000	.500	12.750	.375	.566E+06	.189E+06
5.000	.625	12.750	.375	.989E+06	.330E+06
5.000	.750	12.750	.375	.156E+07	.520E+06
5.000	1.000	12.750	.375	.320E+07	.107E+07
5.000	1.250	12.750	.375	.559E+07	.186E+07
5.000	1.500	12.750	.375	.882E+07	.294E+07
5.000	1.750	12.750	.375	.130E+08	.432E+07
5.000	2.000	12.750	.375	.181E+08	.604E+07
5.000	.250	14.000	.375	.111E+06	.369E+05
5.000	.375	14.000	.375	.305E+06	.102E+06
5.000	.500	14.000	.375	.626E+06	.209E+06
5.000	.625	14.000	.375	.109E+07	.365E+06
5.000	.750	14.000	.375	.173E+07	.575E+06
5.000	1.000	14.000	.375	.354E+07	.118E+07
5.000	1.250	14.000	.375	.619E+07	.206E+07
5.000	1.500	14.000	.375	.976E+07	.325E+07
5.000	1.750	14.000	.375	.144E+08	.478E+07
5.000	2.000	14.000	.375	.200E+08	.668E+07
5.000	.250	16.000	.375	.128E+06	.426E+05
5.000	.375	16.000	.375	.352E+06	.117E+06
5.000	.500	16.000	.375	.723E+06	.241E+06
5.000	.625	16.000	.375	.126E+07	.421E+06
5.000	.750	16.000	.375	.199E+07	.664E+06
5.000	1.000	16.000	.375	.409E+07	.136E+07
5.000	1.250	16.000	.375	.715E+07	.238E+07
5.000	1.500	16.000	.375	.113E+08	.376E+07
5.000	1.750	16.000	.375	.166E+08	.552E+07
5.000	2.000	16.000	.375	.231E+08	.771E+07
5.000	.250	18.000	.375	.145E+06	.483E+05
5.000	.375	18.000	.375	.399E+06	.133E+06
5.000	.500	18.000	.375	.820E+06	.273E+06
5.000	.625	18.000	.375	.143E+07	.477E+06
5.000	.750	18.000	.375	.226E+07	.753E+06
5.000	1.000	18.000	.375	.464E+07	.155E+07
5.000	1.250	18.000	.375	.810E+07	.270E+07
5.000	1.500	18.000	.375	.128E+08	.426E+07
5.000	1.750	18.000	.375	.188E+08	.626E+07
5.000	2.000	18.000	.375	.262E+08	.875E+07
6.000	.250	2.375	.154	.153E+05	.509E+04
6.000	.375	2.375	.154	.421E+05	.140E+05
6.000	.500	2.375	.154	.864E+05	.288E+05
6.000	.625	2.375	.154	.151E+06	.503E+05
6.000	.750	2.375	.154	.238E+06	.794E+05
6.000	1.000	2.375	.154	.489E+06	.163E+06
6.000	1.250	2.375	.154	.854E+06	.285E+06
6.000	1.500	2.375	.154	.135E+07	.449E+06
6.000	1.750	2.375	.154	.198E+07	.660E+06
6.000	2.000	2.375	.154	.276E+07	.922E+06
6.000	.250	3.500	.216	.227E+05	.757E+04
6.000	.375	3.500	.216	.626E+05	.209E+05
6.000	.500	3.500	.216	.129E+06	.428E+05
6.000	.625	3.500	.216	.225E+06	.749E+05
6.000	.750	3.500	.216	.354E+06	.118E+06
6.000	1.000	3.500	.216	.727E+06	.242E+06
6.000	1.250	3.500	.216	.127E+07	.423E+06

Table 6-1
Continued

ROTA STIFF CALCULATION, CYL. VESSEL

VESSEL OD,FT	VESSEL TCK,IN	NOZZLE OD,IN	NOZZLE TCK,IN STD	ROT STIF IN.LB/DEG INPLANE LONGI	OUTPLANE CIRCU
6.000	1.500	3.500	.216	.200E+07	.668E+06
6.000	1.750	3.500	.216	.295E+07	.982E+06
6.000	2.000	3.500	.216	.411E+07	.137E+07
6.000	.250	4.500	.237	.300E+05	.100E+05
6.000	.375	4.500	.237	.828E+05	.276E+05
6.000	.500	4.500	.237	.170E+06	.566E+05
6.000	.625	4.500	.237	.297E+06	.989E+05
6.000	.750	4.500	.237	.468E+06	.156E+06
6.000	1.000	4.500	.237	.961E+06	.320E+06
6.000	1.250	4.500	.237	.168E+07	.560E+06
6.000	1.500	4.500	.237	.265E+07	.883E+06
6.000	1.750	4.500	.237	.389E+07	.130E+07
6.000	2.000	4.500	.237	.544E+07	.181E+07
6.000	.250	6.625	.280	.456E+05	.152E+05
6.000	.375	6.625	.280	.126E+06	.419E+05
6.000	.500	6.625	.280	.258E+06	.860E+05
6.000	.625	6.625	.280	.451E+06	.150E+06
6.000	.750	6.625	.280	.711E+06	.237E+06
6.000	1.000	6.625	.280	.146E+07	.487E+06
6.000	1.250	6.625	.280	.255E+07	.850E+06
6.000	1.500	6.625	.280	.402E+07	.134E+07
6.000	1.750	6.625	.280	.592E+07	.197E+07
6.000	2.000	6.625	.280	.826E+07	.275E+07
6.000	.250	8.625	.322	.603E+05	.201E+05
6.000	.375	8.625	.322	.166E+06	.554E+05
6.000	.500	8.625	.322	.341E+06	.114E+06
6.000	.625	8.625	.322	.596E+06	.199E+06
6.000	.750	8.625	.322	.940E+06	.313E+06
6.000	1.000	8.625	.322	.193E+07	.643E+06
6.000	1.250	8.625	.322	.337E+07	.112E+07
6.000	1.500	8.625	.322	.532E+07	.177E+07
6.000	1.750	8.625	.322	.782E+07	.261E+07
6.000	2.000	8.625	.322	.109E+08	.364E+07
6.000	.250	10.750	.365	.759E+05	.253E+05
6.000	.375	10.750	.365	.209E+06	.698E+05
6.000	.500	10.750	.365	.430E+06	.143E+06
6.000	.625	10.750	.365	.750E+06	.250E+06
6.000	.750	10.750	.365	.118E+07	.395E+06
6.000	1.000	10.750	.365	.243E+07	.810E+06
6.000	1.250	10.750	.365	.425E+07	.142E+07
6.000	1.500	10.750	.365	.670E+07	.223E+07
6.000	1.750	10.750	.365	.984E+07	.328E+07
6.000	2.000	10.750	.365	.137E+08	.458E+07
6.000	.250	12.750	.375	.913E+05	.304E+05
6.000	.375	12.750	.375	.252E+06	.839E+05
6.000	.500	12.750	.375	.517E+06	.172E+06
6.000	.625	12.750	.375	.902E+06	.301E+06
6.000	.750	12.750	.375	.142E+07	.474E+06
6.000	1.000	12.750	.375	.292E+07	.974E+06
6.000	1.250	12.750	.375	.510E+07	.170E+07
6.000	1.500	12.750	.375	.805E+07	.268E+07
6.000	1.750	12.750	.375	.118E+08	.395E+07
6.000	2.000	12.750	.375	.165E+08	.551E+07
6.000	.250	14.000	.375	.101E+06	.337E+05
6.000	.375	14.000	.375	.279E+06	.928E+05
6.000	.500	14.000	.375	.572E+06	.191E+06
6.000	.625	14.000	.375	.999E+06	.333E+06
6.000	.750	14.000	.375	.158E+07	.525E+06
6.000	1.000	14.000	.375	.323E+07	.108E+07
6.000	1.250	14.000	.375	.565E+07	.188E+07
6.000	1.500	14.000	.375	.891E+07	.297E+07

Table 6-1
Continued

ROTA STIFF CALCULATION, CYL. VESSEL

VESSEL OD,FT	VESSEL TCK,IN	NOZZLE OD,IN	NOZZLE TCK,IN STD	ROT STIF IN.LB/DEG INPLANE LONGI	OUTPLANE CIRCU
6.000	1.750	14.000	.375	.131E+08	.437E+07
6.000	2.000	14.000	.375	.183E+08	.610E+07
6.000	.250	16.000	.375	.117E+06	.389E+05
6.000	.375	16.000	.375	.322E+06	.107E+06
6.000	.500	16.000	.375	.660E+06	.220E+06
6.000	.625	16.000	.375	.115E+07	.384E+06
6.000	.750	16.000	.375	.182E+07	.606E+06
6.000	1.000	16.000	.375	.373E+07	.124E+07
6.000	1.250	16.000	.375	.652E+07	.217E+07
6.000	1.500	16.000	.375	.103E+08	.343E+07
6.000	1.750	16.000	.375	.151E+08	.504E+07
6.000	2.000	16.000	.375	.211E+08	.704E+07
6.000	.250	18.000	.375	.132E+06	.441E+05
6.000	.375	18.000	.375	.365E+06	.122E+06
6.000	.500	18.000	.375	.748E+06	.249E+06
6.000	.625	18.000	.375	.131E+07	.436E+06
6.000	.750	18.000	.375	.206E+07	.687E+06
6.000	1.000	18.000	.375	.423E+07	.141E+07
6.000	1.250	18.000	.375	.740E+07	.247E+07
6.000	1.500	18.000	.375	.117E+08	.389E+07
6.000	1.750	18.000	.375	.172E+08	.572E+07
6.000	2.000	18.000	.375	.239E+08	.798E+07
6.000	.250	20.000	.375	.148E+06	.493E+05
6.000	.375	20.000	.375	.408E+06	.136E+06
6.000	.500	20.000	.375	.837E+06	.279E+06
6.000	.625	20.000	.375	.146E+07	.487E+06
6.000	.750	20.000	.375	.231E+07	.769E+06
6.000	1.000	20.000	.375	.473E+07	.158E+07
6.000	1.250	20.000	.375	.827E+07	.276E+07
6.000	1.500	20.000	.375	.130E+08	.435E+07
6.000	1.750	20.000	.375	.192E+08	.639E+07
6.000	2.000	20.000	.375	.268E+08	.893E+07
6.000	.250	22.000	.375	.164E+06	.545E+05
6.000	.375	22.000	.375	.451E+06	.150E+06
6.000	.500	22.000	.375	.925E+06	.308E+06
6.000	.625	22.000	.375	.162E+07	.539E+06
6.000	.750	22.000	.375	.255E+07	.850E+06
6.000	1.000	22.000	.375	.523E+07	.174E+07
6.000	1.250	22.000	.375	.914E+07	.305E+07
6.000	1.500	22.000	.375	.144E+08	.481E+07
6.000	1.750	22.000	.375	.212E+08	.707E+07
6.000	2.000	22.000	.375	.296E+08	.987E+07
7.000	.250	2.375	.154	.141E+05	.471E+04
7.000	.375	2.375	.154	.390E+05	.130E+05
7.000	.500	2.375	.154	.800E+05	.267E+05
7.000	.625	2.375	.154	.140E+06	.466E+05
7.000	.750	2.375	.154	.220E+06	.735E+05
7.000	1.000	2.375	.154	.452E+06	.151E+06
7.000	1.250	2.375	.154	.790E+06	.263E+06
7.000	1.500	2.375	.154	.125E+07	.416E+06
7.000	1.750	2.375	.154	.183E+07	.611E+06
7.000	2.000	2.375	.154	.256E+07	.853E+06
7.000	.250	3.500	.216	.210E+05	.701E+04
7.000	.375	3.500	.216	.580E+05	.193E+05
7.000	.500	3.500	.216	.119E+06	.397E+05
7.000	.625	3.500	.216	.208E+06	.693E+05
7.000	.750	3.500	.216	.328E+06	.109E+06
7.000	1.000	3.500	.216	.673E+06	.224E+06
7.000	1.250	3.500	.216	.118E+07	.392E+06

Table 6-1
Continued

ROTA STIFF CALCULATION, CYL. VESSEL

VESSEL OD,FT	VESSEL TCK,IN	NOZZLE OD,IN	NOZZLE TCK,IN STD	ROT STIF IN.LB/DEG INPLANE LONGI	OUTPLANE CIRCU
7.000	1.500	3.500	.216	.186E+07	.618E+06
7.000	1.750	3.500	.216	.273E+07	.909E+06
7.000	2.000	3.500	.216	.381E+07	.127E+07
7.000	.250	4.500	.237	.278E+05	.927E+04
7.000	.375	4.500	.237	.766E+05	.255E+05
7.000	.500	4.500	.237	.157E+06	.524E+05
7.000	.625	4.500	.237	.275E+06	.916E+05
7.000	.750	4.500	.237	.433E+06	.144E+06
7.000	1.000	4.500	.237	.890E+06	.297E+06
7.000	1.250	4.500	.237	.155E+07	.518E+06
7.000	1.500	4.500	.237	.245E+07	.817E+06
7.000	1.750	4.500	.237	.360E+07	.120E+07
7.000	2.000	4.500	.237	.503E+07	.168E+07
7.000	.250	6.625	.280	.422E+05	.141E+05
7.000	.375	6.625	.280	.116E+06	.388E+05
7.000	.500	6.625	.280	.239E+06	.797E+05
7.000	.625	6.625	.280	.418E+06	.139E+06
7.000	.750	6.625	.280	.659E+06	.220E+06
7.000	1.000	6.625	.280	.135E+07	.451E+06
7.000	1.250	6.625	.280	.236E+07	.787E+06
7.000	1.500	6.625	.280	.373E+07	.124E+07
7.000	1.750	6.625	.280	.548E+07	.183E+07
7.000	2.000	6.625	.280	.765E+07	.255E+07
7.000	.250	8.625	.322	.558E+05	.186E+05
7.000	.375	8.625	.322	.154E+06	.513E+05
7.000	.500	8.625	.322	.316E+06	.105E+06
7.000	.625	8.625	.322	.552E+06	.184E+06
7.000	.750	8.625	.322	.870E+06	.290E+06
7.000	1.000	8.625	.322	.179E+07	.596E+06
7.000	1.250	8.625	.322	.312E+07	.104E+07
7.000	1.500	8.625	.322	.492E+07	.164E+07
7.000	1.750	8.625	.322	.724E+07	.241E+07
7.000	2.000	8.625	.322	.101E+08	.337E+07
7.000	.250	10.750	.365	.703E+05	.234E+05
7.000	.375	10.750	.365	.194E+06	.646E+05
7.000	.500	10.750	.365	.398E+06	.133E+06
7.000	.625	10.750	.365	.695E+06	.232E+06
7.000	.750	10.750	.365	.110E+07	.365E+06
7.000	1.000	10.750	.365	.225E+07	.750E+06
7.000	1.250	10.750	.365	.393E+07	.131E+07
7.000	1.500	10.750	.365	.620E+07	.207E+07
7.000	1.750	10.750	.365	.911E+07	.304E+07
7.000	2.000	10.750	.365	.127E+08	.424E+07
7.000	.250	12.750	.375	.845E+05	.282E+05
7.000	.375	12.750	.375	.233E+06	.777E+05
7.000	.500	12.750	.375	.478E+06	.159E+06
7.000	.625	12.750	.375	.835E+06	.278E+06
7.000	.750	12.750	.375	.132E+07	.439E+06
7.000	1.000	12.750	.375	.271E+07	.902E+06
7.000	1.250	12.750	.375	.473E+07	.158E+07
7.000	1.500	12.750	.375	.745E+07	.248E+07
7.000	1.750	12.750	.375	.110E+08	.365E+07
7.000	2.000	12.750	.375	.153E+08	.510E+07
7.000	.250	14.000	.375	.936E+05	.312E+05
7.000	.375	14.000	.375	.258E+06	.859E+05
7.000	.500	14.000	.375	.529E+06	.176E+06
7.000	.625	14.000	.375	.925E+06	.308E+06
7.000	.750	14.000	.375	.146E+07	.486E+06
7.000	1.000	14.000	.375	.299E+07	.998E+06
7.000	1.250	14.000	.375	.523E+07	.174E+07
7.000	1.500	14.000	.375	.825E+07	.275E+07

Table 6-1
Continued

ROTA STIFF CALCULATION, CYL. VESSEL

VESSEL OD,FT	VESSEL TCK,IN	NOZZLE OD,IN	NOZZLE TCK,IN STD	ROT STIF IN.LB/DEG INPLANE LONGI	OUTPLANE CIRCU
7.000	1.750	14.000	.375	.121E+08	.404E+07
7.000	2.000	14.000	.375	.169E+08	.565E+07
7.000	.250	16.000	.375	.108E+06	.360E+05
7.000	.375	16.000	.375	.298E+06	.992E+05
7.000	.500	16.000	.375	.611E+06	.204E+06
7.000	.625	16.000	.375	.107E+07	.356E+06
7.000	.750	16.000	.375	.168E+07	.561E+06
7.000	1.000	16.000	.375	.346E+07	.115E+07
7.000	1.250	16.000	.375	.604E+07	.201E+07
7.000	1.500	16.000	.375	.953E+07	.318E+07
7.000	1.750	16.000	.375	.140E+08	.467E+07
7.000	2.000	16.000	.375	.196E+08	.652E+07
7.000	.250	18.000	.375	.122E+06	.408E+05
7.000	.375	18.000	.375	.338E+06	.113E+06
7.000	.500	18.000	.375	.693E+06	.231E+06
7.000	.625	18.000	.375	.121E+07	.403E+06
7.000	.750	18.000	.375	.191E+07	.636E+06
7.000	1.000	18.000	.375	.392E+07	.131E+07
7.000	1.250	18.000	.375	.685E+07	.228E+07
7.000	1.500	18.000	.375	.108E+08	.360E+07
7.000	1.750	18.000	.375	.159E+08	.529E+07
7.000	2.000	18.000	.375	.222E+08	.739E+07
7.000	.250	20.000	.375	.137E+06	.457E+05
7.000	.375	20.000	.375	.377E+06	.126E+06
7.000	.500	20.000	.375	.775E+06	.258E+06
7.000	.625	20.000	.375	.135E+07	.451E+06
7.000	.750	20.000	.375	.213E+07	.712E+06
7.000	1.000	20.000	.375	.438E+07	.146E+07
7.000	1.250	20.000	.375	.766E+07	.255E+07
7.000	1.500	20.000	.375	.121E+08	.403E+07
7.000	1.750	20.000	.375	.178E+08	.592E+07
7.000	2.000	20.000	.375	.248E+08	.826E+07
7.000	.250	22.000	.375	.151E+06	.505E+05
7.000	.375	22.000	.375	.417E+06	.139E+06
7.000	.500	22.000	.375	.857E+06	.286E+06
7.000	.625	22.000	.375	.150E+07	.499E+06
7.000	.750	22.000	.375	.236E+07	.787E+06
7.000	1.000	22.000	.375	.485E+07	.162E+07
7.000	1.250	22.000	.375	.847E+07	.282E+07
7.000	1.500	22.000	.375	.134E+08	.445E+07
7.000	1.750	22.000	.375	.196E+08	.654E+07
7.000	2.000	22.000	.375	.274E+08	.914E+07
7.000	.250	24.000	.375	.166E+06	.553E+05
7.000	.375	24.000	.375	.457E+06	.152E+06
7.000	.500	24.000	.375	.938E+06	.313E+06
7.000	.625	24.000	.375	.164E+07	.546E+06
7.000	.750	24.000	.375	.259E+07	.862E+06
7.000	1.000	24.000	.375	.531E+07	.177E+07
7.000	1.250	24.000	.375	.927E+07	.309E+07
7.000	1.500	24.000	.375	.146E+08	.488E+07
7.000	1.750	24.000	.375	.215E+08	.717E+07
7.000	2.000	24.000	.375	.300E+08	.100E+08
7.000	.250	26.000	.375	.180E+06	.601E+05
7.000	.375	26.000	.375	.497E+06	.166E+06
7.000	.500	26.000	.375	.102E+07	.340E+06
7.000	.625	26.000	.375	.178E+07	.594E+06
7.000	.750	26.000	.375	.281E+07	.937E+06
7.000	1.000	26.000	.375	.577E+07	.192E+07
7.000	1.250	26.000	.375	.101E+08	.336E+07
7.000	1.500	26.000	.375	.159E+08	.530E+07
7.000	1.750	26.000	.375	.234E+08	.779E+07
7.000	2.000	26.000	.375	.327E+08	.109E+08

Table 6-1
Continued

ROTA STIFF CALCULATION, CYL. VESSEL

VESSEL OD,FT	VESSEL TCK,IN	NOZZLE OD,IN	NOZZLE TCK,IN STD	ROT STIF IN.LB/DEG INPLANE LONGI	OUTPLANE CIRCU
8.000	.250	2.375	.154	.132E+05	.441E+04
8.000	.375	2.375	.154	.364E+05	.121E+05
8.000	.500	2.375	.154	.748E+05	.249E+05
8.000	.625	2.375	.154	.131E+06	.436E+05
8.000	.750	2.375	.154	.206E+06	.687E+05
8.000	1.000	2.375	.154	.423E+06	.141E+06
8.000	1.250	2.375	.154	.739E+06	.246E+06
8.000	1.500	2.375	.154	.117E+07	.389E+06
8.000	1.750	2.375	.154	.171E+07	.572E+06
8.000	2.000	2.375	.154	.239E+07	.798E+06
8.000	.250	3.500	.216	.197E+05	.656E+04
8.000	.375	3.500	.216	.542E+05	.181E+05
8.000	.500	3.500	.216	.111E+06	.371E+05
8.000	.625	3.500	.216	.194E+06	.648E+05
8.000	.750	3.500	.216	.307E+06	.102E+06
8.000	1.000	3.500	.216	.630E+06	.210E+06
8.000	1.250	3.500	.216	.110E+07	.367E+06
8.000	1.500	3.500	.216	.174E+07	.578E+06
8.000	1.750	3.500	.216	.255E+07	.850E+06
8.000	2.000	3.500	.216	.356E+07	.119E+07
8.000	.250	4.500	.237	.260E+05	.867E+04
8.000	.375	4.500	.237	.717E+05	.239E+05
8.000	.500	4.500	.237	.147E+06	.490E+05
8.000	.625	4.500	.237	.257E+06	.857E+05
8.000	.750	4.500	.237	.405E+06	.135E+06
8.000	1.000	4.500	.237	.832E+06	.277E+06
8.000	1.250	4.500	.237	.145E+07	.485E+06
8.000	1.500	4.500	.237	.229E+07	.764E+06
8.000	1.750	4.500	.237	.337E+07	.112E+07
8.000	2.000	4.500	.237	.471E+07	.157E+07
8.000	.250	6.625	.280	.395E+05	.132E+05
8.000	.375	6.625	.280	.109E+06	.363E+05
8.000	.500	6.625	.280	.224E+06	.745E+05
8.000	.625	6.625	.280	.391E+06	.130E+06
8.000	.750	6.625	.280	.616E+06	.205E+06
8.000	1.000	6.625	.280	.126E+07	.422E+06
8.000	1.250	6.625	.280	.221E+07	.736E+06
8.000	1.500	6.625	.280	.349E+07	.116E+07
8.000	1.750	6.625	.280	.512E+07	.171E+07
8.000	2.000	6.625	.280	.715E+07	.238E+07
8.000	.250	8.625	.322	.522E+05	.174E+05
8.000	.375	8.625	.322	.144E+06	.480E+05
8.000	.500	8.625	.322	.295E+06	.985E+05
8.000	.625	8.625	.322	.516E+06	.172E+06
8.000	.750	8.625	.322	.814E+06	.271E+06
8.000	1.000	8.625	.322	.167E+07	.557E+06
8.000	1.250	8.625	.322	.292E+07	.973E+06
8.000	1.500	8.625	.322	.461E+07	.154E+07
8.000	1.750	8.625	.322	.677E+07	.226E+07
8.000	2.000	8.625	.322	.945E+07	.315E+07
8.000	.250	10.750	.365	.658E+05	.219E+05
8.000	.375	10.750	.365	.181E+06	.604E+05
8.000	.500	10.750	.365	.372E+06	.124E+06
8.000	.625	10.750	.365	.650E+06	.217E+06
8.000	.750	10.750	.365	.103E+07	.342E+06
8.000	1.000	10.750	.365	.210E+07	.701E+06
8.000	1.250	10.750	.365	.368E+07	.123E+07
8.000	1.500	10.750	.365	.580E+07	.193E+07
8.000	1.750	10.750	.365	.853E+07	.284E+07
8.000	2.000	10.750	.365	.119E+08	.397E+07
8.000	.250	12.750	.375	.791E+05	.264E+05
8.000	.375	12.750	.375	.218E+06	.726E+05

Table 6-1
Continued

ROTA STIFF CALCULATION, CYL. VESSEL

VESSEL OD,FT	VESSEL TCK,IN	NOZZLE OD,IN	NOZZLE TCK,IN STD	ROT STIF IN.LB/DEG INPLANE LONGI	OUTPLANE CIRCU
8.000	.500	12.750	.375	.447E+06	.149E+06
8.000	.625	12.750	.375	.781E+06	.260E+06
8.000	.750	12.750	.375	.123E+07	.411E+06
8.000	1.000	12.750	.375	.253E+07	.844E+06
8.000	1.250	12.750	.375	.442E+07	.147E+07
8.000	1.500	12.750	.375	.697E+07	.232E+07
8.000	1.750	12.750	.375	.103E+08	.342E+07
8.000	2.000	12.750	.375	.143E+08	.477E+07
8.000	.250	14.000	.375	.875E+05	.292E+05
8.000	.375	14.000	.375	.241E+06	.804E+05
8.000	.500	14.000	.375	.495E+06	.165E+06
8.000	.625	14.000	.375	.865E+06	.288E+06
8.000	.750	14.000	.375	.136E+07	.455E+06
8.000	1.000	14.000	.375	.280E+07	.934E+06
8.000	1.250	14.000	.375	.489E+07	.163E+07
8.000	1.500	14.000	.375	.772E+07	.257E+07
8.000	1.750	14.000	.375	.113E+08	.378E+07
8.000	2.000	14.000	.375	.158E+08	.528E+07
8.000	.250	16.000	.375	.101E+06	.337E+05
8.000	.375	16.000	.375	.278E+06	.928E+05
8.000	.500	16.000	.375	.572E+06	.191E+06
8.000	.625	16.000	.375	.999E+06	.333E+06
8.000	.750	16.000	.375	.158E+07	.525E+06
8.000	1.000	16.000	.375	.323E+07	.108E+07
8.000	1.250	16.000	.375	.565E+07	.188E+07
8.000	1.500	16.000	.375	.891E+07	.297E+07
8.000	1.750	16.000	.375	.131E+08	.437E+07
8.000	2.000	16.000	.375	.183E+08	.610E+07
8.000	.250	18.000	.375	.115E+06	.382E+05
8.000	.375	18.000	.375	.316E+06	.105E+06
8.000	.500	18.000	.375	.648E+06	.216E+06
8.000	.625	18.000	.375	.113E+07	.377E+06
8.000	.750	18.000	.375	.179E+07	.595E+06
8.000	1.000	18.000	.375	.367E+07	.122E+07
8.000	1.250	18.000	.375	.641E+07	.214E+07
8.000	1.500	18.000	.375	.101E+08	.337E+07
8.000	1.750	18.000	.375	.149E+08	.495E+07
8.000	2.000	18.000	.375	.207E+08	.691E+07
8.000	.250	20.000	.375	.128E+06	.427E+05
8.000	.375	20.000	.375	.353E+06	.118E+06
8.000	.500	20.000	.375	.725E+06	.242E+06
8.000	.625	20.000	.375	.127E+07	.422E+06
8.000	.750	20.000	.375	.200E+07	.666E+06
8.000	1.000	20.000	.375	.410E+07	.137E+07
8.000	1.250	20.000	.375	.716E+07	.239E+07
8.000	1.500	20.000	.375	.113E+08	.377E+07
8.000	1.750	20.000	.375	.166E+08	.554E+07
8.000	2.000	20.000	.375	.232E+08	.773E+07
8.000	.250	22.000	.375	.142E+06	.472E+05
8.000	.375	22.000	.375	.390E+06	.130E+06
8.000	.500	22.000	.375	.801E+06	.267E+06
8.000	.625	22.000	.375	.140E+07	.467E+06
8.000	.750	22.000	.375	.221E+07	.736E+06
8.000	1.000	22.000	.375	.453E+07	.151E+07
8.000	1.250	22.000	.375	.792E+07	.264E+07
8.000	1.500	22.000	.375	.125E+08	.416E+07
8.000	1.750	22.000	.375	.184E+08	.612E+07
8.000	2.000	22.000	.375	.256E+08	.855E+07
8.000	.250	24.000	.375	.155E+06	.517E+05
8.000	.375	24.000	.375	.428E+06	.143E+06
8.000	.500	24.000	.375	.878E+06	.293E+06

Table 6-1
Continued

ROTA STIFF CALCULATION, CYL. VESSEL

VESSEL OD,FT	VESSEL TCK,IN	NOZZLE OD,IN	NOZZLE TCK,IN STD	ROT STIF IN.LB/DEG INPLANE LONGI	OUTPLANE CIRCU
8.000	.625	24.000	.375	.153E+07	.511E+06
8.000	.750	24.000	.375	.242E+07	.806E+06
8.000	1.000	24.000	.375	.497E+07	.166E+07
8.000	1.250	24.000	.375	.868E+07	.289E+07
8.000	1.500	24.000	.375	.137E+08	.456E+07
8.000	1.750	24.000	.375	.201E+08	.671E+07
8.000	2.000	24.000	.375	.281E+08	.936E+07
8.000	.250	26.000	.375	.169E+06	.562E+05
8.000	.375	26.000	.375	.465E+06	.155E+06
8.000	.500	26.000	.375	.954E+06	.318E+06
8.000	.625	26.000	.375	.167E+07	.556E+06
8.000	.750	26.000	.375	.263E+07	.877E+06
8.000	1.000	26.000	.375	.540E+07	.180E+07
8.000	1.250	26.000	.375	.943E+07	.314E+07
8.000	1.500	26.000	.375	.149E+08	.496E+07
8.000	1.750	26.000	.375	.219E+08	.729E+07
8.000	2.000	26.000	.375	.305E+08	.102E+08
8.000	.250	28.000	.375	.182E+06	.608E+05
8.000	.375	28.000	.375	.502E+06	.167E+06
8.000	.500	28.000	.375	.103E+07	.344E+06
8.000	.625	28.000	.375	.180E+07	.600E+06
8.000	.750	28.000	.375	.284E+07	.947E+06
8.000	1.000	28.000	.375	.583E+07	.194E+07
8.000	1.250	28.000	.375	.102E+08	.340E+07
8.000	1.500	28.000	.375	.161E+08	.536E+07
8.000	1.750	28.000	.375	.236E+08	.788E+07
8.000	2.000	28.000	.375	.330E+08	.110E+08
8.000	.250	30.000	.375	.196E+06	.653E+05
8.000	.375	30.000	.375	.540E+06	.180E+06
8.000	.500	30.000	.375	.111E+07	.369E+06
8.000	.625	30.000	.375	.194E+07	.645E+06
8.000	.750	30.000	.375	.305E+07	.102E+07
8.000	1.000	30.000	.375	.627E+07	.209E+07
8.000	1.250	30.000	.375	.109E+08	.365E+07
8.000	1.500	30.000	.375	.173E+08	.576E+07
8.000	1.750	30.000	.375	.254E+08	.846E+07
8.000	2.000	30.000	.375	.354E+08	.118E+08
9.000	.250	2.375	.154	.125E+05	.416E+04
9.000	.375	2.375	.154	.344E+05	.115E+05
9.000	.500	2.375	.154	.705E+05	.235E+05
9.000	.625	2.375	.154	.123E+06	.411E+05
9.000	.750	2.375	.154	.194E+06	.648E+05
9.000	1.000	2.375	.154	.399E+06	.133E+06
9.000	1.250	2.375	.154	.697E+06	.232E+06
9.000	1.500	2.375	.154	.110E+07	.367E+06
9.000	1.750	2.375	.154	.162E+07	.539E+06
9.000	2.000	2.375	.154	.226E+07	.752E+06
9.000	.250	3.500	.216	.186E+05	.618E+04
9.000	.375	3.500	.216	.511E+05	.170E+05
9.000	.500	3.500	.216	.105E+06	.350E+05
9.000	.625	3.500	.216	.183E+06	.611E+05
9.000	.750	3.500	.216	.289E+06	.964E+05
9.000	1.000	3.500	.216	.594E+06	.198E+06
9.000	1.250	3.500	.216	.104E+07	.346E+06
9.000	1.500	3.500	.216	.164E+07	.545E+06
9.000	1.750	3.500	.216	.241E+07	.802E+06
9.000	2.000	3.500	.216	.336E+07	.112E+07
9.000	.250	4.500	.237	.245E+05	.817E+04
9.000	.375	4.500	.237	.676E+05	.225E+05

Table 6-1
Continued

ROTA STIFF CALCULATION, CYL. VESSEL

VESSEL OD,FT	VESSEL TCK,IN	NOZZLE OD,IN	NOZZLE TCK,IN STD	ROT STIF IN.LB/DEG INPLANE LONGI	OUTPLANE CIRCU
9.000	.500	4.500	.237	.139E+06	.462E+05
9.000	.625	4.500	.237	.242E+06	.808E+05
9.000	.750	4.500	.237	.382E+06	.127E+06
9.000	1.000	4.500	.237	.785E+06	.262E+06
9.000	1.250	4.500	.237	.137E+07	.457E+06
9.000	1.500	4.500	.237	.216E+07	.721E+06
9.000	1.750	4.500	.237	.318E+07	.106E+07
9.000	2.000	4.500	.237	.444E+07	.148E+07
9.000	.250	6.625	.280	.373E+05	.124E+05
9.000	.375	6.625	.280	.103E+06	.342E+05
9.000	.500	6.625	.280	.211E+06	.703E+05
9.000	.625	6.625	.280	.368E+06	.123E+06
9.000	.750	6.625	.280	.581E+06	.194E+06
9.000	1.000	6.625	.280	.119E+07	.397E+06
9.000	1.250	6.625	.280	.208E+07	.694E+06
9.000	1.500	6.625	.280	.329E+07	.110E+07
9.000	1.750	6.625	.280	.483E+07	.161E+07
9.000	2.000	6.625	.280	.674E+07	.225E+07
9.000	.250	8.625	.322	.492E+05	.164E+05
9.000	.375	8.625	.322	.136E+06	.452E+05
9.000	.500	8.625	.322	.279E+06	.928E+05
9.000	.625	8.625	.322	.487E+06	.162E+06
9.000	.750	8.625	.322	.768E+06	.256E+06
9.000	1.000	8.625	.322	.158E+07	.525E+06
9.000	1.250	8.625	.322	.275E+07	.918E+06
9.000	1.500	8.625	.322	.434E+07	.145E+07
9.000	1.750	8.625	.322	.638E+07	.213E+07
9.000	2.000	8.625	.322	.891E+07	.297E+07
9.000	.250	10.750	.365	.620E+05	.207E+05
9.000	.375	10.750	.365	.171E+06	.570E+05
9.000	.500	10.750	.365	.351E+06	.117E+06
9.000	.625	10.750	.365	.613E+06	.204E+06
9.000	.750	10.750	.365	.967E+06	.322E+06
9.000	1.000	10.750	.365	.198E+07	.661E+06
9.000	1.250	10.750	.365	.347E+07	.116E+07
9.000	1.500	10.750	.365	.547E+07	.182E+07
9.000	1.750	10.750	.365	.804E+07	.268E+07
9.000	2.000	10.750	.365	.112E+08	.374E+07
9.000	.250	12.750	.375	.746E+05	.249E+05
9.000	.375	12.750	.375	.205E+06	.685E+05
9.000	.500	12.750	.375	.422E+06	.141E+06
9.000	.625	12.750	.375	.737E+06	.246E+06
9.000	.750	12.750	.375	.116E+07	.387E+06
9.000	1.000	12.750	.375	.239E+07	.795E+06
9.000	1.250	12.750	.375	.417E+07	.139E+07
9.000	1.500	12.750	.375	.657E+07	.219E+07
9.000	1.750	12.750	.375	.967E+07	.322E+07
9.000	2.000	12.750	.375	.135E+08	.450E+07
9.000	.250	14.000	.375	.825E+05	.275E+05
9.000	.375	14.000	.375	.227E+06	.758E+05
9.000	.500	14.000	.375	.467E+06	.156E+06
9.000	.625	14.000	.375	.815E+06	.272E+06
9.000	.750	14.000	.375	.129E+07	.429E+06
9.000	1.000	14.000	.375	.264E+07	.880E+06
9.000	1.250	14.000	.375	.461E+07	.154E+07
9.000	1.500	14.000	.375	.728E+07	.243E+07
9.000	1.750	14.000	.375	.107E+08	.357E+07
9.000	2.000	14.000	.375	.149E+08	.498E+07
9.000	.250	16.000	.375	.953E+05	.318E+05
9.000	.375	16.000	.375	.263E+06	.875E+05
9.000	.500	16.000	.375	.539E+06	.180E+06

Table 6-1
Continued

ROTA STIFF CALCULATION, CYL. VESSEL

VESSEL OD,FT	VESSEL TCK,IN	NOZZLE OD,IN	NOZZLE TCK,IN STD	ROT STIF IN.LB/DEG INPLANE LONGI	OUTPLANE CIRCU
9.000	.625	16.000	.375	.941E+06	.314E+06
9.000	.750	16.000	.375	.149F+07	.495E+06
9.000	1.000	16.000	.375	.305E+07	.102E+07
9.000	1.250	16.000	.375	.533E+07	.178E+07
9.000	1.500	16.000	.375	.840E+07	.280E+07
9.000	1.750	16.000	.375	.124E+08	.412E+07
9.000	2.000	16.000	.375	.172E+08	.5[illegible]5E+07
9.000	.250	18.000	.375	.108E+06	.360E+05
9.000	.375	18.000	.375	.298E+06	.992E+05
9.000	.500	18.000	.375	.611E+06	.204E+06
9.000	.625	18.000	.375	.107E+07	.356E+06
9.000	.750	18.000	.375	.168E+07	.561E+06
9.000	1.000	18.000	.375	.346E+07	.115E+07
9.000	1.250	18.000	.375	.604E+07	.201E+07
9.000	1.500	18.000	.375	.953E+07	.318E+07
9.000	1.750	18.000	.375	.140E+08	.467E+07
9.000	2.000	18.000	.375	.196E+08	.652E+07
9.000	.250	20.000	.375	.121E+06	.403E+05
9.000	.375	20.000	.375	.333E+06	.111E+06
9.000	.500	20.000	.375	.683E+06	.228E+06
9.000	.625	20.000	.375	.119E+07	.398E+C6
9.000	.750	20.000	.375	.188E+07	.628E+06
9.000	1.000	20.000	.375	.387E+07	.129E+07
9.000	1.250	20.000	.375	.675E+07	.225E+07
9.000	1.500	20.000	.375	.107E+08	.355E+07
9.000	1.750	20.000	.375	.157E+08	.522E+07
9.000	2.000	20.000	.375	.219E+08	.729E+07
9.000	.250	22.000	.375	.134E+06	.445E+05
9.000	.375	22.000	.375	.368E+06	.123E+06
9.000	.500	22.000	.375	.755E+06	.252E+06
9.000	.625	22.000	.375	.132E+07	.440E+06
9.000	.750	22.000	.375	.208E+07	.694E+06
9.000	1.000	22.000	.375	.427E+07	.142E+07
9.000	1.250	22.000	.375	.747E+07	.249E+07
9.000	1.500	22.000	.375	.118E+08	.393E+07
9.000	1.750	22.000	.375	.173E+08	.577E+07
9.000	2.000	22.000	.375	.242E+08	.806E+07
9.000	.250	24.000	.375	.146E+06	.488E+05
9.000	.375	24.000	.375	.403E+06	.134E+06
9.000	.500	24.000	.375	.828E+06	.276E+06
9.000	.625	24.000	.375	.145E+07	.482E+06
9.000	.750	24.000	.375	.228E+07	.760E+06
9.000	1.000	24.000	.375	.468E+07	.156E+07
9.000	1.250	24.000	.375	.818E+07	.273E+07
9.000	1.500	24.000	.375	.129E+08	.430E+07
9.000	1.750	24.000	.375	.190E+08	.632E+07
9.000	2.000	24.000	.375	.265E+08	.883E+07
9.000	.250	26.000	.375	.159E+06	.530E+05
9.000	.375	26.000	.375	.438E+06	.146E+06
9.000	.500	26.000	.375	.900E+06	.300E+06
9.000	.625	26.000	.375	.157E+07	.524E+06
9.000	.750	26.000	.375	.248E+07	.827E+06
9.000	1.000	26.000	.375	.509E+07	.170E+07
9.000	1.250	26.000	.375	.889E+07	.296E+07
9.000	1.500	26.000	.375	.140E+08	.468E+07
9.000	1.750	26.000	.375	.206E+08	.687E+07
9.000	2.000	26.000	.375	.288E+08	.960E+07
9.000	.250	28.000	.375	.172E+06	.573E+05
9.000	.375	28.000	.375	.474E+06	.158E+06
9.000	.500	28.000	.375	.972E+06	.324E+06
9.000	.625	28.000	.375	.170E+07	.566E+06

Table 6-1
Continued

ROTA STIFF CALCULATION, CYL. VESSEL

VESSEL OD,FT	VESSEL TCK,IN	NOZZLE OD,IN	NOZZLE TCK,IN STD	ROT STIF IN.LB/DEG INPLANE LONGI	OUTPLANE CIRCU
9.000	.750	28.000	.375	.268E+07	.893E+06
9.000	1.000	28.000	.375	.550E+07	.183E+07
9.000	1.250	28.000	.375	.961E+07	.320E+07
9.000	1.500	28.000	.375	.152E+08	.505E+07
9.000	1.750	28.000	.375	.223E+08	.743E+07
9.000	2.000	28.000	.375	.311E+08	.104E+08
9.000	.250	30.000	.375	.185E+06	.615E+05
9.000	.375	30.000	.375	.509E+06	.170E+06
9.000	.500	30.000	.375	.104E+07	.348E+06
9.000	.625	30.000	.375	.182E+07	.608E+06
9.000	.750	30.000	.375	.288E+07	.959E+06
9.000	1.000	30.000	.375	.591E+07	.197E+07
9.000	1.250	30.000	.375	.103E+08	.344E+07
9.000	1.500	30.000	.375	.163E+08	.543E+07
9.000	1.750	30.000	.375	.239E+08	.798E+07
9.000	2.000	30.000	.375	.334E+08	.111E+08
9.000	.250	32.000	.375	.197E+06	.658E+05
9.000	.375	32.000	.375	.544E+06	.181E+06
9.000	.500	32.000	.375	.112E+07	.372E+06
9.000	.625	32.000	.375	.195E+07	.650E+06
9.000	.750	32.000	.375	.308E+07	.103E+07
9.000	1.000	32.000	.375	.632E+07	.211E+07
9.000	1.250	32.000	.375	.110E+08	.368E+07
9.000	1.500	32.000	.375	.174E+08	.580E+07
9.000	1.750	32.000	.375	.256E+08	.853E+07
9.000	2.000	32.000	.375	.357E+08	.119E+08
10.000	.250	2.375	.154	.118E+05	.394E+04
10.000	.375	2.375	.154	.326E+05	.109E+05
10.000	.500	2.375	.154	.669E+05	.223E+05
10.000	.625	2.375	.154	.117E+06	.390E+05
10.000	.750	2.375	.154	.184E+06	.615E+05
10.000	1.000	2.375	.154	.379E+06	.126E+06
10.000	1.250	2.375	.154	.661E+06	.220E+06
10.000	1.500	2.375	.154	.104E+07	.348E+06
10.000	1.750	2.375	.154	.153E+07	.511E+06
10.000	2.000	2.375	.154	.214E+07	.714E+06
10.000	.250	3.500	.216	.176E+05	.587E+04
10.000	.375	3.500	.216	.485E+05	.162E+05
10.000	.500	3.500	.216	.996E+05	.332E+05
10.000	.625	3.500	.216	.174E+06	.580E+05
10.000	.750	3.500	.216	.274E+06	.915E+05
10.000	1.000	3.500	.216	.563E+06	.188E+06
10.000	1.250	3.500	.216	.984E+06	.328E+06
10.000	1.500	3.500	.216	.155E+07	.517E+06
10.000	1.750	3.500	.216	.228E+07	.761E+06
10.000	2.000	3.500	.216	.319E+07	.106E+07
10.000	.250	4.500	.237	.233E+05	.775E+04
10.000	.375	4.500	.237	.641E+05	.214E+05
10.000	.500	4.500	.237	.132E+06	.439E+05
10.000	.625	4.500	.237	.230E+06	.766E+05
10.000	.750	4.500	.237	.363E+06	.121E+06
10.000	1.000	4.500	.237	.744E+06	.248E+06
10.000	1.250	4.500	.237	.130E+07	.433E+06
10.000	1.500	4.500	.237	.205E+07	.684E+06
10.000	1.750	4.500	.237	.302E+07	.101E+07
10.000	2.000	4.500	.237	.421E+07	.140E+07
10.000	.250	6.625	.280	.353E+05	.118E+05
10.000	.375	6.625	.280	.974E+05	.325E+05
10.000	.500	6.625	.280	.200E+06	.667E+05

Table 6-1
Continued

ROTA STIFF CALCULATION, CYL. VESSEL

VESSEL OD,FT	VESSEL TCK,IN	NOZZLE OD,IN	NOZZLE TCK,IN STD	ROT STIF IN.LB/DEG INPLANE LONGI	OUTPLANE CIRCU
10.000	.625	6.625	.280	.349E+06	.116E+06
10.000	.750	6.625	.280	.551E+06	.184E+06
10.000	1.000	6.625	.280	.113E+07	.377E+06
10.000	1.250	6.625	.280	.198E+07	.659E+06
10.000	1.500	6.625	.280	.312E+07	.104E+07
10.000	1.750	6.625	.280	.458E+07	.153E+07
10.000	2.000	6.625	.280	.640E+07	.213E+07
10.000	.250	8.625	.322	.467E+05	.156E+05
10.000	.375	8.625	.322	.129E+06	.429E+05
10.000	.500	8.625	.322	.264E+06	.881E+05
10.000	.625	8.625	.322	.462E+06	.154E+06
10.000	.750	8.625	.322	.728E+06	.243E+06
10.000	1.000	8.625	.322	.149E+07	.498E+06
10.000	1.250	8.625	.322	.261E+07	.870E+06
10.000	1.500	8.625	.322	.412E+07	.137E+07
10.000	1.750	8.625	.322	.606E+07	.202E+07
10.000	2.000	8.625	.322	.846E+07	.282E+07
10.000	.250	10.750	.365	.588E+05	.196E+05
10.000	.375	10.750	.365	.162E+06	.540E+05
10.000	.500	10.750	.365	.333E+06	.111E+06
10.000	.625	10.750	.365	.581E+06	.194E+06
10.000	.750	10.750	.365	.917E+06	.306E+06
10.000	1.000	10.750	.365	.188E+07	.627E+06
10.000	1.250	10.750	.365	.329E+07	.110E+07
10.000	1.500	10.750	.365	.519E+07	.173E+07
10.000	1.750	10.750	.365	.763E+07	.254E+07
10.000	2.000	10.750	.365	.106E+08	.355E+07
10.000	.250	12.750	.375	.707E+05	.236E+05
10.000	.375	12.750	.375	.195E+06	.650E+05
10.000	.500	12.750	.375	.400E+06	.133E+06
10.000	.625	12.750	.375	.699E+06	.233E+06
10.000	.750	12.750	.375	.110E+07	.368E+06
10.000	1.000	12.750	.375	.226E+07	.754E+06
10.000	1.250	12.750	.375	.395E+07	.132E+07
10.000	1.500	12.750	.375	.624E+07	.208E+07
10.000	1.750	12.750	.375	.917E+07	.306E+07
10.000	2.000	12.750	.375	.128E+08	.427E+07
10.000	.250	14.000	.375	.783E+05	.261E+05
10.000	.375	14.000	.375	.216E+06	.719E+05
10.000	.500	14.000	.375	.443E+06	.148E+06
10.000	.625	14.000	.375	.774E+06	.258E+06
10.000	.750	14.000	.375	.122E+07	.407E+06
10.000	1.000	14.000	.375	.251E+07	.835E+06
10.000	1.250	14.000	.375	.438E+07	.146E+07
10.000	1.500	14.000	.375	.690E+07	.230E+07
10.000	1.750	14.000	.375	.101E+08	.338E+07
10.000	2.000	14.000	.375	.142E+08	.472E+07
10.000	.250	16.000	.375	.904E+05	.301E+05
10.000	.375	16.000	.375	.249E+06	.830E+05
10.000	.500	16.000	.375	.511E+06	.170E+06
10.000	.625	16.000	.375	.893E+06	.298E+06
10.000	.750	16.000	.375	.141E+07	.470E+06
10.000	1.000	16.000	.375	.289E+07	.964E+06
10.000	1.250	16.000	.375	.505E+07	.168E+07
10.000	1.500	16.000	.375	.797E+07	.266E+07
10.000	1.750	16.000	.375	.117E+08	.391E+07
10.000	2.000	16.000	.375	.164E+08	.545E+07
10.000	.250	18.000	.375	.102E+06	.342E+05
10.000	.375	18.000	.375	.282E+06	.941E+05
10.000	.500	18.000	.375	.580E+06	.193E+06
10.000	.625	18.000	.375	.101E+07	.338E+06

Table 6-1
Continued

ROTA STIFF CALCULATION, CYL. VESSEL

VESSEL OD,FT	VESSEL TCK,IN	NOZZLE OD,IN	NOZZLE TCK,IN STD	ROT STIF IN.LB/DEG INPLANE LONGI	OUTPLANE CIRCU
10.000	.750	18.000	.375	.160E+07	.533E+06
10.000	1.000	18.000	.375	.328E+07	.109E+07
10.000	1.250	18.000	.375	.573E+07	.191E+07
10.000	1.500	18.000	.375	.904E+07	.301E+07
10.000	1.750	18.000	.375	.133E+08	.443E+07
10.000	2.000	18.000	.375	.186E+08	.618E+07
10.000	.250	20.000	.375	.115E+06	.382E+05
10.000	.375	20.000	.375	.316E+06	.105E+06
10.000	.500	20.000	.375	.648E+06	.216E+06
10.000	.625	20.000	.375	.113E+07	.377E+06
10.000	.750	20.000	.375	.179E+07	.595E+06
10.000	1.000	20.000	.375	.367E+07	.122E+07
10.000	1.250	20.000	.375	.641E+07	.214E+07
10.000	1.500	20.000	.375	.101E+08	.337E+07
10.000	1.750	20.000	.375	.149E+08	.495E+07
10.000	2.000	20.000	.375	.207E+08	.691E+07
10.000	.250	22.000	.375	.127E+06	.422E+05
10.000	.375	22.000	.375	.349E+06	.116E+06
10.000	.500	22.000	.375	.717E+06	.239E+06
10.000	.625	22.000	.375	.125E+07	.417E+06
10.000	.750	22.000	.375	.197E+07	.658E+06
10.000	1.000	22.000	.375	.405E+07	.135E+07
10.000	1.250	22.000	.375	.708E+07	.236E+07
10.000	1.500	22.000	.375	.112E+08	.372E+07
10.000	1.750	22.000	.375	.164E+08	.547E+07
10.000	2.000	22.000	.375	.229E+08	.764E+07
10.000	.250	24.000	.375	.139E+06	.463E+05
10.000	.375	24.000	.375	.383E+06	.128E+06
10.000	.500	24.000	.375	.785E+06	.262E+06
10.000	.625	24.000	.375	.137E+07	.457E+06
10.000	.750	24.000	.375	.216E+07	.721E+06
10.000	1.000	24.000	.375	.444E+07	.148E+07
10.000	1.250	24.000	.375	.776E+07	.259E+07
10.000	1.500	24.000	.375	.122E+08	.408E+07
10.000	1.750	24.000	.375	.180E+08	.600E+07
10.000	2.000	24.000	.375	.251E+08	.838E+07
10.000	.250	26.000	.375	.151E+06	.503E+05
10.000	.375	26.000	.375	.416E+06	.139E+06
10.000	.500	26.000	.375	.854E+06	.285E+06
10.000	.625	26.000	.375	.149E+07	.497E+06
10.000	.750	26.000	.375	.235E+07	.784E+06
10.000	1.000	26.000	.375	.483E+07	.161E+07
10.000	1.250	26.000	.375	.844E+07	.281E+07
10.000	1.500	26.000	.375	.133E+08	.444E+07
10.000	1.750	26.000	.375	.196E+08	.652E+07
10.000	2.000	26.000	.375	.273E+08	.911E+07
10.000	.250	28.000	.375	.163E+06	.543E+05
10.000	.375	28.000	.375	.449E+06	.150E+06
10.000	.500	28.000	.375	.922E+06	.307E+06
10.000	.625	28.000	.375	.161E+07	.537E+06
10.000	.750	28.000	.375	.254E+07	.847E+06
10.000	1.000	28.000	.375	.522E+07	.174E+07
10.000	1.250	28.000	.375	.911E+07	.304E+07
10.000	1.500	28.000	.375	.144E+08	.479E+07
10.000	1.750	28.000	.375	.211E+08	.705E+07
10.000	2.000	28.000	.375	.295E+08	.984E+07
10.000	.250	30.000	.375	.175E+06	.584E+05
10.000	.375	30.000	.375	.483E+06	.161E+06
10.000	.500	30.000	.375	.991E+06	.330E+06
10.000	.625	30.000	.375	.173E+07	.577E+06
10.000	.750	30.000	.375	.273E+07	.910E+06

Table 6-1
Continued

ROTA STIFF CALCULATION, CYL. VESSEL

VESSEL OD,FT	VESSEL TCK,IN	NOZZLE OD,IN	NOZZLE TCK,IN STD	ROT STIF IN.LB/DEG INPLANE LONGI	OUTPLANE CIRCU
10.000	1.000	30.000	.375	.560E+07	.187E+07
10.000	1.250	30.000	.375	.979E+07	.326E+07
10.000	1.500	30.000	.375	.154E+08	.515E+07
10.000	1.750	30.000	.375	.227E+08	.757E+07
10.000	2.000	30.000	.375	.317E+08	.106E+08
10.000	.250	32.000	.375	.187E+06	.624E+05
10.000	.375	32.000	.375	.516E+06	.172E+06
10.000	.500	32.000	.375	.106E+07	.353E+06
10.000	.625	32.000	.375	.185E+07	.617E+06
10.000	.750	32.000	.375	.292E+07	.973E+06
10.000	1.000	32.000	.375	.599E+07	.200E+07
10.000	1.250	32.000	.375	.105E+08	.349E+07
10.000	1.500	32.000	.375	.165E+08	.550E+07
10.000	1.750	32.000	.375	.243E+08	.809E+07
10.000	2.000	32.000	.375	.339E+08	.113E+08
10.000	.250	36.000	.375	.212E+06	.705E+05
10.000	.375	36.000	.375	.583E+06	.194E+06
10.000	.500	36.000	.375	.120E+07	.399E+06
10.000	.625	36.000	.375	.209E+07	.697E+06
10.000	.750	36.000	.375	.330E+07	.110E+07
10.000	1.000	36.000	.375	.677E+07	.226E+07
10.000	1.250	36.000	.375	.118E+08	.394E+07
10.000	1.500	36.000	.375	.187E+08	.622E+07
10.000	1.750	36.000	.375	.274E+08	.914E+07
10.000	2.000	36.000	.375	.383E+08	.128E+08
11.000	.250	2.375	.154	.113E+05	.376E+04
11.000	.375	2.375	.154	.311E+05	.104E+05
11.000	.500	2.375	.154	.638E+05	.213E+05
11.000	.625	2.375	.154	.111E+06	.372E+05
11.000	.750	2.375	.154	.176E+06	.586E+05
11.000	1.000	2.375	.154	.361E+06	.120E+06
11.000	1.250	2.375	.154	.631E+06	.210E+06
11.000	1.500	2.375	.154	.995E+06	.332E+06
11.000	1.750	2.375	.154	.146E+07	.487E+06
11.000	2.000	2.375	.154	.204E+07	.681E+06
11.000	.250	3.500	.216	.168E+05	.559E+04
11.000	.375	3.500	.216	.462E+05	.154E+05
11.000	.500	3.500	.216	.949E+05	.316E+05
11.000	.625	3.500	.216	.166E+06	.553E+05
11.000	.750	3.500	.216	.262E+06	.872E+05
11.000	1.000	3.500	.216	.537E+06	.179E+06
11.000	1.250	3.500	.216	.938E+06	.313E+06
11.000	1.500	3.500	.216	.148E+07	.493E+06
11.000	1.750	3.500	.216	.218E+07	.725E+06
11.000	2.000	3.500	.216	.304E+07	.101E+07
11.000	.250	4.500	.237	.222E+05	.739E+04
11.000	.375	4.500	.237	.611E+05	.204E+05
11.000	.500	4.500	.237	.125E+06	.418E+05
11.000	.625	4.500	.237	.219E+06	.731E+05
11.000	.750	4.500	.237	.346E+06	.115E+06
11.000	1.000	4.500	.237	.710E+06	.237E+06
11.000	1.250	4.500	.237	.124E+07	.413E+06
11.000	1.500	4.500	.237	.196E+07	.652E+06
11.000	1.750	4.500	.237	.288E+07	.958E+06
11.000	2.000	4.500	.237	.402E+07	.134E+07
11.000	.250	6.625	.280	.337E+05	.112E+05
11.000	.375	6.625	.280	.929E+05	.310E+05
11.000	.500	6.625	.280	.191E+06	.636E+05
11.000	.625	6.625	.280	.333E+06	.111E+06

Table 6-1
Continued

ROTA STIFF CALCULATION, CYL. VESSEL

VESSEL OD,FT	VESSEL TCK,IN	NOZZLE OD,IN	NOZZLE TCK,IN STD	ROT STIF IN.LB/DEG INPLANE LONGI	OUTPLANE CIRCU
11.000	.750	6.625	.280	.525E+06	.175E+06
11.000	1.000	6.625	.280	.108E+07	.360E+06
11.000	1.250	6.625	.280	.188E+07	.628E+06
11.000	1.500	6.625	.280	.297E+07	.991E+06
11.000	1.750	6.625	.280	.437E+07	.146E+07
11.000	2.000	6.625	.280	.610E+07	.203E+07
11.000	.250	8.625	.322	.445E+05	.148E+05
11.000	.375	8.625	.322	.123E+06	.409E+05
11.000	.500	8.625	.322	.252E+06	.840E+05
11.000	.625	8.625	.322	.440E+06	.147E+06
11.000	.750	8.625	.322	.694E+06	.231E+06
11.000	1.000	8.625	.322	.143E+07	.475E+06
11.000	1.250	8.625	.322	.249E+07	.830E+06
11.000	1.500	8.625	.322	.393E+07	.131E+07
11.000	1.750	8.625	.322	.577E+07	.192E+07
11.000	2.000	8.625	.322	.806E+07	.269E+07
11.000	.250	10.750	.365	.561E+05	.187E+05
11.000	.375	10.750	.365	.155E+06	.515E+05
11.000	.500	10.750	.365	.317E+06	.106E+06
11.000	.625	10.750	.365	.554E+06	.185E+06
11.000	.750	10.750	.365	.874E+06	.291E+06
11.000	1.000	10.750	.365	.179E+07	.598E+06
11.000	1.250	10.750	.365	.314E+07	.105E+07
11.000	1.500	10.750	.365	.495E+07	.165E+07
11.000	1.750	10.750	.365	.727E+07	.242E+07
11.000	2.000	10.750	.365	.102E+08	.338E+07
11.000	.250	12.750	.375	.674E+05	.225E+05
11.000	.375	12.750	.375	.186E+06	.619E+05
11.000	.500	12.750	.375	.382E+06	.127E+06
11.000	.625	12.750	.375	.666E+06	.222E+06
11.000	.750	12.750	.375	.105E+07	.350E+06
11.000	1.000	12.750	.375	.216E+07	.719E+06
11.000	1.250	12.750	.375	.377E+07	.126E+07
11.000	1.500	12.750	.375	.595E+07	.198E+07
11.000	1.750	12.750	.375	.874E+07	.291E+07
11.000	2.000	12.750	.375	.122E+08	.407E+07
11.000	.250	14.000	.375	.746E+05	.249E+05
11.000	.375	14.000	.375	.206E+06	.686E+05
11.000	.500	14.000	.375	.422E+06	.141E+06
11.000	.625	14.000	.375	.738E+06	.246E+06
11.000	.750	14.000	.375	.116E+07	.388E+06
11.000	1.000	14.000	.375	.239E+07	.796E+06
11.000	1.250	14.000	.375	.417E+07	.139E+07
11.000	1.500	14.000	.375	.658E+07	.219E+07
11.000	1.750	14.000	.375	.968E+07	.323E+07
11.000	2.000	14.000	.375	.135E+08	.450E+07
11.000	.250	16.000	.375	.862E+05	.287E+05
11.000	.375	16.000	.375	.237E+06	.792E+05
11.000	.500	16.000	.375	.487E+06	.162E+06
11.000	.625	16.000	.375	.852E+06	.284E+06
11.000	.750	16.000	.375	.134E+07	.448E+06
11.000	1.000	16.000	.375	.276E+07	.919E+06
11.000	1.250	16.000	.375	.482E+07	.161E+07
11.000	1.500	16.000	.375	.760E+07	.253E+07
11.000	1.750	16.000	.375	.112E+08	.372E+07
11.000	2.000	16.000	.375	.156E+08	.520E+07
11.000	.250	18.000	.375	.977E+05	.326E+05
11.000	.375	18.000	.375	.269E+06	.898E+05
11.000	.500	18.000	.375	.553E+06	.184E+06
11.000	.625	18.000	.375	.966E+06	.322E+06
11.000	.750	18.000	.375	.152E+07	.508E+06

Table 6-1
Continued

ROTA STIFF CALCULATION, CYL. VESSEL

VESSEL OD,FT	VESSEL TCK,IN	NOZZLE OD,IN	NOZZLE TCK,IN STD	ROT STIF IN.LB/DEG INPLANE LONGI	OUTPLANE CIRCU
11.000	1.000	18.000	.375	.313E+07	.104E+07
11.000	1.250	18.000	.375	.546E+07	.182E+07
11.000	1.500	18.000	.375	.862E+07	.287E+07
11.000	1.750	18.000	.375	.127E+08	.422E+07
11.000	2.000	18.000	.375	.177E+08	.590E+07
11.000	.250	20.000	.375	.109E+06	.364E+05
11.000	.375	20.000	.375	.301E+06	.100E+06
11.000	.500	20.000	.375	.618E+06	.206E+06
11.000	.625	20.000	.375	.108E+07	.360E+06
11.000	.750	20.000	.375	.170E+07	.568E+06
11.000	1.000	20.000	.375	.350E+07	.117E+07
11.000	1.250	20.000	.375	.611E+07	.204E+07
11.000	1.500	20.000	.375	.963E+07	.321E+07
11.000	1.750	20.000	.375	.142E+08	.472E+07
11.000	2.000	20.000	.375	.198E+08	.659E+07
11.000	.250	22.000	.375	.121E+06	.403E+05
11.000	.375	22.000	.375	.333E+06	.111E+06
11.000	.500	22.000	.375	.683E+06	.228E+06
11.000	.625	22.000	.375	.119E+07	.398E+06
11.000	.750	22.000	.375	.188E+07	.628E+06
11.000	1.000	22.000	.375	.387E+07	.129E+07
11.000	1.250	22.000	.375	.675E+07	.225E+07
11.000	1.500	22.000	.375	.107E+08	.355E+07
11.000	1.750	22.000	.375	.157E+08	.522E+07
11.000	2.000	22.000	.375	.219E+08	.729E+07
11.000	.250	24.000	.375	.132E+06	.441E+05
11.000	.375	24.000	.375	.365E+06	.122E+06
11.000	.500	24.000	.375	.749E+06	.250E+06
11.000	.625	24.000	.375	.131E+07	.436E+06
11.000	.750	24.000	.375	.206E+07	.688E+06
11.000	1.000	24.000	.375	.424E+07	.141E+07
11.000	1.250	24.000	.375	.740E+07	.247E+07
11.000	1.500	24.000	.375	.117E+08	.389E+07
11.000	1.750	24.000	.375	.172E+08	.572E+07
11.000	2.000	24.000	.375	.240E+08	.799E+07
11.000	.250	26.000	.375	.144E+06	.480E+05
11.000	.375	26.000	.375	.397E+06	.132E+06
11.000	.500	26.000	.375	.814E+06	.271E+06
11.000	.625	26.000	.375	.142E+07	.474E+06
11.000	.750	26.000	.375	.224E+07	.748E+06
11.000	1.000	26.000	.375	.460E+07	.153E+07
11.000	1.250	26.000	.375	.804E+07	.268E+07
11.000	1.500	26.000	.375	.127E+08	.423E+07
11.000	1.750	26.000	.375	.187E+08	.622E+07
11.000	2.000	26.000	.375	.260E+08	.868E+07
11.000	.250	28.000	.375	.155E+06	.518E+05
11.000	.375	28.000	.375	.428E+06	.143E+06
11.000	.500	28.000	.375	.879E+06	.293E+06
11.000	.625	28.000	.375	.154E+07	.512E+06
11.000	.750	28.000	.375	.242E+07	.808E+06
11.000	1.000	28.000	.375	.497E+07	.166E+07
11.000	1.250	28.000	.375	.869E+07	.290E+07
11.000	1.500	28.000	.375	.137E+08	.457E+07
11.000	1.750	28.000	.375	.202E+08	.672E+07
11.000	2.000	28.000	.375	.281E+08	.938E+07
11.000	.250	30.000	.375	.167E+06	.557E+05
11.000	.375	30.000	.375	.460E+06	.153E+06
11.000	.500	30.000	.375	.945E+06	.315E+06
11.000	.625	30.000	.375	.165E+07	.550E+06
11.000	.750	30.000	.375	.260E+07	.868E+06
11.000	1.000	30.000	.375	.534E+07	.178E+07

Table 6-1
Continued

ROTA STIFF CALCULATION, CYL. VESSEL

VESSEL OD,FT	VESSEL TCK,IN	NOZZLE OD,IN	NOZZLE TCK,IN STD	ROT STIF IN.LB/DEG INPLANE LONGI	OUTPLANE CIRCU
11.000	1.250	30.000	.375	.934E+07	.311E+07
11.000	1.500	30.000	.375	.147E+08	.491E+07
11.000	1.750	30.000	.375	.216E+08	.722E+07
11.000	2.000	30.000	.375	.302E+08	.101E+08
11.000	.250	32.000	.375	.179E+06	.595E+05
11.000	.375	32.000	.375	.492E+06	.164E+06
11.000	.500	32.000	.375	.101E+07	.337E+06
11.000	.625	32.000	.375	.176E+07	.588E+06
11.000	.750	32.000	.375	.278E+07	.928E+06
11.000	1.000	32.000	.375	.571E+07	.190E+07
11.000	1.250	32.000	.375	.998E+07	.333E+07
11.000	1.500	32.000	.375	.157E+08	.525E+07
11.000	1.750	32.000	.375	.231E+08	.772E+07
11.000	2.000	32.000	.375	.323E+08	.108E+08
11.000	.250	36.000	.375	.202E+06	.672E+05
11.000	.375	36.000	.375	.556E+06	.185E+06
11.000	.500	36.000	.375	.114E+07	.380E+06
11.000	.625	36.000	.375	.199E+07	.664E+06
11.000	.750	36.000	.375	.314E+07	.105E+07
11.000	1.000	36.000	.375	.645E+07	.215E+07
11.000	1.250	36.000	.375	.113E+08	.376E+07
11.000	1.500	36.000	.375	.178E+08	.593E+07
11.000	1.750	36.000	.375	.261E+08	.871E+07
11.000	2.000	36.000	.375	.365E+08	.122E+08
11.000	.250	40.000	.375	.225E+06	.749E+05
11.000	.375	40.000	.375	.619E+06	.206E+06
11.000	.500	40.000	.375	.127E+07	.424E+06
11.000	.625	40.000	.375	.222E+07	.740E+06
11.000	.750	40.000	.375	.350E+07	.117E+07
11.000	1.000	40.000	.375	.719E+07	.240E+07
11.000	1.250	40.000	.375	.126E+08	.419E+07
11.000	1.500	40.000	.375	.198E+08	.661E+07
11.000	1.750	40.000	.375	.291E+08	.971E+07
11.000	2.000	40.000	.375	.407E+08	.136E+08
12.000	.250	2.375	.154	.108E+05	.360E+04
12.000	.375	2.375	.154	.298E+05	.992E+04
12.000	.500	2.375	.154	.611E+05	.204E+05
12.000	.625	2.375	.154	.107E+06	.356E+05
12.000	.750	2.375	.154	.168E+06	.561E+05
12.000	1.000	2.375	.154	.346E+06	.115E+06
12.000	1.250	2.375	.154	.604E+06	.201E+06
12.000	1.500	2.375	.154	.952E+06	.317E+06
12.000	1.750	2.375	.154	.140E+07	.467E+06
12.000	2.000	2.375	.154	.195E+07	.652E+06
12.000	.250	3.500	.216	.161E+05	.536E+04
12.000	.375	3.500	.216	.443E+05	.148E+05
12.000	.500	3.500	.216	.909E+05	.303E+05
12.000	.625	3.500	.216	.159E+06	.529E+05
12.000	.750	3.500	.216	.250E+06	.835E+05
12.000	1.000	3.500	.216	.514E+06	.171E+06
12.000	1.250	3.500	.216	.898E+06	.299E+06
12.000	1.500	3.500	.216	.142E+07	.472E+06
12.000	1.750	3.500	.216	.208E+07	.694E+06
12.000	2.000	3.500	.216	.291E+07	.970E+06
12.000	.250	4.500	.237	.212E+05	.708E+04
12.000	.375	4.500	.237	.585E+05	.195E+05
12.000	.500	4.500	.237	.120E+06	.400E+05
12.000	.625	4.500	.237	.210E+06	.700E+05
12.000	.750	4.500	.237	.331E+06	.110E+06

Table 6-1
Continued

ROTA STIFF CALCULATION, CYL. VESSEL

VESSEL OD,FT	VESSEL TCK,IN	NOZZLE OD,IN	NOZZLE TCK,IN STD	ROT STIF IN.LB/DEG INPLANE LONGI	OUTPLANE CIRCU
12.000	1.000	4.500	.237	.680E+06	.227E+06
12.000	1.250	4.500	.237	.119E+07	.396E+06
12.000	1.500	4.500	.237	.187E+07	.624E+06
12.000	1.750	4.500	.237	.275E+07	.918E+06
12.000	2.000	4.500	.237	.384E+07	.128E+07
12.000	.250	6.625	.280	.323E+05	.108E+05
12.000	.375	6.625	.280	.889E+05	.296E+05
12.000	.500	6.625	.280	.183E+06	.608E+05
12.000	.625	6.625	.280	.319E+06	.106E+06
12.000	.750	6.625	.280	.503E+06	.168E+06
12.000	1.000	6.625	.280	.103E+07	.344E+06
12.000	1.250	6.625	.280	.180E+07	.601E+06
12.000	1.500	6.625	.280	.285E+07	.949E+06
12.000	1.750	6.625	.280	.418E+07	.139E+07
12.000	2.000	6.625	.280	.584E+07	.195E+07
12.000	.250	8.625	.322	.426E+05	.142E+05
12.000	.375	8.625	.322	.118E+06	.392E+05
12.000	.500	8.625	.322	.241E+06	.804E+05
12.000	.625	8.625	.322	.421E+06	.140E+06
12.000	.750	8.625	.322	.665E+06	.222E+06
12.000	1.000	8.625	.322	.136E+07	.455E+06
12.000	1.250	8.625	.322	.238E+07	.795E+06
12.000	1.500	8.625	.322	.376E+07	.125E+07
12.000	1.750	8.625	.322	.553E+07	.184E+07
12.000	2.000	8.625	.322	.772E+07	.257E+07
12.000	.250	10.750	.365	.537E+05	.179E+05
12.000	.375	10.750	.365	.148E+06	.493E+05
12.000	.500	10.750	.365	.304E+06	.101E+06
12.000	.625	10.750	.365	.531E+06	.177E+06
12.000	.750	10.750	.365	.837E+06	.279E+06
12.000	1.000	10.750	.365	.172E+07	.573E+06
12.000	1.250	10.750	.365	.300E+07	.100E+07
12.000	1.500	10.750	.365	.474E+07	.158E+07
12.000	1.750	10.750	.365	.696E+07	.232E+07
12.000	2.000	10.750	.365	.972E+07	.324E+07
12.000	.250	12.750	.375	.646E+05	.215E+05
12.000	.375	12.750	.375	.178E+06	.593E+05
12.000	.500	12.750	.375	.365E+06	.122E+06
12.000	.625	12.750	.375	.638E+06	.213E+06
12.000	.750	12.750	.375	.101E+07	.336E+06
12.000	1.000	12.750	.375	.207E+07	.689E+06
12.000	1.250	12.750	.375	.361E+07	.120E+07
12.000	1.500	12.750	.375	.569E+07	.190E+07
12.000	1.750	12.750	.375	.837E+07	.279E+07
12.000	2.000	12.750	.375	.117E+08	.390E+07
12.000	.250	14.000	.375	.715E+05	.238E+05
12.000	.375	14.000	.375	.197E+06	.656E+05
12.000	.500	14.000	.375	.404E+06	.135E+06
12.000	.625	14.000	.375	.706E+06	.235E+06
12.000	.750	14.000	.375	.111E+07	.371E+06
12.000	1.000	14.000	.375	.229E+07	.762E+06
12.000	1.250	14.000	.375	.400E+07	.133E+07
12.000	1.500	14.000	.375	.630E+07	.210E+07
12.000	1.750	14.000	.375	.926E+07	.309E+07
12.000	2.000	14.000	.375	.129E+08	.431E+07
12.000	.250	16.000	.375	.825E+05	.275E+05
12.000	.375	16.000	.375	.227E+06	.758E+05
12.000	.500	16.000	.375	.467E+06	.156E+06
12.000	.625	16.000	.375	.815E+06	.272E+06
12.000	.750	16.000	.375	.129E+07	.429E+06
12.000	1.000	16.000	.375	.264E+07	.880E+06

Table 6-1
Continued

ROTA STIFF CALCULATION, CYL. VESSEL

VESSEL OD,FT	VESSEL TCK,IN	NOZZLE OD,IN	NOZZLE TCK,IN STD	ROT STIF IN.LB/DEG INPLANE LONGI	OUTPLANE CIRCU
12.000	1.250	16.000	.375	.461E+07	.154E+07
12.000	1.500	16.000	.375	.728E+07	.243E+07
12.000	1.750	16.000	.375	.107E+08	.357E+07
12.000	2.000	16.000	.375	.149E+08	.498E+07
12.000	.250	18.000	.375	.936E+05	.312E+05
12.000	.375	18.000	.375	.258E+06	.859E+05
12.000	.500	18.000	.375	.529E+06	.176E+06
12.000	.625	18.000	.375	.924E+06	.308E+06
12.000	.750	18.000	.375	.146E+07	.486E+06
12.000	1.000	18.000	.375	.299E+07	.998E+06
12.000	1.250	18.000	.375	.523E+07	.174E+07
12.000	1.500	18.000	.375	.825E+07	.275E+07
12.000	1.750	18.000	.375	.121E+08	.404E+07
12.000	2.000	18.000	.375	.169E+08	.564E+07
12.000	.250	20.000	.375	.105E+06	.349E+05
12.000	.375	20.000	.375	.288E+06	.961E+05
12.000	.500	20.000	.375	.592E+06	.197E+06
12.000	.625	20.000	.375	.103E+07	.345E+06
12.000	.750	20.000	.375	.163E+07	.544E+06
12.000	1.000	20.000	.375	.335E+07	.112E+07
12.000	1.250	20.000	.375	.585E+07	.195E+07
12.000	1.500	20.000	.375	.922E+07	.307E+07
12.000	1.750	20.000	.375	.136E+08	.452E+07
12.000	2.000	20.000	.375	.189E+08	.631E+07
12.000	.250	22.000	.375	.116E+06	.386E+05
12.000	.375	22.000	.375	.319E+06	.106E+06
12.000	.500	22.000	.375	.654E+06	.218E+06
12.000	.625	22.000	.375	.114E+07	.381E+06
12.000	.750	22.000	.375	.180E+07	.601E+06
12.000	1.000	22.000	.375	.370E+07	.123E+07
12.000	1.250	22.000	.375	.647E+07	.216E+07
12.000	1.500	22.000	.375	.102E+08	.340E+07
12.000	1.750	22.000	.375	.150E+08	.500E+07
12.000	2.000	22.000	.375	.209E+08	.698E+07
12.000	.250	24.000	.375	.127E+06	.422E+05
12.000	.375	24.000	.375	.349E+06	.116E+06
12.000	.500	24.000	.375	.717E+06	.239E+06
12.000	.625	24.000	.375	.125E+07	.417E+06
12.000	.750	24.000	.375	.198E+07	.658E+06
12.000	1.000	24.000	.375	.405E+07	.135E+07
12.000	1.250	24.000	.375	.708E+07	.236E+07
12.000	1.500	24.000	.375	.112E+08	.372E+07
12.000	1.750	24.000	.375	.164E+08	.548E+07
12.000	2.000	24.000	.375	.229E+08	.765E+07
12.000	.250	26.000	.375	.138E+06	.459E+05
12.000	.375	26.000	.375	.380E+06	.127E+06
12.000	.500	26.000	.375	.779E+06	.260E+06
12.000	.625	26.000	.375	.136E+07	.454E+06
12.000	.750	26.000	.375	.215E+07	.716E+06
12.000	1.000	26.000	.375	.441E+07	.147E+07
12.000	1.250	26.000	.375	.770E+07	.257E+07
12.000	1.500	26.000	.375	.121E+08	.405E+07
12.000	1.750	26.000	.375	.179E+08	.595E+07
12.000	2.000	26.000	.375	.249E+08	.831E+07
12.000	.250	28.000	.375	.149E+06	.496E+05
12.000	.375	28.000	.375	.410E+06	.137E+06
12.000	.500	28.000	.375	.842E+06	.281E+06
12.000	.625	28.000	.375	.147E+07	.490E+06
12.000	.750	28.000	.375	.232E+07	.773E+06
12.000	1.000	28.000	.375	.476E+07	.159E+07
12.000	1.250	28.000	.375	.832E+07	.277E+07

Table 6-1
Continued

ROTA STIFF CALCULATION, CYL. VESSEL

VESSEL OD,FT	VESSEL TCK,IN	NOZZLE OD,IN	NOZZLE TCK,IN STD	ROT STIF IN.LB/DEG INPLANE LONGI	OUTPLANE CIRCU
12.000	1.500	28.000	.375	.131E+08	.437E+07
12.000	1.750	28.000	.375	.193E+08	.643E+07
12.000	2.000	28.000	.375	.269E+08	.898E+07
12.000	.250	30.000	.375	.160E+06	.533E+05
12.000	.375	30.000	.375	.441E+06	.147E+06
12.000	.500	30.000	.375	.904E+06	.301E+06
12.000	.625	30.000	.375	.158E+07	.527E+06
12.000	.750	30.000	.375	.249E+07	.831E+06
12.000	1.000	30.000	.375	.512E+07	.171E+07
12.000	1.250	30.000	.375	.894E+07	.298E+07
12.000	1.500	30.000	.375	.141E+08	.470E+07
12.000	1.750	30.000	.375	.207E+08	.691E+07
12.000	2.000	30.000	.375	.289E+08	.965E+07
12.000	.250	32.000	.375	.171E+06	.570E+05
12.000	.375	32.000	.375	.471E+06	.157E+06
12.000	.500	32.000	.375	.967E+06	.322E+06
12.000	.625	32.000	.375	.169E+07	.563E+06
12.000	.750	32.000	.375	.266E+07	.888E+06
12.000	1.000	32.000	.375	.547E+07	.182E+07
12.000	1.250	32.000	.375	.956E+07	.319E+07
12.000	1.500	32.000	.375	.151E+08	.502E+07
12.000	1.750	32.000	.375	.222E+08	.739E+07
12.000	2.000	32.000	.375	.309E+08	.103E+08
12.000	.250	36.000	.375	.193E+06	.644E+05
12.000	.375	36.000	.375	.532E+06	.177E+06
12.000	.500	36.000	.375	.109E+07	.364E+06
12.000	.625	36.000	.375	.191E+07	.636E+06
12.000	.750	36.000	.375	.301E+07	.100E+07
12.000	1.000	36.000	.375	.618E+07	.206E+07
12.000	1.250	36.000	.375	.108E+08	.360E+07
12.000	1.500	36.000	.375	.170E+08	.568E+07
12.000	1.750	36.000	.375	.250E+08	.834E+07
12.000	2.000	36.000	.375	.349E+08	.116E+08
12.000	.250	40.000	.375	.215E+06	.717E+05
12.000	.375	40.000	.375	.593E+06	.198E+06
12.000	.500	40.000	.375	.122E+07	.406E+06
12.000	.625	40.000	.375	.213E+07	.709E+06
12.000	.750	40.000	.375	.335E+07	.112E+07
12.000	1.000	40.000	.375	.689E+07	.230E+07
12.000	1.250	40.000	.375	.120E+08	.401E+07
12.000	1.500	40.000	.375	.190E+08	.633E+07
12.000	1.750	40.000	.375	.279E+08	.930E+07
12.000	2.000	40.000	.375	.390E+08	.130E+08
13.000	.250	2.375	.154	.104E+05	.346E+04
13.000	.375	2.375	.154	.286E+05	.953E+04
13.000	.500	2.375	.154	.587E+05	.196E+05
13.000	.625	2.375	.154	.103E+06	.342E+05
13.000	.750	2.375	.154	.162E+06	.539E+05
13.000	1.000	2.375	.154	.332E+06	.111E+06
13.000	1.250	2.375	.154	.580E+06	.193E+06
13.000	1.500	2.375	.154	.915E+06	.305E+06
13.000	1.750	2.375	.154	.135E+07	.448E+06
13.000	2.000	2.375	.154	.188E+07	.626E+06
13.000	.250	3.500	.216	.154E+05	.515E+04
13.000	.375	3.500	.216	.425E+05	.142E+05
13.000	.500	3.500	.216	.873E+05	.291E+05
13.000	.625	3.500	.216	.153E+06	.509E+05
13.000	.750	3.500	.216	.241E+06	.802E+05
13.000	1.000	3.500	.216	.494E+06	.165E+06

Table 6-1
Continued

ROTA STIFF CALCULATION, CYL. VESSEL

VESSEL OD,FT	VESSEL TCK,IN	NOZZLE OD,IN	NOZZLE TCK,IN STD	ROT STIF IN.LB/DEG INPLANE LONGI	OUTPLANE CIRCU
13.000	1.250	3.500	.216	.863E+06	.288E+06
13.000	1.500	3.500	.216	.136E+07	.454E+06
13.000	1.750	3.500	.216	.200E+07	.667E+06
13.000	2.000	3.500	.216	.279E+07	.932E+06
13.000	.250	4.500	.237	.204E+05	.680E+04
13.000	.375	4.500	.237	.562E+05	.187E+05
13.000	.500	4.500	.237	.115E+06	.385E+05
13.000	.625	4.500	.237	.202E+06	.672E+05
13.000	.750	4.500	.237	.318E+06	.106E+06
13.000	1.000	4.500	.237	.653E+06	.218E+06
13.000	1.250	4.500	.237	.114E+07	.380E+06
13.000	1.500	4.500	.237	.180E+07	.600E+06
13.000	1.750	4.500	.237	.265E+07	.882E+06
13.000	2.000	4.500	.237	.369E+07	.123E+07
13.000	.250	6.625	.280	.310E+05	.103E+05
13.000	.375	6.625	.280	.854E+05	.285E+05
13.000	.500	6.625	.280	.175E+06	.585E+05
13.000	.625	6.625	.280	.306E+06	.102E+06
13.000	.750	6.625	.280	.483E+06	.161E+06
13.000	1.000	6.625	.280	.992E+06	.331E+06
13.000	1.250	6.625	.280	.173E+07	.578E+06
13.000	1.500	6.625	.280	.273E+07	.911E+06
13.000	1.750	6.625	.280	.402E+07	.134E+07
13.000	2.000	6.625	.280	.561E+07	.187E+07
13.000	.250	8.625	.322	.410E+05	.137E+05
13.000	.375	8.625	.322	.113E+06	.376E+05
13.000	.500	8.625	.322	.232E+06	.773E+05
13.000	.625	8.625	.322	.405E+06	.135E+06
13.000	.750	8.625	.322	.639E+06	.213E+06
13.000	1.000	8.625	.322	.131E+07	.437E+06
13.000	1.250	8.625	.322	.229E+07	.763E+06
13.000	1.500	8.625	.322	.361E+07	.120E+07
13.000	1.750	8.625	.322	.531E+07	.177E+07
13.000	2.000	8.625	.322	.742E+07	.247E+07
13.000	.250	10.750	.365	.516E+05	.172E+05
13.000	.375	10.750	.365	.142E+06	.474E+05
13.000	.500	10.750	.365	.292E+06	.973E+05
13.000	.625	10.750	.365	.510E+06	.170E+06
13.000	.750	10.750	.365	.804E+06	.268E+06
13.000	1.000	10.750	.365	.165E+07	.550E+06
13.000	1.250	10.750	.365	.288E+07	.961E+06
13.000	1.500	10.750	.365	.455E+07	.152E+07
13.000	1.750	10.750	.365	.669E+07	.223E+07
13.000	2.000	10.750	.365	.934E+07	.311E+07
13.000	.250	12.750	.375	.620E+05	.207E+05
13.000	.375	12.750	.375	.171E+06	.570E+05
13.000	.500	12.750	.375	.351E+06	.117E+06
13.000	.625	12.750	.375	.613E+06	.204E+06
13.000	.750	12.750	.375	.967E+06	.322E+06
13.000	1.000	12.750	.375	.199E+07	.662E+06
13.000	1.250	12.750	.375	.347E+07	.116E+07
13.000	1.500	12.750	.375	.547E+07	.182E+07
13.000	1.750	12.750	.375	.804E+07	.268E+07
13.000	2.000	12.750	.375	.112E+08	.374E+07
13.000	.250	14.000	.375	.687E+05	.229E+05
13.000	.375	14.000	.375	.189E+06	.631E+05
13.000	.500	14.000	.375	.388E+06	.129E+06
13.000	.625	14.000	.375	.679E+06	.226E+06
13.000	.750	14.000	.375	.107E+07	.357E+06
13.000	1.000	14.000	.375	.220E+07	.732E+06
13.000	1.250	14.000	.375	.384E+07	.128E+07

Table 6-1
Continued

ROTA STIFF CALCULATION, CYL. VESSEL

VESSEL OD,FT	VESSEL TCK,IN	NOZZLE OD,IN	NOZZLE TCK,IN STD	ROT STIF IN.LB/DEG INPLANE LONGI	OUTPLANE CIRCU
13.000	1.500	14.000	.375	.605E+07	.202E+07
13.000	1.750	14.000	.375	.890E+07	.297E+07
13.000	2.000	14.000	.375	.124E+08	.414E+07
13.000	.250	16.000	.375	.793E+05	.264E+05
13.000	.375	16.000	.375	.218E+06	.728E+05
13.000	.500	16.000	.375	.448E+06	.149E+06
13.000	.625	16.000	.375	.783E+06	.261E+06
13.000	.750	16.000	.375	.124E+07	.412E+06
13.000	1.000	16.000	.375	.254E+07	.846E+06
13.000	1.250	16.000	.375	.443E+07	.148E+07
13.000	1.500	16.000	.375	.699E+07	.233E+07
13.000	1.750	16.000	.375	.103E+08	.343E+07
13.000	2.000	16.000	.375	.143E+08	.478E+07
13.000	.250	18.000	.375	.899E+05	.300E+05
13.000	.375	18.000	.375	.248E+06	.826E+05
13.000	.500	18.000	.375	.508E+06	.169E+06
13.000	.625	18.000	.375	.888E+06	.296E+06
13.000	.750	18.000	.375	.140E+07	.467E+06
13.000	1.000	18.000	.375	.288E+07	.959E+06
13.000	1.250	18.000	.375	.502E+07	.167E+07
13.000	1.500	18.000	.375	.793E+07	.264E+07
13.000	1.750	18.000	.375	.117E+08	.388E+07
13.000	2.000	18.000	.375	.163E+08	.542E+07
13.000	.250	20.000	.375	.100E+06	.335E+05
13.000	.375	20.000	.375	.277E+06	.923E+05
13.000	.500	20.000	.375	.569E+06	.190E+06
13.000	.625	20.000	.375	.993E+06	.331E+06
13.000	.750	20.000	.375	.157E+07	.522E+06
13.000	1.000	20.000	.375	.322E+07	.107E+07
13.000	1.250	20.000	.375	.562E+07	.187E+07
13.000	1.500	20.000	.375	.886E+07	.295E+07
13.000	1.750	20.000	.375	.130E+08	.434E+07
13.000	2.000	20.000	.375	.182E+08	.606E+07
13.000	.250	22.000	.375	.111E+06	.370E+05
13.000	.375	22.000	.375	.306E+06	.102E+06
13.000	.500	22.000	.375	.629E+06	.210E+06
13.000	.625	22.000	.375	.110E+07	.366E+06
13.000	.750	22.000	.375	.173E+07	.577E+06
13.000	1.000	22.000	.375	.356E+07	.119E+07
13.000	1.250	22.000	.375	.621E+07	.207E+07
13.000	1.500	22.000	.375	.980E+07	.327E+07
13.000	1.750	22.000	.375	.144E+08	.480E+07
13.000	2.000	22.000	.375	.201E+08	.670E+07
13.000	.250	24.000	.375	.122E+06	.406E+05
13.000	.375	24.000	.375	.335E+06	.112E+06
13.000	.500	24.000	.375	.689E+06	.230E+06
13.000	.625	24.000	.375	.120E+07	.401E+06
13.000	.750	24.000	.375	.190E+07	.633E+06
13.000	1.000	24.000	.375	.390E+07	.130E+07
13.000	1.250	24.000	.375	.681E+07	.227E+07
13.000	1.500	24.000	.375	.107E+08	.358E+07
13.000	1.750	24.000	.375	.158E+08	.526E+07
13.000	2.000	24.000	.375	.220E+08	.735E+07
13.000	.250	26.000	.375	.132E+06	.441E+05
13.000	.375	26.000	.375	.365E+06	.122E+06
13.000	.500	26.000	.375	.749E+06	.250E+06
13.000	.625	26.000	.375	.131E+07	.436E+06
13.000	.750	26.000	.375	.206E+07	.688E+06
13.000	1.000	26.000	.375	.424E+07	.141E+07
13.000	1.250	26.000	.375	.740E+07	.247E+07
13.000	1.500	26.000	.375	.117E+08	.389E+07

Table 6-1
Continued

ROTA STIFF CALCULATION, CYL. VESSEL

VESSEL OD,FT	VESSEL TCK,IN	NOZZLE OD,IN	NOZZLE TCK,IN STD	ROT STIF IN.LB/DEG INPLANE LONGI	OUTPLANE CIRCU
13.000	1.750	26.000	.375	.172E+08	.572E+07
13.000	2.000	26.000	.375	.240E+08	.799E+07
13.000	.250	28.000	.375	.143E+06	.477E+05
13.000	.375	28.000	.375	.394E+06	.131E+06
13.000	.500	28.000	.375	.809E+06	.270E+06
13.000	.625	28.000	.375	.141E+07	.471E+06
13.000	.750	28.000	.375	.223E+07	.743E+06
13.000	1.000	28.000	.375	.458E+07	.153E+07
13.000	1.250	28.000	.375	.799E+07	.266E+07
13.000	1.500	28.000	.375	.126E+08	.420E+07
13.000	1.750	28.000	.375	.185E+08	.618E+07
13.000	2.000	28.000	.375	.259E+08	.863E+07
13.000	.250	30.000	.375	.154E+06	.512E+05
13.000	.375	30.000	.375	.423E+06	.141E+06
13.000	.500	30.000	.375	.869E+06	.290E+06
13.000	.625	30.000	.375	.152E+07	.506E+06
13.000	.750	30.000	.375	.239E+07	.798E+06
13.000	1.000	30.000	.375	.492E+07	.164E+07
13.000	1.250	30.000	.375	.859E+07	.286E+07
13.000	1.500	30.000	.375	.135E+08	.452E+07
13.000	1.750	30.000	.375	.199E+08	.664E+07
13.000	2.000	30.000	.375	.278E+08	.927E+07
13.000	.250	32.000	.375	.164E+06	.547E+05
13.000	.375	32.000	.375	.453E+06	.151E+06
13.000	.500	32.000	.375	.929E+06	.310E+06
13.000	.625	32.000	.375	.162E+07	.541E+06
13.000	.750	32.000	.375	.256E+07	.853E+06
13.000	1.000	32.000	.375	.526E+07	.175E+07
13.000	1.250	32.000	.375	.918E+07	.306E+07
13.000	1.500	32.000	.375	.145E+08	.483E+07
13.000	1.750	32.000	.375	.213E+08	.710E+07
13.000	2.000	32.000	.375	.297E+08	.991E+07
13.000	.250	36.000	.375	.185E+06	.618E+05
13.000	.375	36.000	.375	.511E+06	.170E+06
13.000	.500	36.000	.375	.105E+07	.350E+06
13.000	.625	36.000	.375	.183E+07	.611E+06
13.000	.750	36.000	.375	.289E+07	.964E+06
13.000	1.000	36.000	.375	.594E+07	.198E+07
13.000	1.250	36.000	.375	.104E+08	.346E+07
13.000	1.500	36.000	.375	.164E+08	.545E+07
13.000	1.750	36.000	.375	.240E+08	.802E+07
13.000	2.000	36.000	.375	.336E+08	.112E+08
13.000	.250	40.000	.375	.207E+06	.689E+05
13.000	.375	40.000	.375	.570E+06	.190E+06
13.000	.500	40.000	.375	.117E+07	.390E+06
13.000	.625	40.000	.375	.204E+07	.681E+06
13.000	.750	40.000	.375	.322E+07	.107E+07
13.000	1.000	40.000	.375	.662E+07	.221E+07
13.000	1.250	40.000	.375	.116E+08	.385E+07
13.000	1.500	40.000	.375	.182E+08	.608E+07
13.000	1.750	40.000	.375	.268E+08	.893E+07
13.000	2.000	40.000	.375	.374E+08	.125E+08
13.000	.250	48.000	.375	.249E+06	.831E+05
13.000	.375	48.000	.375	.687E+06	.229E+06
13.000	.500	48.000	.375	.141E+07	.470E+06
13.000	.625	48.000	.375	.246E+07	.821E+06
13.000	.750	48.000	.375	.389E+07	.130E+07
13.000	1.000	48.000	.375	.798E+07	.266E+07
13.000	1.250	48.000	.375	.139E+08	.464E+07
13.000	1.500	48.000	.375	.220E+08	.733E+07
13.000	1.750	48.000	.375	.323E+08	.108E+08
13.000	2.000	48.000	.375	.451E+08	.150E+08

Table 6-1
Continued

ROTA STIFF CALCULATION, CYL. VESSEL

VESSEL OD,FT	VESSEL TCK,IN	NOZZLE OD,IN	NOZZLE TCK,IN STD	ROT STIF IN.LB/DEG INPLANE LONGI	OUTPLANE CIRCU
14.000	.250	2.375	.154	.100E+05	.333E+04
14.000	.375	2.375	.154	.276E+05	.918E+04
14.000	.500	2.375	.154	.566E+05	.189E+05
14.000	.625	2.375	.154	.988E+05	.329E+05
14.000	.750	2.375	.154	.156E+06	.520E+05
14.000	1.000	2.375	.154	.320E+06	.107E+06
14.000	1.250	2.375	.154	.559E+06	.186E+06
14.000	1.500	2.375	.154	.882E+06	.294E+06
14.000	1.750	2.375	.154	.130E+07	.432E+06
14.000	2.000	2.375	.154	.181E+07	.603E+06
14.000	.250	3.500	.216	.149E+05	.496E+04
14.000	.375	3.500	.216	.410E+05	.137E+05
14.000	.500	3.500	.216	.842E+05	.281E+05
14.000	.625	3.500	.216	.147E+06	.490E+05
14.000	.750	3.500	.216	.232E+06	.773E+05
14.000	1.000	3.500	.216	.476E+06	.159E+06
14.000	1.250	3.500	.216	.832E+06	.277E+06
14.000	1.500	3.500	.216	.131E+07	.437E+06
14.000	1.750	3.500	.216	.193E+07	.643E+06
14.000	2.000	3.500	.216	.269E+07	.898E+06
14.000	.250	4.500	.237	.197E+05	.655E+04
14.000	.375	4.500	.237	.542E+05	.181E+05
14.000	.500	4.500	.237	.111E+06	.371E+05
14.000	.625	4.500	.237	.194E+06	.648E+05
14.000	.750	4.500	.237	.306E+06	.102E+06
14.000	1.000	4.500	.237	.629E+06	.210E+06
14.000	1.250	4.500	.237	.110E+07	.366E+06
14.000	1.500	4.500	.237	.173E+07	.578E+06
14.000	1.750	4.500	.237	.255E+07	.850E+06
14.000	2.000	4.500	.237	.356E+07	.119E+07
14.000	.250	6.625	.280	.299E+05	.996E+04
14.000	.375	6.625	.280	.823E+05	.274E+05
14.000	.500	6.625	.280	.169E+06	.563E+05
14.000	.625	6.625	.280	.295E+06	.984E+05
14.000	.750	6.625	.280	.466E+06	.155E+06
14.000	1.000	6.625	.280	.956E+06	.319E+06
14.000	1.250	6.625	.280	.167E+07	.557E+06
14.000	1.500	6.625	.280	.263E+07	.878E+06
14.000	1.750	6.625	.280	.387E+07	.129E+07
14.000	2.000	6.625	.280	.541E+07	.180E+07
14.000	.250	8.625	.322	.395E+05	.132E+05
14.000	.375	8.625	.322	.109E+06	.363E+05
14.000	.500	8.625	.322	.223E+06	.744E+05
14.000	.625	8.625	.322	.390E+06	.130E+06
14.000	.750	8.625	.322	.615E+06	.205E+06
14.000	1.000	8.625	.322	.126E+07	.421E+06
14.000	1.250	8.625	.322	.221E+07	.736E+06
14.000	1.500	8.625	.322	.348E+07	.116E+07
14.000	1.750	8.625	.322	.512E+07	.171E+07
14.000	2.000	8.625	.322	.715E+07	.238E+07
14.000	.250	10.750	.365	.497E+05	.166E+05
14.000	.375	10.750	.365	.137E+06	.457E+05
14.000	.500	10.750	.365	.281E+06	.937E+05
14.000	.625	10.750	.365	.491E+06	.164E+06
14.000	.750	10.750	.365	.775E+06	.258E+06
14.000	1.000	10.750	.365	.159E+07	.530E+06
14.000	1.250	10.750	.365	.278E+07	.926E+06
14.000	1.500	10.750	.365	.438E+07	.146E+07
14.000	1.750	10.750	.365	.645E+07	.215E+07
14.000	2.000	10.750	.365	.900E+07	.300E+07
14.000	.250	12.750	.375	.598E+05	.199E+05
14.000	.375	12.750	.375	.165E+06	.549E+05
14.000	.500	12.750	.375	.338E+06	.113E+06

Table 6-1
Continued

ROTA STIFF CALCULATION, CYL. VESSEL

VESSEL OD,FT	VESSEL TCK,IN	NOZZLE OD,IN	NOZZLE TCK,IN STD	ROT STIF IN.LB/DEG INPLANE LONGI	OUTPLANE CIRCU
14.000	.625	12.750	.375	.591E+06	.197E+06
14.000	.750	12.750	.375	.932E+06	.311E+06
14.000	1.000	12.750	.375	.191E+07	.638E+06
14.000	1.250	12.750	.375	.334E+07	.111E+07
14.000	1.500	12.750	.375	.527E+07	.176E+07
14.000	1.750	12.750	.375	.775E+07	.258E+07
14.000	2.000	12.750	.375	.108E+08	.361E+07
14.000	.250	14.000	.375	.662E+05	.221E+05
14.000	.375	14.000	.375	.182E+06	.608E+05
14.000	.500	14.000	.375	.374E+06	.125E+06
14.000	.625	14.000	.375	.654E+06	.218E+06
14.000	.750	14.000	.375	.103E+07	.344E+06
14.000	1.000	14.000	.375	.212E+07	.706E+06
14.000	1.250	14.000	.375	.370E+07	.123E+07
14.000	1.500	14.000	.375	.583E+07	.194E+07
14.000	1.750	14.000	.375	.858E+07	.286E+07
14.000	2.000	14.000	.375	.120E+08	.399E+07
14.000	.250	16.000	.375	.764E+05	.255E+05
14.000	.375	16.000	.375	.210E+06	.702E+05
14.000	.500	16.000	.375	.432E+06	.144E+06
14.000	.625	16.000	.375	.755E+06	.252E+06
14.000	.750	16.000	.375	.119E+07	.397E+06
14.000	1.000	16.000	.375	.244E+07	.815E+06
14.000	1.250	16.000	.375	.427E+07	.142E+07
14.000	1.500	16.000	.375	.674E+07	.225E+07
14.000	1.750	16.000	.375	.990E+07	.330E+07
14.000	2.000	16.000	.375	.138E+08	.461E+07
14.000	.250	18.000	.375	.866E+05	.289E+05
14.000	.375	18.000	.375	.239E+06	.796E+05
14.000	.500	18.000	.375	.490E+06	.163E+06
14.000	.625	18.000	.375	.856E+06	.285E+06
14.000	.750	18.000	.375	.135E+07	.450E+06
14.000	1.000	18.000	.375	.277E+07	.924E+06
14.000	1.250	18.000	.375	.484E+07	.161E+07
14.000	1.500	18.000	.375	.764E+07	.255E+07
14.000	1.750	18.000	.375	.112E+08	.374E+07
14.000	2.000	18.000	.375	.157E+08	.523E+07
14.000	.250	20.000	.375	.968E+05	.323E+05
14.000	.375	20.000	.375	.267E+06	.890E+05
14.000	.500	20.000	.375	.548E+06	.183E+06
14.000	.625	20.000	.375	.957E+06	.319E+06
14.000	.750	20.000	.375	.151E+07	.503E+06
14.000	1.000	20.000	.375	.310E+07	.103E+07
14.000	1.250	20.000	.375	.541E+07	.180E+07
14.000	1.500	20.000	.375	.854E+07	.285E+07
14.000	1.750	20.000	.375	.126E+08	.418E+07
14.000	2.000	20.000	.375	.175E+08	.584E+07
14.000	.250	22.000	.375	.107E+06	.357E+05
14.000	.375	22.000	.375	.295E+06	.984E+05
14.000	.500	22.000	.375	.606E+06	.202E+06
14.000	.625	22.000	.375	.106E+07	.353E+06
14.000	.750	22.000	.375	.167E+07	.556E+06
14.000	1.000	22.000	.375	.343E+07	.114E+07
14.000	1.250	22.000	.375	.599E+07	.200E+07
14.000	1.500	22.000	.375	.944E+07	.315E+07
14.000	1.750	22.000	.375	.139E+08	.463E+07
14.000	2.000	22.000	.375	.194E+08	.646E+07
14.000	.250	24.000	.375	.117E+06	.391E+05
14.000	.375	24.000	.375	.323E+06	.108E+06
14.000	.500	24.000	.375	.664E+06	.221E+06
14.000	.625	24.000	.375	.116E+07	.386E+06

Table 6-1
Continued

ROTA STIFF CALCULATION, CYL. VESSEL

VESSEL OD,FT	VESSEL TCK,IN	NOZZLE OD,IN	NOZZLE TCK,IN STD	ROT STIF IN.LB/DEG INPLANE LONGI	OUTPLANE CIRCU
14.000	.750	24.000	.375	.183E+07	.610E+06
14.000	1.000	24.000	.375	.375E+07	.125E+07
14.000	1.250	24.000	.375	.656E+07	.219E+07
14.000	1.500	24.000	.375	.103E+08	.345E+07
14.000	1.750	24.000	.375	.152E+08	.507E+07
14.000	2.000	24.000	.375	.212E+08	.708E+07
14.000	.250	26.000	.375	.128E+06	.425E+05
14.000	.375	26.000	.375	.351E+06	.117E+06
14.000	.500	26.000	.375	.722E+06	.241E+06
14.000	.625	26.000	.375	.126E+07	.420E+06
14.000	.750	26.000	.375	.199E+07	.663E+06
14.000	1.000	26.000	.375	.408E+07	.136E+07
14.000	1.250	26.000	.375	.713E+07	.238E+07
14.000	1.500	26.000	.375	.112E+08	.375E+07
14.000	1.750	26.000	.375	.165E+08	.551E+07
14.000	2.000	26.000	.375	.231E+08	.770E+07
14.000	.250	28.000	.375	.138E+06	.459E+05
14.000	.375	28.000	.375	.380E+06	.127E+06
14.000	.500	28.000	.375	.779E+06	.260E+06
14.000	.625	28.000	.375	.136E+07	.454E+06
14.000	.750	28.000	.375	.215E+07	.716E+06
14.000	1.000	28.000	.375	.441E+07	.147E+07
14.000	1.250	28.000	.375	.770E+07	.257E+07
14.000	1.500	28.000	.375	.122E+08	.405E+07
14.000	1.750	28.000	.375	.179E+08	.595E+07
14.000	2.000	28.000	.375	.249E+08	.831E+07
14.000	.250	30.000	.375	.148E+06	.493E+05
14.000	.375	30.000	.375	.408E+06	.136E+06
14.000	.500	30.000	.375	.837E+06	.279E+06
14.000	.625	30.000	.375	.146E+07	.488E+06
14.000	.750	30.000	.375	.231E+07	.769E+06
14.000	1.000	30.000	.375	.474E+07	.158E+07
14.000	1.250	30.000	.375	.827E+07	.276E+07
14.000	1.500	30.000	.375	.131E+08	.435E+07
14.000	1.750	30.000	.375	.192E+08	.640E+07
14.000	2.000	30.000	.375	.268E+08	.893E+07
14.000	.250	32.000	.375	.158E+06	.528E+05
14.000	.375	32.000	.375	.436E+06	.145E+06
14.000	.500	32.000	.375	.895E+06	.298E+06
14.000	.625	32.000	.375	.156E+07	.521E+06
14.000	.750	32.000	.375	.247E+07	.822E+06
14.000	1.000	32.000	.375	.506E+07	.169E+07
14.000	1.250	32.000	.375	.885E+07	.295E+07
14.000	1.500	32.000	.375	.140E+08	.465E+07
14.000	1.750	32.000	.375	.205E+08	.684E+07
14.000	2.000	32.000	.375	.286E+08	.955E+07
14.000	.250	36.000	.375	.179E+06	.596E+05
14.000	.375	36.000	.375	.493E+06	.164E+06
14.000	.500	36.000	.375	.101E+07	.337E+06
14.000	.625	36.000	.375	.177E+07	.589E+06
14.000	.750	36.000	.375	.279E+07	.929E+06
14.000	1.000	36.000	.375	.572E+07	.191E+07
14.000	1.250	36.000	.375	.999E+07	.333E+07
14.000	1.500	36.000	.375	.158E+08	.525E+07
14.000	1.750	36.000	.375	.232E+08	.772E+07
14.000	2.000	36.000	.375	.324E+08	.108E+08
14.000	.250	40.000	.375	.199E+06	.664E+05
14.000	.375	40.000	.375	.549E+06	.183E+06
14.000	.500	40.000	.375	.113E+07	.376E+06
14.000	.625	40.000	.375	.197E+07	.656E+06
14.000	.750	40.000	.375	.311E+07	.104E+07

Table 6-1
Continued

ROTA STIFF CALCULATION, CYL. VESSEL

VESSEL OD,FT	VESSEL TCK,IN	NOZZLE OD,IN	NOZZLE TCK,IN STD	ROT STIF IN.LB/DEG INPLANE LONGI	OUTPLANE CIRCU
14.000	1.000	40.000	.375	.638E+07	.213E+07
14.000	1.250	40.000	.375	.111E+08	.371E+07
14.000	1.500	40.000	.375	.176E+08	.586E+07
14.000	1.750	40.000	.375	.258E+08	.861E+07
14.000	2.000	40.000	.375	.361E+08	.120E+08
14.000	.250	48.000	.375	.240E+06	.801E+05
14.000	.375	48.000	.375	.662E+06	.221E+06
14.000	.500	48.000	.375	.136E+07	.453E+06
14.000	.625	48.000	.375	.237E+07	.791E+06
14.000	.750	48.000	.375	.374E+07	.125E+07
14.000	1.000	48.000	.375	.769E+07	.256E+07
14.000	1.250	48.000	.375	.134E+08	.448E+07
14.000	1.500	48.000	.375	.212E+08	.706E+07
14.000	1.750	48.000	.375	.311E+08	.104E+08
14.000	2.000	48.000	.375	.435E+08	.145E+08
15.000	.250	2.375	.154	.966E+04	.322E+04
15.000	.375	2.375	.154	.266E+05	.887E+04
15.000	.500	2.375	.154	.546E+05	.182E+05
15.000	.625	2.375	.154	.955E+05	.318E+05
15.000	.750	2.375	.154	.151E+06	.502E+05
15.000	1.000	2.375	.154	.309E+06	.103E+06
15.000	1.250	2.375	.154	.540E+06	.180E+06
15.000	1.500	2.375	.154	.852E+06	.284E+06
15.000	1.750	2.375	.154	.125E+07	.417E+06
15.000	2.000	2.375	.154	.175E+07	.583E+06
15.000	.250	3.500	.216	.144E+05	.479E+04
15.000	.375	3.500	.216	.396E+05	.132E+05
15.000	.500	3.500	.216	.813E+05	.271E+05
15.000	.625	3.500	.216	.142E+06	.473E+05
15.000	.750	3.500	.216	.224E+06	.747E+05
15.000	1.000	3.500	.216	.460E+06	.153E+06
15.000	1.250	3.500	.216	.803E+06	.268E+06
15.000	1.500	3.500	.216	.127E+07	.422E+06
15.000	1.750	3.500	.216	.186E+07	.621E+06
15.000	2.000	3.500	.216	.260E+07	.867E+06
15.000	.250	4.500	.237	.190E+05	.633E+04
15.000	.375	4.500	.237	.523E+05	.174E+05
15.000	.500	4.500	.237	.107E+06	.358E+05
15.000	.625	4.500	.237	.188E+06	.626E+05
15.000	.750	4.500	.237	.296E+06	.987E+05
15.000	1.000	4.500	.237	.608E+06	.203E+06
15.000	1.250	4.500	.237	.106E+07	.354E+06
15.000	1.500	4.500	.237	.167E+07	.558E+06
15.000	1.750	4.500	.237	.246E+07	.821E+06
15.000	2.000	4.500	.237	.344E+07	.115E+07
15.000	.250	6.625	.280	.289E+05	.962E+04
15.000	.375	6.625	.280	.795E+05	.265E+05
15.000	.500	6.625	.280	.163E+06	.544E+05
15.000	.625	6.625	.280	.285E+06	.951E+05
15.000	.750	6.625	.280	.450E+06	.150E+06
15.000	1.000	6.625	.280	.924E+06	.308E+06
15.000	1.250	6.625	.280	.161E+07	.538E+06
15.000	1.500	6.625	.280	.255E+07	.848E+06
15.000	1.750	6.625	.280	.374E+07	.125E+07
15.000	2.000	6.625	.280	.522E+07	.174E+07
15.000	.250	8.625	.322	.381E+05	.127E+05
15.000	.375	8.625	.322	.105E+06	.350E+05
15.000	.500	8.625	.322	.216E+06	.719E+05
15.000	.625	8.625	.322	.377E+06	.126E+06

Table 6-1
Continued

ROTA STIFF CALCULATION, CYL. VESSEL

VESSEL OD,FT	VESSEL TCK,IN	NOZZLE OD,IN	NOZZLE TCK,IN STD	ROT STIF IN.LB/DEG INPLANE LONGI	OUTPLANE CIRCU
15.000	.750	8.625	.322	.595E+06	.198E+06
15.000	1.000	8.625	.322	.122E+07	.407E+06
15.000	1.250	8.625	.322	.213E+07	.711E+06
15.000	1.500	8.625	.322	.336E+07	.112E+07
15.000	1.750	8.625	.322	.494E+07	.165E+07
15.000	2.000	8.625	.322	.690E+07	.230E+07
15.000	.250	10.750	.365	.480E+05	.160E+05
15.000	.375	10.750	.365	.132E+06	.441E+05
15.000	.500	10.750	.365	.272E+06	.906E+05
15.000	.625	10.750	.365	.475E+06	.158E+06
15.000	.750	10.750	.365	.749E+06	.250E+06
15.000	1.000	10.750	.365	.154E+07	.512E+06
15.000	1.250	10.750	.365	.268E+07	.895E+06
15.000	1.500	10.750	.365	.424E+07	.141E+07
15.000	1.750	10.750	.365	.623E+07	.208E+07
15.000	2.000	10.750	.365	.869E+07	.290E+07
15.000	.250	12.750	.375	.578E+05	.193E+05
15.000	.375	12.750	.375	.159E+06	.530E+05
15.000	.500	12.750	.375	.327E+06	.109E+06
15.000	.625	12.750	.375	.571E+06	.190E+06
15.000	.750	12.750	.375	.900E+06	.300E+06
15.000	1.000	12.750	.375	.185E+07	.616E+06
15.000	1.250	12.750	.375	.323E+07	.108E+07
15.000	1.500	12.750	.375	.509E+07	.170E+07
15.000	1.750	12.750	.375	.749E+07	.250E+07
15.000	2.000	12.750	.375	.105E+08	.348E+07
15.000	.250	14.000	.375	.639E+05	.213E+05
15.000	.375	14.000	.375	.176E+06	.587E+05
15.000	.500	14.000	.375	.362E+06	.121E+06
15.000	.625	14.000	.375	.632E+06	.211E+06
15.000	.750	14.000	.375	.996E+06	.332E+06
15.000	1.000	14.000	.375	.205E+07	.682E+06
15.000	1.250	14.000	.375	.357E+07	.119E+07
15.000	1.500	14.000	.375	.564E+07	.188E+07
15.000	1.750	14.000	.375	.829E+07	.276E+07
15.000	2.000	14.000	.375	.116E+08	.386E+07
15.000	.250	16.000	.375	.738E+05	.246E+05
15.000	.375	16.000	.375	.203E+06	.678E+05
15.000	.500	16.000	.375	.417E+06	.139E+06
15.000	.625	16.000	.375	.729E+06	.243E+06
15.000	.750	16.000	.375	.115E+07	.383E+06
15.000	1.000	16.000	.375	.236E+07	.787E+06
15.000	1.250	16.000	.375	.413E+07	.138E+07
15.000	1.500	16.000	.375	.651E+07	.217E+07
15.000	1.750	16.000	.375	.957E+07	.319E+07
15.000	2.000	16.000	.375	.134E+08	.445E+07
15.000	.250	18.000	.375	.837E+05	.279E+05
15.000	.375	18.000	.375	.231E+06	.769E+05
15.000	.500	18.000	.375	.473E+06	.158E+06
15.000	.625	18.000	.375	.827E+06	.276E+06
15.000	.750	18.000	.375	.130E+07	.435E+06
15.000	1.000	18.000	.375	.268E+07	.893E+06
15.000	1.250	18.000	.375	.468E+07	.156E+07
15.000	1.500	18.000	.375	.738E+07	.246E+07
15.000	1.750	18.000	.375	.108E+08	.362E+07
15.000	2.000	18.000	.375	.151E+08	.505E+07
15.000	.250	20.000	.375	.936E+05	.312E+05
15.000	.375	20.000	.375	.258E+06	.859E+05
15.000	.500	20.000	.375	.529E+06	.176E+06
15.000	.625	20.000	.375	.925E+06	.308E+06
15.000	.750	20.000	.375	.146E+07	.486E+06

Table 6-1
Continued

ROTA STIFF CALCULATION, CYL. VESSEL

VESSEL OD,FT	VESSEL TCK,IN	NOZZLE OD,IN	NOZZLE TCK,IN STD	ROT STIF IN.LB/DEG INPLANE LONGI	OUTPLANE CIRCU
15.000	1.000	20.000	.375	.299E+07	.998E+06
15.000	1.250	20.000	.375	.523E+07	.174E+07
15.000	1.500	20.000	.375	.825E+07	.275E+07
15.000	1.750	20.000	.375	.121E+08	.404E+07
15.000	2.000	20.000	.375	.169E+08	.565E+07
15.000	.250	22.000	.375	.103E+06	.345E+05
15.000	.375	22.000	.375	.285E+06	.950E+05
15.000	.500	22.000	.375	.585E+06	.195E+06
15.000	.625	22.000	.375	.102E+07	.341E+06
15.000	.750	22.000	.375	.161E+07	.538E+06
15.000	1.000	22.000	.375	.331E+07	.110E+07
15.000	1.250	22.000	.375	.578E+07	.193E+07
15.000	1.500	22.000	.375	.912E+07	.304E+07
15.000	1.750	22.000	.375	.134E+08	.447E+07
15.000	2.000	22.000	.375	.187E+08	.624E+07
15.000	.250	24.000	.375	.113E+06	.378E+05
15.000	.375	24.000	.375	.312E+06	.104E+06
15.000	.500	24.000	.375	.641E+06	.214E+06
15.000	.625	24.000	.375	.112E+07	.373E+06
15.000	.750	24.000	.375	.177E+07	.589E+06
15.000	1.000	24.000	.375	.363E+07	.121E+07
15.000	1.250	24.000	.375	.634E+07	.211E+07
15.000	1.500	24.000	.375	.999E+07	.333E+07
15.000	1.750	24.000	.375	.147E+08	.490E+07
15.000	2.000	24.000	.375	.205E+08	.684E+07
15.000	.250	26.000	.375	.123E+06	.411E+05
15.000	.375	26.000	.375	.340E+06	.113E+06
15.000	.500	26.000	.375	.697E+06	.232E+06
15.000	.625	26.000	.375	.122E+07	.406E+06
15.000	.750	26.000	.375	.192E+07	.640E+06
15.000	1.000	26.000	.375	.394E+07	.131E+07
15.000	1.250	26.000	.375	.689E+07	.230E+07
15.000	1.500	26.000	.375	.109E+08	.362E+07
15.000	1.750	26.000	.375	.160E+08	.532E+07
15.000	2.000	26.000	.375	.223E+08	.744E+07
15.000	.250	28.000	.375	.133E+06	.444E+05
15.000	.375	28.000	.375	.367E+06	.122E+06
15.000	.500	28.000	.375	.753E+06	.251E+06
15.000	.625	28.000	.375	.132E+07	.438E+06
15.000	.750	28.000	.375	.208E+07	.692E+06
15.000	1.000	28.000	.375	.426E+07	.142E+07
15.000	1.250	28.000	.375	.744E+07	.248E+07
15.000	1.500	28.000	.375	.117E+08	.391E+07
15.000	1.750	28.000	.375	.173E+08	.575E+07
15.000	2.000	28.000	.375	.241E+08	.803E+07
15.000	.250	30.000	.375	.143E+06	.477E+05
15.000	.375	30.000	.375	.394E+06	.131E+06
15.000	.500	30.000	.375	.809E+06	.270E+06
15.000	.625	30.000	.375	.141E+07	.471E+06
15.000	.750	30.000	.375	.223E+07	.743E+06
15.000	1.000	30.000	.375	.458E+07	.153E+07
15.000	1.250	30.000	.375	.799E+07	.266E+07
15.000	1.500	30.000	.375	.126E+08	.420E+07
15.000	1.750	30.000	.375	.185E+08	.618E+07
15.000	2.000	30.000	.375	.259E+08	.863E+07
15.000	.250	32.000	.375	.153E+06	.510E+05
15.000	.375	32.000	.375	.421E+06	.140E+06
15.000	.500	32.000	.375	.865E+06	.288E+06
15.000	.625	32.000	.375	.151E+07	.504E+06
15.000	.750	32.000	.375	.238E+07	.794E+06
15.000	1.000	32.000	.375	.489E+07	.163E+07

Table 6-1
Continued

ROTA STIFF CALCULATION, CYL. VESSEL

VESSEL OD,FT	VESSEL TCK,IN	NOZZLE OD,IN	NOZZLE TCK,IN STD	ROT STIF IN.LB/DEG INPLANE LONGI	OUTPLANE CIRCU
15.000	1.250	32.000	.375	.855E+07	.285E+07
15.000	1.500	32.000	.375	.135E+08	.449E+07
15.000	1.750	32.000	.375	.198E+08	.661E+07
15.000	2.000	32.000	.375	.277E+08	.923E+07
15.000	.250	36.000	.375	.173E+06	.576E+05
15.000	.375	36.000	.375	.476E+06	.159E+06
15.000	.500	36.000	.375	.977E+06	.326E+06
15.000	.625	36.000	.375	.171E+07	.569E+06
15.000	.750	36.000	.375	.269E+07	.897E+06
15.000	1.000	36.000	.375	.553E+07	.184E+07
15.000	1.250	36.000	.375	.965E+07	.322E+07
15.000	1.500	36.000	.375	.152E+08	.508E+07
15.000	1.750	36.000	.375	.224E+08	.746E+07
15.000	2.000	36.000	.375	.313E+08	.104E+08
15.000	.250	40.000	.375	.192E+06	.642E+05
15.000	.375	40.000	.375	.530E+06	.177E+06
15.000	.500	40.000	.375	.109E+07	.363E+06
15.000	.625	40.000	.375	.190E+07	.634E+06
15.000	.750	40.000	.375	.300E+07	.100E+07
15.000	1.000	40.000	.375	.616E+07	.205E+07
15.000	1.250	40.000	.375	.108E+08	.359E+07
15.000	1.500	40.000	.375	.170E+08	.566E+07
15.000	1.750	40.000	.375	.250E+08	.832E+07
15.000	2.000	40.000	.375	.348E+08	.116E+08
15.000	.250	48.000	.375	.232E+06	.774E+05
15.000	.375	48.000	.375	.639E+06	.213E+06
15.000	.500	48.000	.375	.131E+07	.438E+06
15.000	.625	48.000	.375	.229E+07	.764E+06
15.000	.750	48.000	.375	.362E+07	.121E+07
15.000	1.000	48.000	.375	.743E+07	.248E+07
15.000	1.250	48.000	.375	.130E+08	.432E+07
15.000	1.500	48.000	.375	.205E+08	.682E+07
15.000	1.750	48.000	.375	.301E+08	.100E+08
15.000	2.000	48.000	.375	.420E+08	.140E+08
16.000	.250	2.375	.154	.935E+04	.312E+04
16.000	.375	2.375	.154	.258E+05	.859E+04
16.000	.500	2.375	.154	.529E+05	.176E+05
16.000	.625	2.375	.154	.924E+05	.308E+05
16.000	.750	2.375	.154	.146E+06	.486E+05
16.000	1.000	2.375	.154	.299E+06	.998E+05
16.000	1.250	2.375	.154	.523E+06	.174E+06
16.000	1.500	2.375	.154	.825E+06	.275E+06
16.000	1.750	2.375	.154	.121E+07	.404E+06
16.000	2.000	2.375	.154	.169E+07	.564E+06
16.000	.250	3.500	.216	.139E+05	.464E+04
16.000	.375	3.500	.216	.383E+05	.128E+05
16.000	.500	3.500	.216	.787E+05	.262E+05
16.000	.625	3.500	.216	.138E+06	.458E+05
16.000	.750	3.500	.216	.217E+06	.723E+05
16.000	1.000	3.500	.216	.445E+06	.148E+06
16.000	1.250	3.500	.216	.778E+06	.259E+06
16.000	1.500	3.500	.216	.123E+07	.409E+06
16.000	1.750	3.500	.216	.180E+07	.601E+06
16.000	2.000	3.500	.216	.252E+07	.840E+06
16.000	.250	4.500	.237	.184E+05	.613E+04
16.000	.375	4.500	.237	.507E+05	.169E+05
16.000	.500	4.500	.237	.104E+06	.347E+05
16.000	.625	4.500	.237	.182E+06	.606E+05
16.000	.750	4.500	.237	.287E+06	.956E+05

Table 6-1
Continued

ROTA STIFF CALCULATION, CYL. VESSEL

VESSEL OD,FT	VESSEL TCK,IN	NOZZLE OD,IN	NOZZLE TCK,IN STD	ROT STIF IN.LB/DEG INPLANE LONGI	OUTPLANE CIRCU
16.000	1.000	4.500	.237	.589E+06	.196E+06
16.000	1.250	4.500	.237	.103E+07	.343E+06
16.000	1.500	4.500	.237	.162E+07	.541E+06
16.000	1.750	4.500	.237	.238E+07	.795E+06
16.000	2.000	4.500	.237	.333E+07	.111E+07
16.000	.250	6.625	.280	.279E+05	.932E+04
16.000	.375	6.625	.280	.770E+05	.257E+05
16.000	.500	6.625	.280	.158E+06	.527E+05
16.000	.625	6.625	.280	.276E+06	.921E+05
16.000	.750	6.625	.280	.436E+06	.145E+06
16.000	1.000	6.625	.280	.894E+06	.298E+06
16.000	1.250	6.625	.280	.156E+07	.521E+06
16.000	1.500	6.625	.280	.246E+07	.821E+06
16.000	1.750	6.625	.280	.362E+07	.121E+07
16.000	2.000	6.625	.280	.506E+07	.169E+07
16.000	.250	8.625	.322	.369E+05	.123E+05
16.000	.375	8.625	.322	.102E+06	.339E+05
16.000	.500	8.625	.322	.209E+06	.696E+05
16.000	.625	8.625	.322	.365E+06	.122E+06
16.000	.750	8.625	.322	.576E+06	.192E+06
16.000	1.000	8.625	.322	.118E+07	.394E+06
16.000	1.250	8.625	.322	.206E+07	.688E+06
16.000	1.500	8.625	.322	.326E+07	.109E+07
16.000	1.750	8.625	.322	.479E+07	.160E+07
16.000	2.000	8.625	.322	.669E+07	.223E+07
16.000	.250	10.750	.365	.465E+05	.155E+05
16.000	.375	10.750	.365	.128E+06	.427E+05
16.000	.500	10.750	.365	.263E+06	.877E+05
16.000	.625	10.750	.365	.460E+06	.153E+06
16.000	.750	10.750	.365	.725E+06	.242E+06
16.000	1.000	10.750	.365	.149E+07	.496E+06
16.000	1.250	10.750	.365	.260E+07	.867E+06
16.000	1.500	10.750	.365	.410E+07	.137E+07
16.000	1.750	10.750	.365	.603E+07	.201E+07
16.000	2.000	10.750	.365	.842E+07	.281E+07
16.000	.250	12.750	.375	.559E+05	.186E+05
16.000	.375	12.750	.375	.154E+06	.514E+05
16.000	.500	12.750	.375	.316E+06	.105E+06
16.000	.625	12.750	.375	.553E+06	.184E+06
16.000	.750	12.750	.375	.872E+06	.291E+06
16.000	1.000	12.750	.375	.179E+07	.596E+06
16.000	1.250	12.750	.375	.313E+07	.104E+07
16.000	1.500	12.750	.375	.493E+07	.164E+07
16.000	1.750	12.750	.375	.725E+07	.242E+07
16.000	2.000	12.750	.375	.101E+08	.337E+07
16.000	.250	14.000	.375	.619E+05	.206E+05
16.000	.375	14.000	.375	.171E+06	.569E+05
16.000	.500	14.000	.375	.350E+06	.117E+06
16.000	.625	14.000	.375	.612E+06	.204E+06
16.000	.750	14.000	.375	.965E+06	.322E+06
16.000	1.000	14.000	.375	.198E+07	.660E+06
16.000	1.250	14.000	.375	.346E+07	.115E+07
16.000	1.500	14.000	.375	.546E+07	.182E+07
16.000	1.750	14.000	.375	.802E+07	.267E+07
16.000	2.000	14.000	.375	.112E+08	.373E+07
16.000	.250	16.000	.375	.715E+05	.238E+05
16.000	.375	16.000	.375	.197E+06	.656E+05
16.000	.500	16.000	.375	.404E+06	.135E+06
16.000	.625	16.000	.375	.706E+06	.235E+06
16.000	.750	16.000	.375	.111E+07	.371E+06
16.000	1.000	16.000	.375	.229E+07	.762E+06

Table 6-1
Continued

ROTA STIFF CALCULATION, CYL. VESSEL

VESSEL OD,FT	VESSEL TCK,IN	NOZZLE OD,IN	NOZZLE TCK,IN STD	ROT STIF IN.LB/DEG INPLANE LONGI	OUTPLANE CIRCU
16.000	1.250	16.000	.375	.399E+07	.133E+07
16.000	1.500	16.000	.375	.630E+07	.210E+07
16.000	1.750	16.000	.375	.926E+07	.309E+07
16.000	2.000	16.000	.375	.129E+08	.431E+07
16.000	.250	18.000	.375	.810E+05	.270E+05
16.000	.375	18.000	.375	.223E+06	.744E+05
16.000	.500	18.000	.375	.458E+06	.153E+06
16.000	.625	18.000	.375	.801E+06	.267E+06
16.000	.750	18.000	.375	.126E+07	.421E+06
16.000	1.000	18.000	.375	.259E+07	.864E+06
16.000	1.250	18.000	.375	.453E+07	.151E+07
16.000	1.500	18.000	.375	.714E+07	.238E+07
16.000	1.750	18.000	.375	.105E+08	.350E+07
16.000	2.000	18.000	.375	.147E+08	.489E+07
16.000	.250	20.000	.375	.906E+05	.302E+05
16.000	.375	20.000	.375	.250E+06	.832E+05
16.000	.500	20.000	.375	.512E+06	.171E+06
16.000	.625	20.000	.375	.895E+06	.298E+06
16.000	.750	20.000	.375	.141E+07	.471E+06
16.000	1.000	20.000	.375	.290E+07	.966E+06
16.000	1.250	20.000	.375	.506E+07	.169E+07
16.000	1.500	20.000	.375	.799E+07	.266E+07
16.000	1.750	20.000	.375	.117E+08	.391E+07
16.000	2.000	20.000	.375	.164E+08	.547E+07
16.000	.250	22.000	.375	.100E+06	.334E+05
16.000	.375	22.000	.375	.276E+06	.920E+05
16.000	.500	22.000	.375	.567E+06	.189E+06
16.000	.625	22.000	.375	.990E+06	.330E+06
16.000	.750	22.000	.375	.156E+07	.520E+06
16.000	1.000	22.000	.375	.321E+07	.107E+07
16.000	1.250	22.000	.375	.560E+07	.187E+07
16.000	1.500	22.000	.375	.883E+07	.294E+07
16.000	1.750	22.000	.375	.130E+08	.433E+07
16.000	2.000	22.000	.375	.181E+08	.604E+07
16.000	.250	24.000	.375	.110E+06	.366E+05
16.000	.375	24.000	.375	.302E+06	.101E+06
16.000	.500	24.000	.375	.621E+06	.207E+06
16.000	.625	24.000	.375	.108E+07	.361E+06
16.000	.750	24.000	.375	.171E+07	.570E+06
16.000	1.000	24.000	.375	.351E+07	.117E+07
16.000	1.250	24.000	.375	.613E+07	.204E+07
16.000	1.500	24.000	.375	.968E+07	.323E+07
16.000	1.750	24.000	.375	.142E+08	.474E+07
16.000	2.000	24.000	.375	.199E+08	.662E+07
16.000	.250	26.000	.375	.119E+06	.398E+05
16.000	.375	26.000	.375	.329E+06	.110E+06
16.000	.500	26.000	.375	.675E+06	.225E+06
16.000	.625	26.000	.375	.118E+07	.393E+06
16.000	.750	26.000	.375	.186E+07	.620E+06
16.000	1.000	26.000	.375	.382E+07	.127E+07
16.000	1.250	26.000	.375	.667E+07	.222E+07
16.000	1.500	26.000	.375	.105E+08	.351E+07
16.000	1.750	26.000	.375	.155E+08	.516E+07
16.000	2.000	26.000	.375	.216E+08	.720E+07
16.000	.250	28.000	.375	.129E+06	.430E+05
16.000	.375	28.000	.375	.355E+06	.118E+06
16.000	.500	28.000	.375	.729E+06	.243E+06
16.000	.625	28.000	.375	.127E+07	.425E+06
16.000	.750	28.000	.375	.201E+07	.670E+06
16.000	1.000	28.000	.375	.412E+07	.137E+07
16.000	1.250	28.000	.375	.721E+07	.240E+07

Table 6-1
Continued

ROTA STIFF CALCULATION, CYL. VESSEL

VESSEL OD,FT	VESSEL TCK,IN	NOZZLE OD,IN	NOZZLE TCK,IN STD	ROT STIF IN.LB/DEG INPLANE LONGI	OUTPLANE CIRCU
16.000	1.500	28.000	.375	.114E+08	.379E+07
16.000	1.750	28.000	.375	.167E+08	.557E+07
16.000	2.000	28.000	.375	.233E+08	.778E+07
16.000	.250	30.000	.375	.138E+06	.462E+05
16.000	.375	30.000	.375	.382E+06	.127E+06
16.000	.500	30.000	.375	.783E+06	.261E+06
16.000	.625	30.000	.375	.137E+07	.456E+06
16.000	.750	30.000	.375	.216E+07	.719E+06
16.000	1.000	30.000	.375	.443E+07	.148E+07
16.000	1.250	30.000	.375	.774E+07	.258E+07
16.000	1.500	30.000	.375	.122E+08	.407E+07
16.000	1.750	30.000	.375	.180E+08	.598E+07
16.000	2.000	30.000	.375	.251E+08	.836E+07
16.000	.250	32.000	.375	.148E+06	.493E+05
16.000	.375	32.000	.375	.408E+06	.136E+06
16.000	.500	32.000	.375	.837E+06	.279E+06
16.000	.625	32.000	.375	.146E+07	.488E+06
16.000	.750	32.000	.375	.231E+07	.769E+06
16.000	1.000	32.000	.375	.474E+07	.158E+07
16.000	1.250	32.000	.375	.828E+07	.276E+07
16.000	1.500	32.000	.375	.131E+08	.435E+07
16.000	1.750	32.000	.375	.192E+08	.640E+07
16.000	2.000	32.000	.375	.268E+08	.893E+07
16.000	.250	36.000	.375	.167E+06	.557E+05
16.000	.375	36.000	.375	.461E+06	.154E+06
16.000	.500	36.000	.375	.946E+06	.315E+06
16.000	.625	36.000	.375	.165E+07	.551E+06
16.000	.750	36.000	.375	.261E+07	.869E+06
16.000	1.000	36.000	.375	.535E+07	.178E+07
16.000	1.250	36.000	.375	.935E+07	.312E+07
16.000	1.500	36.000	.375	.147E+08	.491E+07
16.000	1.750	36.000	.375	.217E+08	.723E+07
16.000	2.000	36.000	.375	.303E+08	.101E+08
16.000	.250	40.000	.375	.186E+06	.621E+05
16.000	.375	40.000	.375	.514E+06	.171E+06
16.000	.500	40.000	.375	.105E+07	.351E+06
16.000	.625	40.000	.375	.184E+07	.614E+06
16.000	.750	40.000	.375	.291E+07	.968E+06
16.000	1.000	40.000	.375	.596E+07	.199E+07
16.000	1.250	40.000	.375	.104E+08	.347E+07
16.000	1.500	40.000	.375	.164E+08	.548E+07
16.000	1.750	40.000	.375	.242E+08	.805E+07
16.000	2.000	40.000	.375	.337E+08	.112E+08
16.000	.250	48.000	.375	.225E+06	.749E+05
16.000	.375	48.000	.375	.619E+06	.206E+06
16.000	.500	48.000	.375	.127E+07	.424E+06
16.000	.625	48.000	.375	.222E+07	.740E+06
16.000	.750	48.000	.375	.350E+07	.117E+07
16.000	1.000	48.000	.375	.719E+07	.240E+07
16.000	1.250	48.000	.375	.126E+08	.419E+07
16.000	1.500	48.000	.375	.198E+08	.660E+07
16.000	1.750	48.000	.375	.291E+08	.971E+07
16.000	2.000	48.000	.375	.407E+08	.136E+08
17.000	.250	2.375	.154	.907E+04	.302E+04
17.000	.375	2.375	.154	.250E+05	.833E+04
17.000	.500	2.375	.154	.513E+05	.171E+05
17.000	.625	2.375	.154	.897E+05	.299E+05
17.000	.750	2.375	.154	.141E+06	.471E+05
17.000	1.000	2.375	.154	.290E+06	.968E+05

Table 6-1
Continued

ROTA STIFF CALCULATION, CYL. VESSEL

VESSEL OD,FT	VESSEL TCK,IN	NOZZLE OD,IN	NOZZLE TCK,IN STD	ROT STIF IN.LB/DEG INPLANE LONGI	OUTPLANE CIRCU
17.000	1.250	2.375	.154	.507E+06	.169E+06
17.000	1.500	2.375	.154	.800E+06	.267E+06
17.000	1.750	2.375	.154	.118E+07	.392E+06
17.000	2.000	2.375	.154	.164E+07	.547E+06
17.000	.250	3.500	.216	.135E+05	.450E+04
17.000	.375	3.500	.216	.372E+05	.124E+05
17.000	.500	3.500	.216	.764E+05	.255E+05
17.000	.625	3.500	.216	.133E+06	.445E+05
17.000	.750	3.500	.216	.210E+06	.701E+05
17.000	1.000	3.500	.216	.432E+06	.144E+06
17.000	1.250	3.500	.216	.755E+06	.252E+06
17.000	1.500	3.500	.216	.119E+07	.397E+06
17.000	1.750	3.500	.216	.175E+07	.583E+06
17.000	2.000	3.500	.216	.244E+07	.815E+06
17.000	.250	4.500	.237	.178E+05	.595E+04
17.000	.375	4.500	.237	.492E+05	.164E+05
17.000	.500	4.500	.237	.101E+06	.336E+05
17.000	.625	4.500	.237	.176E+06	.588E+05
17.000	.750	4.500	.237	.278E+06	.927E+05
17.000	1.000	4.500	.237	.571E+06	.190E+06
17.000	1.250	4.500	.237	.997E+06	.332E+06
17.000	1.500	4.500	.237	.157E+07	.524E+06
17.000	1.750	4.500	.237	.231E+07	.771E+06
17.000	2.000	4.500	.237	.323E+07	.108E+07
17.000	.250	6.625	.280	.271E+05	.904E+04
17.000	.375	6.625	.280	.747E+05	.249E+05
17.000	.500	6.625	.280	.153E+06	.511E+05
17.000	.625	6.625	.280	.268E+06	.893E+05
17.000	.750	6.625	.280	.423E+06	.141E+06
17.000	1.000	6.625	.280	.868E+06	.289E+06
17.000	1.250	6.625	.280	.152E+07	.505E+06
17.000	1.500	6.625	.280	.239E+07	.797E+06
17.000	1.750	6.625	.280	.351E+07	.117E+07
17.000	2.000	6.625	.280	.491E+07	.164E+07
17.000	.250	8.625	.322	.358E+05	.119E+05
17.000	.375	8.625	.322	.987E+05	.329E+05
17.000	.500	8.625	.322	.203E+06	.676E+05
17.000	.625	8.625	.322	.354E+06	.118E+06
17.000	.750	8.625	.322	.558E+06	.186E+06
17.000	1.000	8.625	.322	.115E+07	.382E+06
17.000	1.250	8.625	.322	.200E+07	.668E+06
17.000	1.500	8.625	.322	.316E+07	.105E+07
17.000	1.750	8.625	.322	.464E+07	.155E+07
17.000	2.000	8.625	.322	.649E+07	.216E+07
17.000	.250	10.750	.365	.451E+05	.150E+05
17.000	.375	10.750	.365	.124E+06	.414E+05
17.000	.500	10.750	.365	.255E+06	.851E+05
17.000	.625	10.750	.365	.446E+06	.149E+06
17.000	.750	10.750	.365	.703E+06	.234E+06
17.000	1.000	10.750	.365	.144E+07	.481E+06
17.000	1.250	10.750	.365	.252E+07	.841E+06
17.000	1.500	10.750	.365	.398E+07	.133E+07
17.000	1.750	10.750	.365	.585E+07	.195E+07
17.000	2.000	10.750	.365	.817E+07	.272E+07
17.000	.250	12.750	.375	.542E+05	.181E+05
17.000	.375	12.750	.375	.149E+06	.498E+05
17.000	.500	12.750	.375	.307E+06	.102E+06
17.000	.625	12.750	.375	.536E+06	.179E+06
17.000	.750	12.750	.375	.846E+06	.282E+06
17.000	1.000	12.750	.375	.174E+07	.579E+06
17.000	1.250	12.750	.375	.303E+07	.101E+07

Table 6-1
Continued

ROTA STIFF CALCULATION, CYL. VESSEL

VESSEL OD,FT	VESSEL TCK,IN	NOZZLE OD,IN	NOZZLE TCK,IN STD	ROT STIF IN.LB/DEG INPLANE LONGI	OUTPLANE CIRCU
17.000	1.500	12.750	.375	.478E+07	.159E+07
17.000	1.750	12.750	.375	.703E+07	.234E+07
17.000	2.000	12.750	.375	.982E+07	.327E+07
17.000	.250	14.000	.375	.600E+05	.200E+05
17.000	.375	14.000	.375	.165E+06	.552E+05
17.000	.500	14.000	.375	.340E+06	.113E+06
17.000	.625	14.000	.375	.593E+06	.198E+06
17.000	.750	14.000	.375	.936E+06	.312E+06
17.000	1.000	14.000	.375	.192E+07	.640E+06
17.000	1.250	14.000	.375	.336E+07	.112E+07
17.000	1.500	14.000	.375	.529E+07	.176E+07
17.000	1.750	14.000	.375	.778E+07	.259E+07
17.000	2.000	14.000	.375	.109E+08	.362E+07
17.000	.250	16.000	.375	.693E+05	.231E+05
17.000	.375	16.000	.375	.191E+06	.637E+05
17.000	.500	16.000	.375	.392E+06	.131E+06
17.000	.625	16.000	.375	.685E+06	.228E+06
17.000	.750	16.000	.375	.108E+07	.360E+06
17.000	1.000	16.000	.375	.222E+07	.739E+06
17.000	1.250	16.000	.375	.388E+07	.129E+07
17.000	1.500	16.000	.375	.611E+07	.204E+07
17.000	1.750	16.000	.375	.899E+07	.300E+07
17.000	2.000	16.000	.375	.125E+08	.418E+07
17.000	.250	18.000	.375	.786E+05	.262E+05
17.000	.375	18.000	.375	.217E+06	.722E+05
17.000	.500	18.000	.375	.445E+06	.148E+06
17.000	.625	18.000	.375	.777E+06	.259E+06
17.000	.750	18.000	.375	.123E+07	.408E+06
17.000	1.000	18.000	.375	.252E+07	.838E+06
17.000	1.250	18.000	.375	.439E+07	.146E+07
17.000	1.500	18.000	.375	.693E+07	.231E+07
17.000	1.750	18.000	.375	.102E+08	.340E+07
17.000	2.000	18.000	.375	.142E+08	.474E+07
17.000	.250	20.000	.375	.879E+05	.293E+05
17.000	.375	20.000	.375	.242E+06	.807E+05
17.000	.500	20.000	.375	.497E+06	.166E+06
17.000	.625	20.000	.375	.868E+06	.289E+06
17.000	.750	20.000	.375	.137E+07	.457E+06
17.000	1.000	20.000	.375	.281E+07	.937E+06
17.000	1.250	20.000	.375	.491E+07	.164E+07
17.000	1.500	20.000	.375	.775E+07	.258E+07
17.000	1.750	20.000	.375	.114E+08	.380E+07
17.000	2.000	20.000	.375	.159E+08	.530E+07
17.000	.250	22.000	.375	.972E+05	.324E+05
17.000	.375	22.000	.375	.268E+06	.893E+05
17.000	.500	22.000	.375	.550E+06	.183E+06
17.000	.625	22.000	.375	.960E+06	.320E+06
17.000	.750	22.000	.375	.151E+07	.505E+06
17.000	1.000	22.000	.375	.311E+07	.104E+07
17.000	1.250	22.000	.375	.543E+07	.181E+07
17.000	1.500	22.000	.375	.857E+07	.286E+07
17.000	1.750	22.000	.375	.126E+08	.420E+07
17.000	2.000	22.000	.375	.176E+08	.586E+07
17.000	.250	24.000	.375	.106E+06	.355E+05
17.000	.375	24.000	.375	.293E+06	.978E+05
17.000	.500	24.000	.375	.602E+06	.201E+06
17.000	.625	24.000	.375	.105E+07	.351E+06
17.000	.750	24.000	.375	.166E+07	.553E+06
17.000	1.000	24.000	.375	.341E+07	.114E+07
17.000	1.250	24.000	.375	.595E+07	.198E+07
17.000	1.500	24.000	.375	.939E+07	.313E+07

Table 6-1
Continued

ROTA STIFF CALCULATION, CYL. VESSEL

VESSEL OD,FT	VESSEL TCK,IN	NOZZLE OD,IN	NOZZLE TCK,IN STD	ROT STIF IN.LB/DEG INPLANE LONGI	OUTPLANE CIRCU
17.000	1.750	24.000	.375	.138E+08	.460E+07
17.000	2.000	24.000	.375	.193E+08	.642E+07
17.000	.250	26.000	.375	.116E+06	.386E+05
17.000	.375	26.000	.375	.319E+06	.106E+06
17.000	.500	26.000	.375	.655E+06	.218E+06
17.000	.625	26.000	.375	.114E+07	.381E+06
17.000	.750	26.000	.375	.180E+07	.601E+06
17.000	1.000	26.000	.375	.370E+07	.123E+07
17.000	1.250	26.000	.375	.647E+07	.216E+07
17.000	1.500	26.000	.375	.102E+08	.340E+07
17.000	1.750	26.000	.375	.150E+08	.500E+07
17.000	2.000	26.000	.375	.210E+08	.698E+07
17.000	.250	28.000	.375	.125E+06	.417E+05
17.000	.375	28.000	.375	.345E+06	.115E+06
17.000	.500	28.000	.375	.707E+06	.236E+06
17.000	.625	28.000	.375	.124E+07	.412E+06
17.000	.750	28.000	.375	.195E+07	.650E+06
17.000	1.000	28.000	.375	.400E+07	.133E+07
17.000	1.250	28.000	.375	.699E+07	.233E+07
17.000	1.500	28.000	.375	.110E+08	.368E+07
17.000	1.750	28.000	.375	.162E+08	.540E+07
17.000	2.000	28.000	.375	.226E+08	.754E+07
17.000	.250	30.000	.375	.134E+06	.448E+05
17.000	.375	30.000	.375	.370E+06	.123E+06
17.000	.500	30.000	.375	.760E+06	.253E+06
17.000	.625	30.000	.375	.133E+07	.442E+06
17.000	.750	30.000	.375	.209E+07	.698E+06
17.000	1.000	30.000	.375	.430E+07	.143E+07
17.000	1.250	30.000	.375	.751E+07	.250E+07
17.000	1.500	30.000	.375	.118E+08	.395E+07
17.000	1.750	30.000	.375	.174E+08	.581E+07
17.000	2.000	30.000	.375	.243E+08	.811E+07
17.000	.250	32.000	.375	.144E+06	.479E+05
17.000	.375	32.000	.375	.396E+06	.132E+06
17.000	.500	32.000	.375	.812E+06	.271E+06
17.000	.625	32.000	.375	.142E+07	.473E+06
17.000	.750	32.000	.375	.224E+07	.746E+06
17.000	1.000	32.000	.375	.460E+07	.153E+07
17.000	1.250	32.000	.375	.803E+07	.268E+07
17.000	1.500	32.000	.375	.127E+08	.422E+07
17.000	1.750	32.000	.375	.186E+08	.621E+07
17.000	2.000	32.000	.375	.260E+08	.867E+07
17.000	.250	36.000	.375	.162E+06	.541E+05
17.000	.375	36.000	.375	.447E+06	.149E+06
17.000	.500	36.000	.375	.918E+06	.306E+06
17.000	.625	36.000	.375	.160E+07	.534E+06
17.000	.750	36.000	.375	.253E+07	.843E+06
17.000	1.000	36.000	.375	.519E+07	.173E+07
17.000	1.250	36.000	.375	.907E+07	.302E+07
17.000	1.500	36.000	.375	.143E+08	.477E+07
17.000	1.750	36.000	.375	.210E+08	.701E+07
17.000	2.000	36.000	.375	.294E+08	.979E+07
17.000	.250	40.000	.375	.181E+06	.603E+05
17.000	.375	40.000	.375	.498E+06	.166E+06
17.000	.500	40.000	.375	.102E+07	.341E+06
17.000	.625	40.000	.375	.179E+07	.596E+06
17.000	.750	40.000	.375	.282E+07	.939E+06
17.000	1.000	40.000	.375	.579E+07	.193E+07
17.000	1.250	40.000	.375	.101E+08	.337E+07
17.000	1.500	40.000	.375	.159E+08	.531E+07
17.000	1.750	40.000	.375	.234E+08	.781E+07

Table 6-1
Continued

ROTA STIFF CALCULATION, CYL. VESSEL

VESSEL OD,FT	VESSEL TCK,IN	NOZZLE OD,IN	NOZZLE TCK,IN STD	ROT STIF IN.LB/DEG INPLANE LONGI	OUTPLANE CIRCU
17.000	2.000	40.000	.375	.327E+08	.109E+08
17.000	.250	48.000	.375	.218E+06	.727E+05
17.000	.375	48.000	.375	.601E+06	.200E+06
17.000	.500	48.000	.375	.123E+07	.411E+06
17.000	.625	48.000	.375	.215E+07	.718E+06
17.000	.750	48.000	.375	.340E+07	.113E+07
17.000	1.000	48.000	.375	.698E+07	.233E+07
17.000	1.250	48.000	.375	.122E+08	.406E+07
17.000	1.500	48.000	.375	.192E+08	.641E+07
17.000	1.750	48.000	.375	.283E+08	.942E+07
17.000	2.000	48.000	.375	.395E+08	.132E+08
18.000	.250	2.375	.154	.882E+04	.294E+04
18.000	.375	2.375	.154	.243E+05	.810E+04
18.000	.500	2.375	.154	.499E+05	.166E+05
18.000	.625	2.375	.154	.871E+05	.290E+05
18.000	.750	2.375	.154	.137E+06	.458E+05
18.000	1.000	2.375	.154	.282E+06	.941E+05
18.000	1.250	2.375	.154	.493E+06	.164E+06
18.000	1.500	2.375	.154	.778E+06	.259E+06
18.000	1.750	2.375	.154	.114E+07	.381E+06
18.000	2.000	2.375	.154	.160E+07	.532E+06
18.000	.250	3.500	.216	.131E+05	.437E+04
18.000	.375	3.500	.216	.362E+05	.121E+05
18.000	.500	3.500	.216	.742E+05	.247E+05
18.000	.625	3.500	.216	.130E+06	.432E+05
18.000	.750	3.500	.216	.205E+06	.682E+05
18.000	1.000	3.500	.216	.420E+06	.140E+06
18.000	1.250	3.500	.216	.733E+06	.244E+06
18.000	1.500	3.500	.216	.116E+07	.386E+06
18.000	1.750	3.500	.216	.170E+07	.567E+06
18.000	2.000	3.500	.216	.237E+07	.792E+06
18.000	.250	4.500	.237	.173E+05	.578E+04
18.000	.375	4.500	.237	.478E+05	.159E+05
18.000	.500	4.500	.237	.981E+05	.327E+05
18.000	.625	4.500	.237	.171E+06	.571E+05
18.000	.750	4.500	.237	.270E+06	.901E+05
18.000	1.000	4.500	.237	.555E+06	.185E+06
18.000	1.250	4.500	.237	.969E+06	.323E+06
18.000	1.500	4.500	.237	.153E+07	.510E+06
18.000	1.750	4.500	.237	.225E+07	.749E+06
18.000	2.000	4.500	.237	.314E+07	.105E+07
18.000	.250	6.625	.280	.263E+05	.878E+04
18.000	.375	6.625	.280	.726E+05	.242E+05
18.000	.500	6.625	.280	.149E+06	.497E+05
18.000	.625	6.625	.280	.260E+06	.868E+05
18.000	.750	6.625	.280	.411E+06	.137E+06
18.000	1.000	6.625	.280	.843E+06	.281E+06
18.000	1.250	6.625	.280	.147E+07	.491E+06
18.000	1.500	6.625	.280	.232E+07	.774E+06
18.000	1.750	6.625	.280	.342E+07	.114E+07
18.000	2.000	6.625	.280	.477E+07	.159E+07
18.000	.250	8.625	.322	.348E+05	.116E+05
18.000	.375	8.625	.322	.959E+05	.320E+05
18.000	.500	8.625	.322	.197E+06	.657E+05
18.000	.625	8.625	.322	.344E+06	.115E+06
18.000	.750	8.625	.322	.543E+06	.181E+06
18.000	1.000	8.625	.322	.111E+07	.371E+06
18.000	1.250	8.625	.322	.195E+07	.649E+06
18.000	1.500	8.625	.322	.307E+07	.102E+07

Table 6-1
Continued

ROTA STIFF CALCULATION, CYL. VESSEL

VESSEL OD,FT	VESSEL TCK,IN	NOZZLE OD,IN	NOZZLE TCK,IN STD	ROT STIF IN.LB/DEG INPLANE LONGI	OUTPLANE CIRCU
18.000	1.750	8.625	.322	.451E+07	.150E+07
18.000	2.000	8.625	.322	.630E+07	.210E+07
18.000	.250	10.750	.365	.438E+05	.146E+05
18.000	.375	10.750	.365	.121E+06	.403E+05
18.000	.500	10.750	.365	.248E+06	.827E+05
18.000	.625	10.750	.365	.433E+06	.144E+06
18.000	.750	10.750	.365	.683E+06	.228E+06
18.000	1.000	10.750	.365	.140E+07	.468E+06
18.000	1.250	10.750	.365	.245E+07	.817E+06
18.000	1.500	10.750	.365	.387E+07	.129E+07
18.000	1.750	10.750	.365	.568E+07	.189E+07
18.000	2.000	10.750	.365	.794E+07	.265E+07
18.000	.250	12.750	.375	.527E+05	.176E+05
18.000	.375	12.750	.375	.145E+06	.484E+05
18.000	.500	12.750	.375	.298E+06	.994E+05
18.000	.625	12.750	.375	.521E+06	.174E+06
18.000	.750	12.750	.375	.822E+06	.274E+06
18.000	1.000	12.750	.375	.169E+07	.562E+06
18.000	1.250	12.750	.375	.295E+07	.982E+06
18.000	1.500	12.750	.375	.465E+07	.155E+07
18.000	1.750	12.750	.375	.683E+07	.228E+07
18.000	2.000	12.750	.375	.954E+07	.318E+07
18.000	.250	14.000	.375	.584E+05	.195E+05
18.000	.375	14.000	.375	.161E+06	.536E+05
18.000	.500	14.000	.375	.330E+06	.110E+06
18.000	.625	14.000	.375	.577E+06	.192E+06
18.000	.750	14.000	.375	.910E+06	.303E+06
18.000	1.000	14.000	.375	.187E+07	.622E+06
18.000	1.250	14.000	.375	.326E+07	.109E+07
18.000	1.500	14.000	.375	.515E+07	.172E+07
18.000	1.750	14.000	.375	.756E+07	.252E+07
18.000	2.000	14.000	.375	.106E+08	.352E+07
18.000	.250	16.000	.375	.674E+05	.225E+05
18.000	.375	16.000	.375	.186E+06	.619E+05
18.000	.500	16.000	.375	.381E+06	.127E+06
18.000	.625	16.000	.375	.666E+06	.222E+06
18.000	.750	16.000	.375	.105E+07	.350E+06
18.000	1.000	16.000	.375	.216E+07	.719E+06
18.000	1.250	16.000	.375	.377E+07	.126E+07
18.000	1.500	16.000	.375	.594E+07	.198E+07
18.000	1.750	16.000	.375	.873E+07	.291E+07
18.000	2.000	16.000	.375	.122E+08	.406E+07
18.000	.250	18.000	.375	.764E+05	.255E+05
18.000	.375	18.000	.375	.210E+06	.702E+05
18.000	.500	18.000	.375	.432E+06	.144E+06
18.000	.625	18.000	.375	.755E+06	.252E+06
18.000	.750	18.000	.375	.119E+07	.397E+06
18.000	1.000	18.000	.375	.244E+07	.815E+06
18.000	1.250	18.000	.375	.427E+07	.142E+07
18.000	1.500	18.000	.375	.674E+07	.225E+07
18.000	1.750	18.000	.375	.990E+07	.330E+07
18.000	2.000	18.000	.375	.138E+08	.461E+07
18.000	.250	20.000	.375	.854E+05	.285E+05
18.000	.375	20.000	.375	.235E+06	.785E+05
18.000	.500	20.000	.375	.483E+06	.161E+06
18.000	.625	20.000	.375	.844E+06	.281E+06
18.000	.750	20.000	.375	.133E+07	.444E+06
18.000	1.000	20.000	.375	.273E+07	.911E+06
18.000	1.250	20.000	.375	.477E+07	.159E+07
18.000	1.500	20.000	.375	.753E+07	.251E+07
18.000	1.750	20.000	.375	.111E+08	.369E+07

Table 6-1
Continued

ROTA STIFF CALCULATION, CYL. VESSEL

VESSEL OD,FT	VESSEL TCK,IN	NOZZLE OD,IN	NOZZLE TCK,IN STD	ROT STIF IN.LB/DEG INPLANE LONGI	OUTPLANE CIRCU
18.000	2.000	20.000	.375	.155E+08	.515E+07
18.000	.250	22.000	.375	.944E+05	.315E+05
18.000	.375	22.000	.375	.260E+06	.867E+05
18.000	.500	22.000	.375	.534E+06	.178E+06
18.000	.625	22.000	.375	.933E+06	.311E+06
18.000	.750	22.000	.375	.147E+07	.491E+06
18.000	1.000	22.000	.375	.302E+07	.101E+07
18.000	1.250	22.000	.375	.528E+07	.176E+07
18.000	1.500	22.000	.375	.833E+07	.278E+07
18.000	1.750	22.000	.375	.122E+08	.408E+07
18.000	2.000	22.000	.375	.171E+08	.570E+07
18.000	.250	24.000	.375	.103E+06	.345E+05
18.000	.375	24.000	.375	.285E+06	.950E+05
18.000	.500	24.000	.375	.585E+06	.195E+06
18.000	.625	24.000	.375	.102E+07	.341E+06
18.000	.750	24.000	.375	.161E+07	.538E+06
18.000	1.000	24.000	.375	.331E+07	.110E+07
18.000	1.250	24.000	.375	.578E+07	.193E+07
18.000	1.500	24.000	.375	.912E+07	.304E+07
18.000	1.750	24.000	.375	.134E+08	.447E+07
18.000	2.000	24.000	.375	.187E+08	.624E+07
18.000	.250	26.000	.375	.112E+06	.375E+05
18.000	.375	26.000	.375	.310E+06	.103E+06
18.000	.500	26.000	.375	.636E+06	.212E+06
18.000	.625	26.000	.375	.111E+07	.371E+06
18.000	.750	26.000	.375	.175E+07	.585E+06
18.000	1.000	26.000	.375	.360E+07	.120E+07
18.000	1.250	26.000	.375	.629E+07	.210E+07
18.000	1.500	26.000	.375	.992E+07	.331E+07
18.000	1.750	26.000	.375	.146E+08	.486E+07
18.000	2.000	26.000	.375	.204E+08	.679E+07
18.000	.250	28.000	.375	.122E+06	.405E+05
18.000	.375	28.000	.375	.335E+06	.112E+06
18.000	.500	28.000	.375	.687E+06	.229E+06
18.000	.625	28.000	.375	.120E+07	.400E+06
18.000	.750	28.000	.375	.189E+07	.631E+06
18.000	1.000	28.000	.375	.389E+07	.130E+07
18.000	1.250	28.000	.375	.679E+07	.226E+07
18.000	1.500	28.000	.375	.107E+08	.357E+07
18.000	1.750	28.000	.375	.158E+08	.525E+07
18.000	2.000	28.000	.375	.220E+08	.733E+07
18.000	.250	30.000	.375	.131E+06	.435E+05
18.000	.375	30.000	.375	.360E+06	.120E+06
18.000	.500	30.000	.375	.738E+06	.246E+06
18.000	.625	30.000	.375	.129E+07	.430E+06
18.000	.750	30.000	.375	.204E+07	.678E+06
18.000	1.000	30.000	.375	.418E+07	.139E+07
18.000	1.250	30.000	.375	.730E+07	.243E+07
18.000	1.500	30.000	.375	.115E+08	.384E+07
18.000	1.750	30.000	.375	.169E+08	.564E+07
18.000	2.000	30.000	.375	.236E+08	.788E+07
18.000	.250	32.000	.375	.140E+06	.465E+05
18.000	.375	32.000	.375	.385E+06	.128E+06
18.000	.500	32.000	.375	.790E+06	.263E+06
18.000	.625	32.000	.375	.138E+07	.460E+06
18.000	.750	32.000	.375	.218E+07	.725E+06
18.000	1.000	32.000	.375	.447E+07	.149E+07
18.000	1.250	32.000	.375	.780E+07	.260E+07
18.000	1.500	32.000	.375	.123E+08	.410E+07
18.000	1.750	32.000	.375	.181E+08	.603E+07
18.000	2.000	32.000	.375	.253E+08	.842E+07

Table 6-1
Continued

ROTA STIFF CALCULATION, CYL. VESSEL

VESSEL OD,FT	VESSEL TCK,IN	NOZZLE OD,IN	NOZZLE TCK,IN STD	ROT STIF IN.LB/DEG INPLANE LONGI	OUTPLANE CIRCU
18.000	.250	36.000	.375	.158E+06	.525E+05
18.000	.375	36.000	.375	.434E+06	.145E+06
18.000	.500	36.000	.375	.892E+06	.297E+06
18.000	.625	36.000	.375	.156E+07	.519E+06
18.000	.750	36.000	.375	.246E+07	.819E+06
18.000	1.000	36.000	.375	.504E+07	.168E+07
18.000	1.250	36.000	.375	.881E+07	.294E+07
18.000	1.500	36.000	.375	.139E+08	.463E+07
18.000	1.750	36.000	.375	.204E+08	.681E+07
18.000	2.000	36.000	.375	.285E+08	.951E+07
18.000	.250	40.000	.375	.176E+06	.586E+05
18.000	.375	40.000	.375	.484E+06	.161E+06
18.000	.500	40.000	.375	.994E+06	.331E+06
18.000	.625	40.000	.375	.174E+07	.579E+06
18.000	.750	40.000	.375	.274E+07	.913E+06
18.000	1.000	40.000	.375	.562E+07	.187E+07
18.000	1.250	40.000	.375	.982E+07	.327E+07
18.000	1.500	40.000	.375	.155E+08	.516E+07
18.000	1.750	40.000	.375	.228E+08	.759E+07
18.000	2.000	40.000	.375	.318E+08	.106E+08
18.000	.250	48.000	.375	.212E+06	.706E+05
18.000	.375	48.000	.375	.584E+06	.195E+06
18.000	.500	48.000	.375	.120E+07	.399E+06
18.000	.625	48.000	.375	.209E+07	.698E+06
18.000	.750	48.000	.375	.330E+07	.110E+07
18.000	1.000	48.000	.375	.678E+07	.226E+07
18.000	1.250	48.000	.375	.118E+08	.395E+07
18.000	1.500	48.000	.375	.187E+08	.623E+07
18.000	1.750	48.000	.375	.275E+08	.915E+07
18.000	2.000	48.000	.375	.383E+08	.128E+08
19.000	.250	2.375	.154	.858E+04	.286E+04
19.000	.375	2.375	.154	.237E+05	.788E+04
19.000	.500	2.375	.154	.486E+05	.162E+05
19.000	.625	2.375	.154	.848E+05	.283E+05
19.000	.750	2.375	.154	.134E+06	.446E+05
19.000	1.000	2.375	.154	.275E+06	.915E+05
19.000	1.250	2.375	.154	.480E+06	.160E+06
19.000	1.500	2.375	.154	.757E+06	.252E+06
19.000	1.750	2.375	.154	.111E+07	.371E+06
19.000	2.000	2.375	.154	.155E+07	.518E+06
19.000	.250	3.500	.216	.128E+05	.426E+04
19.000	.375	3.500	.216	.352E+05	.117E+05
19.000	.500	3.500	.216	.722E+05	.241E+05
19.000	.625	3.500	.216	.126E+06	.421E+05
19.000	.750	3.500	.216	.199E+06	.664E+05
19.000	1.000	3.500	.216	.409E+06	.136E+06
19.000	1.250	3.500	.216	.714E+06	.238E+06
19.000	1.500	3.500	.216	.113E+07	.375E+06
19.000	1.750	3.500	.216	.166E+07	.552E+06
19.000	2.000	3.500	.216	.231E+07	.771E+06
19.000	.250	4.500	.237	.169E+05	.563E+04
19.000	.375	4.500	.237	.465E+05	.155E+05
19.000	.500	4.500	.237	.955E+05	.318E+05
19.000	.625	4.500	.237	.167E+06	.556E+05
19.000	.750	4.500	.237	.263E+06	.877E+05
19.000	1.000	4.500	.237	.540E+06	.180E+06
19.000	1.250	4.500	.237	.943E+06	.314E+06
19.000	1.500	4.500	.237	.149E+07	.496E+06
19.000	1.750	4.500	.237	.219E+07	.729E+06

Table 6-1
Continued

ROTA STIFF CALCULATION, CYL. VESSEL

VESSEL OD,FT	VESSEL TCK,IN	NOZZLE OD,IN	NOZZLE TCK,IN STD	ROT STIF IN.LB/DEG INPLANE LONGI	OUTPLANE CIRCU
19.000	2.000	4.500	.237	.306E+07	.102E+07
19.000	.250	6.625	.280	.256E+05	.855E+04
19.000	.375	6.625	.280	.707E+05	.236E+05
19.000	.500	6.625	.280	.145E+06	.484E+05
19.000	.625	6.625	.280	.253E+06	.845E+05
19.000	.750	6.625	.280	.400E+06	.133E+06
19.000	1.000	6.625	.280	.821E+06	.274E+06
19.000	1.250	6.625	.280	.143E+07	.478E+06
19.000	1.500	6.625	.280	.226E+07	.754E+06
19.000	1.750	6.625	.280	.332E+07	.111E+07
19.000	2.000	6.625	.280	.464E+07	.155E+07
19.000	.250	8.625	.322	.339E+05	.113E+05
19.000	.375	8.625	.322	.934E+05	.311E+05
19.000	.500	8.625	.322	.192E+06	.639E+05
19.000	.625	8.625	.322	.335E+06	.112E+06
19.000	.750	8.625	.322	.528E+06	.176E+06
19.000	1.000	8.625	.322	.108E+07	.361E+06
19.000	1.250	8.625	.322	.189E+07	.631E+06
19.000	1.500	8.625	.322	.299E+07	.996E+06
19.000	1.750	8.625	.322	.439E+07	.146E+07
19.000	2.000	8.625	.322	.613E+07	.204E+07
19.000	.250	10.750	.365	.427E+05	.142E+05
19.000	.375	10.750	.365	.118E+06	.392E+05
19.000	.500	10.750	.365	.241E+06	.805E+05
19.000	.625	10.750	.365	.422E+06	.141E+06
19.000	.750	10.750	.365	.665E+06	.222E+06
19.000	1.000	10.750	.365	.137E+07	.455E+06
19.000	1.250	10.750	.365	.239E+07	.795E+06
19.000	1.500	10.750	.365	.376E+07	.125E+07
19.000	1.750	10.750	.365	.553E+07	.184E+07
19.000	2.000	10.750	.365	.772E+07	.257E+07
19.000	.250	12.750	.375	.513E+05	.171E+05
19.000	.375	12.750	.375	.141E+06	.471E+05
19.000	.500	12.750	.375	.290E+06	.968E+05
19.000	.625	12.750	.375	.507E+06	.169E+06
19.000	.750	12.750	.375	.800E+06	.267E+06
19.000	1.000	12.750	.375	.164E+07	.547E+06
19.000	1.250	12.750	.375	.287E+07	.956E+06
19.000	1.500	12.750	.375	.452E+07	.151E+07
19.000	1.750	12.750	.375	.665E+07	.222E+07
19.000	2.000	12.750	.375	.929E+07	.310E+07
19.000	.250	14.000	.375	.568E+05	.189E+05
19.000	.375	14.000	.375	.157E+06	.522E+05
19.000	.500	14.000	.375	.321E+06	.107E+06
19.000	.625	14.000	.375	.561E+06	.187E+06
19.000	.750	14.000	.375	.885E+06	.295E+06
19.000	1.000	14.000	.375	.182E+07	.606E+06
19.000	1.250	14.000	.375	.317E+07	.106E+07
19.000	1.500	14.000	.375	.501E+07	.167E+07
19.000	1.750	14.000	.375	.736E+07	.245E+07
19.000	2.000	14.000	.375	.103E+08	.343E+07
19.000	.250	16.000	.375	.656E+05	.219E+05
19.000	.375	16.000	.375	.181E+06	.602E+05
19.000	.500	16.000	.375	.371E+06	.124E+06
19.000	.625	16.000	.375	.648E+06	.216E+06
19.000	.750	16.000	.375	.102E+07	.341E+06
19.000	1.000	16.000	.375	.210E+07	.699E+06
19.000	1.250	16.000	.375	.367E+07	.122E+07
19.000	1.500	16.000	.375	.578E+07	.193E+07
19.000	1.750	16.000	.375	.850E+07	.283E+07
19.000	2.000	16.000	.375	.119E+08	.396E+07

Table 6-1
Continued

ROTA STIFF CALCULATION, CYL. VESSEL

VESSEL OD,FT	VESSEL TCK,IN	NOZZLE OD,IN	NOZZLE TCK,IN STD	ROT STIF IN.LB/DEG INPLANE LONGI	OUTPLANE CIRCU
19.000	.250	18.000	.375	.743E+05	.248E+05
19.000	.375	18.000	.375	.205E+06	.683E+05
19.000	.500	18.000	.375	.421E+06	.140E+06
19.000	.625	18.000	.375	.735E+06	.245E+06
19.000	.750	18.000	.375	.116E+07	.386E+06
19.000	1.000	18.000	.375	.238E+07	.793E+06
19.000	1.250	18.000	.375	.416E+07	.139E+07
19.000	1.500	18.000	.375	.656E+07	.219E+07
19.000	1.750	18.000	.375	.964E+07	.321E+07
19.000	2.000	18.000	.375	.135E+08	.449E+07
19.000	.250	20.000	.375	.831E+05	.277E+05
19.000	.375	20.000	.375	.229E+06	.764E+05
19.000	.500	20.000	.375	.470E+06	.157E+06
19.000	.625	20.000	.375	.821E+06	.274E+06
19.000	.750	20.000	.375	.130E+07	.432E+06
19.000	1.000	20.000	.375	.266E+07	.887E+06
19.000	1.250	20.000	.375	.465E+07	.155E+07
19.000	1.500	20.000	.375	.733E+07	.244E+07
19.000	1.750	20.000	.375	.108E+08	.359E+07
19.000	2.000	20.000	.375	.150E+08	.502E+07
19.000	.250	22.000	.375	.919E+05	.306E+05
19.000	.375	22.000	.375	.253E+06	.844E+05
19.000	.500	22.000	.375	.520E+06	.173E+06
19.000	.625	22.000	.375	.908E+06	.303E+06
19.000	.750	22.000	.375	.143E+07	.478E+06
19.000	1.000	22.000	.375	.294E+07	.980E+06
19.000	1.250	22.000	.375	.514E+07	.171E+07
19.000	1.500	22.000	.375	.811E+07	.270E+07
19.000	1.750	22.000	.375	.119E+08	.397E+07
19.000	2.000	22.000	.375	.166E+08	.555E+07
19.000	.250	24.000	.375	.101E+06	.336E+05
19.000	.375	24.000	.375	.277E+06	.925E+05
19.000	.500	24.000	.375	.570E+06	.190E+06
19.000	.625	24.000	.375	.995E+06	.332E+06
19.000	.750	24.000	.375	.157E+07	.523E+06
19.000	1.000	24.000	.375	.322E+07	.107E+07
19.000	1.250	24.000	.375	.563E+07	.188E+07
19.000	1.500	24.000	.375	.888E+07	.296E+07
19.000	1.750	24.000	.375	.131E+08	.435E+07
19.000	2.000	24.000	.375	.182E+08	.608E+07
19.000	.250	26.000	.375	.109E+06	.365E+05
19.000	.375	26.000	.375	.302E+06	.101E+06
19.000	.500	26.000	.375	.619E+06	.206E+06
19.000	.625	26.000	.375	.108E+07	.361E+06
19.000	.750	26.000	.375	.171E+07	.569E+06
19.000	1.000	26.000	.375	.350E+07	.117E+07
19.000	1.250	26.000	.375	.612E+07	.204E+07
19.000	1.500	26.000	.375	.965E+07	.322E+07
19.000	1.750	26.000	.375	.142E+08	.473E+07
19.000	2.000	26.000	.375	.198E+08	.661E+07
19.000	.250	28.000	.375	.118E+06	.394E+05
19.000	.375	28.000	.375	.326E+06	.109E+06
19.000	.500	28.000	.375	.669E+06	.223E+06
19.000	.625	28.000	.375	.117E+07	.390E+06
19.000	.750	28.000	.375	.184E+07	.615E+06
19.000	1.000	28.000	.375	.378E+07	.126E+07
19.000	1.250	28.000	.375	.661E+07	.220E+07
19.000	1.500	28.000	.375	.104E+08	.348E+07
19.000	1.750	28.000	.375	.153E+08	.511E+07
19.000	2.000	28.000	.375	.214E+08	.714E+07
19.000	.250	30.000	.375	.127E+06	.424E+05

Table 6-1
Continued

ROTA STIFF CALCULATION, CYL. VESSEL

VESSEL OD,FT	VESSEL TCK,IN	NOZZLE OD,IN	NOZZLE TCK,IN STD	ROT STIF IN.LB/DEG INPLANE LONGI	OUTPLANE CIRCU
19.000	.375	30.000	.375	.350E+06	.117E+06
19.000	.500	30.000	.375	.719E+06	.240E+06
19.000	.625	30.000	.375	.126E+07	.419E+06
19.000	.750	30.000	.375	.198E+07	.660E+06
19.000	1.000	30.000	.375	.407E+07	.136E+07
19.000	1.250	30.000	.375	.710E+07	.237E+07
19.000	1.500	30.000	.375	.112E+08	.373E+07
19.000	1.750	30.000	.375	.165E+08	.549E+07
19.000	2.000	30.000	.375	.230E+08	.767E+07
19.000	.250	32.000	.375	.136E+06	.453E+05
19.000	.375	32.000	.375	.374E+06	.125E+06
19.000	.500	32.000	.375	.769E+06	.256E+06
19.000	.625	32.000	.375	.134E+07	.448E+06
19.000	.750	32.000	.375	.212E+07	.706E+06
19.000	1.000	32.000	.375	.435E+07	.145E+07
19.000	1.250	32.000	.375	.759E+07	.253E+07
19.000	1.500	32.000	.375	.120E+08	.399E+07
19.000	1.750	32.000	.375	.176E+08	.587E+07
19.000	2.000	32.000	.375	.246E+08	.820E+07
19.000	.250	36.000	.375	.153E+06	.511E+05
19.000	.375	36.000	.375	.423E+06	.141E+06
19.000	.500	36.000	.375	.868E+06	.289E+06
19.000	.625	36.000	.375	.152E+07	.505E+06
19.000	.750	36.000	.375	.239E+07	.797E+06
19.000	1.000	36.000	.375	.491E+07	.164E+07
19.000	1.250	36.000	.375	.858E+07	.286E+07
19.000	1.500	36.000	.375	.135E+08	.451E+07
19.000	1.750	36.000	.375	.199E+08	.663E+07
19.000	2.000	36.000	.375	.278E+08	.926E+07
19.000	.250	40.000	.375	.171E+06	.570E+05
19.000	.375	40.000	.375	.471E+06	.157E+06
19.000	.500	40.000	.375	.967E+06	.322E+06
19.000	.625	40.000	.375	.169E+07	.563E+06
19.000	.750	40.000	.375	.267E+07	.889E+06
19.000	1.000	40.000	.375	.547E+07	.182E+07
19.000	1.250	40.000	.375	.956E+07	.319E+07
19.000	1.500	40.000	.375	.151E+08	.503E+07
19.000	1.750	40.000	.375	.222E+08	.739E+07
19.000	2.000	40.000	.375	.310E+08	.103E+08
19.000	.250	48.000	.375	.206E+06	.687E+05
19.000	.375	48.000	.375	.568E+06	.189E+06
19.000	.500	48.000	.375	.117E+07	.389E+06
19.000	.625	48.000	.375	.204E+07	.679E+06
19.000	.750	48.000	.375	.321E+07	.107E+07
19.000	1.000	48.000	.375	.660E+07	.220E+07
19.000	1.250	48.000	.375	.115E+08	.384E+07
19.000	1.500	48.000	.375	.182E+08	.606E+07
19.000	1.750	48.000	.375	.267E+08	.891E+07
19.000	2.000	48.000	.375	.373E+08	.124E+08
20.000	.250	2.375	.154	.837E+04	.279E+04
20.000	.375	2.375	.154	.231E+05	.768E+04
20.000	.500	2.375	.154	.473E+05	.158E+05
20.000	.625	2.375	.154	.827E+05	.276E+05
20.000	.750	2.375	.154	.130E+06	.435E+05
20.000	1.000	2.375	.154	.268E+06	.892E+05
20.000	1.250	2.375	.154	.468E+06	.156E+06
20.000	1.500	2.375	.154	.738E+06	.246E+06
20.000	1.750	2.375	.154	.108E+07	.362E+06
20.000	2.000	2.375	.154	.151E+07	.505E+06

Table 6-1
Continued

ROTA STIFF CALCULATION, CYL. VESSEL

VESSEL OD,FT	VESSEL TCK,IN	NOZZLE OD,IN	NOZZLE TCK,IN STD	ROT STIF IN.LB/DEG INPLANE LONGI	OUTPLANE CIRCU
20.000	.250	3.500	.216	.124E+05	.415E+04
20.000	.375	3.500	.216	.343E+05	.114E+05
20.000	.500	3.500	.216	.704E+05	.235E+05
20.000	.625	3.500	.216	.123E+06	.410E+05
20.000	.750	3.500	.216	.194E+06	.647E+05
20.000	1.000	3.500	.216	.398E+06	.133E+06
20.000	1.250	3.500	.216	.696E+06	.232E+06
20.000	1.500	3.500	.216	.110E+07	.366E+06
20.000	1.750	3.500	.216	.161E+07	.538E+06
20.000	2.000	3.500	.216	.225E+07	.751E+06
20.000	.250	4.500	.237	.164E+05	.548E+04
20.000	.375	4.500	.237	.453E+05	.151E+05
20.000	.500	4.500	.237	.931E+05	.310E+05
20.000	.625	4.500	.237	.163E+06	.542E+05
20.000	.750	4.500	.237	.256E+06	.855E+05
20.000	1.000	4.500	.237	.526E+06	.175E+06
20.000	1.250	4.500	.237	.920E+06	.307E+06
20.000	1.500	4.500	.237	.145E+07	.484E+06
20.000	1.750	4.500	.237	.213E+07	.711E+06
20.000	2.000	4.500	.237	.298E+07	.993E+06
20.000	.250	6.625	.280	.250E+05	.833E+04
20.000	.375	6.625	.280	.689E+05	.230E+05
20.000	.500	6.625	.280	.141E+06	.471E+05
20.000	.625	6.625	.280	.247E+06	.823E+05
20.000	.750	6.625	.280	.390E+06	.130E+06
20.000	1.000	6.625	.280	.800E+06	.267E+06
20.000	1.250	6.625	.280	.140E+07	.466E+06
20.000	1.500	6.625	.280	.220E+07	.735E+06
20.000	1.750	6.625	.280	.324E+07	.108E+07
20.000	2.000	6.625	.280	.452E+07	.151E+07
20.000	.250	8.625	.322	.330E+05	.110E+05
20.000	.375	8.625	.322	.910E+05	.303E+05
20.000	.500	8.625	.322	.187E+06	.623E+05
20.000	.625	8.625	.322	.326E+06	.109E+06
20.000	.750	8.625	.322	.515E+06	.172E+06
20.000	1.000	8.625	.322	.106E+07	.352E+06
20.000	1.250	8.625	.322	.185E+07	.616E+06
20.000	1.500	8.625	.322	.291E+07	.971E+06
20.000	1.750	8.625	.322	.428E+07	.143E+07
20.000	2.000	8.625	.322	.598E+07	.199E+07
20.000	.250	10.750	.365	.416E+05	.139E+05
20.000	.375	10.750	.365	.115E+06	.382E+05
20.000	.500	10.750	.365	.235E+06	.784E+05
20.000	.625	10.750	.365	.411E+06	.137E+06
20.000	.750	10.750	.365	.648E+06	.216E+06
20.000	1.000	10.750	.365	.133E+07	.444E+06
20.000	1.250	10.750	.365	.233E+07	.775E+06
20.000	1.500	10.750	.365	.367E+07	.122E+07
20.000	1.750	10.750	.365	.539E+07	.180E+07
20.000	2.000	10.750	.365	.753E+07	.251E+07
20.000	.250	12.750	.375	.500E+05	.167E+05
20.000	.375	12.750	.375	.138E+06	.459E+05
20.000	.500	12.750	.375	.283E+06	.943E+05
20.000	.625	12.750	.375	.494E+06	.165E+06
20.000	.750	12.750	.375	.780E+06	.260E+06
20.000	1.000	12.750	.375	.160E+07	.533E+06
20.000	1.250	12.750	.375	.280E+07	.932E+06
20.000	1.500	12.750	.375	.441E+07	.147E+07
20.000	1.750	12.750	.375	.648E+07	.216E+07
20.000	2.000	12.750	.375	.905E+07	.302E+07
20.000	.250	14.000	.375	.554E+05	.185E+05

Table 6-1
Continued

ROTA STIFF CALCULATION, CYL. VESSEL

VESSEL OD,FT	VESSEL TCK,IN	NOZZLE OD,IN	NOZZLE TCK,IN STD	ROT STIF IN.LB/DEG INPLANE LONGI	OUTPLANE CIRCU
20.000	.375	14.000	.375	.153E+06	.508E+05
20.000	.500	14.000	.375	.313E+06	.104E+06
20.000	.625	14.000	.375	.547E+06	.182E+06
20.000	.750	14.000	.375	.863E+06	.288E+06
20.000	1.000	14.000	.375	.177E+07	.590E+06
20.000	1.250	14.000	.375	.309E+07	.103E+07
20.000	1.500	14.000	.375	.488E+07	.163E+07
20.000	1.750	14.000	.375	.718E+07	.239E+07
20.000	2.000	14.000	.375	.100E+08	.334E+07
20.000	.250	16.000	.375	.639E+05	.213E+05
20.000	.375	16.000	.375	.176E+06	.587E+05
20.000	.500	16.000	.375	.362E+06	.121E+06
20.000	.625	16.000	.375	.632E+06	.211E+06
20.000	.750	16.000	.375	.996E+06	.332E+06
20.000	1.000	16.000	.375	.205E+07	.682E+06
20.000	1.250	16.000	.375	.357E+07	.119E+07
20.000	1.500	16.000	.375	.564E+07	.188E+07
20.000	1.750	16.000	.375	.829E+07	.276E+07
20.000	2.000	16.000	.375	.116E+08	.386E+07
20.000	.250	18.000	.375	.725E+05	.242E+05
20.000	.375	18.000	.375	.200E+06	.666E+05
20.000	.500	18.000	.375	.410E+06	.137E+06
20.000	.625	18.000	.375	.716E+06	.239E+06
20.000	.750	18.000	.375	.113E+07	.377E+06
20.000	1.000	18.000	.375	.232E+07	.773E+06
20.000	1.250	18.000	.375	.405E+07	.135E+07
20.000	1.500	18.000	.375	.639E+07	.213E+07
20.000	1.750	18.000	.375	.939E+07	.313E+07
20.000	2.000	18.000	.375	.131E+08	.437E+07
20.000	.250	20.000	.375	.810E+05	.270E+05
20.000	.375	20.000	.375	.223E+06	.744E+05
20.000	.500	20.000	.375	.458E+06	.153E+06
20.000	.625	20.000	.375	.801E+06	.267E+06
20.000	.750	20.000	.375	.126E+07	.421E+06
20.000	1.000	20.000	.375	.259E+07	.864E+06
20.000	1.250	20.000	.375	.453E+07	.151E+07
20.000	1.500	20.000	.375	.714E+07	.238E+07
20.000	1.750	20.000	.375	.105E+08	.350E+07
20.000	2.000	20.000	.375	.147E+08	.489E+07
20.000	.250	22.000	.375	.896E+05	.299E+05
20.000	.375	22.000	.375	.247E+06	.823E+05
20.000	.500	22.000	.375	.507E+06	.169E+06
20.000	.625	22.000	.375	.885E+06	.295E+06
20.000	.750	22.000	.375	.140E+07	.466E+06
20.000	1.000	22.000	.375	.287E+07	.956E+06
20.000	1.250	22.000	.375	.501E+07	.167E+07
20.000	1.500	22.000	.375	.790E+07	.263E+07
20.000	1.750	22.000	.375	.116E+08	.387E+07
20.000	2.000	22.000	.375	.162E+08	.541E+07
20.000	.250	24.000	.375	.982E+05	.327E+05
20.000	.375	24.000	.375	.270E+06	.902E+05
20.000	.500	24.000	.375	.555E+06	.185E+06
20.000	.625	24.000	.375	.970E+06	.323E+06
20.000	.750	24.000	.375	.153E+07	.510E+06
20.000	1.000	24.000	.375	.314E+07	.105E+07
20.000	1.250	24.000	.375	.549E+07	.183E+07
20.000	1.500	24.000	.375	.866E+07	.289E+07
20.000	1.750	24.000	.375	.127E+08	.424E+07
20.000	2.000	24.000	.375	.178E+08	.592E+07
20.000	.250	26.000	.375	.107E+06	.356E+05
20.000	.375	26.000	.375	.294E+06	.980E+05

Table 6-1
Continued

ROTA STIFF CALCULATION, CYL. VESSEL

VESSEL OD, FT	VESSEL TCK, IN	NOZZLE OD, IN	NOZZLE TCK, IN STD	ROT STIF IN.LB/DEG INPLANE LONGI	OUTPLANE CIRCU
20.000	.500	26.000	.375	.604E+06	.201E+06
20.000	.625	26.000	.375	.105E+07	.352E+06
20.000	.750	26.000	.375	.166E+07	.555E+06
20.000	1.000	26.000	.375	.341E+07	.114E+07
20.000	1.250	26.000	.375	.597E+07	.199E+07
20.000	1.500	26.000	.375	.941E+07	.314E+07
20.000	1.750	26.000	.375	.138E+08	.461E+07
20.000	2.000	26.000	.375	.193E+08	.644E+07
20.000	.250	28.000	.375	.115E+06	.384E+05
20.000	.375	28.000	.375	.318E+06	.106E+06
20.000	.500	28.000	.375	.652E+06	.217E+06
20.000	.625	28.000	.375	.114E+07	.380E+06
20.000	.750	28.000	.375	.180E+07	.599E+06
20.000	1.000	28.000	.375	.369E+07	.123E+07
20.000	1.250	28.000	.375	.644E+07	.215E+07
20.000	1.500	28.000	.375	.102E+08	.339E+07
20.000	1.750	28.000	.375	.149E+08	.498E+07
20.000	2.000	28.000	.375	.209E+08	.696E+07
20.000	.250	30.000	.375	.124E+06	.413E+05
20.000	.375	30.000	.375	.341E+06	.114E+06
20.000	.500	30.000	.375	.701E+06	.234E+06
20.000	.625	30.000	.375	.122E+07	.408E+06
20.000	.750	30.000	.375	.193E+07	.644E+06
20.000	1.000	30.000	.375	.396E+07	.132E+07
20.000	1.250	30.000	.375	.692E+07	.231E+07
20.000	1.500	30.000	.375	.109E+08	.364E+07
20.000	1.750	30.000	.375	.161E+08	.535E+07
20.000	2.000	30.000	.375	.224E+08	.747E+07
20.000	.250	32.000	.375	.132E+06	.441E+05
20.000	.375	32.000	.375	.365E+06	.122E+06
20.000	.500	32.000	.375	.749E+06	.250E+06
20.000	.625	32.000	.375	.131E+07	.436E+06
20.000	.750	32.000	.375	.206E+07	.688E+06
20.000	1.000	32.000	.375	.424E+07	.141E+07
20.000	1.250	32.000	.375	.740E+07	.247E+07
20.000	1.500	32.000	.375	.117E+08	.389E+07
20.000	1.750	32.000	.375	.172E+08	.572E+07
20.000	2.000	32.000	.375	.240E+08	.799E+07
20.000	.250	36.000	.375	.150E+06	.499E+05
20.000	.375	36.000	.375	.412E+06	.137E+06
20.000	.500	36.000	.375	.846E+06	.282E+06
20.000	.625	36.000	.375	.148E+07	.493E+06
20.000	.750	36.000	.375	.233E+07	.777E+06
20.000	1.000	36.000	.375	.479E+07	.160E+07
20.000	1.250	36.000	.375	.836E+07	.279E+07
20.000	1.500	36.000	.375	.132E+08	.440E+07
20.000	1.750	36.000	.375	.194E+08	.646E+07
20.000	2.000	36.000	.375	.271E+08	.902E+07
20.000	.250	40.000	.375	.167E+06	.556E+05
20.000	.375	40.000	.375	.459E+06	.153E+06
20.000	.500	40.000	.375	.943E+06	.314E+06
20.000	.625	40.000	.375	.165E+07	.549E+06
20.000	.750	40.000	.375	.260E+07	.866E+06
20.000	1.000	40.000	.375	.533E+07	.178E+07
20.000	1.250	40.000	.375	.932E+07	.311E+07
20.000	1.500	40.000	.375	.147E+08	.490E+07
20.000	1.750	40.000	.375	.216E+08	.720E+07
20.000	2.000	40.000	.375	.302E+08	.101E+08
20.000	.250	48.000	.375	.201E+06	.670E+05
20.000	.375	48.000	.375	.554E+06	.185E+06
20.000	.500	48.000	.375	.114E+07	.379E+06

Table 6-1
Continued

ROTA STIFF CALCULATION, CYL. VESSEL

VESSEL OD,FT	VESSEL TCK,IN	NOZZLE OD,IN	NOZZLE TCK,IN STD	ROT STIF IN.LB/DEG INPLANE LONGI	OUTPLANE CIRCU
20.000	.625	48.000	.375	.199E+07	.662E+06
20.000	.750	48.000	.375	.313E+07	.104E+07
20.000	1.000	48.000	.375	.643E+07	.214E+07
20.000	1.250	48.000	.375	.112E+08	.374E+07
20.000	1.500	48.000	.375	.177E+08	.591E+07
20.000	1.750	48.000	.375	.261E+08	.868E+07
20.000	2.000	48.000	.375	.364E+08	.121E+08

7

Pressure and Stress Ratios

By merely multiplying or dividing, P/S ratios may be used to readily determine:

1. Allowable working pressure
2. Working stress
3. Wall thickness required

This extreme simplicity arises because in the formulas devised to predict the stresses in a pipe under internal pressure, the P/S ratio may be equated to a quantity that is dependent only on the diameter and thickness of the pipe and the applicable allowance for threading, mechanical strength, and/or corrosion.

The general formula, adopted by the ASME Boiler Code in the section on power boilers and the ANSI Code for Pressure Piping is:

$$P = \frac{2\, S_E\, (t_m - A)}{D - 2y\, (t_m - A)}$$

This formula may be written as:

$$P/S = \frac{2(t_m - A)}{D - 2y(t_m - A)}$$

where P = Maximum internal service pressure, lbs/in.^{2}
S_E = Allowable stress in material due to internal pressure
t_m = Minimum pipe wall thickness, in.
A = Allowance for threading, mechanical strength, and/or corrosion, in.
D = Outside diameter of pipe, in.
y = Coefficient having values, as follows:

Temperature (°F)	Ferritic Seals (Carbon and Alloys except Austenitic)	Austenitic Steels (Cr-Ni stainless, such as Types 304, 316, and 347)
900	0.4	0.4
950	0.5	0.4
1,000	0.7	0.4
1,050	0.7	0.4
1,100	0.7	0.5
1,150	0.7	0.7

The y value in the general formula reflects the effect of creep at high temperatures. In some ANSI Code sections that do not cover temperatures over 900°F, the y value of .4 is directly inserted in the formula; the formula with y = .4 is known as the "modified lame" formula. In Sections 4 and 8 of ANSI B31 the Barlow formula is used, which is a special case of the general formula in which y = 0. In addition, Section 8 is based on nominal thickness rather than minimum thickness; the tabulated P/S ratios for y = 0 may be placed on a nominal wall basis by multiplying by 8/7.

Tables 7-1 through 7-4 give the precalculated values for the right-hand side of the preceding general equation for each pipe size and weight based on a wall thickness 87½% of nominal and for values of C varying from 0.0 to 100 in. in increments of .005 in. For any pipe size, wall thickness, and corrosion allowance the allowable working pressure is found merely by multiplying the P/S ratio by the allowable stress. Obviously, this relieves the designer from making annoying multiple arithmetical manipulations which might be subject to error.

(Text continued on page 250.)

Table 7-1
Pressure/Stress Ratios Where Y = 0.0

NOMINAL PIPE SIZE	SCHEDULE NUMBER AND/OR WEIGHT	WALL THICKNESS	CORROSION ALLOWANCE-INCHES Y=0.0										
			0.000	0.005	0.010	0.015	0.020	0.025	0.030	0.035	0.040	0.045	0.050
1/8	10S	.049	.2117	.1870	.1623	.1377	.1130	.0883	.0636	.0389	.0142		
1/8	40 ST 40S	.068	.2938	.2691	.2444	.2198	.1951	.1704	.1457	.1210	.0963	.0716	.0469
1/8	80 ST 80S	.095	.4105	.3858	.3611	.3364	.3117	.2870	.2623	.2377	.2130	.1883	.1636
1/4	10S	.065	.2106	.1921	.1736	.1551	.1366	.1181	.0995	.0810	.0625	.0440	.0255
1/4	40 ST 40S	.088	.2852	.2667	.2481	.2296	.2111	.1926	.1741	.1556	.1370	.1185	.1000
1/4	80 ST 80S	.119	.3856	.3671	.3486	.3301	.3116	.2931	.2745	.2560	.2375	.2190	.2005
3/8	10S	.065	.1685	.1537	.1389	.1241	.1093	.0944	.0796	.0648	.0500	.0352	.0204
3/8	40 ST 40S	.091	.2359	.2211	.2063	.1915	.1767	.1619	.1470	.1322	.1174	.1026	.0878
3/8	80 ST 80S	.126	.3267	.3119	.2970	.2822	.2674	.2526	.2378	.2230	.2081	.1933	.1785
1/2	10S	.083	.1729	.1610	.1491	.1372	.1253	.1134	.1015	.0896	.0777	.0658	.0539
1/2	40 ST 40S	.109	.2271	.2152	.2033	.1914	.1795	.1676	.1557	.1437	.1318	.1199	.1080
1/2	80 ST 80S	.147	.3062	.2943	.2824	.2705	.2586	.2467	.2348	.2229	.2110	.1991	.1872
1/2	160	.187	.3896	.3777	.3658	.3539	.3420	.3301	.3182	.3062	.2943	.2824	.2705
1/2	XX	.294	.6125	.6006	.5887	.5768	.5649	.5530	.5411	.5292	.5173	.5054	.4935
3/4	5S	.065	.1083	.0988	.0893	.0798	.0702	.0607	.0512	.0417	.0321	.0226	.0131
3/4	10S	.083	.1383	.1288	.1193	.1098	.1002	.0907	.0812	.0717	.0621	.0526	.0431
3/4	40S	.113	.1883	.1788	.1693	.1598	.1502	.1407	.1312	.1217	.1121	.1026	.0931
3/4	80S	.154	.2567	.2471	.2376	.2281	.2186	.2090	.1995	.1900	.1805	.1710	.1614
3/4		.188	.3133	.3038	.2943	.2848	.2752	.2657	.2562	.2467	.2371	.2276	.2181
3/4	160	.218	.3633	.3538	.3443	.3348	.3252	.3157	.3062	.2967	.2871	.2776	.2681
3/4	XX	.308	.5133	.5038	.4943	.4848	.4752	.4657	.4562	.4467	.4371	.4276	.4181
1	5S	.065	.0865	.0789	.0713	.0637	.0561	.0485	.0409	.0333	.0257	.0181	.0105
1	10S	.109	.1451	.1375	.1298	.1222	.1146	.1070	.0994	.0918	.0842	.0766	.0690
1	40 ST 40S	.133	.1770	.1694	.1618	.1542	.1466	.1390	.1314	.1238	.1162	.1086	.1010
1	80 ST 80S	.179	.2382	.2306	.2230	.2154	.2078	.2002	.1926	.1850	.1774	.1698	.1622
1		.219	.2914	.2838	.2762	.2686	.2610	.2534	.2458	.2382	.2306	.2230	.2154
1	160	.250	.3327	.3251	.3175	.3099	.3023	.2947	.2871	.2795	.2719	.2643	.2567
1	XXO	.358	.4764	.4688	.4612	.4536	.4460	.4384	.4308	.4232	.4156	.4080	.4004
11/4	5S	.065	.0685	.0625	.0565	.0505	.0444	.0384	.0324	.0264	.0203	.0143	.0083
11/4	10S	.109	.1149	.1089	.1029	.0968	.0908	.0848	.0788	.0727	.0667	.0607	.0547
11/4	40 ST 40S	.140	.1476	.1416	.1355	.1295	.1235	.1175	.1114	.1054	.0994	.0934	.0873
11/4	80 ST 80S	.191	.2014	.1953	.1893	.1833	.1773	.1712	.1652	.1592	.1532	.1471	.1411
11/4	160	.250	.2636	.2575	.2515	.2455	.2395	.2334	.2274	.2214	.2154	.2093	.2033
11/4	XX	.382	.4027	.3967	.3907	.3846	.3786	.3726	.3666	.3605	.3545	.3485	.3425

Table 7-1
Continued

NOMINAL PIPE SIZE	SCHEDULE NUMBER AND/OR WEIGHT	WALL THICKNESS	CORROSION ALLOWANCE-INCHES Y=0.0										
			0.000	0.005	0.010	0.015	0.020	0.025	0.030	0.035	0.040	0.045	0.050
11/2	5S	.065	.0599	.0546	.0493	.0441	.0388	.0336	.0283	.0230	.0178	.0125	.0072
11/2	10S	.109	.1004	.0951	.0899	.0846	.0793	.0741	.0688	.0636	.0583	.0530	.0478
11/2	40 ST 40S	.145	.1336	.1283	.1230	.1178	.1125	.1072	.1020	.0967	.0914	.0862	.0809
11/2	80 ST 80S	.200	.1842	.1789	.1737	.1684	.1632	.1579	.1526	.1474	.1421	.1368	.1316
11/2	160	.281	.2588	.2536	.2483	.2430	.2378	.2325	.2272	.2220	.2167	.2114	.2062
11/2	XX	.400	.3684	.3632	.3579	.3526	.3474	.3421	.3368	.3316	.3263	.3211	.3158
2	5S	.065	.0479	.0437	.0395	.0353	.0311	.0268	.0226	.0184	.0142	.0100	.0058
2	10S	.109	.0803	.0761	.0719	.0677	.0635	.0593	.0551	.0508	.0466	.0424	.0382
2	40 ST 40S	.154	.1135	.1093	.1051	.1008	.0966	.0924	.0882	.0840	.0798	.0756	.0714
2		.167	.1231	.1188	.1146	.1104	.1062	.1020	.0978	.0936	.0894	.0852	.0809
2		.188	.1385	.1343	.1301	.1259	.1217	.1175	.1133	.1091	.1048	.1006	.0964
2	80 ST 80S	.218	.1606	.1564	.1522	.1480	.1438	.1396	.1354	.1312	.1269	.1227	.1185
2		.250	.1842	.1800	.1758	.1716	.1674	.1632	.1589	.1547	.1505	.1463	.1421
2		.312	.2299	.2257	.2215	.2173	.2131	.2088	.2046	.2004	.1962	.1920	.1878
2	160	.343	.2527	.2485	.2443	.2401	.2359	.2317	.2275	.2233	.2191	.2148	.2106
2	XX	.436	.3213	.3171	.3128	.3086	.3044	.3002	.2960	.2918	.2876	.2834	.2792
21/2	5S	.083	.0505	.0470	.0436	.0401	.0366	.0331	.0297	.0262	.0227	.0192	.0157
21/2	10S	.120	.0730	.0696	.0661	.0626	.0591	.0557	.0522	.0487	.0452	.0417	.0383
21/2	40 ST 40S	.203	.1236	.1201	.1166	.1131	.1097	.1062	.1027	.0992	.0957	.0923	.0888
21/2		.217	.1321	.1286	.1251	.1217	.1182	.1147	.1112	.1077	.1043	.1008	.0973
21/2	80 ST 805	.276	.1680	.1645	.1610	.1576	.1541	.1506	.1471	.1437	.1402	.1367	.1332
21/2	160	.375	.2283	.2248	.2213	.2178	.2143	.2109	.2074	.2039	.2004	.1970	.1935
21/2	XX	.552	.3360	.3325	.3290	.3256	.3221	.3186	.3151	.3117	.3082	.3047	.3012
3	5S	.083	.0415	.0386	.0358	.0329	.0301	.0272	.0244	.0215	.0186	.0158	.0129
3	10S	.120	.0600	.0571	.0543	.0514	.0486	.0457	.0429	.0400	.0371	.0343	.0314
3		.125	.0625	.0596	.0568	.0539	.0511	.0482	.0454	.0425	.0396	.0368	.0339
3		.148	.0740	.0711	.0683	.0654	.0626	.0597	.0569	.0540	.0511	.0483	.0454
3		.188	.0940	.0911	.0883	.0854	.0826	.0797	.0769	.0740	.0711	.0683	.0654
3	40 ST 40S	.216	.1080	.1051	.1023	.0994	.0966	.0937	.0909	.0880	.0851	.0823	.0794
3		.241	.1205	.1176	.1148	.1119	.1091	.1062	.1034	.1005	.0976	.0948	.0919
3		.254	.1270	.1241	.1213	.1184	.1156	.1127	.1099	.1070	.1041	.1013	.0984
3		.289	.1445	.1416	.1388	.1359	.1331	.1302	.1274	.1245	.1216	.1188	.1159
3	80 XS 805	.300	.1500	.1471	.1443	.1414	.1386	.1357	.1329	.1300	.1271	.1243	.1214
3		.312	.1560	.1531	.1503	.1474	.1446	.1417	.1389	.1360	.1331	.1303	.1274
3		.406	.2030	.2001	.1973	.1944	.1916	.1887	.1859	.1830	.1801	.1773	.1744

Table 7-1
Continued

NOMINAL PIPE SIZE	SCHEDULE NUMBER AND/OR WEIGHT	WALL THICKNESS	CORROSION ALLOWANCE-INCHES Y=0.0										
			0.000	0.005	0.010	0.015	0.020	0.025	0.030	0.035	0.040	0.045	0.050
3	160	.438	.2190	.2161	.2133	.2104	.2076	.2047	.2019	.1990	.1961	.1933	.1904
3	XX	.600	.3000	.2971	.2943	.2914	.2886	.2857	.2829	.2800	.2771	.2743	.2714
31/2	5S	.083	.0363	.0338	.0313	.0288	.0263	.0238	.0213	.0188	.0163	.0138	.0113
31/2	10S	.120	.0525	.0500	.0475	.0450	.0425	.0400	.0375	.0350	.0325	.0300	.0275
31/2		.128	.0560	.0535	.0510	.0485	.0460	.0435	.0410	.0385	.0360	.0335	.0310
31/2		.134	.0586	.0561	.0536	.0511	.0486	.0461	.0436	.0411	.0386	.0361	.0336
31/2		.148	.0647	.0622	.0597	.0572	.0547	.0522	.0497	.0472	.0447	.0422	.0397
31/2		.188	.0822	.0797	.0772	.0747	.0722	.0697	.0672	.0647	.0622	.0597	.0572
31/2	40 ST 40S	.226	.0989	.0964	.0939	.0914	.0889	.0864	.0839	.0814	.0789	.0764	.0739
31/2		.281	.1229	.1204	.1179	.1154	.1129	.1104	.1079	.1054	.1029	.1004	.0979
31/2	80 XS 80S	.318	.1391	.1366	.1341	.1316	.1291	.1266	.1241	.1216	.1191	.1166	.1141
31/2		.344	.1505	.1480	.1455	.1430	.1405	.1380	.1355	.1330	.1305	.1280	.1255
31/2		.469	.2052	.2027	.2002	.1977	.1952	.1927	.1902	.1877	.1852	.1827	.1802
31/2		.636	.2782	.2757	.2732	.2707	.2682	.2657	.2632	.2607	.2582	.2557	.2532
4	5S	.083	.0323	.0301	.0278	.0256	.0234	.0212	.0189	.0167	.0145	.0123	.0101
4	10S	.120	.0467	.0444	.0422	.0400	.0378	.0356	.0333	.0311	.0289	.0267	.0244
4		.128	.0498	.0476	.0453	.0431	.0409	.0387	.0364	.0342	.0320	.0298	.0276
4		.134	.0521	.0499	.0477	.0454	.0432	.0410	.0388	.0366	.0343	.0321	.0299
4		.142	.0552	.0530	.0508	.0486	.0463	.0441	.0419	.0397	.0374	.0352	.0330
4		.165	.0642	.0619	.0597	.0575	.0553	.0531	.0508	.0486	.0464	.0442	.0419
4		.188	.0731	.0709	.0687	.0664	.0642	.0620	.0598	.0576	.0553	.0531	.0509
4		.205	.0797	.0775	.0753	.0731	.0708	.0686	.0664	.0642	.0619	.0597	.0575
4	40 ST40S	.237	.0922	.0899	.0877	.0855	.0833	.0811	.0788	.0766	.0744	.0722	.0699
4		.250	.0972	.0950	.0928	.0906	.0883	.0861	.0839	.0817	.0794	.0772	.0750
4		.271	.1054	.1032	.1009	.0987	.0965	.0943	.0921	.0898	.0876	.0854	.0832
4		.281	.1093	.1071	.1048	.1026	.1004	.0982	.0959	.0937	.0915	.0893	.0871
4		.300	.1167	.1144	.1122	.1100	.1078	.1056	.1033	.1011	.0989	.0967	.0944
4		.312	.1213	.1191	.1169	.1147	.1124	.1102	.1080	.1058	.1036	.1013	.0991
4	80 XS 80S	.337	.1311	.1288	.1266	.1244	.1222	.1199	.1177	.1155	.1133	.1111	.1088
4		.375	.1458	.1436	.1414	.1392	.1369	.1347	.1325	.1303	.1281	.1258	.1236
4	120	.438	.1703	.1681	.1659	.1637	.1614	.1592	.1570	.1548	.1526	.1503	.1481
4		.500	.1944	.1922	.1900	.1878	.1856	.1833	.1811	.1789	.1767	.1744	.1722
4	160	.531	.2065	.2043	.2021	.1998	.1976	.1954	.1932	.1909	.1887	.1865	.1843
4	XX	.674	.2621	.2599	.2577	.2554	.2532	.2510	.2488	.2466	.2443	.2421	.2399
5	5S	.109	.0343	.0325	.0307	.0289	.0271	.0253	.0235	.0217	.0199	.0181	.0163
5	10S	.134	.0422	.0404	.0386	.0368	.0350	.0332	.0314	.0296	.0278	.0260	.0242

Table 7-1
Continued

NOMINAL PIPE SIZE	SCHEDULE NUMBER AND/OR WEIGHT	WALL THICKNESS	CORROSION ALLOWANCE-INCHES Y=0.0										
			0.000	0.005	0.010	0.015	0.020	0.025	0.030	0.035	0.040	0.045	0.050
5	40 ST 40S	.258	.0812	.0794	.0776	.0758	.0740	.0722	.0704	.0686	.0668	.0650	.0632
5		.352	.1107	.1089	.1071	.1053	.1035	.1017	.0999	.0981	.0964	.0946	.0928
5	80 XS 80S	.375	.1180	.1162	.1144	.1126	.1108	.1090	.1072	.1054	.1036	.1018	.1000
5		.438	.1378	.1360	.1342	.1324	.1306	.1288	.1270	.1252	.1234	.1216	.1198
5	120	.500	.1573	.1555	.1537	.1519	.1501	.1483	.1465	.1447	.1429	.1411	.1393
5	160	.625	.1966	.1948	.1930	.1912	.1894	.1876	.1858	.1840	.1822	.1804	.1786
5	XX	.750	.2359	.2341	.2323	.2305	.2287	.2269	.2251	.2234	.2216	.2198	.2180
6	5S	.109	.0288	.0273	.0258	.0243	.0228	.0212	.0197	.0182	.0167	.0152	.0137
6	10S	.134	.0354	.0339	.0324	.0309	.0294	.0278	.0263	.0248	.0233	.0218	.0203
6		.169	.0446	.0431	.0416	.0401	.0386	.0371	.0356	.0341	.0326	.0311	.0295
6		.180	.0475	.0460	.0445	.0430	.0415	.0400	.0385	.0370	.0355	.0340	.0325
6		.188	.0497	.0482	.0466	.0451	.0436	.0421	.0406	.0391	.0376	.0361	.0346
6		.219	.0578	.0563	.0548	.0533	.0518	.0503	.0488	.0473	.0458	.0443	.0428
6		.250	.0660	.0645	.0630	.0615	.0600	.0585	.0570	.0555	.0540	.0525	.0509
6		.277	.0732	.0717	.0702	.0686	.0671	.0656	.0641	.0626	.0611	.0596	.0581
6	40 ST 40S	.280	.0740	.0725	.0709	.0694	.0679	.0664	.0649	.0634	.0619	.0604	.0589
6		.375	.0991	.0975	.0960	.0945	.0930	.0915	.0900	.0885	.0870	.0855	.0840
6	80 XS 80S	.432	.1141	.1126	.1111	.1096	.1081	.1066	.1051	.1035	.1020	.1005	.0990
6		.500	.1321	.1306	.1291	.1275	.1260	.1245	.1230	.1215	.1200	.1185	.1170
6	120	.562	.1485	.1469	.1454	.1439	.1424	.1409	.1394	.1379	.1364	.1349	.1334
6	160	.718	.1897	.1882	.1866	.1851	.1836	.1821	.1806	.1791	.1776	.1761	.1746
6	XX	.864	.2282	.2267	.2252	.2237	.2222	.2207	.2192	.2177	.2162	.2146	.2131
8	5S	.109	.0221	.0210	.0198	.0186	.0175	.0163	.0152	.0140	.0128	.0117	.0105
8	10S	.148	.0300	.0289	.0277	.0266	.0254	.0242	.0231	.0219	.0208	.0196	.0184
8		.158	.0321	.0309	.0297	.0286	.0274	.0263	.0251	.0239	.0228	.0216	.0205
8		.165	.0335	.0323	.0312	.0300	.0288	.0277	.0265	.0254	.0242	.0230	.0219
8		.188	.0381	.0370	.0358	.0347	.0335	.0323	.0312	.0300	.0289	.0277	.0266
8		.203	.0412	.0400	.0389	.0377	.0366	.0354	.0342	.0331	.0319	.0308	.0296
8		.219	.0444	.0433	.0421	.0410	.0398	.0386	.0375	.0363	.0352	.0340	.0328
8		.238	.0483	.0471	.0460	.0448	.0437	.0425	.0413	.0402	.0390	.0379	.0367
8	20	.250	.0507	.0496	.0484	.0472	.0461	.0449	.0438	.0426	.0414	.0403	.0391
8	30	.277	.0562	.0550	.0539	.0527	.0516	.0504	.0492	.0481	.0469	.0458	.0446
8	40 ST 40S	.322	.0653	.0642	.0630	.0619	.0607	.0595	.0584	.0572	.0561	.0549	.0537
8		.344	.0698	.0686	.0675	.0663	.0652	.0640	.0628	.0617	.0605	.0594	.0582
8		.352	.0714	.0703	.0691	.0679	.0668	.0656	.0645	.0633	.0621	.0610	.0598
8		.375	.0761	.0749	.0738	.0726	.0714	.0703	.0691	.0680	.0668	.0657	.0645

Table 7-1
Continued

NOMINAL PIPE SIZE	SCHEDULE NUMBER AND/OR WEIGHT	WALL THICKNESS	CORROSION ALLOWANCE-INCHES Y=0.0										
			0.000	0.005	0.010	0.015	0.020	0.025	0.030	0.035	0.040	0.045	0.050
8	60	.406	.0824	.0812	.0801	.0789	.0777	.0766	.0754	.0743	.0731	.0719	.0708
8		.469	.0952	.0940	.0928	.0917	.0905	.0894	.0882	.0870	.0859	.0847	.0836
8	80 XS 80S	.500	.1014	.1003	.0991	.0980	.0968	.0957	.0945	.0933	.0922	.0910	.0899
8	100	.593	.1203	.1192	.1180	.1168	.1157	.1145	.1134	.1122	.1110	.1099	.1087
8		.625	.1268	.1257	.1245	.1233	.1222	.1210	.1199	.1187	.1175	.1164	.1152
8	120	.718	.1457	.1445	.1434	.1422	.1410	.1399	.1387	.1376	.1364	.1352	.1341
8	140	.812	.1648	.1636	.1624	.1613	.1601	.1590	.1578	.1566	.1555	.1543	.1532
8	XX	.875	.1775	.1764	.1752	.1741	.1729	.1717	.1706	.1694	.1683	.1671	.1659
8	160	.906	.1838	.1827	.1815	.1803	.1792	.1780	.1769	.1757	.1746	.1734	.1722
10	5S	.134	.0218	.0209	.0200	.0190	.0181	.0172	.0162	.0153	.0144	.0134	.0125
10	10S	.165	.0269	.0259	.0250	.0241	.0231	.0222	.0213	.0203	.0194	.0185	.0176
10		.188	.0306	.0297	.0287	.0278	.0269	.0260	.0250	.0241	.0232	.0222	.0213
10		.203	.0330	.0321	.0312	.0303	.0293	.0284	.0275	.0265	.0256	.0247	.0237
10		.219	.0357	.0347	.0338	.0329	.0319	.0310	.0301	.0291	.0282	.0273	.0263
10	20	.250	.0407	.0398	.0388	.0379	.0370	.0360	.0351	.0342	.0333	.0323	.0314
10		.279	.0454	.0445	.0436	.0426	.0417	.0408	.0398	.0389	.0380	.0370	.0361
10	30	.307	.0500	.0490	.0481	.0472	.0463	.0453	.0444	.0435	.0425	.0416	.0407
10		.348	.0567	.0557	.0548	.0539	.0529	.0520	.0511	.0501	.0492	.0483	.0473
10	40 ST 40S	.365	.0594	.0585	.0576	.0566	.0557	.0548	.0538	.0529	.0520	.0510	.0501
10		.395	.0643	.0634	.0624	.0615	.0606	.0597	.0587	.0578	.0569	.0559	.0550
10	60 XS 80S	.500	.0814	.0805	.0795	.0786	.0777	.0767	.0758	.0749	.0740	.0730	.0721
10		.531	.0864	.0855	.0846	.0837	.0827	.0818	.0809	.0799	.0790	.0781	.0771
10	80	.593	.0965	.0956	.0947	.0937	.0928	.0919	.0910	.0900	.0891	.0882	.0872
10	100	.718	.1169	.1160	.1150	.1141	.1132	.1122	.1113	.1104	.1094	.1085	.1076
10		.750	.1221	.1212	.1202	.1193	.1184	.1174	.1165	.1156	.1147	.1137	.1128
10	120	.843	.1372	.1363	.1354	.1344	.1335	.1326	.1317	.1307	.1298	.1289	.1279
10	140	1.000	.1628	.1619	.1609	.1600	.1591	.1581	.1572	.1563	.1553	.1544	.1535
10		1.062	.1729	.1720	.1710	.1701	.1692	.1682	.1673	.1664	.1654	.1645	.1636
10	160	1.125	.1831	.1822	.1813	.1803	.1794	.1785	.1776	.1766	.1757	.1748	.1738
12	5S	.156	.0214	.0206	.0198	.0191	.0183	.0175	.0167	.0159	.0151	.0144	.0136
12	10S	.180	.0247	.0239	.0231	.0224	.0216	.0208	.0200	.0192	.0184	.0176	.0169
12		.203	.0279	.0271	.0263	.0255	.0247	.0239	.0232	.0224	.0216	.0208	.0200
12		.219	.0301	.0293	.0285	.0277	.0269	.0261	.0254	.0246	.0238	.0230	.0222
12		.238	.0327	.0319	.0311	.0303	.0295	.0287	.0280	.0272	.0264	.0256	.0248
12	20	.250	.0343	.0335	.0327	.0320	.0312	.0304	.0296	.0288	.0280	.0273	.0265
12		.279	.0383	.0375	.0367	.0359	.0352	.0344	.0336	.0328	.0320	.0312	.0305

Table 7-1
Continued

NOMINAL PIPE SIZE	SCHEDULE NUMBER AND/OR WEIGHT	WALL THICKNESS	CORROSION ALLOWANCE-INCHES									Y=0.0	
			0.000	0.005	0.010	0.015	0.020	0.025	0.030	0.035	0.040	0.045	0.050
12		.300	.0412	.0404	.0396	.0388	.0380	.0373	.0365	.0357	.0349	.0341	.0333
12	30	.330	.0453	.0445	.0437	.0429	.0422	.0414	.0406	.0398	.0390	.0382	.0375
12		.344	.0472	.0464	.0456	.0449	.0441	.0433	.0425	.0417	.0409	.0402	.0394
12	ST 40S	.375	.0515	.0507	.0499	.0491	.0483	.0475	.0468	.0460	.0452	.0444	.0436
12	40	.406	.0557	.0549	.0542	.0534	.0526	.0518	.0510	.0502	.0495	.0487	.0479
12		.438	.0601	.0593	.0585	.0578	.0570	.0562	.0554	.0546	.0538	.0531	.0523
12	XS 80S	.500	.0686	.0678	.0671	.0663	.0655	.0647	.0639	.0631	.0624	.0616	.0608
12	60	.562	.0771	.0764	.0756	.0748	.0740	.0732	.0724	.0716	.0709	.0701	.0693
12		.625	.0858	.0850	.0842	.0834	.0826	.0819	.0811	.0803	.0795	.0787	.0779
12	80	.687	.0943	.0935	.0927	.0919	.0912	.0904	.0896	.0888	.0880	.0872	.0865
12	100	.843	.1157	.1149	.1141	.1134	.1126	.1118	.1110	.1102	.1094	.1086	.1079
12		.875	.1201	.1193	.1185	.1177	.1170	.1162	.1154	.1146	.1138	.1130	.1123
12	120	1.000	.1373	.1365	.1357	.1349	.1341	.1333	.1325	.1318	.1310	.1302	.1294
12	140	1.125	.1544	.1536	.1528	.1521	.1513	.1505	.1497	.1489	.1481	.1474	.1466
12		1.219	.1673	.1665	.1657	.1650	.1642	.1634	.1626	.1618	.1610	.1603	.1595
12	160	1.312	.1801	.1793	.1785	.1777	.1769	.1762	.1754	.1746	.1738	.1730	.1722
14		.188	.0235	.0228	.0221	.0214	.0206	.0199	.0192	.0185	.0178	.0171	.0164
14		.220	.0275	.0268	.0261	.0254	.0246	.0239	.0232	.0225	.0218	.0211	.0204
14		.238	.0297	.0290	.0283	.0276	.0269	.0262	.0255	.0247	.0240	.0233	.0226
14	10	.250	.0313	.0305	.0298	.0291	.0284	.0277	.0270	.0262	.0255	.0248	.0241
14	20	.312	.0390	.0383	.0376	.0369	.0361	.0354	.0347	.0340	.0333	.0326	.0319
14	30ST	.375	.0469	.0462	.0454	.0447	.0440	.0433	.0426	.0419	.0412	.0404	.0397
14		.406	.0507	.0500	.0493	.0486	.0479	.0472	.0465	.0457	.0450	.0443	.0436
14	40	.438	.0547	.0540	.0533	.0526	.0519	.0512	.0505	.0497	.0490	.0483	.0476
14		.469	.0586	.0579	.0572	.0565	.0558	.0551	.0543	.0536	.0529	.0522	.0515
14	XS	.500	.0625	.0618	.0611	.0604	.0596	.0589	.0582	.0575	.0568	.0561	.0554
14	60	.593	.0741	.0734	.0727	.0720	.0713	.0706	.0698	.0691	.0684	.0677	.0670
14		.625	.0781	.0774	.0767	.0760	.0753	.0746	.0738	.0731	.0724	.0717	.0710
14		.656	.0820	.0813	.0806	.0799	.0791	.0784	.0777	.0770	.0763	.0756	.0749
14	80	.750	.0938	.0930	.0923	.0916	.0909	.0902	.0895	.0887	.0880	.0873	.0866
14	100	.937	.1171	.1164	.1157	.1150	.1143	.1136	.1128	.1121	.1114	.1107	.1100
14	120	1.093	.1366	.1359	.1352	.1345	.1338	.1331	.1323	.1316	.1309	.1302	.1295
14	140	1.250	.1563	.1555	.1548	.1541	.1534	.1527	.1520	.1512	.1505	.1498	.1491
14		1.344	.1680	.1673	.1666	.1659	.1651	.1644	.1637	.1630	.1623	.1616	.1609
14	160	1.406	.1757	.1750	.1743	.1736	.1729	.1722	.1715	.1707	.1700	.1693	.1686
16		.188	.0206	.0199	.0193	.0187	.0181	.0174	.0168	.0162	.0156	.0149	.0143

Table 7-1
Continued

NOMINAL PIPE SIZE	SCHEDULE NUMBER AND/OR WEIGHT	WALL THICKNESS	CORROSION ALLOWANCE-INCHES Y=0.0										
			0.000	0.005	0.010	0.015	0.020	0.025	0.030	0.035	0.040	0.045	0.050
16		.238	.0260	.0254	.0248	.0242	.0235	.0229	.0223	.0217	.0210	.0204	.0198
16	10	.250	.0273	.0267	.0261	.0255	.0248	.0242	.0236	.0230	.0223	.0217	.0211
16		.281	.0307	.0301	.0295	.0289	.0282	.0276	.0270	.0264	.0257	.0251	.0245
16	20	.312	.0341	.0335	.0329	.0322	.0316	.0310	.0304	.0297	.0291	.0285	.0279
16		.344	.0376	.0370	.0364	.0357	.0351	.0345	.0339	.0332	.0326	.0320	.0314
16	30 ST	.375	.0410	.0404	.0398	.0391	.0385	.0379	.0373	.0366	.0360	.0354	.0348
16		.406	.0444	.0438	.0432	.0425	.0419	.0413	.0407	.0400	.0394	.0388	.0382
16		.438	.0479	.0473	.0467	.0460	.0454	.0448	.0442	.0435	.0429	.0423	.0417
16		.469	.0513	.0507	.0500	.0494	.0488	.0482	.0475	.0469	.0463	.0457	.0450
16	40 XS	.500	.0547	.0541	.0534	.0528	.0522	.0516	.0509	.0503	.0497	.0491	.0484
16		.531	.0581	.0575	.0568	.0562	.0556	.0550	.0543	.0537	.0531	.0525	.0518
16	60	.656	.0717	.0711	.0705	.0699	.0692	.0686	.0680	.0674	.0667	.0661	.0655
16		.688	.0752	.0746	.0740	.0734	.0727	.0721	.0715	.0709	.0702	.0696	.0690
16		.750	.0820	.0814	.0808	.0802	.0795	.0789	.0783	.0777	.0770	.0764	.0758
16	80	.843	.0922	.0916	.0910	.0903	.0897	.0891	.0885	.0878	.0872	.0866	.0860
16	100	1.031	.1128	.1121	.1115	.1109	.1103	.1096	.1090	.1084	.1078	.1071	.1065
16	120	1.218	.1332	.1326	.1320	.1313	.1307	.1301	.1295	.1288	.1282	.1276	.1270
16	140	1.438	.1573	.1567	.1560	.1554	.1548	.1542	.1535	.1529	.1523	.1517	.1510
16		1.500	.1641	.1634	.1628	.1622	.1616	.1609	.1603	.1597	.1591	.1584	.1578
16	160	1.593	.1742	.1736	.1730	.1724	.1717	.1711	.1705	.1699	.1692	.1686	.1680
18	10	.250	.0243	.0237	.0232	.0226	.0221	.0215	.0210	.0204	.0199	.0193	.0187
18	20	.312	.0303	.0298	.0292	.0287	.0281	.0276	.0270	.0264	.0259	.0253	.0248
18	ST	.375	.0365	.0359	.0353	.0348	.0342	.0337	.0331	.0326	.0320	.0315	.0309
18	30	.438	.0426	.0420	.0415	.0409	.0404	.0398	.0392	.0387	.0381	.0376	.0370
18	XS	.500	.0486	.0481	.0475	.0469	.0464	.0458	.0453	.0447	.0442	.0436	.0431
18	40	.562	.0546	.0541	.0535	.0530	.0524	.0519	.0513	.0507	.0502	.0496	.0491
18		.594	.0577	.0572	.0566	.0561	.0555	.0550	.0544	.0539	.0533	.0527	.0522
18		.625	.0608	.0602	.0597	.0591	.0585	.0580	.0574	.0569	.0563	.0558	.0552
18		.719	.0699	.0693	.0688	.0682	.0677	.0671	.0666	.0660	.0655	.0649	.0643
18	60	.750	.0729	.0724	.0718	.0712	.0707	.0701	.0696	.0690	.0685	.0679	.0674
18		.812	.0789	.0784	.0778	.0773	.0767	.0762	.0756	.0751	.0745	.0739	.0734
18	80	.937	.0911	.0905	.0900	.0894	.0889	.0883	.0878	.0872	.0867	.0861	.0855
18	100	1.156	.1124	.1118	.1113	.1107	.1102	.1096	.1091	.1085	.1079	.1074	.1068
18	120	1.375	.1337	.1331	.1326	.1320	.1315	.1309	.1303	.1298	.1292	.1287	.1281
18	140	1.562	.1519	.1513	.1507	.1502	.1496	.1491	.1485	.1480	.1474	.1469	.1463
18		1.688	.1641	.1636	.1630	.1624	.1619	.1613	.1608	.1602	.1597	.1591	.1586

Table 7-1
Continued

NOMINAL PIPE SIZE	SCHEDULE NUMBER AND/OR WEIGHT	WALL THICKNESS	CORROSION ALLOWANCE-INCHES									Y=0.0	
			0.000	0.005	0.010	0.015	0.020	0.025	0.030	0.035	0.040	0.045	0.050
18	160	1.781	.1732	.1726	.1720	.1715	.1709	.1704	.1698	.1693	.1687	.1682	.1676
20	10	.250	.0219	.0214	.0209	.0204	.0199	.0194	.0189	.0184	.0179	.0174	.0169
20		.312	.0273	.0268	.0263	.0258	.0253	.0248	.0243	.0238	.0233	.0228	.0223
20	20 ST	.375	.0328	.0323	.0318	.0313	.0308	.0303	.0298	.0293	.0288	.0283	.0278
20		.438	.0383	.0378	.0373	.0368	.0363	.0358	.0353	.0348	.0343	.0338	.0333
20	30 XS	.500	.0437	.0432	.0427	.0422	.0417	.0412	.0407	.0402	.0397	.0393	.0387
20		.562	.0492	.0487	.0482	.0477	.0472	.0467	.0462	.0457	.0452	.0447	.0442
20	40	.593	.0519	.0514	.0509	.0504	.0499	.0494	.0489	.0484	.0479	.0474	.0469
20		.625	.0547	.0542	.0537	.0532	.0527	.0522	.0517	.0512	.0507	.0502	.0497
20	60	.812	.0710	.0705	.0700	.0695	.0690	.0685	.0680	.0675	.0670	.0665	.0660
20		.875	.0766	.0761	.0756	.0751	.0746	.0741	.0736	.0731	.0726	.0721	.0716
20		.906	.0793	.0788	.0783	.0778	.0773	.0768	.0763	.0758	.0753	.0748	.0743
20	80	1.031	.0902	.0897	.0892	.0887	.0882	.0877	.0872	.0867	.0862	.0857	.0852
20		1.250	.1094	.1089	.1084	.1079	.1074	.1069	.1064	.1059	.1054	.1049	.1044
20	100	1.281	.1121	.1116	.1111	.1106	.1101	.1096	.1091	.1086	.1081	.1076	.1071
20	120	1.500	.1312	.1307	.1302	.1297	.1292	.1287	.1282	.1277	.1272	.1267	.1262
20	140	1.750	.1531	.1526	.1521	.1516	.1511	.1506	.1501	.1496	.1491	.1486	.1481
20		1.844	.1613	.1608	.1603	.1598	.1593	.1588	.1583	.1578	.1573	.1568	.1563
20	160	1.968	.1722	.1717	.1712	.1707	.1702	.1697	.1692	.1687	.1682	.1677	.1672
22	LG	.250	.0199	.0194	.0190	.0185	.0181	.0176	.0172	.0167	.0162	.0158	.0153
22	ST	.375	.0298	.0294	.0289	.0285	.0280	.0276	.0271	.0266	.0262	.0257	.0253
22	XS	.500	.0398	.0393	.0389	.0384	.0380	.0375	.0370	.0366	.0361	.0357	.0352
24	10	.250	.0182	.0178	.0174	.0170	.0166	.0161	.0157	.0153	.0149	.0145	.0141
24		.312	.0227	.0223	.0219	.0215	.0211	.0207	.0202	.0198	.0194	.0190	.0186
24	20 ST	.375	.0273	.0269	.0265	.0261	.0257	.0253	.0248	.0244	.0240	.0236	.0232
24		.438	.0319	.0315	.0311	.0307	.0303	.0299	.0294	.0290	.0286	.0282	.0278
24	XS	.500	.0365	.0360	.0356	.0352	.0348	.0344	.0340	.0335	.0331	.0327	.0323
24	30	.562	.0410	.0406	.0401	.0397	.0393	.0389	.0385	.0381	.0376	.0372	.0368
24		.625	.0456	.0452	.0447	.0443	.0439	.0435	.0431	.0427	.0422	.0418	.0414
24	40	.687	.0501	.0497	.0493	.0488	.0484	.0480	.0476	.0472	.0468	.0463	.0459
24		.750	.0547	.0543	.0539	.0534	.0530	.0526	.0522	.0518	.0514	.0509	.0505
24	60	.968	.0706	.0702	.0697	.0693	.0689	.0685	.0681	.0677	.0672	.0668	.0664
24		1.031	.0752	.0748	.0743	.0739	.0735	.0731	.0727	.0723	.0718	.0714	.0710
24	80	1.218	.0888	.0884	.0880	.0876	.0871	.0867	.0863	.0859	.0855	.0851	.0846
24	100	1.531	.1116	.1112	.1108	.1104	.1100	.1096	.1091	.1087	.1083	.1079	.1075

Table 7-1
Continued

NOMINAL PIPE SIZE	SCHEDULE NUMBER AND/OR WEIGHT	WALL THICKNESS	CORROSION ALLOWANCE-INCHES									Y=0.0	
			0.000	0.005	0.010	0.015	0.020	0.025	0.030	0.035	0.040	0.045	0.050
24	120	1.812	.1321	.1317	.1313	.1309	.1305	.1300	.1296	.1292	.1288	.1284	.1280
24	140	2.062	.1504	.1499	.1495	.1491	.1487	.1483	.1479	.1474	.1470	.1466	.1462
24		2.188	.1595	.1591	.1587	.1583	.1579	.1575	.1570	.1566	.1562	.1558	.1554
24	160	2.343	.1708	.1704	.1700	.1696	.1692	.1688	.1683	.1679	.1675	.1671	.1667
26	ST	.375	.0252	.0249	.0245	.0241	.0237	.0233	.0229	.0225	.0222	.0218	.0214
26	XS	.500	.0337	.0333	.0329	.0325	.0321	.0317	.0313	.0310	.0306	.0302	.0298
30	10	.312	.0182	.0179	.0175	.0172	.0169	.0165	.0162	.0159	.0155	.0152	.0149
30	ST	.375	.0219	.0215	.0212	.0209	.0205	.0202	.0199	.0195	.0192	.0189	.0185
30		.438	.0255	.0252	.0249	.0245	.0242	.0239	.0235	.0232	.0229	.0225	.0222
30	20 XS	.500	.0292	.0288	.0285	.0282	.0278	.0275	.0272	.0268	.0265	.0262	.0258
30		.562	.0328	.0324	.0321	.0318	.0314	.0311	.0308	.0304	.0301	.0298	.0294
30	30	.625	.0365	.0361	.0358	.0355	.0351	.0348	.0345	.0341	.0338	.0335	.0331
34	ST	.375	.0193	.0190	.0187	.0184	.0181	.0178	.0175	.0172	.0169	.0167	.0164
34	XS	.500	.0257	.0254	.0251	.0249	.0246	.0243	.0240	.0237	.0234	.0231	.0228
36	ST	.375	.0182	.0180	.0177	.0174	.0171	.0168	.0166	.0163	.0160	.0157	.0155
36	XS	.500	.0243	.0240	.0237	.0235	.0232	.0229	.0226	.0224	.0221	.0218	.0215
42	ST	.375	.0156	.0154	.0151	.0149	.0147	.0144	.0142	.0140	.0137	.0135	.0132
42	XS	.500	.0208	.0206	.0204	.0201	.0199	.0196	.0194	.0192	.0189	.0187	.0185
48	ST	.375	.0137	.0135	.0133	.0130	.0128	.0126	.0124	.0122	.0120	.0118	.0116
48	XS	.500	.0182	.0180	.0178	.0176	.0174	.0172	.0170	.0168	.0166	.0164	.0161

Table 7-1
Continued

NOM-INAL PIPE SIZE	SCHEDULE NUMBER AND/OR WEIGHT	WALL THICK-NESS	CORROSION ALLOWANCE-INCHES									Y=0.0
			0.055	0.060	0.065	0.070	0.075	0.080	0.085	0.90	0.095	0.100
1/8	10S	.049	0.0000									
1/8	40 ST 40S	.068	.0222									
1/8	80 ST 80S	.095	.1389	.1142	.0895	.0648	.0401	.0154				
1/4	10S	.065	.0069									
1/4	40 ST 40S	.088	.0815	.0630	.0444	.0259	.0074					
1/4	80 ST 80S	.119	.1819	.1634	.1449	.1264	.1079	.0894	.0708	.0523	.0338	.0153
3/8	10S	.065	.0056									
3/8	40 ST 40S	.091	.0730	.0581	.0433	.0285	.0137					
3/8	80 ST 80S	.126	.1637	.1489	.1341	.1193	.1044	.0896	.0748	.0600	.0452	.0304
1/2	10S	.083	.0420	.0301	.0182	.0063						
1/2	40 ST 40S	.109	.0961	.0842	.0723	.0604	.0485	.0366	.0247	.0128	.0009	
1/2	80 ST 80S	.147	.1753	.1634	.1515	.1396	.1277	.1158	.1039	.0920	.0801	.0682
1/2	160	.187	.2586	.2467	.2348	.2229	.2110	.1991	.1872	.1753	.1634	.1515
1/2	XX	.294	.4815	.4696	.4577	.4458	.4339	.4220	.4101	.3982	.3863	.3744
3/4	5S	.065	.0036									
3/4	10S	.083	.0336	.0240	.0145	.0050						
3/4	40S	.113	.0836	.0740	.0645	.0550	.0455	.0360	.0264	.0169	.0074	
3/4	80S	.154	.1519	.1424	.1329	.1233	.1138	.1043	.0948	.0852	.0757	.0662
3/4		.188	.2086	.1990	.1895	.1800	.1705	.1610	.1514	.1419	.1324	.1229
3/4	160	.218	.2586	.2490	.2395	.2300	.2205	.2110	.2014	.1919	.1824	.1729
3/4	XX	.308	.4086	.3990	.3895	.3800	.3705	.3610	.3514	.3419	.3324	.3229
1	5S	.065	.0029									
1	10S	.109	.0614	.0538	.0462	.0386	.0310	.0234	.0158	.0082	.0006	
1	40 ST 40S	.133	.0933	.0857	.0781	.0705	.0629	.0553	.0477	.0401	.0325	.0249
1	80 ST 80S	.179	.1546	.1470	.1394	.1317	.1241	.1165	.1089	.1013	.0937	.0861
1		.219	.2078	.2002	.1926	.1850	.1774	.1698	.1622	.1546	.1470	.1394
1	160	.250	.2490	.2414	.2338	.2262	.2186	.2110	.2034	.1958	.1882	.1806
1	XXO	.358	.3928	.3852	.3776	.3700	.3624	.3548	.3471	.3395	.3319	.3243
11/4	5S	.065	.0023									
11/4	10S	.109	.0486	.0426	.0366	.0306	.0245	.0185	.0125	.0065	.0005	
11/4	40 ST 40S	.140	.0813	.0753	.0693	.0633	.0572	.0512	.0452	.0392	.0331	.0271
11/4	80 ST 80S	.191	.1351	.1291	.1230	.1170	.1110	.1050	.0989	.0929	.0869	.0809
11/4	160	.250	.1973	.1913	.1852	.1792	.1732	.1672	.1611	.1551	.1491	.1431
11/4	XX	.382	.3364	.3304	.3244	.3184	.3123	.3063	.3003	.2943	.2883	.2822

Table 7-1
Continued

NOMINAL PIPE SIZE	SCHEDULE NUMBER AND/OR WEIGHT	WALL THICKNESS	CORROSION ALLOWANCE-INCHES									Y=0.0
			0.055	0.060	0.065	0.070	0.075	0.080	0.085	0.90	0.095	0.100
11/2	5S	.065	.0020									
11/2	10S	.109	.0425	.0372	.0320	.0267	.0214	.0162	.0109	.0057	.0004	
11/2	40 ST 40S	.145	.0757	.0704	.0651	.0599	.0546	.0493	.0441	.0388	.0336	.0283
11/2	80 ST 80S	.200	.1263	.1211	.1158	.1105	.1053	.1000	.0947	.0895	.0842	.0789
11/2	160	.281	.2009	.1957	.1904	.1851	.1799	.1746	.1693	.1641	.1588	.1536
11/2	XX	.400	.3105	.3053	.3000	.2947	.2895	.2842	.2789	.2737	.2684	.2632
2	5S	.065	.0016									
2	10S	.109	.0340	.0298	.0256	.0214	.0172	.0129	.0087	.0045	.0003	
2	40 ST 40S	.154	.0672	.0629	.0587	.0545	.0503	.0461	.0419	.0377	.0335	.0293
2		.167	.0767	.0725	.0683	.0641	.0599	.0557	.0515	.0473	.0431	.0388
2		.188	.0922	.0880	.0838	.0796	.0754	.0712	.0669	.0627	.0585	.0543
2	80 ST 80S	.218	.1143	.1101	.1059	.1017	.0975	.0933	.0891	.0848	.0806	.0764
2		.250	.1379	.1337	.1295	.1253	.1211	.1168	.1126	.1084	.1042	.1000
2		.312	.1836	.1794	.1752	.1709	.1667	.1625	.1583	.1541	.1499	.1457
2	160	.343	.2064	.2022	.1980	.1938	.1896	.1854	.1812	.1769	.1727	.1685
2	XX	.436	.2749	.2707	.2665	.2623	.2581	.2539	.2497	.2455	.2413	.2371
21/2	5S	.083	.0123	.0088	.0053	.0018						
21/2	10S	.120	.0348	.0313	.0278	.0243	.0209	.0174	.0139	.0104	.0070	.0035
21/2	40 ST 40S	.203	.0853	.0818	.0783	.0749	.0714	.0679	.0644	.0610	.0575	.0540
21/2		.217	.0938	.0903	.0869	.0834	.0799	.0764	.0730	.0695	.0660	.0625
21/2	80 ST 805	.276	.1297	.1263	.1228	.1193	.1158	.1123	.1089	.1054	.1019	.0984
21/2	160	.375	.1900	.1865	.1830	.1796	.1761	.1726	.1691	.1657	.1622	.1587
21/2	XX	.552	.2977	.2943	.2908	.2873	.2838	.2803	.2769	.2734	.2699	.2664
3	5S	.083	.0101	.0072	.0044	.0015						
3	10S	.120	.0286	.0257	.0229	.0200	.0171	.0143	.0114	.0086	.0057	.0029
3		.125	.0311	.0282	.0254	.0225	.0196	.0168	.0139	.0111	.0082	.0054
3		.148	.0426	.0397	.0369	.0340	.0311	.0283	.0254	.0226	.0197	.0169
3		.188	.0626	.0597	.0569	.0540	.0511	.0483	.0454	.0426	.0397	.0369
3	40 ST 40S	.216	.0766	.0737	.0709	.0680	.0651	.0623	.0594	.0566	.0537	.0509
3		.241	.0891	.0862	.0834	.0805	.0776	.0748	.0719	.0691	.0662	.0634
3		.254	.0956	.0927	.0899	.0870	.0841	.0813	.0784	.0756	.0727	.0699
3		.289	.1131	.1102	.1074	.1045	.1016	.0988	.0959	.0931	.0902	.0874
3	80 XS 805	.300	.1186	.1157	.1129	.1100	.1071	.1043	.1014	.0986	.0957	.0929
3		.312	.1246	.1217	.1189	.1160	.1131	.1103	.1074	.1046	.1017	.0989
3		.406	.1716	.1687	.1659	.1630	.1601	.1573	.1544	.1516	.1487	.1459

Table 7-1
Continued

NOMINAL PIPE SIZE	SCHEDULE NUMBER AND/OR WEIGHT	WALL THICKNESS	CORROSION ALLOWANCE-INCHES									Y=0.0
			0.055	0.060	0.065	0.070	0.075	0.080	0.085	0.90	0.095	0.100
3	160	.438	.1876	.1847	.1819	.1790	.1761	.1733	.1704	.1676	.1647	.1619
3	XX	.600	.2686	.2657	.2629	.2600	.2571	.2543	.2514	.2486	.2457	.2429
31/2	5S	.083	.0088	.0063	.0038	.0013						
31/2	10S	.120	.0250	.0225	.0200	.0175	.0150	.0125	.0100	.0075	.0050	.0025
31/2		.128	.0285	.0260	.0235	.0210	.0185	.0160	.0135	.0110	.0085	.0060
31/2		.134	.0311	.0286	.0261	.0236	.0211	.0186	.0161	.0136	.0111	.0086
31/2		.148	.0372	.0347	.0322	.0297	.0272	.0248	.0223	.0198	.0173	.0148
31/2		.188	.0547	.0522	.0497	.0473	.0448	.0423	.0398	.0373	.0348	.0323
31/2	40 ST 40S	.226	.0714	.0689	.0664	.0639	.0614	.0589	.0564	.0539	.0514	.0489
31/2		.281	.0954	.0929	.0904	.0879	.0854	.0829	.0804	.0779	.0754	.0729
31/2	80 XS 80S	.318	.1116	.1091	.1066	.1041	.1016	.0991	.0966	.0941	.0916	.0891
31/2		.344	.1230	.1205	.1180	.1155	.1130	.1105	.1080	.1055	.1030	.1005
31/2		.469	.1777	.1752	.1727	.1702	.1677	.1652	.1627	.1602	.1577	.1552
31/2		.636	.2507	.2482	.2457	.2432	.2407	.2382	.2357	.2332	.2307	.2282
4	5S	.083	.0078	.0056	.0034	.0012						
4	10S	.120	.0222	.0200	.0178	.0156	.0133	.0111	.0089	.0067	.0044	.0022
4		.128	.0253	.0231	.0209	.0187	.0164	.0142	.0120	.0098	.0076	.0053
4		.134	.0277	.0254	.0232	.0210	.0188	.0166	.0143	.0121	.0099	.0077
4		.142	.0308	.0286	.0263	.0241	.0219	.0197	.0174	.0152	.0130	.0108
4		.165	.0397	.0375	.0353	.0331	.0308	.0286	.0264	.0242	.0219	.0197
4		.188	.0487	.0464	.0442	.0420	.0398	.0376	.0353	.0331	.0309	.0287
4		.205	.0553	.0531	.0508	.0486	.0464	.0442	.0419	.0397	.0375	.0353
4	40 ST40S	.237	.0677	.0655	.0633	.0611	.0588	.0566	.0544	.0522	.0499	.0477
4		.250	.0728	.0706	.0683	.0661	.0639	.0617	.0594	.0572	.0550	.0528
4		.271	.0809	.0787	.0765	.0743	.0721	.0698	.0676	.0654	.0632	.0609
4		.281	.0848	.0826	.0804	.0782	.0759	.0737	.0715	.0693	.0671	.0648
4		.300	.0922	.0900	.0878	.0856	.0833	.0811	.0789	.0767	.0744	.0722
4		.312	.0969	.0947	.0924	.0902	.0880	.0858	.0836	.0813	.0791	.0769
4	80 XS 80S	.337	.1066	.1044	.1022	.0999	.0977	.0955	.0933	.0911	.0888	.0866
4		.375	.1214	.1192	.1169	.1147	.1125	.1103	.1081	.1058	.1036	.1014
4	120	.438	.1459	.1437	.1414	.1392	.1370	.1348	.1326	.1303	.1281	.1259
4		.500	.1700	.1678	.1656	.1633	.1611	.1589	.1567	.1544	.1522	.1500
4	160	.531	.1821	.1798	.1776	.1754	.1732	.1709	.1687	.1665	.1643	.1621
4	XX	.674	.2377	.2354	.2332	.2310	.2288	.2266	.2243	.2221	.2199	.2177
5	5S	.109	.0145	.0127	.0109	.0091	.0073	.0055	.0037	.0019	.0001	
5	10S	.134	.0224	.0206	.0188	.0170	.0152	.0134	.0116	.0098	.0080	.0062

Table 7-1
Continued

NOMINAL PIPE SIZE	SCHEDULE NUMBER AND/OR WEIGHT	WALL THICKNESS	CORROSION ALLOWANCE-INCHES									Y=0.0
			0.055	0.060	0.065	0.070	0.075	0.080	0.085	0.90	0.095	0.100
5	40 ST 40S	.258	.0614	.0596	.0578	.0560	.0542	.0524	.0506	.0488	.0470	.0452
5		.352	.0910	.0892	.0874	.0856	.0838	.0820	.0802	.0784	.0766	.0748
5	80 XS 80S	.375	.0982	.0964	.0946	.0928	.0910	.0892	.0874	.0856	.0838	.0820
5		.438	.1180	.1162	.1144	.1126	.1108	.1090	.1072	.1054	.1036	.1018
5	120	.500	.1375	.1357	.1339	.1321	.1303	.1285	.1267	.1249	.1231	.1213
5	160	.625	.1768	.1750	.1732	.1714	.1696	.1679	.1661	.1643	.1625	.1607
5	XX	.750	.2162	.2144	.2126	.2108	.2090	.2072	.2054	.2036	.2018	.2000
6	5S	.109	.0122	.0107	.0092	.0077	.0062	.0046	.0031	.0016	.0001	
6	10S	.134	.0188	.0173	.0158	.0143	.0128	.0112	.0097	.0082	.0067	.0052
6		.169	.0280	.0265	.0250	.0235	.0220	.0205	.0190	.0175	.0160	.0145
6		.180	.0309	.0294	.0279	.0264	.0249	.0234	.0219	.0204	.0189	.0174
6		.188	.0331	.0315	.0300	.0285	.0270	.0255	.0240	.0225	.0210	.0195
6		.219	.0412	.0397	.0382	.0367	.0352	.0337	.0322	.0307	.0292	.0277
6		.250	.0494	.0479	.0464	.0449	.0434	.0419	.0404	.0389	.0374	.0358
6		.277	.0566	.0551	.0535	.0520	.0505	.0490	.0475	.0460	.0445	.0430
6	40 ST 40S	.280	.0574	.0558	.0543	.0528	.0513	.0498	.0483	.0468	.0453	.0438
6		.375	.0825	.0809	.0794	.0779	.0764	.0749	.0734	.0719	.0704	.0689
6	80 XS 80S	.432	.0975	.0960	.0945	.0930	.0915	.0900	.0885	.0869	.0854	.0839
6		.500	.1155	.1140	.1125	.1109	.1094	.1079	.1064	.1049	.1034	.1019
6	120	.562	.1318	.1303	.1288	.1273	.1258	.1243	.1228	.1213	.1198	.1183
6	160	.718	.1731	.1715	.1700	.1685	.1670	.1655	.1640	.1625	.1610	.1595
6	XX	.864	.2116	.2101	.2086	.2071	.2056	.2041	.2026	.2011	.1995	.1980
8	5S	.109	.0094	.0082	.0070	.0059	.0047	.0036	.0024	.0012	.0001	
8	10S	.148	.0173	.0161	.0150	.0138	.0126	.0115	.0103	.0092	.0080	.0068
8		.158	.0193	.0181	.0170	.0158	.0147	.0135	.0123	.0112	.0100	.0089
8		.165	.0207	.0196	.0184	.0172	.0161	.0149	.0138	.0126	.0114	.0103
8		.188	.0254	.0242	.0231	.0219	.0208	.0196	.0184	.0173	.0161	.0150
8		.203	.0284	.0273	.0261	.0250	.0238	.0226	.0215	.0203	.0192	.0180
8		.219	.0317	.0305	.0294	.0282	.0270	.0259	.0247	.0236	.0224	.0212
8		.238	.0355	.0344	.0332	.0321	.0309	.0297	.0286	.0274	.0263	.0251
8	20	.250	.0380	.0368	.0357	.0345	.0333	.0322	.0310	.0299	.0287	.0275
8	30	.277	.0434	.0423	.0411	.0400	.0388	.0377	.0365	.0353	.0342	.0330
8	40 ST 40S	.322	.0526	.0514	.0503	.0491	.0479	.0468	.0456	.0445	.0433	.0421
8		.344	.0570	.0559	.0547	.0536	.0524	.0512	.0501	.0489	.0478	.0466
8		.352	.0587	.0575	.0563	.0552	.0540	.0529	.0517	.0506	.0494	.0482
8		.375	.0633	.0622	.0610	.0599	.0587	.0575	.0564	.0552	.0541	.0529

Table 7-1
Continued

NOM-INAL PIPE SIZE	SCHEDULE NUMBER AND/OR WEIGHT	WALL THICK-NESS	CORROSION ALLOWANCE-INCHES									Y=0.0
			0.055	0.060	0.065	0.070	0.075	0.080	0.085	0.90	0.095	0.100
8	60	.406	.0696	.0685	.0673	.0661	.0650	.0638	.0627	.0615	.0603	.0592
8		.469	.0824	.0812	.0801	.0789	.0778	.0766	.0754	.0743	.0731	.0720
8	80 XS 80S	.500	.0887	.0875	.0864	.0852	.0841	.0829	.0817	.0806	.0794	.0783
8	100	.593	.1076	.1064	.1052	.1041	.1029	.1018	.1006	.0994	.0983	.0971
8		.625	.1141	.1129	.1117	.1106	.1094	.1083	.1071	.1059	.1048	.1036
8	120	.718	.1329	.1318	.1306	.1294	.1283	.1271	.1260	.1248	.1237	.1225
8	140	.812	.1520	.1508	.1497	.1485	.1474	.1462	.1450	.1439	.1427	.1416
8	XX	.875	.1648	.1636	.1625	.1613	.1601	.1590	.1578	.1567	.1555	.1543
8	160	.906	.1711	.1699	.1688	.1676	.1664	.1653	.1641	.1630	.1618	.1606
10	5S	.134	.0116	.0107	.0097	.0088	.0079	.0069	.0060	.0051	.0041	.0032
10	10S	.165	.0166	.0157	.0148	.0138	.0129	.0120	.0110	.0101	.0092	.0083
10		.188	.0204	.0194	.0185	.0176	.0167	.0157	.0148	.0139	.0129	.0120
10		.203	.0228	.0219	.0210	.0200	.0191	.0182	.0172	.0163	.0154	.0144
10		.219	.0254	.0245	.0236	.0226	.0217	.0208	.0198	.0189	.0180	.0170
10	20	.250	.0305	.0295	.0286	.0277	.0267	.0258	.0249	.0240	.0230	.0221
10		.279	.0352	.0343	.0333	.0324	.0315	.0305	.0296	.0287	.0277	.0268
10	30	.307	.0397	.0388	.0379	.0370	.0360	.0351	.0342	.0332	.0323	.0314
10		.348	.0464	.0455	.0446	.0436	.0427	.0418	.0408	.0399	.0390	.0380
10	40 ST 40S	.365	.0492	.0483	.0473	.0464	.0455	.0445	.0436	.0427	.0417	.0408
10		.395	.0541	.0531	.0522	.0513	.0503	.0494	.0485	.0476	.0466	.0457
10	60 XS 80S	.500	.0712	.0702	.0693	.0684	.0674	.0665	.0656	.0647	.0637	.0628
10		.531	.0762	.0753	.0743	.0734	.0725	.0716	.0706	.0697	.0688	.0678
10	80	.593	.0863	.0854	.0844	.0835	.0826	.0817	.0807	.0798	.0789	.0779
10	100	.718	.1067	.1057	.1048	.1039	.1029	.1020	.1011	.1001	.0992	.0983
10		.750	.1119	.1109	.1100	.1091	.1081	.1072	.1063	.1053	.1044	.1035
10	120	.843	.1270	.1261	.1251	.1242	.1233	.1223	.1214	.1205	.1196	.1186
10	140	1.000	.1526	.1516	.1507	.1498	.1488	.1479	.1470	.1460	.1451	.1442
10		1.062	.1627	.1617	.1608	.1599	.1589	.1580	.1571	.1561	.1552	.1543
10	160	1.125	.1729	.1720	.1710	.1701	.1692	.1683	.1673	.1664	.1655	.1645
12	5S	.156	.0128	.0120	.0112	.0104	.0096	.0089	.0081	.0073	.0065	.0057
12	10S	.180	.0161	.0153	.0145	.0137	.0129	.0122	.0114	.0106	.0098	.0090
12		.203	.0192	.0185	.0177	.0169	.0161	.0153	.0145	.0137	.0130	.0122
12		.219	.0214	.0206	.0199	.0191	.0183	.0175	.0167	.0159	.0152	.0144
12		.238	.0240	.0233	.0225	.0217	.0209	.0201	.0193	.0185	.0178	.0170
12	20	.250	.0257	.0249	.0241	.0233	.0225	.0218	.0210	.0202	.0194	.0186
12		.279	.0297	.0289	.0281	.0273	.0265	.0257	.0250	.0242	.0234	.0226

Table 7-1
Continued

NOMINAL PIPE SIZE	SCHEDULE NUMBER AND/OR WEIGHT	WALL THICKNESS	CORROSION ALLOWANCE-INCHES									Y=0.0
			0.055	0.060	0.065	0.070	0.075	0.080	0.085	0.90	0.095	0.100
12		.300	.0325	.0318	.0310	.0302	.0294	.0286	.0278	.0271	.0263	.0255
12	30	.330	.0367	.0359	.0351	.0343	.0335	.0327	.0320	.0312	.0304	.0296
12		.344	.0386	.0378	.0370	.0362	.0355	.0347	.0339	.0331	.0323	.0315
12	ST 40S	.375	.0428	.0421	.0413	.0405	.0397	.0389	.0381	.0374	.0366	.0358
12	40	.406	.0471	.0463	.0455	.0447	.0440	.0432	.0424	.0416	.0408	.0400
12		.438	.0515	.0507	.0499	.0491	.0484	.0476	.0468	.0460	.0452	.0444
12	XS 80S	.500	.0600	.0592	.0584	.0576	.0569	.0561	.0553	.0545	.0537	.0529
12	60	.562	.0685	.0677	.0669	.0662	.0654	.0646	.0638	.0630	.0622	.0615
12		.625	.0772	.0764	.0756	.0748	.0740	.0732	.0725	.0717	.0709	.0701
12	80	.687	.0857	.0849	.0841	.0833	.0825	.0817	.0810	.0802	.0794	.0786
12	100	.843	.1071	.1063	.1055	.1047	.1039	.1032	.1024	.1016	.1008	.1000
12		.875	.1115	.1107	.1099	.1091	.1083	.1075	.1068	.1060	.1052	.1044
12	120	1.000	.1286	.1278	.1271	.1263	.1255	.1247	.1239	.1231	.1224	.1216
12	140	1.125	.1458	.1450	.1442	.1434	.1426	.1419	.1411	.1403	.1395	.1387
12		1.219	.1587	.1579	.1571	.1563	.1555	.1548	.1540	.1532	.1524	.1516
12	160	1.312	.1715	.1707	.1699	.1691	.1683	.1675	.1667	.1660	.1652	.1644
14		.188	.0156	.0149	.0142	.0135	.0128	.0121	.0114	.0106	.0099	.0092
14		.220	.0196	.0189	.0182	.0175	.0168	.0161	.0154	.0146	.0139	.0132
14		.238	.0219	.0212	.0205	.0197	.0190	.0183	.0176	.0169	.0162	.0155
14	10	.250	.0234	.0227	.0220	.0212	.0205	.0198	.0191	.0184	.0177	.0170
14	20	.312	.0311	.0304	.0297	.0290	.0283	.0276	.0269	.0261	.0254	.0247
14	30ST	.375	.0390	.0383	.0376	.0369	.0362	.0354	.0347	.0340	.0333	.0326
14		.406	.0429	.0422	.0415	.0407	.0400	.0393	.0386	.0379	.0372	.0365
14	40	.438	.0469	.0462	.0455	.0447	.0440	.0433	.0426	.0419	.0412	.0405
14		.469	.0508	.0501	.0493	.0486	.0479	.0472	.0465	.0458	.0451	.0443
14	XS	.500	.0546	.0539	.0532	.0525	.0518	.0511	.0504	.0496	.0489	.0482
14	60	.593	.0663	.0656	.0648	.0641	.0634	.0627	.0620	.0613	.0606	.0598
14		.625	.0703	.0696	.0688	.0681	.0674	.0667	.0660	.0653	.0646	.0638
14		.656	.0741	.0734	.0727	.0720	.0713	.0706	.0699	.0691	.0684	.0677
14	80	.750	.0859	.0852	.0845	.0837	.0830	.0823	.0816	.0809	.0802	.0795
14	100	.937	.1093	.1086	.1078	.1071	.1064	.1057	.1050	.1043	.1036	.1028
14	120	1.093	.1288	.1281	.1273	.1266	.1259	.1252	.1245	.1238	.1231	.1223
14	140	1.250	.1484	.1477	.1470	.1462	.1455	.1448	.1441	.1434	.1427	.1420
14		1.344	.1601	.1594	.1587	.1580	.1573	.1566	.1559	.1551	.1544	.1537
14	160	1.406	.1679	.1672	.1665	.1657	.1650	.1643	.1636	.1629	.1622	.1615
16		.188	.0137	.0131	.0124	.0118	.0112	.0106	.0099	.0093	.0087	.0081

Table 7-1
Continued

NOM-INAL PIPE SIZE	SCHEDULE NUMBER AND/OR WEIGHT	WALL THICK-NESS	CORROSION ALLOWANCE-INCHES									Y=0.0
			0.055	0.060	0.065	0.070	0.075	0.080	0.085	0.90	0.095	0.100
16		.238	.0192	.0185	.0179	.0173	.0167	.0160	.0154	.0148	.0142	.0135
16	10	.250	.0205	.0198	.0192	.0186	.0180	.0173	.0167	.0161	.0155	.0148
16		.281	.0239	.0232	.0226	.0220	.0214	.0207	.0201	.0195	.0189	.0182
16	20	.312	.0272	.0266	.0260	.0254	.0247	.0241	.0235	.0229	.0222	.0216
16		.344	.0307	.0301	.0295	.0289	.0282	.0276	.0270	.0264	.0257	.0251
16	30 ST	.375	.0341	.0335	.0329	.0323	.0316	.0310	.0304	.0298	.0291	.0285
16		.406	.0375	.0369	.0363	.0357	.0350	.0344	.0338	.0332	.0325	.0319
16		.438	.0410	.0404	.0398	.0392	.0385	.0379	.0373	.0367	.0360	.0354
16		.469	.0444	.0438	.0432	.0425	.0419	.0413	.0407	.0400	.0394	.0388
16	40 XS	.500	.0478	.0472	.0466	.0459	.0453	.0447	.0441	.0434	.0428	.0422
16		.531	.0512	.0506	.0500	.0493	.0487	.0481	.0475	.0468	.0462	.0456
16	60	.656	.0649	.0642	.0636	.0630	.0624	.0617	.0611	.0605	.0599	.0592
16		.688	.0684	.0677	.0671	.0665	.0659	.0652	.0646	.0640	.0634	.0627
16		.750	.0752	.0745	.0739	.0733	.0727	.0720	.0714	.0708	.0702	.0695
16	80	.843	.0853	.0847	.0841	.0835	.0828	.0822	.0816	.0810	.0803	.0797
16	100	1.031	.1059	.1053	.1046	.1040	.1034	.1028	.1021	.1015	.1009	.1003
16	120	1.218	.1263	.1257	.1251	.1245	.1238	.1232	.1226	.1220	.1213	.1207
16	140	1.438	.1504	.1498	.1492	.1485	.1479	.1473	.1467	.1460	.1454	.1448
16		1.500	.1572	.1566	.1559	.1553	.1547	.1541	.1534	.1528	.1522	.1516
16	160	1.593	.1674	.1667	.1661	.1655	.1649	.1642	.1636	.1630	.1624	.1617
18	10	.250	.0182	.0176	.0171	.0165	.0160	.0154	.0149	.0143	.0138	.0132
18	20	.312	.0242	.0237	.0231	.0226	.0220	.0214	.0209	.0203	.0198	.0192
18	ST	.375	.0303	.0298	.0292	.0287	.0281	.0276	.0270	.0265	.0259	.0253
18	30	.438	.0365	.0359	.0354	.0348	.0343	.0337	.0331	.0326	.0320	.0315
18	XS	.500	.0425	.0419	.0414	.0408	.0403	.0397	.0392	.0386	.0381	.0375
18	40	.562	.0485	.0480	.0474	.0469	.0463	.0457	.0452	.0446	.0441	.0435
18		.594	.0516	.0511	.0505	.0500	.0494	.0489	.0483	.0477	.0472	.0466
18		.625	.0547	.0541	.0535	.0530	.0524	.0519	.0513	.0508	.0502	.0497
18		.719	.0638	.0632	.0627	.0621	.0616	.0610	.0605	.0599	.0593	.0588
18	60	.750	.0668	.0662	.0657	.0651	.0646	.0640	.0635	.0629	.0624	.0618
18		.812	.0728	.0723	.0717	.0712	.0706	.0701	.0695	.0689	.0684	.0678
18	80	.937	.0850	.0844	.0839	.0833	.0828	.0822	.0817	.0811	.0805	.0800
18	100	1.156	.1063	.1057	.1052	.1046	.1041	.1035	.1029	.1024	.1018	.1013
18	120	1.375	.1276	.1270	.1265	.1259	.1253	.1248	.1242	.1237	.1231	.1226
18	140	1.562	.1457	.1452	.1446	.1441	.1435	.1430	.1424	.1419	.1413	.1407
18		1.688	.1580	.1574	.1569	.1563	.1558	.1552	.1547	.1541	.1536	.1530

Table 7-1
Continued

NOMINAL PIPE SIZE	SCHEDULE NUMBER AND/OR WEIGHT	WALL THICKNESS	CORROSION ALLOWANCE-INCHES Y=0.0									
			0.055	0.060	0.065	0.070	0.075	0.080	0.085	0.90	0.095	0.100
18	160	1.781	.1670	.1665	.1659	.1654	.1648	.1643	.1637	.1632	.1626	.1620
20	10	.250	.0164	.0159	.0154	.0149	.0144	.0139	.0134	.0129	.0124	.0119
20		.312	.0218	.0213	.0208	.0203	.0198	.0193	.0188	.0183	.0178	.0173
20	20 ST	.375	.0273	.0268	.0263	.0258	.0253	.0248	.0243	.0238	.0233	.0228
20		.438	.0328	.0323	.0318	.0313	.0308	.0303	.0298	.0293	.0288	.0283
20	30 XS	.500	.0382	.0377	.0373	.0367	.0362	.0357	.0353	.0347	.0343	.0337
20		.562	.0437	.0432	.0427	.0422	.0417	.0412	.0407	.0402	.0397	.0392
20	40	.593	.0464	.0459	.0454	.0449	.0444	.0439	.0434	.0429	.0424	.0419
20		.625	.0492	.0487	.0482	.0477	.0472	.0467	.0462	.0457	.0452	.0447
20	60	.812	.0655	.0650	.0645	.0640	.0635	.0630	.0625	.0620	.0615	.0610
20		.875	.0711	.0706	.0701	.0696	.0691	.0686	.0681	.0676	.0671	.0666
20		.906	.0738	.0733	.0728	.0723	.0718	.0713	.0708	.0703	.0698	.0693
20	80	1.031	.0847	.0842	.0837	.0832	.0827	.0822	.0817	.0812	.0807	.0802
20		1.250	.1039	.1034	.1029	.1024	.1019	.1014	.1009	.1004	.0999	.0994
20	100	1.281	.1066	.1061	.1056	.1051	.1046	.1041	.1036	.1031	.1026	.1021
20	120	1.500	.1258	.1252	.1247	.1242	.1237	.1232	.1227	.1222	.1218	.1212
20	140	1.750	.1476	.1471	.1466	.1461	.1456	.1451	.1446	.1441	.1436	.1431
20		1.844	.1558	.1553	.1548	.1543	.1538	.1533	.1528	.1523	.1518	.1513
20	160	1.968	.1667	.1662	.1657	.1652	.1647	.1642	.1637	.1632	.1627	.1622
22	LG	.250	.0149	.0144	.0140	.0135	.0131	.0126	.0122	.0117	.0113	.0108
22	ST	.375	.0248	.0244	.0239	.0235	.0230	.0226	.0221	.0216	.0212	.0207
22	XS	.500	.0348	.0343	.0339	.0334	.0330	.0325	.0320	.0316	.0311	.0307
24	10	.250	.0136	.0132	.0128	.0124	.0120	.0116	.0111	.0107	.0103	.0099
24		.312	.0182	.0177	.0173	.0169	.0165	.0161	.0157	.0152	.0148	.0144
24	20 ST	.375	.0228	.0223	.0219	.0215	.0211	.0207	.0203	.0198	.0194	.0190
24		.438	.0274	.0269	.0265	.0261	.0257	.0253	.0249	.0244	.0240	.0236
24	XS	.500	.0319	.0315	.0310	.0306	.0302	.0298	.0294	.0290	.0285	.0281
24	30	.562	.0364	.0360	.0356	.0351	.0347	.0343	.0339	.0335	.0331	.0326
24		.625	.0410	.0406	.0402	.0397	.0393	.0389	.0385	.0381	.0377	.0372
24	40	.687	.0455	.0451	.0447	.0443	.0438	.0434	.0430	.0426	.0422	.0418
24		.750	.0501	.0497	.0493	.0489	.0484	.0480	.0476	.0472	.0468	.0464
24	60	.968	.0660	.0656	.0652	.0647	.0643	.0639	.0635	.0631	.0627	.0622
24		1.031	.0706	.0702	.0698	.0693	.0689	.0685	.0681	.0677	.0673	.0668
24	80	1.218	.0842	.0838	.0834	.0830	.0826	.0821	.0817	.0813	.0809	.0805
24	100	1.531	.1071	.1066	.1062	.1058	.1054	.1050	.1046	.1041	.1037	.1033

Table 7-1
Continued

NOMINAL PIPE SIZE	SCHEDULE NUMBER AND/OR WEIGHT	WALL THICKNESS	CORROSION ALLOWANCE-INCHES									Y=0.0
			0.055	0.060	0.065	0.070	0.075	0.080	0.085	0.90	0.095	0.100
24	120	1.812	.1275	.1271	.1267	.1263	.1259	.1255	.1250	.1246	.1242	.1238
24	140	2.062	.1458	.1454	.1449	.1445	.1441	.1437	.1433	.1429	.1424	.1420
24		2.188	.1550	.1545	.1541	.1537	.1533	.1529	.1525	.1520	.1516	.1512
24	160	2.343	.1663	.1658	.1654	.1650	.1646	.1642	.1638	.1633	.1629	.1625
26	ST	.375	.0210	.0206	.0202	.0199	.0195	.0191	.0187	.0183	.0179	.0175
26	XS	.500	.0294	.0290	.0287	.0283	.0279	.0275	.0271	.0267	.0263	.0260
30	10	.312	.0145	.0142	.0139	.0135	.0132	.0129	.0125	.0122	.0119	.0115
30	ST	.375	.0182	.0179	.0175	.0172	.0169	.0165	.0162	.0159	.0155	.0152
30		.438	.0219	.0215	.0212	.0209	.0206	.0202	.0199	.0195	.0192	.0189
30	20 XS	.500	.0255	.0252	.0248	.0245	.0242	.0238	.0235	.0232	.0228	.0225
30		.562	.0291	.0288	.0284	.0281	.0278	.0274	.0271	.0268	.0264	.0261
30	30	.625	.0328	.0325	.0321	.0318	.0315	.0311	.0308	.0305	.0301	.0298
34	ST	.375	.0161	.0158	.0155	.0152	.0149	.0146	.0143	.0140	.0137	.0134
34	XS	.500	.0225	.0222	.0219	.0216	.0213	.0210	.0207	.0204	.0201	.0199
36	ST	.375	.0152	.0149	.0146	.0143	.0141	.0138	.0135	.0132	.0130	.0127
36	XS	.500	.0212	.0210	.0207	.0204	.0201	.0199	.0196	.0193	.0190	.0187
42	ST	.375	.0130	.0128	.0125	.0123	.0121	.0118	.0116	.0113	.0111	.0109
42	XS	.500	.0182	.0180	.0177	.0175	.0173	.0170	.0168	.0165	.0163	.0161
48	ST	.375	.0114	.0112	.0110	.0108	.0105	.0103	.0101	.0099	.0097	.0095
48	XS	.500	.0159	.0157	.0155	.0153	.0151	.0149	.0147	.0145	.0143	.0141

Table 7-2
Pressure/Stress Ratios Where Y = 0.4

NOMINAL PIPE SIZE	SCHEDULE NUMBER AND/OR WEIGHT	WALL THICKNESS	CORROSION ALLOWANCE-INCHES Y=0.4										
			0.000	0.005	0.010	0.015	0.020	0.025	0.030	0.035	0.040	0.045	0.050
1/8	10S	.049	.2313	.2022	.1736	.1457	.1183	.0915	.0652	.0395	.0143		
1/8	40 ST 40S	.068	.3330	.3016	.2709	.2409	.2116	.1828	.1547	.1271	.1002	.0737	.0478
1/8	80 ST 80S	.095	.4911	.4562	.4221	.3887	.3561	.3243	.2931	.2626	.2328	.2036	.1750
1/4	10S	.065	.2300	.2081	.1866	.1654	.1445	.1239	.1037	.0837	.0641	.0448	.0257
1/4	40 ST 40S	.088	.3219	.2985	.2755	.2529	.2306	.2087	.1871	.1659	.1450	.1244	.1042
1/4	80 ST 80S	.119	.4560	.4303	.4051	.3803	.3559	.3320	.3084	.2852	.2624	.2400	.2179
3/8	10S	.065	.1807	.1638	.1471	.1306	.1143	.0982	.0822	.0665	.0510	.0357	.0205
3/8	40 ST 40S	.091	.2605	.2426	.2249	.2074	.1901	.1731	.1562	.1396	.1232	.1070	.0910
3/8	80 ST 80S	.126	.3758	.3563	.3371	.3181	.2994	.2810	.2628	.2448	.2271	.2095	.1922
1/2	10S	.083	.1858	.1721	.1586	.1452	.1319	.1188	.1058	.0929	.0802	.0676	.0551
1/2	40 ST 40S	.109	.2498	.2354	.2213	.2072	.1933	.1796	.1660	.1525	.1392	.1260	.1129
1/2	80 ST 80S	.147	.3490	.3336	.3184	.3034	.2885	.2737	.2592	.2447	.2305	.2163	.2024
1/2	160	.187	.4615	.4449	.4285	.4122	.3962	.3803	.3645	.3490	.3336	.3184	.3034
1/2	XX	.294	.8113	.7905	.7700	.7498	.7298	.7100	.6905	.6712	.6522	.6334	.6148
3/4	5S	.065	.1132	.1029	.0926	.0824	.0723	.0622	.0523	.0424	.0326	.0228	.0132
3/4	10S	.083	.1464	.1358	.1253	.1148	.1044	.0941	.0839	.0738	.0637	.0538	.0439
3/4	40S	.113	.2037	.1926	.1816	.1707	.1598	.1491	.1385	.1279	.1174	.1070	.0967
3/4	80S	.154	.2860	.2743	.2626	.2510	.2395	.2281	.2168	.2056	.1945	.1835	.1726
3/4		.188	.3582	.3458	.3335	.3214	.3093	.2973	.2854	.2737	.2620	.2504	.2389
3/4	160	.218	.4251	.4121	.3993	.3865	.3739	.3613	.3489	.3366	.3244	.3123	.3003
3/4	XX	.308	.6460	.6310	.6161	.6014	.5868	.5723	.5580	.5438	.5298	.5159	.5021
1	5S	.065	.0896	.0815	.0734	.0654	.0574	.0494	.0416	.0337	.0259	.0182	.0105
1	10S	.109	.1540	.1454	.1370	.1285	.1201	.1118	.1035	.0953	.0872	.0790	.0710
1	40 ST 40S	.133	.1905	.1817	.1730	.1643	.1557	.1472	.1387	.1302	.1218	.1135	.1052
1	80 ST 80S	.179	.2633	.2540	.2448	.2357	.2266	.2176	.2087	.1998	.1909	.1821	.1734
1		.219	.3299	.3202	.3105	.3010	.2915	.2820	.2726	.2633	.2540	.2448	.2357
1	160	.250	.3838	.3737	.3637	.3537	.3439	.3341	.3243	.3146	.3050	.2955	.2860
1	XXO	.358	.5886	.5770	.5656	.5542	.5429	.5316	.5205	.5094	.4984	.4875	.4767
11/4	5S	.065	.0705	.0641	.0578	.0515	.0452	.0390	.0328	.0266	.0205	.0144	.0083
11/4	10S	.109	.1204	.1138	.1073	.1007	.0942	.0878	.0813	.0749	.0685	.0622	.0559
11/4	40 ST 40S	.140	.1569	.1501	.1433	.1366	.1299	.1233	.1166	.1101	.1035	.0970	.0905
11/4	80 ST 80S	.191	.2190	.2119	.2048	.1978	.1908	.1838	.1769	.1700	.1632	.1563	.1496
11/4	160	.250	.2946	.2871	.2796	.2722	.2648	.2575	.2502	.2429	.2357	.2285	.2213
11/4	XX	.382	.4800	.4715	.4630	.4546	.4462	.4378	.4295	.4213	.4131	.4049	.3968

Table 7-2
Continued

NOMINAL PIPE SIZE	SCHEDULE NUMBER AND/OR WEIGHT	WALL THICKNESS	CORROSION ALLOWANCE-INCHES										Y=0.4
			0.000	0.005	0.010	0.015	0.020	0.025	0.030	0.035	0.040	0.045	0.050
11/2	5S	.065	.0613	.0558	.0503	.0449	.0394	.0340	.0286	.0232	.0179	.0126	.0073
11/2	10S	.109	.1046	.0989	.0932	.0876	.0819	.0763	.0708	.0652	.0597	.0542	.0487
11/2	40 ST 40S	.145	.1411	.1352	.1294	.1236	.1178	.1120	.1063	.1006	.0949	.0893	.0836
11/2	80 ST 80S	.200	.1989	.1927	.1867	.1806	.1745	.1685	.1626	.1566	.1507	.1448	.1389
11/2	160	.281	.2887	.2822	.2757	.2692	.2628	.2563	.2500	.2436	.2373	.2310	.2247
11/2	XX	.400	.4321	.4249	.4177	.4105	.4034	.3963	.3893	.3823	.3753	.3684	.3614
2	5S	.065	.0488	.0445	.0401	.0358	.0314	.0271	.0228	.0186	.0143	.0100	.0058
2	10S	.109	.0830	.0785	.0740	.0696	.0651	.0607	.0563	.0519	.0475	.0432	.0388
2	40 ST 40S	.154	.1189	.1143	.1097	.1051	.1005	.0960	.0914	.0869	.0824	.0779	.0735
2		.167	.1294	.1248	.1201	.1155	.1109	.1063	.1018	.0972	.0927	.0882	.0837
2		.188	.1467	.1419	.1372	.1326	.1279	.1233	.1186	.1140	.1094	.1049	.1003
2	80 ST 80S	.218	.1717	.1669	.1621	.1573	.1526	.1478	.1431	.1384	.1337	.1291	.1244
2		.250	.1989	.1940	.1891	.1842	.1794	.1745	.1697	.1649	.1602	.1554	.1507
2		.312	.2532	.2481	.2430	.2379	.2329	.2279	.2229	.2179	.2129	.2080	.2030
2	160	.343	.2812	.2760	.2708	.2656	.2605	.2553	.2502	.2452	.2401	.2350	.2300
2	XX	.436	.3686	.3631	.3576	.3521	.3466	.3412	.3358	.3303	.3250	.3196	.3142
21/2	5S	.083	.0516	.0479	.0443	.0407	.0372	.0336	.0300	.0265	.0229	.0194	.0158
21/2	10S	.120	.0752	.0716	.0679	.0642	.0606	.0569	.0533	.0497	.0461	.0424	.0389
21/2	40 ST 40S	.203	.1300	.1261	.1223	.1185	.1147	.1109	.1071	.1033	.0996	.0958	.0921
21/2		.217	.1395	.1356	.1317	.1279	.1240	.1202	.1164	.1126	.1088	.1050	.1012
21/2	80 ST 805	.276	.1801	.1761	.1721	.1682	.1642	.1603	.1563	.1524	.1485	.1446	.1407
21/2	160	.375	.2512	.2470	.2428	.2386	.2344	.2303	.2262	.2220	.2179	.2138	.2097
21/2	XX	.552	.3882	.3835	.3789	.3743	.3697	.3651	.3606	.3560	.3515	.3470	.3425
3	5S	.083	.0422	.0392	.0363	.0334	.0304	.0275	.0246	.0217	.0188	.0159	.0130
3	10S	.120	.0615	.0585	.0555	.0525	.0495	.0466	.0436	.0407	.0377	.0348	.0318
3		.125	.0641	.0611	.0581	.0551	.0521	.0492	.0462	.0432	.0403	.0373	.0344
3		.148	.0763	.0732	.0702	.0672	.0642	.0612	.0582	.0552	.0522	.0492	.0463
3		.188	.0977	.0946	.0915	.0885	.0854	.0823	.0793	.0763	.0732	.0702	.0672
3	40 ST 40S	.216	.1129	.1098	.1066	.1035	.1005	.0974	.0943	.0912	.0881	.0851	.0820
3		.241	.1266	.1235	.1203	.1172	.1140	.1109	.1078	.1047	.1016	.0985	.0954
3		.254	.1338	.1306	.1275	.1243	.1212	.1180	.1149	.1118	.1087	.1056	.1025
3		.289	.1534	.1501	.1469	.1437	.1406	.1374	.1342	.1310	.1279	.1247	.1216
3	80 XS 805	.300	.1596	.1563	.1531	.1499	.1467	.1435	.1403	.1371	.1340	.1308	.1276
3		.312	.1664	.1631	.1599	.1567	.1534	.1502	.1470	.1438	.1406	.1374	.1343
3		.406	.2209	.2176	.2142	.2108	.2075	.2041	.2008	.1975	.1941	.1908	.1875

Table 7-2
Continued

NOMINAL PIPE SIZE	SCHEDULE NUMBER AND/OR WEIGHT	WALL THICKNESS	CORROSION ALLOWANCE-INCHES								Y=0.4		
			0.000	0.005	0.010	0.015	0.020	0.025	0.030	0.035	0.040	0.045	0.050
3	160	.438	.2400	.2366	.2332	.2298	.2264	.2230	.2196	.2162	.2128	.2095	.2061
3	XX	.600	.3409	.3372	.3335	.3299	.3262	.3226	.3189	.3153	.3117	.3081	.3045
31/2	5S	.083	.0368	.0343	.0317	.0291	.0266	.0240	.0215	.0190	.0164	.0139	.0114
31/2	10S	.120	.0536	.0510	.0484	.0458	.0432	.0407	.0381	.0355	.0329	.0304	.0278
31/2		.128	.0573	.0547	.0521	.0495	.0469	.0443	.0417	.0391	.0365	.0340	.0314
31/2		.134	.0600	.0574	.0548	.0522	.0496	.0470	.0444	.0418	.0392	.0367	.0341
31/2		.148	.0665	.0638	.0612	.0586	.0560	.0534	.0508	.0482	.0456	.0430	.0404
31/2		.188	.0850	.0824	.0797	.0771	.0744	.0718	.0691	.0665	.0638	.0612	.0586
31/2	40 ST 40S	.226	.1029	.1002	.0975	.0948	.0922	.0895	.0868	.0841	.0814	.0788	.0761
31/2		.281	.1293	.1265	.1238	.1210	.1183	.1155	.1128	.1101	.1074	.1046	.1019
31/2	80 XS 80S	.318	.1473	.1445	.1417	.1389	.1362	.1334	.1306	.1278	.1251	.1223	.1196
31/2		.344	.1601	.1573	.1545	.1517	.1489	.1461	.1433	.1405	.1377	.1349	.1321
31/2		.469	.2235	.2206	.2176	.2147	.2117	.2088	.2058	.2029	.2000	.1971	.1942
31/2		.636	.3131	.3099	.3068	.3036	.3005	.2974	.2942	.2911	.2880	.2849	.2818
4	5S	.083	.0327	.0304	.0281	.0259	.0236	.0213	.0191	.0168	.0146	.0123	.0101
4	10S	.120	.0476	.0452	.0429	.0407	.0384	.0361	.0338	.0315	.0292	.0270	.0247
4		.128	.0508	.0485	.0462	.0439	.0416	.0393	.0370	.0347	.0324	.0301	.0279
4		.134	.0532	.0509	.0486	.0463	.0440	.0417	.0394	.0371	.0348	.0325	.0303
4		.142	.0565	.0541	.0518	.0495	.0472	.0449	.0426	.0403	.0380	.0357	.0334
4		.165	.0659	.0635	.0612	.0589	.0565	.0542	.0519	.0496	.0473	.0450	.0427
4		.188	.0753	.0730	.0706	.0683	.0659	.0636	.0612	.0589	.0566	.0543	.0519
4		.205	.0823	.0800	.0776	.0753	.0729	.0705	.0682	.0659	.0635	.0612	.0589
4	40 ST40S	.237	.0957	.0933	.0909	.0885	.0861	.0838	.0814	.0790	.0767	.0743	.0720
4		.250	.1012	.0988	.0964	.0940	.0916	.0892	.0868	.0844	.0821	.0797	.0773
4		.271	.1100	.1076	.1052	.1028	.1004	.0980	.0956	.0932	.0908	.0884	.0860
4		.281	.1143	.1118	.1094	.1070	.1046	.1022	.0998	.0974	.0950	.0926	.0902
4		.300	.1224	.1199	.1175	.1151	.1126	.1102	.1078	.1054	.1030	.1006	.0982
4		.312	.1275	.1251	.1226	.1202	.1177	.1153	.1129	.1105	.1080	.1056	.1032
4	80 XS 80S	.337	.1383	.1358	.1334	.1309	.1284	.1260	.1235	.1211	.1187	.1162	.1138
4		.375	.1549	.1524	.1499	.1474	.1449	.1424	.1399	.1374	.1350	.1325	.1300
4	120	.438	.1828	.1802	.1777	.1751	.1726	.1701	.1675	.1650	.1625	.1600	.1574
4		.500	.2108	.2082	.2056	.2030	.2004	.1978	.1953	.1927	.1901	.1875	.1850
4	160	.531	.2251	.2225	.2198	.2172	.2146	.2120	.2093	.2067	.2041	.2015	.1989
4	XX	.674	.2928	.2900	.2873	.2845	.2818	.2790	.2763	.2735	.2708	.2681	.2654
5	5S	.109	.0348	.0329	.0311	.0292	.0274	.0256	.0237	.0219	.0201	.0182	.0164
5	10S	.134	.0429	.0410	.0392	.0373	.0355	.0336	.0318	.0299	.0281	.0262	.0244

Table 7-2
Continued

NOMINAL PIPE SIZE	SCHEDULE NUMBER AND/OR WEIGHT	WALL THICKNESS	CORROSION ALLOWANCE-INCHES Y=0.4										
			0.000	0.005	0.010	0.015	0.020	0.025	0.030	0.035	0.040	0.045	0.050
5	40 ST 40S	.258	.0839	.0820	.0800	.0781	.0762	.0743	.0724	.0705	.0686	.0667	.0648
5		.352	.1159	.1139	.1119	.1100	.1080	.1061	.1041	.1022	.1002	.0983	.0963
5	80 XS 80S	.375	.1238	.1218	.1199	.1179	.1159	.1139	.1120	.1100	.1081	.1061	.1042
5		.438	.1458	.1438	.1418	.1398	.1378	.1358	.1338	.1318	.1298	.1278	.1258
5	120	.500	.1678	.1658	.1638	.1617	.1597	.1577	.1556	.1536	.1516	.1496	.1475
5	160	.625	.2134	.2113	.2092	.2071	.2049	.2028	.2007	.1987	.1966	.1945	.1924
5	XX	.750	.2605	.2583	.2561	.2540	.2518	.2496	.2474	.2453	.2431	.2409	.2388
6	5S	.109	.0291	.0276	.0260	.0245	.0230	.0214	.0199	.0184	.0168	.0153	.0138
6	10S	.134	.0359	.0344	.0328	.0313	.0297	.0282	.0266	.0251	.0235	.0220	.0205
6		.169	.0455	.0439	.0423	.0408	.0392	.0377	.0361	.0345	.0330	.0314	.0299
6		.180	.0485	.0469	.0453	.0438	.0422	.0407	.0391	.0375	.0360	.0344	.0329
6		.188	.0507	.0491	.0475	.0460	.0444	.0428	.0413	.0397	.0382	.0366	.0351
6		.219	.0592	.0576	.0561	.0545	.0529	.0513	.0498	.0482	.0466	.0451	.0435
6		.250	.0678	.0662	.0646	.0631	.0615	.0599	.0583	.0567	.0552	.0536	.0520
6		.277	.0754	.0738	.0722	.0706	.0690	.0674	.0658	.0642	.0626	.0610	.0595
6	40 ST 40S	.280	.0762	.0746	.0730	.0714	.0698	.0682	.0666	.0650	.0635	.0619	.0603
6		.375	.1031	.1015	.0999	.0982	.0966	.0950	.0934	.0917	.0901	.0885	.0869
6	80 XS 80S	.432	.1196	.1179	.1163	.1146	.1130	.1113	.1097	.1080	.1064	.1047	.1031
6		.500	.1394	.1378	.1361	.1344	.1327	.1311	.1294	.1277	.1261	.1244	.1227
6	120	.562	.1578	.1561	.1544	.1527	.1510	.1493	.1476	.1459	.1442	.1426	.1409
6	160	.718	.2052	.2035	.2017	.1999	.1982	.1964	.1947	.1929	.1912	.1894	.1877
6	XX	.864	.2512	.2493	.2475	.2457	.2439	.2420	.2402	.2384	.2366	.2348	.2330
8	5S	.109	.0223	.0211	.0200	.0188	.0176	.0164	.0153	.0141	.0129	.0117	.0106
8	10S	.148	.0304	.0292	.0280	.0268	.0257	.0245	.0233	.0221	.0209	.0197	.0186
8		.158	.0325	.0313	.0301	.0289	.0277	.0265	.0254	.0242	.0230	.0218	.0206
8		.165	.0339	.0327	.0316	.0304	.0292	.0280	.0268	.0256	.0244	.0233	.0221
8		.188	.0387	.0375	.0363	.0352	.0340	.0328	.0316	.0304	.0292	.0280	.0268
8		.203	.0419	.0407	.0395	.0383	.0371	.0359	.0347	.0335	.0323	.0311	.0299
8		.219	.0452	.0440	.0428	.0416	.0404	.0392	.0380	.0369	.0357	.0345	.0333
8		.238	.0492	.0480	.0468	.0456	.0444	.0432	.0420	.0408	.0396	.0384	.0372
8	20	.250	.0518	.0506	.0494	.0482	.0470	.0457	.0445	.0433	.0421	.0409	.0398
8	30	.277	.0575	.0563	.0551	.0539	.0527	.0514	.0502	.0490	.0478	.0466	.0454
8	40 ST 40S	.322	.0671	.0659	.0646	.0634	.0622	.0610	.0598	.0586	.0573	.0561	.0549
8		.344	.0718	.0706	.0694	.0681	.0669	.0657	.0645	.0632	.0620	.0608	.0596
8		.352	.0735	.0723	.0711	.0698	.0686	.0674	.0662	.0649	.0637	.0625	.0613
8		.375	.0785	.0772	.0760	.0748	.0736	.0723	.0711	.0699	.0686	.0674	.0662

Table 7-2
Continued

NOMINAL PIPE SIZE	SCHEDULE NUMBER AND/OR WEIGHT	WALL THICKNESS	CORROSION ALLOWANCE-INCHES Y=0.4										
			0.000	0.005	0.010	0.015	0.020	0.025	0.030	0.035	0.040	0.045	0.050
8	60	.406	.0852	.0839	.0827	.0815	.0802	.0790	.0778	.0765	.0753	.0741	.0728
8		.469	.0989	.0977	.0964	.0952	.0939	.0927	.0914	.0902	.0889	.0877	.0865
8	80 XS 80S	.500	.1057	.1045	.1032	.1020	.1007	.0995	.0982	.0970	.0957	.0945	.0932
8	100	.593	.1264	.1251	.1238	.1226	.1213	.1200	.1187	.1175	.1162	.1149	.1137
8		.625	.1336	.1323	.1310	.1297	.1285	.1272	.1259	.1246	.1233	.1221	.1208
8	120	.718	.1547	.1534	.1521	.1508	.1495	.1482	.1469	.1456	.1443	.1430	.1417
8	140	.812	.1764	.1750	.1737	.1724	.1711	.1697	.1684	.1671	.1658	.1645	.1632
8	XX	.875	.1911	.1898	.1884	.1871	.1857	.1844	.1831	.1817	.1804	.1791	.1777
8	160	.906	.1984	.1971	.1957	.1944	.1930	.1917	.1903	.1890	.1877	.1863	.1850
10	5S	.134	.0220	.0211	.0201	.0192	.0182	.0173	.0163	.0154	.0145	.0135	.0126
10	10S	.165	.0272	.0262	.0253	.0243	.0234	.0224	.0215	.0205	.0196	.0186	.0177
10		.188	.0310	.0300	.0291	.0281	.0272	.0262	.0253	.0243	.0234	.0224	.0215
10		.203	.0335	.0325	.0316	.0306	.0297	.0287	.0278	.0268	.0259	.0249	.0240
10		.219	.0362	.0352	.0343	.0333	.0323	.0314	.0304	.0295	.0285	.0276	.0266
10	20	.250	.0414	.0404	.0395	.0385	.0375	.0366	.0356	.0347	.0337	.0327	.0318
10		.279	.0463	.0453	.0443	.0434	.0424	.0414	.0405	.0395	.0386	.0376	.0366
10	30	.307	.0510	.0500	.0491	.0481	.0471	.0462	.0452	.0442	.0433	.0423	.0413
10		.348	.0580	.0570	.0560	.0550	.0541	.0531	.0521	.0512	.0502	.0492	.0483
10	40 ST 40S	.365	.0609	.0599	.0589	.0579	.0570	.0560	.0550	.0541	.0531	.0521	.0511
10		.395	.0660	.0650	.0640	.0631	.0621	.0611	.0601	.0592	.0582	.0572	.0562
10	60 XS 80S	.500	.0841	.0831	.0821	.0812	.0802	.0792	.0782	.0772	.0762	.0752	.0742
10		.531	.0895	.0885	.0875	.0865	.0856	.0846	.0836	.0826	.0816	.0806	.0796
10	80	.593	.1004	.0994	.0984	.0974	.0964	.0954	.0944	.0934	.0924	.0914	.0904
10	100	.718	.1226	.1216	.1206	.1195	.1185	.1175	.1165	.1155	.1145	.1134	.1124
10		.750	.1284	.1273	.1263	.1253	.1243	.1232	.1222	.1212	.1202	.1191	.1181
10	120	.843	.1452	.1442	.1431	.1421	.1410	.1400	.1390	.1379	.1369	.1359	.1348
10	140	1.000	.1741	.1731	.1720	.1709	.1699	.1688	.1678	.1667	.1656	.1646	.1635
10		1.062	.1857	.1847	.1836	.1825	.1814	.1804	.1793	.1782	.1772	.1761	.1750
10	160	1.125	.1976	.1965	.1955	.1944	.1933	.1922	.1911	.1901	.1890	.1879	.1868
12	5S	.156	.0216	.0208	.0200	.0192	.0184	.0176	.0168	.0160	.0152	.0144	.0136
12	10S	.180	.0250	.0242	.0234	.0226	.0218	.0210	.0202	.0194	.0186	.0178	.0170
12		.203	.0282	.0274	.0266	.0258	.0250	.0242	.0234	.0226	.0218	.0210	.0202
12		.219	.0304	.0296	.0288	.0280	.0272	.0264	.0256	.0248	.0240	.0232	.0224
12		.238	.0331	.0323	.0315	.0307	.0299	.0291	.0283	.0275	.0267	.0259	.0251
12	20	.250	.0348	.0340	.0332	.0324	.0316	.0308	.0300	.0292	.0284	.0276	.0268
12		.279	.0389	.0381	.0373	.0365	.0357	.0349	.0340	.0332	.0324	.0316	.0308

Table 7-2
Continued

NOMINAL PIPE SIZE	SCHEDULE NUMBER AND/OR WEIGHT	WALL THICKNESS	CORROSION ALLOWANCE-INCHES Y=0.4										
			0.000	0.005	0.010	0.015	0.020	0.025	0.030	0.035	0.040	0.045	0.050
12		.300	.0419	.0411	.0402	.0394	.0386	.0378	.0370	.0362	.0354	.0346	.0338
12	30	.330	.0461	.0453	.0445	.0437	.0429	.0421	.0413	.0404	.0396	.0388	.0380
12		.344	.0481	.0473	.0465	.0457	.0449	.0441	.0432	.0424	.0416	.0408	.0400
12	ST 40S	.375	.0526	.0517	.0509	.0501	.0493	.0485	.0477	.0468	.0460	.0452	.0444
12	40	.406	.0570	.0562	.0554	.0545	.0537	.0529	.0521	.0513	.0504	.0496	.0488
12		.438	.0616	.0608	.0600	.0591	.0583	.0575	.0567	.0558	.0550	.0542	.0534
12	XS 80S	.500	.0706	.0697	.0689	.0681	.0673	.0664	.0656	.0648	.0639	.0631	.0623
12	60	.562	.0796	.0788	.0779	.0771	.0763	.0754	.0746	.0738	.0729	.0721	.0713
12		.625	.0888	.0880	.0872	.0863	.0855	.0846	.0838	.0830	.0821	.0813	.0804
12	80	.687	.0980	.0971	.0963	.0955	.0946	.0938	.0929	.0921	.0912	.0904	.0895
12	100	.843	.1213	.1205	.1196	.1187	.1179	.1170	.1162	.1153	.1144	.1136	.1127
12		.875	.1262	.1253	.1244	.1236	.1227	.1218	.1210	.1201	.1193	.1184	.1175
12	120	1.000	.1452	.1444	.1435	.1426	.1417	.1408	.1400	.1391	.1382	.1373	.1365
12	140	1.125	.1646	.1637	.1628	.1619	.1610	.1601	.1592	.1584	.1575	.1566	.1557
12		1.219	.1793	.1784	.1775	.1766	.1757	.1748	.1739	.1730	.1721	.1712	.1703
12	160	1.312	.1941	.1931	.1922	.1913	.1904	.1895	.1886	.1877	.1868	.1859	.1850
14		.188	.0237	.0230	.0223	.0215	.0208	.0201	.0194	.0186	.0179	.0172	.0165
14		.220	.0278	.0271	.0263	.0256	.0249	.0242	.0234	.0227	.0220	.0213	.0205
14		.238	.0301	.0294	.0286	.0279	.0272	.0265	.0257	.0250	.0243	.0235	.0228
14	10	.250	.0316	.0309	.0302	.0295	.0287	.0280	.0273	.0265	.0258	.0251	.0243
14	20	.312	.0396	.0389	.0381	.0374	.0367	.0359	.0352	.0345	.0337	.0330	.0323
14	30ST	.375	.0478	.0470	.0463	.0455	.0448	.0441	.0433	.0426	.0418	.0411	.0404
14		.406	.0518	.0511	.0503	.0496	.0488	.0481	.0473	.0466	.0459	.0451	.0444
14	40	.438	.0560	.0552	.0545	.0537	.0530	.0522	.0515	.0508	.0500	.0493	.0485
14		.469	.0600	.0593	.0585	.0578	.0570	.0563	.0555	.0548	.0541	.0533	.0526
14	XS	.500	.0641	.0634	.0626	.0619	.0611	.0604	.0596	.0589	.0581	.0574	.0566
14	60	.593	.0764	.0756	.0749	.0741	.0734	.0726	.0718	.0711	.0703	.0696	.0688
14		.625	.0806	.0799	.0791	.0784	.0776	.0768	.0761	.0753	.0746	.0738	.0731
14		.656	.0848	.0840	.0833	.0825	.0817	.0810	.0802	.0794	.0787	.0779	.0772
14	80	.750	.0974	.0966	.0959	.0951	.0943	.0936	.0928	.0920	.0912	.0905	.0897
14	100	.937	.1229	.1221	.1213	.1205	.1197	.1190	.1182	.1174	.1166	.1158	.1150
14	120	1.093	.1445	.1437	.1429	.1421	.1413	.1405	.1397	.1389	.1381	.1373	.1366
14	140	1.250	.1667	.1659	.1650	.1642	.1634	.1626	.1618	.1610	.1602	.1594	.1586
14		1.344	.1801	.1793	.1785	.1776	.1768	.1760	.1752	.1744	.1736	.1727	.1719
14	160	1.406	.1890	.1882	.1874	.1866	.1857	.1849	.1841	.1833	.1824	.1816	.1808
16		.188	.0207	.0201	.0195	.0188	.0182	.0176	.0169	.0163	.0157	.0150	.0144

Table 7-2
Continued

NOMINAL PIPE SIZE	SCHEDULE NUMBER AND/OR WEIGHT	WALL THICKNESS	CORROSION ALLOWANCE-INCHES Y=0.4										
			0.000	0.005	0.010	0.015	0.020	0.025	0.030	0.035	0.040	0.045	0.050
16		.238	.0263	.0257	.0250	.0244	.0238	.0231	.0225	.0218	.0212	.0206	.0199
16	10	.250	.0276	.0270	.0264	.0257	.0251	.0245	.0238	.0232	.0225	.0219	.0213
16		.281	.0311	.0305	.0298	.0292	.0286	.0279	.0273	.0266	.0260	.0254	.0247
16	20	.312	.0346	.0340	.0333	.0327	.0320	.0314	.0307	.0301	.0295	.0288	.0282
16		.344	.0382	.0376	.0369	.0363	.0356	.0350	.0343	.0337	.0331	.0324	.0318
16	30 ST	.375	.0417	.0411	.0404	.0398	.0391	.0385	.0378	.0372	.0365	.0359	.0353
16		.406	.0452	.0446	.0439	.0433	.0426	.0420	.0413	.0407	.0400	.0394	.0387
16		.438	.0488	.0482	.0475	.0469	.0462	.0456	.0450	.0443	.0437	.0430	.0424
16		.469	.0524	.0517	.0511	.0504	.0498	.0491	.0485	.0478	.0472	.0465	.0459
16	40 XS	.500	.0559	.0553	.0546	.0540	.0533	.0526	.0520	.0513	.0507	.0500	.0494
16		.531	.0595	.0588	.0581	.0575	.0568	.0562	.0555	.0549	.0542	.0536	.0529
16	60	.656	.0739	.0732	.0725	.0719	.0712	.0706	.0699	.0692	.0686	.0679	.0673
16		.688	.0776	.0769	.0763	.0756	.0749	.0743	.0736	.0729	.0723	.0716	.0710
16		.750	.0848	.0841	.0835	.0828	.0821	.0815	.0808	.0801	.0795	.0788	.0782
16	80	.843	.0957	.0951	.0944	.0937	.0930	.0924	.0917	.0910	.0904	.0897	.0890
16	100	1.031	.1181	.1174	.1167	.1160	.1154	.1147	.1140	.1133	.1126	.1119	.1113
16	120	1.218	.1407	.1400	.1393	.1386	.1379	.1372	.1365	.1358	.1352	.1345	.1338
16	140	1.438	.1678	.1671	.1664	.1657	.1650	.1643	.1636	.1629	.1622	.1615	.1607
16		1.500	.1756	.1749	.1742	.1734	.1727	.1720	.1713	.1706	.1699	.1692	.1684
16	160	1.593	.1873	.1866	.1858	.1851	.1844	.1837	.1830	.1822	.1815	.1808	.1801
18	10	.250	.0245	.0240	.0234	.0228	.0223	.0217	.0211	.0206	.0200	.0195	.0189
18	20	.312	.0307	.0301	.0296	.0290	.0284	.0279	.0273	.0267	.0262	.0256	.0250
18	ST	.375	.0370	.0364	.0359	.0353	.0347	.0341	.0336	.0330	.0324	.0319	.0313
18	30	.438	.0433	.0427	.0422	.0416	.0410	.0404	.0399	.0393	.0387	.0382	.0376
18	XS	.500	.0496	.0490	.0484	.0478	.0473	.0467	.0461	.0455	.0450	.0444	.0438
18	40	.562	.0559	.0553	.0547	.0541	.0535	.0530	.0524	.0518	.0512	.0506	.0501
18		.594	.0591	.0585	.0580	.0574	.0568	.0562	.0556	.0550	.0545	.0539	.0533
18		.625	.0623	.0617	.0611	.0605	.0599	.0594	.0588	.0582	.0576	.0570	.0565
18		.719	.0719	.0713	.0707	.0702	.0696	.0690	.0684	.0678	.0672	.0666	.0660
18	60	.750	.0751	.0745	.0739	.0733	.0728	.0722	.0716	.0710	.0704	.0698	.0692
18		.812	.0815	.0809	.0803	.0797	.0792	.0786	.0780	.0774	.0768	.0762	.0756
18	80	.937	.0945	.0939	.0933	.0927	.0922	.0916	.0910	.0904	.0898	.0892	.0886
18	100	1.156	.1177	.1171	.1165	.1159	.1152	.1146	.1140	.1134	.1128	.1122	.1116
18	120	1.375	.1412	.1406	.1400	.1394	.1388	.1381	.1375	.1369	.1363	.1357	.1350
18	140	1.562	.1617	.1611	.1604	.1598	.1592	.1585	.1579	.1573	.1567	.1560	.1554
18		1.688	.1756	.1750	.1744	.1737	.1731	.1725	.1718	.1712	.1706	.1699	.1693

Table 7-2
Continued

NOMINAL PIPE SIZE	SCHEDULE NUMBER AND/OR WEIGHT	WALL THICKNESS	CORROSION ALLOWANCE-INCHES Y=0.4										
			0.000	0.005	0.010	0.015	0.020	0.025	0.030	0.035	0.040	0.045	0.050
18	160	1.781	.1860	.1854	.1848	.1841	.1835	.1828	.1822	.1816	.1809	.1803	.1796
20	10	.250	.0221	.0216	.0211	.0205	.0200	.0195	.0190	.0185	.0180	.0175	.0170
20		.312	.0276	.0271	.0266	.0261	.0256	.0250	.0245	.0240	.0235	.0230	.0225
20	20 ST	.375	.0332	.0327	.0322	.0317	.0312	.0307	.0302	.0297	.0291	.0286	.0281
20		.438	.0389	.0384	.0379	.0374	.0369	.0363	.0358	.0353	.0348	.0343	.0338
20	30 XS	.500	.0445	.0440	.0435	.0430	.0425	.0419	.0414	.0409	.0404	.0399	.0394
20		.562	.0502	.0496	.0491	.0486	.0481	.0476	.0470	.0465	.0460	.0455	.0450
20	40	.593	.0530	.0525	.0519	.0514	.0509	.0504	.0499	.0493	.0488	.0483	.0478
20		.625	.0559	.0554	.0549	.0543	.0538	.0533	.0528	.0523	.0517	.0512	.0507
20	60	.812	.0731	.0726	.0721	.0715	.0710	.0705	.0700	.0694	.0689	.0684	.0678
20		.875	.0790	.0784	.0779	.0774	.0769	.0763	.0758	.0753	.0747	.0742	.0737
20		.906	.0819	.0813	.0808	.0803	.0797	.0792	.0787	.0781	.0776	.0771	.0765
20	80	1.031	.0936	.0931	.0925	.0920	.0914	.0909	.0904	.0898	.0893	.0888	.0882
20		1.250	.1144	.1138	.1133	.1127	.1122	.1116	.1111	.1106	.1100	.1095	.1089
20	100	1.281	.1173	.1168	.1163	.1157	.1152	.1146	.1141	.1135	.1130	.1124	.1119
20	120	1.500	.1385	.1380	.1374	.1369	.1363	.1357	.1352	.1346	.1341	.1335	.1330
20	140	1.750	.1631	.1625	.1620	.1614	.1608	.1603	.1597	.1592	.1586	.1580	.1575
20		1.844	.1725	.1719	.1713	.1708	.1702	.1696	.1691	.1685	.1679	.1673	.1668
20	160	1.968	.1849	.1844	.1838	.1832	.1826	.1821	.1815	.1809	.1803	.1798	.1792
22	LG	.250	.0200	.0196	.0191	.0187	.0182	.0177	.0173	.0168	.0164	.0159	.0154
22	ST	.375	.0302	.0297	.0293	.0288	.0283	.0279	.0274	.0269	.0265	.0260	.0255
22	XS	.500	.0404	.0399	.0395	.0390	.0385	.0381	.0376	.0371	.0367	.0362	.0357
24	10	.250	.0184	.0179	.0175	.0171	.0167	.0163	.0158	.0154	.0150	.0146	.0141
24		.312	.0230	.0225	.0221	.0217	.0213	.0208	.0204	.0200	.0196	.0191	.0187
24	20 ST	.375	.0276	.0272	.0268	.0264	.0259	.0255	.0251	.0247	.0242	.0238	.0234
24		.438	.0324	.0319	.0315	.0311	.0306	.0302	.0298	.0294	.0289	.0285	.0281
24	XS	.500	.0370	.0366	.0361	.0357	.0353	.0349	.0344	.0340	.0336	.0331	.0327
24	30	.562	.0417	.0412	.0408	.0404	.0399	.0395	.0391	.0387	.0382	.0378	.0374
24		.625	.0464	.0460	.0456	.0451	.0447	.0443	.0438	.0434	.0430	.0425	.0421
24	40	.687	.0511	.0507	.0503	.0498	.0494	.0490	.0485	.0481	.0477	.0472	.0468
24		.750	.0559	.0555	.0550	.0546	.0542	.0537	.0533	.0529	.0524	.0520	.0516
24	60	.968	.0726	.0722	.0718	.0713	.0709	.0704	.0700	.0695	.0691	.0687	.0682
24		1.031	.0775	.0771	.0766	.0762	.0757	.0753	.0749	.0744	.0740	.0735	.0731
24	80	1.218	.0921	.0916	.0912	.0907	.0903	.0898	.0894	.0890	.0885	.0881	.0876
24	100	1.531	.1169	.1164	.1159	.1155	.1150	.1146	.1141	.1137	.1132	.1128	.1123

Table 7-2
Continued

NOMINAL PIPE SIZE	SCHEDULE NUMBER AND/OR WEIGHT	WALL THICKNESS	CORROSION ALLOWANCE-INCHES Y=0.4										
			0.000	0.005	0.010	0.015	0.020	0.025	0.030	0.035	0.040	0.045	0.050
24	120	1.812	.1395	.1390	.1386	.1381	.1376	.1372	.1367	.1363	.1358	.1353	.1349
24	140	2.062	.1600	.1595	.1590	.1586	.1581	.1576	.1571	.1567	.1562	.1557	.1553
24		2.188	.1704	.1699	.1695	.1690	.1685	.1680	.1676	.1671	.1666	.1661	.1657
24	160	2.343	.1834	.1829	.1824	.1819	.1815	.1810	.1805	.1800	.1795	.1791	.1786
26	ST	.375	.0255	.0251	.0247	.0243	.0239	.0235	.0231	.0228	.0224	.0220	.0216
26	XS	.500	.0341	.0337	.0333	.0329	.0325	.0321	.0317	.0313	.0310	.0306	.0302
30	10	.312	.0183	.0180	.0177	.0173	.0170	.0166	.0163	.0160	.0156	.0153	.0150
30	ST	.375	.0221	.0217	.0214	.0211	.0207	.0204	.0200	.0197	.0194	.0190	.0187
30		.438	.0258	.0255	.0251	.0248	.0245	.0241	.0238	.0234	.0231	.0228	.0224
30	20 XS	.500	.0295	.0292	.0288	.0285	.0281	.0278	.0275	.0271	.0268	.0264	.0261
30		.562	.0332	.0329	.0325	.0322	.0319	.0315	.0312	.0308	.0305	.0301	.0298
30	30	.625	.0370	.0367	.0363	.0360	.0356	.0353	.0349	.0346	.0343	.0339	.0336
34	ST	.375	.0195	.0192	.0189	.0186	.0183	.0180	.0177	.0174	.0171	.0168	.0165
34	XS	.500	.0260	.0257	.0254	.0251	.0248	.0245	.0242	.0239	.0236	.0233	.0230
36	ST	.375	.0184	.0181	.0178	.0175	.0172	.0170	.0167	.0164	.0161	.0158	.0155
36	XS	.500	.0245	.0243	.0240	.0237	.0234	.0231	.0228	.0226	.0223	.0220	.0217
42	ST	.375	.0157	.0155	.0152	.0150	.0148	.0145	.0143	.0140	.0138	.0136	.0133
42	XS	.500	.0210	.0208	.0205	.0203	.0200	.0198	.0196	.0193	.0191	.0188	.0186
48	ST	.375	.0137	.0135	.0133	.0131	.0129	.0127	.0125	.0123	.0121	.0119	.0116
48	XS	.500	.0184	.0182	.0179	.0177	.0175	.0173	.0171	.0169	.0167	.0165	.0163

Table 7-2
Continued

NOMINAL PIPE SIZE	SCHEDULE NUMBER AND/OR WEIGHT	WALL THICKNESS	CORROSION ALLOWANCE-INCHES									Y=0.4
			0.055	0.060	0.065	0.070	0.075	0.080	0.085	0.90	0.095	0.100
1/8	10S	.049	0.0000									
1/8	40 ST 40S	.068	.0224									
1/8	80 ST 80S	.095	.1471	.1197	.0928	.0665	.0408	.0155				
1/4	10S	.065	.0070									
1/4	40 ST 40S	.088	.0842	.0646	.0452	.0262	.0074					
1/4	80 ST 80S	.119	.1962	.1749	.1538	.1331	.1127	.0927	.0729	.0534	.0343	.0154
3/8	10S	.065	.0056									
3/8	40 ST 40S	.091	.0752	.0595	.0441	.0288	.0138					
3/8	80 ST 80S	.126	.1752	.1583	.1417	.1252	.1090	.0930	.0771	.0615	.0460	.0307
1/2	10S	.083	.0427	.0304	.0183	.0063						
1/2	40 ST 40S	.109	.1000	.0872	.0745	.0619	.0495	.0372	.0249	.0129	.0009	
1/2	80 ST 80S	.147	.1885	.1748	.1613	.1478	.1346	.1214	.1084	.0955	.0827	.0701
1/2	160	.187	.2885	.2737	.2592	.2447	.2305	.2163	.2024	.1885	.1748	.1613
1/2	XX	.294	.5964	.5783	.5603	.5426	.5251	.5077	.4906	.4737	.4569	.4404
3/4	5S	.065	.0036									
3/4	10S	.083	.0340	.0243	.0146	.0050						
3/4	40S	.113	.0865	.0763	.0662	.0562	.0463	.0365	.0267	.0170	.0074	
3/4	80S	.154	.1617	.1510	.1403	.1297	.1192	.1088	.0985	.0882	.0781	.0680
3/4		.188	.2276	.2163	.2051	.1940	.1830	.1720	.1612	.1504	.1398	.1292
3/4	160	.218	.2884	.2766	.2649	.2533	.2418	.2304	.2191	.2079	.1967	.1857
3/4	XX	.308	.4884	.4748	.4614	.4481	.4349	.4219	.4089	.3961	.3833	.3707
1	5S	.065	.0029									
1	10S	.109	.0630	.0550	.0471	.0392	.0314	.0236	.0159	.0082	.0006	
1	40 ST 40S	.133	.0970	.0888	.0807	.0726	.0646	.0566	.0486	.0408	.0329	.0252
1	80 ST 80S	.179	.1647	.1561	.1476	.1391	.1306	.1222	.1139	.1056	.0974	.0892
1		.219	.2266	.2176	.2087	.1998	.1909	.1821	.1734	.1647	.1561	.1476
1	160	.250	.2766	.2673	.2580	.2487	.2396	.2305	.2214	.2125	.2035	.1947
1	XXO	.358	.4660	.4553	.4447	.4342	.4238	.4134	.4031	.3929	.3828	.3727
11/4	5S	.065	.0023									
11/4	10S	.109	.0496	.0434	.0371	.0310	.0248	.0187	.0126	.0065	.0005	
11/4	40 ST 40S	.140	.0841	.0776	.0713	.0649	.0586	.0523	.0460	.0398	.0336	.0274
11/4	80 ST 80S	.191	.1428	.1361	.1294	.1228	.1162	.1096	.1030	.0965	.0900	.0836
11/4	160	.250	.2142	.2071	.2001	.1931	.1861	.1791	.1722	.1654	.1586	.1518
11/4	XX	.382	.3888	.3807	.3728	.3648	.3569	.3491	.3413	.3335	.3258	.3181

Table 7-2
Continued

NOMINAL PIPE SIZE	SCHEDULE NUMBER AND/OR WEIGHT	WALL THICKNESS	CORROSION ALLOWANCE-INCHES									Y=0.4
			0.055	0.060	0.065	0.070	0.075	0.080	0.085	0.90	0.095	0.100
11/2	5S	.065	.0020									
11/2	10S	.109	.0432	.0378	.0324	.0270	.0216	.0163	.0110	.0057	.0004	
11/2	40 ST 40S	.145	.0780	.0724	.0669	.0613	.0558	.0503	.0449	.0394	.0340	.0286
11/2	80 ST 80S	.200	.1330	.1272	.1214	.1156	.1099	.1042	.0985	.0928	.0871	.0815
11/2	160	.281	.2185	.2123	.2061	.1999	.1938	.1877	.1816	.1756	.1696	.1636
11/2	XX	.400	.3546	.3477	.3409	.3341	.3274	.3207	.3140	.3073	.3007	.2941
2	5S	.065	.0016									
2	10S	.109	.0345	.0301	.0258	.0216	.0173	.0130	.0088	.0045	.0003	
2	40 ST 40S	.154	.0690	.0646	.0602	.0557	.0513	.0470	.0426	.0383	.0339	.0296
2		.167	.0792	.0747	.0702	.0658	.0614	.0570	.0526	.0482	.0438	.0395
2		.188	.0957	.0912	.0867	.0822	.0777	.0732	.0688	.0644	.0599	.0555
2	80 ST 80S	.218	.1198	.1152	.1106	.1060	.1014	.0969	.0923	.0878	.0833	.0788
2		.250	.1459	.1412	.1365	.1319	.1272	.1226	.1179	.1133	.1087	.1042
2		.312	.1981	.1932	.1884	.1835	.1787	.1738	.1690	.1642	.1595	.1547
2	160	.343	.2250	.2200	.2150	.2101	.2051	.2002	.1953	.1904	.1856	.1807
2	XX	.436	.3089	.3036	.2983	.2931	.2878	.2826	.2774	.2722	.2670	.2619
21/2	5S	.083	.0123	.0088	.0053	.0018						
21/2	10S	.120	.0353	.0317	.0281	.0246	.0210	.0175	.0140	.0105	.0070	.0035
21/2	40 ST 40S	.203	.0883	.0846	.0809	.0772	.0735	.0698	.0661	.0625	.0588	.0552
21/2		.217	.0975	.0937	.0900	.0863	.0826	.0788	.0751	.0715	.0678	.0641
21/2	80 ST 805	.276	.1368	.1330	.1291	.1253	.1215	.1176	.1138	.1100	.1062	.1025
21/2	160	.375	.2056	.2016	.1975	.1935	.1894	.1854	.1814	.1774	.1734	.1695
21/2	XX	.552	.3380	.3335	.3291	.3246	.3202	.3158	.3114	.3070	.3026	.2982
3	5S	.083	.0101	.0072	.0044	.0015						
3	10S	.120	.0289	.0260	.0231	.0202	.0173	.0144	.0115	.0086	.0057	.0029
3		.125	.0315	.0285	.0256	.0227	.0198	.0169	.0140	.0111	.0082	.0054
3		.148	.0433	.0404	.0374	.0345	.0315	.0286	.0257	.0228	.0199	.0170
3		.188	.0642	.0612	.0582	.0552	.0522	.0492	.0463	.0433	.0404	.0374
3	40 ST 40S	.216	.0790	.0760	.0729	.0699	.0669	.0639	.0609	.0579	.0549	.0519
3		.241	.0924	.0893	.0862	.0832	.0801	.0771	.0741	.0710	.0680	.0650
3		.254	.0994	.0963	.0932	.0901	.0871	.0840	.0810	.0779	.0749	.0719
3		.289	.1184	.1153	.1122	.1091	.1060	.1028	.0998	.0967	.0936	.0905
3	80 XS 805	.300	.1245	.1213	.1182	.1151	.1119	.1088	.1057	.1026	.0995	.0964
3		.312	.1311	.1279	.1248	.1216	.1185	.1154	.1123	.1091	.1060	.1029
3		.406	.1842	.1809	.1776	.1744	.1711	.1678	.1646	.1614	.1581	.1549

Table 7-2
Continued

NOM-INAL PIPE SIZE	SCHEDULE NUMBER AND/OR WEIGHT	WALL THICK-NESS	CORRUSION ALLOWANCE-INCHES									Y=0.4
			0.055	0.060	0.065	0.070	0.075	0.080	0.085	0.90	0.095	0.100
3	160	.438	.2028	.1995	.1961	.1928	.1895	.1862	.1829	.1796	.1763	.1731
3	XX	.600	.3009	.2973	.2937	.2902	.2866	.2831	.2795	.2760	.2725	.2690
31/2	5S	.083	.0088	.0063	.0038	.0013						
31/2	10S	.120	.0253	.0227	.0202	.0176	.0151	.0126	.0100	.0075	.0050	.0025
31/2		.128	.0288	.0263	.0237	.0212	.0186	.0161	.0136	.0110	.0085	.0060
31/2		.134	.0315	.0290	.0264	.0239	.0213	.0188	.0162	.0137	.0112	.0087
31/2		.148	.0378	.0352	.0327	.0301	.0276	.0250	.0224	.0199	.0174	.0148
31/2		.188	.0560	.0534	.0508	.0482	.0456	.0430	.0404	.0378	.0352	.0327
31/2	40 ST 40S	.226	.0735	.0708	.0682	.0655	.0629	.0603	.0577	.0551	.0525	.0498
31/2		.281	.0992	.0965	.0938	.0911	.0885	.0858	.0831	.0804	.0778	.0751
31/2	80 XS 80S	.318	.1168	.1141	.1114	.1087	.1059	.1032	.1005	.0978	.0951	.0924
31/2		.344	.1294	.1266	.1238	.1211	.1183	.1156	.1129	.1101	.1074	.1047
31/2		.469	.1913	.1884	.1855	.1826	.1797	.1769	.1740	.1712	.1683	.1655
31/2		.636	.2787	.2756	.2725	.2695	.2664	.2633	.2603	.2573	.2542	.2512
4	5S	.083	.0079	.0056	.0034	.0012						
4	10S	.120	.0224	.0202	.0179	.0157	.0134	.0112	.0089	.0067	.0045	.0022
4		.128	.0256	.0233	.0211	.0188	.0166	.0143	.0121	.0098	.0076	.0053
4		.134	.0280	.0257	.0234	.0212	.0189	.0167	.0144	.0122	.0099	.0077
4		.142	.0312	.0289	.0266	.0243	.0221	.0198	.0176	.0153	.0131	.0108
4		.165	.0404	.0381	.0358	.0335	.0312	.0289	.0267	.0244	.0221	.0199
4		.188	.0496	.0473	.0450	.0427	.0404	.0381	.0358	.0336	.0313	.0290
4		.205	.0565	.0542	.0519	.0496	.0473	.0450	.0427	.0404	.0381	.0358
4	40 ST40S	.237	.0696	.0673	.0649	.0626	.0603	.0579	.0556	.0533	.0510	.0487
4		.250	.0750	.0726	.0703	.0679	.0656	.0632	.0609	.0586	.0562	.0539
4		.271	.0837	.0813	.0789	.0766	.0742	.0718	.0695	.0671	.0648	.0625
4		.281	.0878	.0854	.0831	.0807	.0783	.0760	.0736	.0713	.0689	.0666
4		.300	.0958	.0934	.0910	.0886	.0862	.0838	.0815	.0791	.0767	.0744
4		.312	.1008	.0984	.0960	.0936	.0912	.0888	.0864	.0841	.0817	.0793
4	80 XS 80S	.337	.1114	.1089	.1065	.1041	.1017	.0993	.0969	.0945	.0921	.0897
4		.375	.1276	.1251	.1227	.1202	.1178	.1154	.1129	.1105	.1081	.1057
4	120	.438	.1549	.1524	.1499	.1474	.1449	.1425	.1400	.1375	.1350	.1326
4		.500	.1824	.1798	.1773	.1748	.1722	.1697	.1671	.1646	.1621	.1596
4	160	.531	.1964	.1938	.1912	.1886	.1861	.1835	.1809	.1784	.1758	.1733
4	XX	.674	.2626	.2599	.2572	.2545	.2518	.2491	.2464	.2438	.2411	.2384
5	5S	.109	.0146	.0128	.0110	.0092	.0073	.0055	.0037	.0019	.0001	
5	10S	.134	.0226	.0208	.0189	.0171	.0153	.0135	.0116	.0098	.0080	.0062

Table 7-2
Continued

NOMINAL PIPE SIZE	SCHEDULE NUMBER AND/OR WEIGHT	WALL THICKNESS	CORROSION ALLOWANCE-INCHES Y=0.4									
			0.055	0.060	0.065	0.070	0.075	0.080	0.085	0.90	0.095	0.100
5	40 ST 40S	.258	.0629	.0610	.0592	.0573	.0554	.0535	.0516	.0498	.0479	.0460
5		.352	.0944	.0925	.0905	.0886	.0867	.0847	.0828	.0809	.0790	.0771
5	80 XS 80S	.375	.1022	.1003	.0983	.0964	.0944	.0925	.0906	.0886	.0867	.0848
5		.438	.1239	.1219	.1199	.1179	.1160	.1140	.1120	.1101	.1081	.1062
5	120	.500	.1455	.1435	.1415	.1395	.1375	.1355	.1335	.1315	.1295	.1275
5	160	.625	.1903	.1882	.1861	.1841	.1820	.1799	.1779	.1758	.1737	.1717
5	XX	.750	.2366	.2345	.2323	.2302	.2280	.2259	.2238	.2216	.2195	.2174
6	5S	.109	.0122	.0107	.0092	.0077	.0062	.0047	.0031	.0016	.0001	
6	10S	.134	.0189	.0174	.0159	.0143	.0128	.0113	.0098	.0083	.0067	.0052
6		.169	.0284	.0268	.0253	.0237	.0222	.0207	.0191	.0176	.0161	.0145
6		.180	.0313	.0298	.0282	.0267	.0252	.0236	.0221	.0205	.0190	.0175
6		.188	.0335	.0320	.0304	.0289	.0273	.0258	.0242	.0227	.0212	.0196
6		.219	.0419	.0404	.0388	.0373	.0357	.0342	.0326	.0311	.0295	.0280
6		.250	.0504	.0489	.0473	.0457	.0442	.0426	.0410	.0395	.0379	.0364
6		.277	.0579	.0563	.0547	.0531	.0516	.0500	.0484	.0469	.0453	.0437
6	40 ST 40S	.280	.0587	.0571	.0555	.0540	.0524	.0508	.0493	.0477	.0461	.0446
6		.375	.0853	.0837	.0820	.0804	.0788	.0772	.0756	.0740	.0724	.0708
6	80 XS 805	.432	.1015	.0998	.0982	.0966	.0949	.0933	.0917	.0901	.0885	.0868
6		.500	.1211	.1194	.1177	.1161	.1144	.1128	.1111	.1095	.1079	.1062
6	120	.562	.1392	.1375	.1358	.1342	.1325	.1308	.1291	.1275	.1258	.1241
6	160	.718	.1859	.1842	.1824	.1807	.1790	.1772	.1755	.1738	.1721	.1703
6	XX	.864	.2312	.2294	.2276	.2258	.2240	.2222	.2204	.2186	.2169	.2151
8	5S	.109	.0094	.0082	.0071	.0059	.0047	.0036	.0024	.0012	.0001	
8	10'S	.148	.0174	.0162	.0150	.0139	.0127	.0115	.0104	.0092	.0080	.0069
8		.158	.0195	.0183	.0171	.0159	.0148	.0136	.0124	.0112	.0101	.0089
8		.165	.0209	.0197	.0185	.0174	.0162	.0150	.0138	.0127	.0115	.0103
8		.188	.0257	.0245	.0233	.0221	.0209	.0197	.0186	.0174	.0162	.0150
8		.203	.0288	.0276	.0264	.0252	.0240	.0228	.0217	.0205	.0193	.0181
8		.219	.0321	.0309	.0297	.0285	.0273	.0262	.0250	.0238	.0226	.0214
8		.238	.0360	.0349	.0337	.0325	.0313	.0301	.0289	.0277	.0265	.0254
8	20	.250	.0386	.0374	.0362	.0350	.0338	.0326	.0314	.0302	.0290	.0278
8	30	.277	.0442	.0430	.0418	.0406	.0394	.0382	.0370	.0358	.0346	.0335
8	40 ST 40S	.322	.0537	.0525	.0513	.0501	.0489	.0477	.0465	.0453	.0441	.0429
8		.344	.0584	.0572	.0559	.0547	.0535	.0523	.0511	.0499	.0487	.0475
8		.352	.0601	.0589	.0576	.0564	.0552	.0540	.0528	.0516	.0504	.0492
8		.375	.0650	.0638	.0625	.0613	.0601	.0589	.0577	.0565	.0553	.0540

Table 7-2
Continued

NOMINAL PIPE SIZE	SCHEDULE NUMBER AND/OR WEIGHT	WALL THICKNESS	CORROSION ALLOWANCE-INCHES									Y=0.4
			0.055	0.060	0.065	0.070	0.075	0.080	0.085	0.90	0.095	0.100
8	60	.406	.0716	.0704	.0692	.0679	.0667	.0655	.0643	.0631	.0618	.0606
8		.469	.0852	.0840	.0827	.0815	.0803	.0790	.0778	.0766	.0753	.0741
8	80 XS 80S	.500	.0920	.0907	.0895	.0882	.0870	.0857	.0845	.0833	.0820	.0808
8	100	.593	.1124	.1111	.1099	.1086	.1073	.1061	.1048	.1036	.1023	.1011
8		.625	.1195	.1182	.1170	.1157	.1144	.1132	.1119	.1106	.1094	.1081
8	120	.718	.1404	.1391	.1378	.1365	.1352	.1339	.1327	.1314	.1301	.1288
8	140	.812	.1618	.1605	.1592	.1579	.1566	.1553	.1540	.1527	.1514	.1501
8	XX	.875	.1764	.1751	.1738	.1724	.1711	.1698	.1685	.1671	.1658	.1645
8	160	.906	.1836	.1823	.1810	.1796	.1783	.1770	.1756	.1743	.1730	.1717
10	5S	.134	.0116	.0107	.0098	.0088	.0079	.0069	.0060	.0051	.0041	.0032
10	10S	.165	.0167	.0158	.0149	.0139	.0130	.0120	.0111	.0102	.0092	.0083
10		.188	.0205	.0196	.0186	.0177	.0168	.0158	.0149	.0139	.0130	.0121
10		.203	.0230	.0221	.0211	.0202	.0192	.0183	.0174	.0164	.0155	.0145
10		.219	.0257	.0247	.0238	.0228	.0219	.0209	.0200	.0191	.0181	.0172
10	20	.250	.0308	.0299	.0289	.0280	.0270	.0261	.0251	.0242	.0232	.0223
10		.279	.0357	.0347	.0338	.0328	.0319	.0309	.0300	.0290	.0281	.0271
10	30	.307	.0404	.0394	.0385	.0375	.0365	.0356	.0346	.0337	.0327	.0318
10		.348	.0473	.0463	.0454	.0444	.0434	.0425	.0415	.0406	.0396	.0386
10	40 ST 40S	.365	.0502	.0492	.0482	.0473	.0463	.0453	.0444	.0434	.0425	.0415
10		.395	.0553	.0543	.0533	.0524	.0514	.0504	.0494	.0485	.0475	.0465
10	60 XS 80S	.500	.0732	.0723	.0713	.0703	.0693	.0683	.0673	.0664	.0654	.0644
10		.531	.0786	.0776	.0766	.0756	.0747	.0737	.0727	.0717	.0707	.0697
10	80	.593	.0894	.0884	.0874	.0864	.0854	.0844	.0834	.0824	.0814	.0804
10	100	.718	.1114	.1104	.1094	.1084	.1074	.1063	.1053	.1043	.1033	.1023
10		.750	.1171	.1161	.1151	.1140	.1130	.1120	.1110	.1100	.1090	.1080
10	120	.843	.1338	.1328	.1317	.1307	.1297	.1286	.1276	.1266	.1256	.1245
10	140	1.000	.1625	.1614	.1604	.1593	.1583	.1572	.1562	.1551	.1541	.1530
10		1.062	.1740	.1729	.1718	.1708	.1697	.1687	.1676	.1665	.1655	.1644
10	160	1.125	.1858	.1847	.1836	.1825	.1815	.1804	.1793	.1783	.1772	.1761
12	5S	.156	.0129	.0121	.0113	.0105	.0097	.0089	.0081	.0073	.0065	.0057
12	10S	.180	.0162	.0154	.0146	.0138	.0130	.0122	.0114	.0106	.0098	.0091
12		.203	.0194	.0186	.0178	.0170	.0162	.0154	.0146	.0138	.0130	.0122
12		.219	.0216	.0208	.0200	.0192	.0184	.0176	.0168	.0160	.0152	.0145
12		.238	.0243	.0235	.0227	.0219	.0211	.0203	.0195	.0187	.0179	.0171
12	20	.250	.0260	.0252	.0244	.0236	.0228	.0220	.0212	.0204	.0196	.0188
12		.279	.0300	.0292	.0284	.0276	.0268	.0260	.0252	.0244	.0236	.0228

Table 7-2
Continued

NOMINAL PIPE SIZE	SCHEDULE NUMBER AND/OR WEIGHT	WALL THICKNESS	CORROSION ALLOWANCE-INCHES Y=0.4									
			0.055	0.060	0.065	0.070	0.075	0.080	0.085	0.90	0.095	0.100
12		.300	.0330	.0322	.0314	.0306	.0298	.0290	.0282	.0274	.0266	.0258
12	30	.330	.0372	.0364	.0356	.0348	.0340	.0332	.0324	.0316	.0308	.0300
12		.344	.0392	.0384	.0376	.0368	.0360	.0352	.0343	.0335	.0327	.0319
12	ST 40S	.375	.0436	.0428	.0420	.0412	.0403	.0395	.0387	.0379	.0371	.0363
12	40	.406	.0480	.0472	.0464	.0456	.0447	.0439	.0431	.0423	.0415	.0407
12		.438	.0526	.0518	.0509	.0501	.0493	.0485	.0477	.0469	.0460	.0452
12	XS 80S	.500	.0615	.0607	.0598	.0590	.0582	.0574	.0565	.0557	.0549	.0541
12	60	.562	.0704	.0696	.0688	.0680	.0671	.0663	.0655	.0646	.0638	.0630
12		.625	.0796	.0788	.0779	.0771	.0763	.0754	.0746	.0738	.0730	.0721
12	80	.687	.0887	.0879	.0870	.0862	.0853	.0845	.0837	.0828	.0820	.0812
12	100	.843	.1119	.1110	.1102	.1093	.1085	.1076	.1067	.1059	.1050	.1042
12		.875	.1167	.1158	.1150	.1141	.1132	.1124	.1115	.1107	.1098	.1090
12	120	1.000	.1356	.1347	.1339	.1330	.1321	.1313	.1304	.1295	.1286	.1278
12	140	1.125	.1548	.1539	.1530	.1522	.1513	.1504	.1495	.1486	.1478	.1469
12		1.219	.1694	.1685	.1677	.1668	.1659	.1650	.1641	.1632	.1623	.1614
12	160	1.312	.1841	.1832	.1823	.1814	.1805	.1796	.1787	.1778	.1769	.1760
14		.188	.0157	.0150	.0143	.0136	.0129	.0121	.0114	.0107	.0100	.0092
14		.220	.0198	.0191	.0183	.0176	.0169	.0162	.0155	.0147	.0140	.0133
14		.238	.0221	.0214	.0206	.0199	.0192	.0185	.0177	.0170	.0163	.0156
14	10	.250	.0236	.0229	.0222	.0214	.0207	.0200	.0193	.0185	.0178	.0171
14	20	.312	.0315	.0308	.0301	.0293	.0286	.0279	.0271	.0264	.0257	.0250
14	30ST	.375	.0396	.0389	.0382	.0374	.0367	.0360	.0352	.0345	.0338	.0330
14		.406	.0436	.0429	.0422	.0414	.0407	.0399	.0392	.0385	.0377	.0370
14	40	.438	.0478	.0470	.0463	.0456	.0448	.0441	.0433	.0426	.0419	.0411
14		.469	.0518	.0511	.0503	.0496	.0488	.0481	.0474	.0466	.0459	.0451
14	XS	.500	.0559	.0551	.0544	.0536	.0529	.0521	.0514	.0506	.0499	.0492
14	60	.593	.0681	.0673	.0666	.0658	.0651	.0643	.0636	.0628	.0621	.0613
14		.625	.0723	.0715	.0708	.0700	.0693	.0685	.0678	.0670	.0663	.0655
14		.656	.0764	.0757	.0749	.0741	.0734	.0726	.0719	.0711	.0704	.0696
14	80	.750	.0889	.0882	.0874	.0867	.0859	.0851	.0844	.0836	.0828	.0821
14	100	.937	.1143	.1135	.1127	.1119	.1111	.1104	.1096	.1088	.1080	.1073
14	120	1.093	.1358	.1350	.1342	.1334	.1326	.1318	.1310	.1302	.1294	.1286
14	140	1.250	.1578	.1569	.1561	.1553	.1545	.1537	.1529	.1521	.1513	.1505
14		1.344	.1711	.1703	.1695	.1687	.1678	.1670	.1662	.1654	.1646	.1638
14	160	1.406	.1800	.1792	.1783	.1775	.1767	.1759	.1751	.1742	.1734	.1726
16		.188	.0136	.0131	.0125	.0119	.0112	.0106	.0100	.0093	.0087	.0081

Table 7-2
Continued

NOMINAL PIPE SIZE	SCHEDULE NUMBER AND/OR WEIGHT	WALL THICKNESS	CORROSION ALLOWANCE-INCHES									Y=0.4
			0.055	0.060	0.065	0.070	0.075	0.080	0.085	0.90	0.095	0.100
16		.238	.0193	.0187	.0180	.0174	.0168	.0161	.0155	.0149	.0142	.0136
16	10	.250	.0206	.0200	.0194	.0187	.0181	.0175	.0168	.0162	.0156	.0149
16		.281	.0241	.0235	.0228	.0222	.0215	.0209	.0203	.0196	.0190	.0184
16	20	.312	.0276	.0269	.0263	.0256	.0250	.0244	.0237	.0231	.0224	.0218
16		.344	.0311	.0305	.0299	.0292	.0286	.0279	.0273	.0267	.0260	.0254
16	30 ST	.375	.0346	.0340	.0333	.0327	.0320	.0314	.0308	.0301	.0295	.0288
16		.406	.0381	.0375	.0368	.0362	.0355	.0349	.0342	.0336	.0330	.0323
16		.438	.0417	.0411	.0404	.0398	.0391	.0385	.0378	.0372	.0366	.0359
16		.469	.0452	.0446	.0439	.0433	.0426	.0420	.0413	.0407	.0401	.0394
16	40 XS	.500	.0487	.0481	.0474	.0468	.0461	.0455	.0449	.0442	.0436	.0429
16		.531	.0523	.0516	.0510	.0503	.0497	.0490	.0484	.0477	.0471	.0464
16	60	.656	.0666	.0659	.0653	.0646	.0640	.0633	.0627	.0620	.0613	.0607
16		.688	.0703	.0696	.0690	.0683	.0677	.0670	.0663	.0657	.0650	.0644
16		.750	.0775	.0768	.0762	.0755	.0748	.0742	.0735	.0728	.0722	.0715
16	80	.843	.0883	.0877	.0870	.0863	.0857	.0850	.0843	.0837	.0830	.0823
16	100	1.031	.1106	.1099	.1092	.1085	.1079	.1072	.1065	.1058	.1051	.1045
16	120	1.218	.1331	.1324	.1317	.1310	.1303	.1296	.1289	.1282	.1275	.1268
16	140	1.438	.1600	.1593	.1586	.1579	.1572	.1565	.1558	.1551	.1544	.1537
16		1.500	.1677	.1670	.1663	.1656	.1649	.1642	.1635	.1628	.1621	.1613
16	160	1.593	.1794	.1786	.1779	.1772	.1765	.1758	.1751	.1744	.1736	.1729
18	10	.250	.0183	.0178	.0172	.0166	.0161	.0155	.0149	.0144	.0138	.0133
18	20	.312	.0245	.0239	.0233	.0228	.0222	.0216	.0211	.0205	.0199	.0194
18	ST	.375	.0307	.0302	.0296	.0290	.0284	.0279	.0273	.0267	.0262	.0256
18	30	.438	.0370	.0364	.0359	.0353	.0347	.0342	.0336	.0330	.0324	.0319
18	XS	.500	.0432	.0427	.0421	.0415	.0409	.0404	.0398	.0392	.0386	.0381
18	40	.562	.0495	.0489	.0483	.0478	.0472	.0466	.0460	.0455	.0449	.0443
18		.594	.0527	.0521	.0516	.0510	.0504	.0498	.0493	.0487	.0481	.0475
18		.625	.0559	.0553	.0547	.0541	.0536	.0530	.0524	.0518	.0512	.0507
18		.719	.0655	.0649	.0643	.0637	.0631	.0625	.0620	.0614	.0608	.0602
18	60	.750	.0686	.0681	.0675	.0669	.0663	.0657	.0651	.0645	.0640	.0634
18		.812	.0750	.0744	.0738	.0733	.0727	.0721	.0715	.0709	.0703	.0697
18	80	.937	.0880	.0874	.0868	.0862	.0856	.0850	.0844	.0838	.0832	.0826
18	100	1.156	.1110	.1104	.1098	.1092	.1086	.1080	.1074	.1068	.1062	.1056
18	120	1.375	.1344	.1338	.1332	.1326	.1320	.1313	.1307	.1301	.1295	.1289
18	140	1.562	.1548	.1541	.1535	.1529	.1523	.1516	.1510	.1504	.1498	.1491
18		1.688	.1687	.1680	.1674	.1668	.1661	.1655	.1649	.1642	.1636	.1630

Table 7-2
Continued

NOMINAL PIPE SIZE	SCHEDULE NUMBER AND/OR WEIGHT	WALL THICKNESS	CORROSION ALLOWANCE-INCHES									Y=0.4
			0.055	0.060	0.065	0.070	0.075	0.080	0.085	0.90	0.095	0.100
18	160	1.781	.1790	.1784	.1777	.1771	.1765	.1758	.1752	.1745	.1739	.1733
20	10	.250	.0165	.0160	.0155	.0150	.0145	.0140	.0134	.0129	.0124	.0119
20		.312	.0220	.0215	.0210	.0205	.0200	.0195	.0189	.0184	.0179	.0174
20	20 ST	.375	.0276	.0271	.0266	.0261	.0256	.0251	.0246	.0240	.0235	.0230
20		.438	.0333	.0327	.0322	.0317	.0312	.0307	.0302	.0297	.0292	.0286
20	30 XS	.500	.0388	.0383	.0378	.0373	.0368	.0363	.0358	.0352	.0347	.0342
20		.562	.0445	.0439	.0434	.0429	.0424	.0419	.0413	.0408	.0403	.0398
20	40	.593	.0473	.0467	.0462	.0457	.0452	.0447	.0442	.0436	.0431	.0426
20		.625	.0502	.0497	.0491	.0486	.0481	.0476	.0471	.0465	.0460	.0455
20	60	.812	.0673	.0668	.0663	.0657	.0652	.0647	.0642	.0636	.0631	.0626
20		.875	.0731	.0726	.0721	.0716	.0710	.0705	.0700	.0694	.0689	.0684
20		.906	.0760	.0755	.0750	.0744	.0739	.0734	.0728	.0723	.0718	.0712
20	80	1.031	.0877	.0871	.0866	.0861	.0855	.0850	.0845	.0839	.0834	.0829
20		1.250	.1084	.1078	.1073	.1067	.1062	.1057	.1051	.1046	.1040	.1035
20	100	1.281	.1113	.1108	.1102	.1097	.1092	.1086	.1081	.1075	.1070	.1064
20	120	1.500	.1324	.1319	.1313	.1307	.1302	.1296	.1291	.1285	.1280	.1274
20	140	1.750	.1569	.1563	.1558	.1552	.1546	.1541	.1535	.1529	.1524	.1518
20		1.844	.1662	.1656	.1651	.1645	.1639	.1634	.1628	.1622	.1617	.1611
20	160	1.968	.1786	.1780	.1775	.1769	.1763	.1757	.1752	.1746	.1740	.1735
22	LG	.250	.0150	.0145	.0141	.0136	.0131	.0127	.0122	.0118	.0113	.0108
22	ST	.375	.0251	.0246	.0242	.0237	.0232	.0228	.0223	.0218	.0214	.0209
22	XS	.500	.0353	.0348	.0343	.0339	.0334	.0329	.0325	.0320	.0315	.0311
24	10	.250	.0137	.0133	.0129	.0125	.0120	.0116	.0112	.0108	.0104	.0099
24		.312	.0183	.0179	.0175	.0170	.0166	.0162	.0158	.0153	.0149	.0145
24	20 ST	.375	.0230	.0225	.0221	.0217	.0213	.0208	.0204	.0200	.0196	.0192
24		.438	.0277	.0272	.0268	.0264	.0260	.0255	.0251	.0247	.0243	.0238
24	XS	.500	.0323	.0319	.0314	.0310	.0306	.0302	.0297	.0293	.0289	.0284
24	30	.562	.0369	.0365	.0361	.0356	.0352	.0348	.0344	.0339	.0335	.0331
24		.625	.0417	.0412	.0408	.0404	.0400	.0395	.0391	.0387	.0382	.0378
24	40	.687	.0464	.0459	.0455	.0451	.0446	.0442	.0438	.0433	.0429	.0425
24		.750	.0511	.0507	.0503	.0498	.0494	.0490	.0485	.0481	.0477	.0472
24	60	.968	.0678	.0674	.0669	.0665	.0660	.0656	.0652	.0647	.0643	.0638
24		1.031	.0726	.0722	.0718	.0713	.0709	.0704	.0700	.0696	.0691	.0687
24	80	1.218	.0872	.0867	.0863	.0858	.0854	.0849	.0845	.0840	.0836	.0832
24	100	1.531	.1118	.1114	.1109	.1105	.1100	.1096	.1091	.1087	.1082	.1078

Table 7-2
Continued

NOMINAL PIPE SIZE	SCHEDULE NUMBER AND/OR WEIGHT	WALL THICKNESS	CORROSION ALLOWANCE-INCHES									Y=0.4
			0.055	0.060	0.065	0.070	0.075	0.080	0.085	0.90	0.095	0.100
24	120	1.812	.1344	.1339	.1335	.1330	.1325	.1321	.1316	.1312	.1307	.1302
24	140	2.062	.1548	.1543	.1539	.1534	.1529	.1524	.1520	.1515	.1510	.1506
24		2.188	.1652	.1647	.1643	.1638	.1633	.1628	.1624	.1619	.1614	.1609
24	160	2.343	.1781	.1776	.1771	.1767	.1762	.1757	.1752	.1748	.1743	.1738
26	ST	.375	.0212	.0208	.0204	.0200	.0196	.0192	.0188	.0185	.0181	.0177
26	XS	.500	.0298	.0294	.0290	.0286	.0282	.0278	.0274	.0270	.0266	.0262
30	10	.312	.0146	.0143	.0139	.0136	.0133	.0129	.0126	.0123	.0119	.0116
30	ST	.375	.0183	.0180	.0177	.0173	.0170	.0167	.0163	.0160	.0156	.0153
30		.438	.0221	.0217	.0214	.0211	.0207	.0204	.0200	.0197	.0194	.0190
30	20 XS	.500	.0258	.0254	.0251	.0247	.0244	.0241	.0237	.0234	.0230	.0227
30		.562	.0295	.0291	.0288	.0284	.0281	.0278	.0274	.0271	.0267	.0264
30	30	.625	.0332	.0329	.0325	.0322	.0319	.0315	.0312	.0308	.0305	.0302
34	ST	.375	.0162	.0159	.0156	.0153	.0150	.0147	.0144	.0141	.0138	.0135
34	XS	.500	.0227	.0224	.0221	.0218	.0215	.0212	.0209	.0206	.0203	.0200
36	ST	.375	.0153	.0150	.0147	.0144	.0141	.0139	.0136	.0133	.0130	.0127
36	XS	.500	.0214	.0211	.0209	.0206	.0203	.0200	.0197	.0195	.0192	.0189
42	ST	.375	.0131	.0128	.0126	.0124	.0121	.0119	.0116	.0114	.0112	.0109
42	XS	.500	.0183	.0181	.0179	.0176	.0174	.0171	.0169	.0167	.0164	.0162
48	ST	.375	.0114	.0112	.0110	.0108	.0106	.0104	.0102	.0100	.0098	.0095
48	XS	.500	.0160	.0158	.0156	.0154	.0152	.0150	.0148	.0146	.0144	.0141

Table 7-3
Pressure/Stress Ratios Where Y = 0.5

NOMINAL PIPE SIZE	SCHEDULE NUMBER AND/OR WEIGHT	WALL THICKNESS	CORROSION ALLOWANCE-INCHES										Y=0.5
			0.000	0.005	0.010	0.015	0.020	0.025	0.030	0.035	0.040	0.045	0.050
1/8	10S	.049	.2366	.2063	.1767	.1478	.1197	.0923	.0657	.0397	.0143		
1/8	40 ST 40S	.068	.3444	.3110	.2785	.2469	.2161	.1862	.1571	.1288	.1012	.0743	.0480
1/8	80 ST 80S	.095	.5165	.4780	.4407	.4045	.3693	.3351	.3020	.2697	.2383	.2078	.1782
1/4	10S	.065	.2354	.2125	.1901	.1681	.1466	.1255	.1048	.0844	.0645	.0450	.0258
1/4	40 ST 40S	.088	.3326	.3077	.2833	.2594	.2360	.2131	.1907	.1687	.1471	.1260	.1053
1/4	80 ST 80S	.119	.4778	.4497	.4222	.3953	.3691	.3434	.3182	.2936	.2695	.2459	.2228
3/8	10S	.065	.1840	.1665	.1493	.1323	.1156	.0991	.0829	.0670	.0513	.0358	.0206
3/8	40 ST 40S	.091	.2675	.2486	.2300	.2118	.1938	.1761	.1587	.1416	.1247	.1081	.0918
3/8	80 ST 80S	.126	.3904	.3695	.3488	.3286	.3087	.2891	.2699	.2509	.2323	.2140	.1960
1/2	10S	.083	.1893	.1751	.1611	.1473	.1337	.1202	.1069	.0938	.0808	.0680	.0554
1/2	40 ST 40S	.109	.2562	.2411	.2263	.2116	.1972	.1829	.1688	.1549	.1412	.1276	.1142
1/2	80 ST 80S	.147	.3616	.3451	.3289	.3129	.2970	.2814	.2661	.2509	.2359	.2211	.2065
1/2	160	.187	.4838	.4656	.4476	.4299	.4125	.3953	.3783	.3616	.3451	.3289	.3129
1/2	XX	.294	.8829	.8584	.8342	.8105	.7872	.7643	.7417	.7195	.6977	.6762	.6551
3/4	5S	.065	.1145	.1039	.0935	.0831	.0728	.0626	.0525	.0426	.0327	.0229	.0132
3/4	10S	.083	.1486	.1377	.1269	.1161	.1055	.0950	.0846	.0743	.0641	.0540	.0440
3/4	40S	.113	.2079	.1964	.1849	.1736	.1624	.1514	.1404	.1295	.1188	.1082	.0976
3/4	80S	.154	.2945	.2820	.2697	.2575	.2454	.2334	.2216	.2099	.1984	.1869	.1756
3/4		.188	.3715	.3582	.3451	.3320	.3192	.3064	.2938	.2814	.2690	.2569	.2448
3/4	160	.218	.4440	.4299	.4159	.4021	.3884	.3749	.3615	.3483	.3353	.3224	.3096
3/4	XX	.308	.6906	.6735	.6565	.6398	.6234	.6071	.5910	.5751	.5594	.5439	.5286
1	5S	.065	.0904	.0821	.0739	.0658	.0577	.0497	.0417	.0338	.0260	.0182	.0105
1	10S	.109	.1564	.1476	.1389	.1302	.1216	.1131	.1046	.0962	.0879	.0797	.0715
1	40 ST 40S	.133	.1942	.1851	.1760	.1671	.1582	.1494	.1406	.1319	.1233	.1148	.1063
1	80 ST 80S	.179	.2704	.2607	.2510	.2414	.2319	.2225	.2131	.2038	.1946	.1855	.1765
1		.219	.3412	.3308	.3205	.3103	.3002	.2902	.2803	.2704	.2607	.2510	.2414
1	160	.250	.3991	.3882	.3774	.3667	.3561	.3456	.3352	.3249	.3146	.3045	.2944
1	XXO	.358	.6254	.6124	.5995	.5867	.5740	.5615	.5491	.5368	.5246	.5125	.5006
11/4	5S	.065	.0710	.0645	.0581	.0518	.0454	.0392	.0329	.0267	.0205	.0144	.0083
11/4	10S	.109	.1219	.1152	.1084	.1018	.0951	.0885	.0820	.0755	.0690	.0626	.0562
11/4	40 ST 40S	.140	.1593	.1524	.1454	.1385	.1316	.1248	.1180	.1113	.1046	.0979	.0913
11/4	80 ST 80S	.191	.2239	.2165	.2091	.2018	.1945	.1873	.1801	.1730	.1659	.1588	.1518
11/4	160	.250	.3036	.2956	.2877	.2798	.2720	.2643	.2566	.2489	.2414	.2338	.2263
11/4	XX	.382	.5042	.4948	.4855	.4762	.4670	.4579	.4488	.4398	.4309	.4220	.4132

Table 7-2
Continued

NOM-INAL PIPE SIZE	SCHEDULE NUMBER AND/OR WEIGHT	WALL THICK-NESS	CORROSION ALLOWANCE-INCHES										Y=0.5
			0.000	0.005	0.010	0.015	0.020	0.025	0.030	0.035	0.040	0.045	0.050
11/2	5S	.065	.0617	.0561	.0506	.0451	.0396	.0341	.0287	.0233	.0179	.0126	.0073
11/2	10S	.109	.1057	.0999	.0941	.0883	.0826	.0769	.0713	.0656	.0600	.0545	.0489
11/2	40 ST 40S	.145	.1431	.1371	.1311	.1251	.1192	.1133	.1075	.1016	.0958	.0901	.0843
11/2	80 ST 80S	.200	.2029	.1965	.1902	.1839	.1777	.1714	.1652	.1591	.1530	.1469	.1408
11/2	160	.281	.2973	.2904	.2835	.2766	.2698	.2631	.2564	.2497	.2430	.2364	.2299
11/2	XX	.400	.4516	.4437	.4359	.4281	.4204	.4127	.4051	.3975	.3899	.3824	.3750
2	5S	.065	.0491	.0447	.0403	.0359	.0315	.0272	.0229	.0186	.0143	.0101	.0058
2	10S	.109	.0837	.0791	.0746	.0701	.0656	.0611	.0566	.0522	.0477	.0433	.0390
2	40 ST 40S	.154	.1203	.1156	.1109	.1062	.1015	.0969	.0923	.0877	.0831	.0785	.0740
2		.167	.1311	.1263	.1216	.1169	.1122	.1075	.1028	.0982	.0935	.0889	.0844
2		.188	.1488	.1440	.1392	.1344	.1296	.1248	.1201	.1153	.1106	.1060	.1013
2	80 ST 80S	.218	.1747	.1697	.1647	.1598	.1549	.1501	.1452	.1404	.1356	.1308	.1260
2		.250	.2029	.1978	.1927	.1877	.1827	.1777	.1727	.1677	.1628	.1579	.1530
2		.312	.2598	.2544	.2491	.2437	.2385	.2332	.2280	.2227	.2176	.2124	.2072
2	160	.343	.2893	.2838	.2783	.2729	.2674	.2620	.2567	.2513	.2460	.2407	.2354
2	XX	.436	.3827	.3768	.3709	.3649	.3591	.3532	.3474	.3416	.3359	.3301	.3244
21/2	5S	.083	.0518	.0482	.0445	.0409	.0373	.0337	.0301	.0265	.0230	.0194	.0159
21/2	10S	.120	.0758	.0721	.0683	.0646	.0609	.0572	.0536	.0499	.0463	.0426	.0390
21/2	40 ST 40S	.203	.1317	.1278	.1238	.1199	.1160	.1121	.1083	.1044	.1006	.0967	.0929
21/2		.217	.1414	.1374	.1335	.1295	.1256	.1217	.1178	.1139	.1100	.1061	.1023
21/2	80 ST 805	.276	.1834	.1793	.1751	.1710	.1669	.1629	.1588	.1548	.1507	.1467	.1427
21/2	160	.375	.2577	.2532	.2488	.2444	.2401	.2357	.2314	.2271	.2228	.2185	.2142
21/2	XX	.552	.4038	.3988	.3938	.3889	.3839	.3790	.3741	.3692	.3643	.3595	.3546
3	5S	.083	.0424	.0394	.0364	.0335	.0305	.0276	.0247	.0217	.0188	.0159	.0130
3	10S	.120	.0619	.0588	.0558	.0528	.0498	.0468	.0438	.0408	.0378	.0349	.0319
3		.125	.0645	.0615	.0584	.0554	.0524	.0494	.0464	.0434	.0404	.0375	.0345
3		.148	.0768	.0738	.0707	.0676	.0646	.0616	.0585	.0555	.0525	.0495	.0465
3		.188	.0986	.0955	.0924	.0892	.0861	.0830	.0799	.0768	.0738	.0707	.0676
3	40 ST 40S	.216	.1142	.1110	.1078	.1046	.1015	.0983	.0952	.0921	.0889	.0858	.0827
3		.241	.1282	.1250	.1218	.1186	.1154	.1122	.1090	.1058	.1027	.0995	.0964
3		.254	.1356	.1324	.1291	.1259	.1227	.1194	.1162	.1130	.1099	.1067	.1035
3		.289	.1558	.1524	.1491	.1458	.1426	.1393	.1360	.1328	.1295	.1263	.1231
3	80 XS 805	.300	.1622	.1588	.1555	.1522	.1489	.1456	.1423	.1390	.1358	.1325	.1293
3		.312	.1692	.1658	.1625	.1592	.1558	.1525	.1492	.1459	.1426	.1394	.1361
3		.406	.2259	.2224	.2189	.2154	.2119	.2084	.2049	.2014	.1980	.1945	.1911

Table 7-3
Continued

NOMINAL PIPE SIZE	SCHEDULE NUMBER AND/OR WEIGHT	WALL THICKNESS	CORROSION ALLOWANCE-INCHES									Y=0.5	
			0.000	0.005	0.010	0.015	0.020	0.025	0.030	0.035	0.040	0.045	0.050
3	160	.438	.2459	.2423	.2387	.2352	.2316	.2281	.2245	.2210	.2175	.2140	.2105
3	XX	.600	.3529	.3490	.3451	.3411	.3372	.3333	.3295	.3256	.3217	.3179	.3140
31/2	5S	.083	.0370	.0344	.0318	.0292	.0267	.0241	.0215	.0190	.0164	.0139	.0114
31/2	10S	.120	.0539	.0513	.0487	.0460	.0434	.0408	.0382	.0356	.0330	.0305	.0279
31/2		.128	.0576	.0550	.0523	.0497	.0471	.0445	.0419	.0393	.0367	.0341	.0315
31/2		.134	.0604	.0577	.0551	.0525	.0498	.0472	.0446	.0420	.0394	.0368	.0342
31/2		.148	.0669	.0642	.0616	.0589	.0563	.0537	.0510	.0484	.0458	.0432	.0406
31/2		.188	.0858	.0831	.0804	.0777	.0750	.0723	.0696	.0669	.0642	.0616	.0589
31/2	40 ST 40S	.226	.1040	.1013	.0985	.0957	.0930	.0903	.0875	.0848	.0821	.0794	.0767
31/2		.281	.1310	.1282	.1253	.1225	.1197	.1169	.1141	.1113	.1085	.1057	.1030
31/2	80 XS 80S	.318	.1495	.1466	.1438	.1409	.1380	.1352	.1323	.1295	.1267	.1238	.1210
31/2		.344	.1627	.1598	.1569	.1540	.1511	.1482	.1453	.1425	.1396	.1368	.1339
31/2		.469	.2286	.2255	.2225	.2194	.2163	.2132	.2102	.2071	.2041	.2011	.1980
31/2		.636	.3232	.3198	.3165	.3131	.3098	.3065	.3032	.2998	.2965	.2932	.2900
4	5S	.083	.0328	.0305	.0282	.0259	.0237	.0214	.0191	.0169	.0146	.0124	.0101
4	10S	.120	.0478	.0455	.0431	.0408	.0385	.0362	.0339	.0316	.0293	.0270	.0247
4		.128	.0510	.0487	.0464	.0441	.0417	.0394	.0371	.0348	.0325	.0302	.0279
4		.134	.0535	.0512	.0488	.0465	.0442	.0419	.0395	.0372	.0349	.0326	.0303
4		.142	.0568	.0544	.0521	.0498	.0474	.0451	.0428	.0405	.0382	.0359	.0336
4		.165	.0663	.0639	.0616	.0592	.0568	.0545	.0522	.0498	.0475	.0452	.0428
4		.188	.0759	.0735	.0711	.0687	.0664	.0640	.0616	.0593	.0569	.0546	.0522
4		.205	.0830	.0806	.0782	.0758	.0734	.0710	.0687	.0663	.0639	.0616	.0592
4	40 ST40S	.237	.0966	.0942	.0917	.0893	.0869	.0845	.0821	.0797	.0773	.0749	.0725
4		.250	.1022	.0997	.0973	.0949	.0924	.0900	.0876	.0851	.0827	.0803	.0779
4		.271	.1113	.1088	.1063	.1038	.1014	.0989	.0965	.0941	.0916	.0892	.0868
4		.281	.1156	.1131	.1106	.1082	.1057	.1032	.1008	.0983	.0959	.0934	.0910
4		.300	.1239	.1214	.1189	.1164	.1139	.1114	.1090	.1065	.1040	.1016	.0991
4		.312	.1292	.1267	.1241	.1216	.1191	.1167	.1142	.1117	.1092	.1067	.1043
4	80 XS 80S	.337	.1402	.1377	.1352	.1326	.1301	.1276	.1251	.1226	.1201	.1176	.1151
4		.375	.1573	.1547	.1521	.1496	.1470	.1445	.1419	.1394	.1368	.1343	.1318
4	120	.438	.1862	.1835	.1809	.1783	.1756	.1730	.1704	.1678	.1652	.1626	.1600
4		.500	.2154	.2127	.2099	.2072	.2045	.2018	.1991	.1965	.1938	.1911	.1884
4	160	.531	.2303	.2275	.2248	.2220	.2193	.2165	.2138	.2111	.2084	.2057	.2030
4	XX	.674	.3016	.2987	.2958	.2928	.2899	.2870	.2841	.2812	.2783	.2755	.2726
5	5S	.109	.0349	.0330	.0312	.0293	.0275	.0256	.0238	.0219	.0201	.0183	.0164
5	10S	.134	.0431	.0412	.0393	.0374	.0356	.0337	.0319	.0300	.0282	.0263	.0245

Table 7-3
Continued

NOMINAL PIPE SIZE	SCHEDULE NUMBER AND/OR WEIGHT	WALL THICKNESS	CORROSION ALLOWANCE-INCHES									Y=0.5	
			0.000	0.005	0.010	0.015	0.020	0.025	0.030	0.035	0.040	0.045	0.050
5	40 ST 40S	.258	.0846	.0826	.0807	.0788	.0768	.0749	.0729	.0710	.0691	.0672	.0652
5		.352	.1172	.1152	.1132	.1112	.1092	.1072	.1052	.1032	.1012	.0992	.0973
5	80 XS 80S	.375	.1254	.1233	.1213	.1193	.1173	.1153	.1133	.1112	.1092	.1072	.1053
5		.438	.1480	.1459	.1438	.1418	.1397	.1377	.1356	.1336	.1315	.1295	.1274
5	120	.500	.1707	.1686	.1665	.1644	.1623	.1602	.1581	.1560	.1539	.1518	.1497
5	160	.625	.2180	.2158	.2136	.2114	.2092	.2070	.2049	.2027	.2005	.1983	.1962
5	XX	.750	.2675	.2652	.2629	.2606	.2583	.2560	.2537	.2514	.2492	.2469	.2446
6	5S	.109	.0292	.0277	.0261	.0246	.0230	.0215	.0199	.0184	.0169	.0153	.0138
6	10S	.134	.0360	.0345	.0329	.0314	.0298	.0282	.0267	.0251	.0236	.0221	.0205
6		.169	.0457	.0441	.0425	.0409	.0394	.0378	.0362	.0347	.0331	.0315	.0300
6		.180	.0487	.0471	.0455	.0440	.0424	.0408	.0392	.0377	.0361	.0345	.0330
6		.188	.0509	.0493	.0478	.0462	.0446	.0430	.0414	.0399	.0383	.0367	.0352
6		.219	.0596	.0580	.0564	.0548	.0532	.0516	.0500	.0484	.0468	.0453	.0437
6		.250	.0683	.0667	.0651	.0635	.0619	.0603	.0587	.0571	.0555	.0539	.0523
6		.277	.0759	.0743	.0727	.0711	.0695	.0678	.0662	.0646	.0630	.0614	.0598
6	40 ST 40S	.280	.0768	.0752	.0736	.0719	.0703	.0687	.0671	.0655	.0639	.0623	.0607
6		.375	.1042	.1025	.1009	.0992	.0976	.0959	.0942	.0926	.0909	.0893	.0876
6	80 XS 805	.432	.1210	.1193	.1176	.1159	.1142	.1126	.1109	.1092	.1075	.1058	.1042
6		.500	.1414	.1397	.1380	.1362	.1345	.1328	.1311	.1294	.1277	.1260	.1242
6	120	.562	.1604	.1586	.1568	.1551	.1533	.1516	.1498	.1481	.1464	.1446	.1429
6	160	.718	.2095	.2077	.2059	.2040	.2022	.2004	.1985	.1967	.1949	.1931	.1913
6	XX	.864	.2576	.2557	.2538	.2519	.2500	.2480	.2461	.2442	.2423	.2404	.2386
8	5S	.109	.0224	.0212	.0200	.0188	.0176	.0165	.0153	.0141	.0129	.0117	.0106
8	10S	.148	.0305	.0293	.0281	.0269	.0257	.0245	.0233	.0222	.0210	.0198	.0186
8		.158	.0326	.0314	.0302	.0290	.0278	.0266	.0254	.0242	.0230	.0219	.0207
8		.165	.0340	.0328	.0317	.0305	.0293	.0281	.0269	.0257	.0245	.0233	.0221
8		.188	.0389	.0377	.0365	.0353	.0341	.0329	.0317	.0305	.0293	.0281	.0269
8		.203	.0421	.0408	.0396	.0384	.0372	.0360	.0348	.0336	.0324	.0312	.0300
8		.219	.0454	.0442	.0430	.0418	.0406	.0394	.0382	.0370	.0358	.0346	.0334
8		.238	.0495	.0483	.0471	.0458	.0446	.0434	.0422	.0410	.0398	.0386	.0374
8	20	.250	.0520	.0508	.0496	.0484	.0472	.0460	.0447	.0435	.0423	.0411	.0399
8	30	.277	.0578	.0566	.0554	.0542	.0529	.0517	.0505	.0493	.0481	.0468	.0456
8	40 ST 40S	.322	.0675	.0663	.0651	.0638	.0626	.0614	.0601	.0589	.0577	.0564	.0552
8		.344	.0723	.0711	.0698	.0686	.0674	.0661	.0649	.0636	.0624	.0612	.0599
8		.352	.0741	.0728	.0716	.0703	.0691	.0678	.0666	.0654	.0641	.0629	.0617
8		.375	.0791	.0778	.0766	.0753	.0741	.0729	.0716	.0704	.0691	.0679	.0666

Table 7-3
Continued

NOMINAL PIPE SIZE	SCHEDULE NUMBER AND/OR WEIGHT	WALL THICKNESS	CORROSION ALLOWANCE-INCHES Y=0.5										
			0.000	0.005	0.010	0.015	0.020	0.025	0.030	0.035	0.040	0.045	0.050
8	60	.406	.0859	.0847	.0834	.0821	.0809	.0796	.0784	.0771	.0759	.0746	.0734
8		.469	.0999	.0986	.0974	.0961	.0948	.0935	.0923	.0910	.0897	.0885	.0872
8	80 XS 80S	.500	.1069	.1056	.1043	.1030	.1017	.1005	.0992	.0979	.0966	.0954	.0941
8	100	.593	.1280	.1267	.1254	.1241	.1228	.1215	.1202	.1189	.1176	.1163	.1150
8		.625	.1354	.1341	.1328	.1314	.1301	.1288	.1275	.1262	.1249	.1236	.1223
8	120	.718	.1571	.1558	.1544	.1531	.1517	.1504	.1491	.1477	.1464	.1451	.1437
8	140	.812	.1795	.1782	.1768	.1754	.1741	.1727	.1713	.1699	.1686	.1672	.1659
8	XX	.875	.1948	.1934	.1920	.1907	.1893	.1879	.1865	.1851	.1837	.1823	.1810
8	160	.906	.2024	.2010	.1996	.1982	.1968	.1954	.1940	.1926	.1912	.1899	.1885
10	5S	.134	.0221	.0211	.0202	.0192	.0183	.0173	.0164	.0154	.0145	.0135	.0126
10	10S	.165	.0272	.0263	.0253	.0244	.0234	.0225	.0215	.0206	.0196	.0187	.0177
10		.188	.0311	.0301	.0292	.0282	.0273	.0263	.0253	.0244	.0234	.0225	.0215
10		.203	.0336	.0326	.0317	.0307	.0298	.0288	.0278	.0269	.0259	.0250	.0240
10		.219	.0363	.0353	.0344	.0334	.0324	.0315	.0305	.0296	.0286	.0277	.0267
10	20	.250	.0415	.0406	.0396	.0386	.0377	.0367	.0357	.0348	.0338	.0329	.0319
10		.279	.0465	.0455	.0445	.0436	.0426	.0416	.0406	.0397	.0387	.0377	.0368
10	30	.307	.0513	.0503	.0493	.0483	.0474	.0464	.0454	.0444	.0435	.0425	.0415
10		.348	.0583	.0573	.0563	.0554	.0544	.0534	.0524	.0514	.0505	.0495	.0485
10	40 ST 40S	.365	.0612	.0603	.0593	.0583	.0573	.0563	.0553	.0543	.0534	.0524	.0514
10		.395	.0664	.0654	.0645	.0635	.0625	.0615	.0605	.0595	.0585	.0575	.0566
10	60 XS 80S	.500	.0848	.0838	.0828	.0818	.0808	.0798	.0788	.0778	.0768	.0758	.0748
10		.531	.0903	.0893	.0883	.0873	.0863	.0853	.0843	.0833	.0822	.0812	.0802
10	80	.593	.1014	.1004	.0994	.0984	.0973	.0963	.0953	.0943	.0932	.0922	.0912
10	100	.718	.1241	.1231	.1220	.1210	.1199	.1189	.1179	.1168	.1158	.1147	.1137
10		.750	.1300	.1290	.1279	.1269	.1258	.1248	.1237	.1227	.1216	.1206	.1195
10	120	.843	.1473	.1463	.1452	.1441	.1431	.1420	.1409	.1399	.1388	.1377	.1367
10	140	1.000	.1772	.1761	.1750	.1739	.1728	.1717	.1706	.1695	.1684	.1673	.1662
10		1.062	.1892	.1881	.1870	.1859	.1848	.1837	.1826	.1815	.1804	.1793	.1782
10	160	1.125	.2016	.2005	.1993	.1982	.1971	.1960	.1949	.1937	.1926	.1915	.1904
12	5S	.156	.0216	.0208	.0200	.0192	.0184	.0176	.0168	.0160	.0153	.0145	.0137
12	10S	.180	.0250	.0242	.0234	.0226	.0218	.0210	.0202	.0194	.0186	.0178	.0170
12		.203	.0283	.0275	.0266	.0258	.0250	.0242	.0234	.0226	.0218	.0210	.0202
12		.219	.0305	.0297	.0289	.0281	.0273	.0265	.0257	.0249	.0241	.0233	.0225
12		.238	.0332	.0324	.0316	.0308	.0300	.0292	.0284	.0276	.0267	.0259	.0251
12	20	.250	.0349	.0341	.0333	.0325	.0317	.0309	.0301	.0292	.0284	.0276	.0268
12		.279	.0390	.0382	.0374	.0366	.0358	.0350	.0342	.0334	.0325	.0317	.0309

Table 7-3
Continued

NOMINAL PIPE SIZE	SCHEDULE NUMBER AND/OR WEIGHT	WALL THICKNESS	CORROSION ALLOWANCE-INCHES									Y=0.5	
			0.000	0.005	0.010	0.015	0.020	0.025	0.030	0.035	0.040	0.045	0.050
12		.300	.0420	.0412	.0404	.0396	.0388	.0380	.0371	.0363	.0355	.0347	.0339
12	30	.330	.0463	.0455	.0447	.0439	.0431	.0422	.0414	.0406	.0398	.0390	.0382
12		.344	.0484	.0475	.0467	.0459	.0451	.0443	.0434	.0426	.0418	.0410	.0402
12	ST 40S	.375	.0528	.0520	.0512	.0504	.0495	.0487	.0479	.0471	.0462	.0454	.0446
12	40	.406	.0573	.0565	.0557	.0548	.0540	.0532	.0524	.0515	.0507	.0499	.0491
12		.438	.0520	.0611	.0603	.0595	.0587	.0578	.0570	.0562	.0553	.0545	.0537
12	XS 80S	.500	.0711	.0702	.0694	.0685	.0677	.0669	.0660	.0652	.0644	.0635	.0627
12	60	.562	.0802	.0794	.0785	.0777	.0768	.0760	.0752	.0743	.0735	.0726	.0718
12		.625	.0896	.0888	.0879	.0871	.0862	.0854	.0845	.0837	.0828	.0820	.0811
12	80	.687	.0990	.0981	.0972	.0964	.0955	.0946	.0938	.0929	.0921	.0912	.0904
12	100	.843	.1228	.1219	.1210	.1202	.1193	.1184	.1175	.1166	.1158	.1149	.1140
12		.875	.1278	.1269	.1260	.1251	.1242	.1233	.1225	.1216	.1207	.1198	.1189
12	120	1.000	.1474	.1465	.1456	.1447	.1438	.1429	.1420	.1411	.1402	.1393	.1384
12	140	1.125	.1673	.1664	.1655	.1646	.1637	.1627	.1618	.1609	.1600	.1591	.1582
12		1.219	.1826	.1817	.1807	.1798	.1789	.1779	.1770	.1761	.1751	.1742	.1733
12	160	1.312	.1979	.1970	.1960	.1951	.1941	.1932	.1922	.1913	.1903	.1894	.1885
14		.188	.0238	.0230	.0223	.0216	.0209	.0201	.0194	.0187	.0179	.0172	.0165
14		.220	.0279	.0271	.0264	.0257	.0250	.0242	.0235	.0228	.0220	.0213	.0206
14		.238	.0302	.0295	.0287	.0280	.0273	.0265	.0258	.0251	.0243	.0236	.0229
14	10	.250	.0317	.0310	.0303	.0295	.0288	.0281	.0273	.0266	.0259	.0251	.0244
14	20	.312	.0398	.0390	.0383	.0375	.0368	.0361	.0353	.0346	.0338	.0331	.0324
14	30ST	.375	.0480	.0473	.0465	.0458	.0450	.0443	.0435	.0428	.0420	.0413	.0405
14		.406	.0521	.0513	.0506	.0498	.0491	.0483	.0476	.0468	.0461	.0453	.0446
14	40	.438	.0563	.0555	.0548	.0540	.0533	.0525	.0518	.0510	.0503	.0495	.0488
14		.469	.0604	.0596	.0589	.0581	.0574	.0566	.0559	.0551	.0543	.0536	.0528
14	XS	.500	.0645	.0638	.0630	.0622	.0615	.0607	.0600	.0592	.0584	.0577	.0569
14	60	.593	.0770	.0762	.0754	.0747	.0739	.0731	.0724	.0716	.0708	.0701	.0693
14		.625	.0813	.0805	.0798	.0790	.0782	.0774	.0767	.0759	.0751	.0744	.0736
14		.656	.0855	.0847	.0840	.0832	.0824	.0816	.0809	.0801	.0793	.0785	.0778
14	80	.750	.0984	.0976	.0968	.0960	.0952	.0944	.0937	.0929	.0921	.0913	.0905
14	100	.937	.1244	.1236	.1228	.1220	.1212	.1204	.1196	.1188	.1180	.1172	.1164
14	120	1.093	.1466	.1458	.1450	.1442	.1434	.1425	.1417	.1409	.1401	.1393	.1384
14	140	1.250	.1695	.1687	.1678	.1670	.1661	.1653	.1645	.1636	.1628	.1620	.1611
14		1.344	.1834	.1826	.1817	.1809	.1800	.1792	.1783	.1775	.1766	.1758	.1749
14	160	1.406	.1927	.1918	.1910	.1901	.1893	.1884	.1875	.1867	.1858	.1850	.1841
16		.188	.0208	.0201	.0195	.0189	.0182	.0176	.0170	.0163	.0157	.0150	.0144

Table 7-3
Continued

NOMINAL PIPE SIZE	SCHEDULE NUMBER AND/OR WEIGHT	WALL THICKNESS	CORROSION ALLOWANCE-INCHES									Y=0.5	
			0.000	0.005	0.010	0.015	0.020	0.025	0.030	0.035	0.040	0.045	0.050
16		.238	.0264	.0257	.0251	.0245	.0238	.0232	.0225	.0219	.0213	.0206	.0200
16	10	.250	.0277	.0271	.0264	.0258	.0252	.0245	.0239	.0232	.0226	.0220	.0213
16		.281	.0312	.0306	.0299	.0293	.0286	.0280	.0274	.0267	.0261	.0254	.0248
16	20	.312	.0347	.0341	.0334	.0328	.0321	.0315	.0308	.0302	.0296	.0289	.0283
16		.344	.0383	.0377	.0370	.0364	.0358	.0351	.0345	.0338	.0332	.0325	.0319
16	30 ST	.375	.0419	.0412	.0406	.0399	.0393	.0386	.0380	.0373	.0367	.0360	.0354
16		.406	.0454	.0448	.0441	.0435	.0428	.0422	.0415	.0408	.0402	.0395	.0389
16		.438	.0491	.0484	.0478	.0471	.0465	.0458	.0452	.0445	.0438	.0432	.0425
16		.469	.0526	.0520	.0513	.0507	.0500	.0494	.0487	.0480	.0474	.0467	.0461
16	40 XS	.500	.0562	.0556	.0549	.0542	.0536	.0529	.0523	.0516	.0510	.0503	.0496
16		.531	.0598	.0592	.0585	.0578	.0572	.0565	.0558	.0552	.0545	.0539	.0532
16	60	.656	.0744	.0737	.0731	.0724	.0717	.0711	.0704	.0697	.0691	.0684	.0677
16		.688	.0782	.0775	.0768	.0762	.0755	.0748	.0742	.0735	.0728	.0721	.0715
16		.750	.0855	.0849	.0842	.0835	.0828	.0821	.0815	.0808	.0801	.0794	.0788
16	80	.843	.0967	.0960	.0953	.0946	.0939	.0932	.0925	.0919	.0912	.0905	.0898
16	100	1.031	.1195	.1188	.1181	.1174	.1167	.1160	.1153	.1146	.1139	.1132	.1125
16	120	1.218	.1427	.1420	.1413	.1406	.1399	.1391	.1384	.1377	.1370	.1363	.1356
16	140	1.438	.1707	.1700	.1692	.1685	.1678	.1670	.1663	.1656	.1648	.1641	.1634
16		1.500	.1787	.1780	.1772	.1765	.1758	.1750	.1743	.1735	.1728	.1721	.1713
16	160	1.593	.1909	.1901	.1894	.1886	.1879	.1871	.1864	.1856	.1849	.1841	.1834
18	10	.250	.0246	.0240	.0235	.0229	.0223	.0218	.0212	.0206	.0201	.0195	.0189
18	20	.312	.0308	.0302	.0297	.0291	.0285	.0279	.0274	.0268	.0262	.0257	.0251
18	ST	.375	.0371	.0366	.0360	.0354	.0348	.0343	.0337	.0331	.0325	.0320	.0314
18	30	.438	.0435	.0429	.0424	.0418	.0412	.0406	.0400	.0395	.0389	.0383	.0377
18	XS	.500	.0498	.0492	.0487	.0481	.0475	.0469	.0463	.0457	.0452	.0446	.0440
18	40	.562	.0562	.0556	.0550	.0544	.0538	.0532	.0527	.0521	.0515	.0509	.0503
18		.594	.0595	.0589	.0583	.0577	.0571	.0565	.0559	.0554	.0548	.0542	.0536
18		.625	.0627	.0621	.0615	.0609	.0603	.0597	.0591	.0585	.0580	.0574	.0568
18		.719	.0724	.0718	.0712	.0706	.0701	.0695	.0689	.0683	.0677	.0671	.0665
18	60	.750	.0757	.0751	.0745	.0739	.0733	.0727	.0721	.0715	.0709	.0703	.0697
18		.812	.0822	.0816	.0810	.0804	.0798	.0792	.0786	.0780	.0774	.0768	.0762
18	80	.937	.0954	.0948	.0942	.0936	.0930	.0924	.0918	.0912	.0906	.0900	.0894
18	100	1.156	.1191	.1185	.1178	.1172	.1166	.1160	.1153	.1147	.1141	.1135	.1129
18	120	1.375	.1433	.1426	.1420	.1413	.1407	.1401	.1394	.1388	.1382	.1375	.1369
18	140	1.562	.1643	.1637	.1630	.1624	.1617	.1611	.1604	.1598	.1591	.1585	.1579
18		1.688	.1788	.1781	.1775	.1768	.1761	.1755	.1748	.1742	.1735	.1729	.1722

Table 7-3
Continued

NOM-INAL PIPE SIZE	SCHEDULE NUMBER AND/OR WEIGHT	WALL THICK-NESS	CORROSION ALLOWANCE-INCHES Y=0.5										
			0.000	0.005	0.010	0.015	0.020	0.025	0.030	0.035	0.040	0.045	0.050
18	160	1.781	.1896	.1889	.1882	.1876	.1869	.1862	.1856	.1849	.1843	.1836	.1829
20	10	.250	.0221	.0216	.0211	.0206	.0201	.0196	.0191	.0185	.0180	.0175	.0170
20		.312	.0277	.0272	.0267	.0261	.0256	.0251	.0246	.0241	.0236	.0231	.0226
20	20 ST	.375	.0334	.0328	.0323	.0318	.0313	.0308	.0303	.0297	.0292	.0287	.0282
20		.438	.0391	.0386	.0380	.0375	.0370	.0365	.0360	.0354	.0349	.0344	.0339
20	30 XS	.500	.0447	.0442	.0437	.0432	.0426	.0421	.0416	.0411	.0406	.0400	.0395
20		.562	.0504	.0499	.0494	.0488	.0483	.0478	.0473	.0467	.0462	.0457	.0452
20	40	.593	.0533	.0527	.0522	.0517	.0512	.0506	.0501	.0496	.0491	.0485	.0480
20		.625	.0562	.0557	.0552	.0546	.0541	.0536	.0531	.0525	.0520	.0515	.0510
20	60	.812	.0737	.0731	.0726	.0721	.0715	.0710	.0704	.0699	.0694	.0688	.0683
20		.875	.0796	.0791	.0785	.0780	.0774	.0769	.0764	.0758	.0753	.0748	.0742
20		.906	.0825	.0820	.0815	.0809	.0804	.0798	.0793	.0788	.0782	.0777	.0771
20	80	1.031	.0945	.0939	.0934	.0928	.0923	.0917	.0912	.0906	.0901	.0896	.0890
20		1.250	.1157	.1151	.1146	.1140	.1135	.1129	.1124	.1118	.1112	.1107	.1101
20	100	1.281	.1187	.1182	.1176	.1171	.1165	.1159	.1154	.1148	.1143	.1137	.1131
20	120	1.500	.1405	.1399	.1393	.1388	.1382	.1376	.1370	.1365	.1359	.1353	.1348
20	140	1.750	.1658	.1652	.1646	.1641	.1635	.1629	.1623	.1617	.1611	.1606	.1600
20		1.844	.1755	.1749	.1743	.1737	.1731	.1726	.1720	.1714	.1708	.1702	.1696
20	160	1.968	.1884	.1878	.1872	.1866	.1860	.1854	.1848	.1842	.1836	.1830	.1825
22	LG	.250	.0201	.0196	.0192	.0187	.0182	.0178	.0173	.0168	.0164	.0159	.0155
22	ST	.375	.0303	.0298	.0293	.0289	.0284	.0279	.0275	.0270	.0265	.0261	.0256
22	XS	.500	.0406	.0401	.0396	.0392	.0387	.0382	.0377	.0373	.0368	.0363	.0359
24	10	.250	.0184	.0180	.0175	.0171	.0167	.0163	.0159	.0154	.0150	.0146	.0142
24		.312	.0230	.0226	.0222	.0217	.0213	.0209	.0205	.0200	.0196	.0192	.0188
24	20 ST	.375	.0277	.0273	.0269	.0264	.0260	.0256	.0252	.0247	.0243	.0239	.0234
24		.438	.0325	.0320	.0316	.0312	.0307	.0303	.0299	.0294	.0290	.0286	.0282
24	XS	.500	.0371	.0367	.0363	.0358	.0354	.0350	.0345	.0341	.0337	.0333	.0328
24	30	.562	.0418	.0414	.0410	.0405	.0401	.0397	.0392	.0388	.0384	.0379	.0375
24		.625	.0466	.0462	.0458	.0453	.0449	.0445	.0440	.0436	.0432	.0427	.0423
24	40	.687	.0514	.0509	.0505	.0501	.0496	.0492	.0488	.0483	.0479	.0474	.0470
24		.750	.0562	.0558	.0553	.0549	.0545	.0540	.0536	.0531	.0527	.0523	.0518
24	60	.968	.0732	.0727	.0723	.0718	.0714	.0709	.0705	.0700	.0696	.0691	.0687
24		1.031	.0781	.0777	.0772	.0768	.0763	.0759	.0754	.0750	.0745	.0741	.0736
24	80	1.218	.0929	.0925	.0920	.0916	.0911	.0907	.0902	.0898	.0893	.0888	.0884
24	100	1.531	.1182	.1178	.1173	.1168	.1164	.1159	.1154	.1150	.1145	.1140	.1136

Table 7-3
Continued

NOMINAL PIPE SIZE	SCHEDULE NUMBER AND/OR WEIGHT	WALL THICKNESS	CORROSION ALLOWANCE-INCHES									Y=0.5	
			0.000	0.005	0.010	0.015	0.020	0.025	0.030	0.035	0.040	0.045	0.050
24	120	1.812	.1415	.1410	.1405	.1400	.1396	.1391	.1386	.1381	.1377	.1372	.1367
24	140	2.062	.1626	.1621	.1616	.1611	.1606	.1601	.1597	.1592	.1587	.1582	.1577
24		2.188	.1734	.1729	.1724	.1719	.1714	.1709	.1704	.1699	.1694	.1690	.1685
24	160	2.343	.1868	.1863	.1858	.1853	.1848	.1843	.1838	.1833	.1828	.1823	.1818
26	ST	.375	.0256	.0252	.0248	.0244	.0240	.0236	.0232	.0228	.0224	.0220	.0216
26	XS	.500	.0342	.0338	.0334	.0330	.0326	.0322	.0318	.0314	.0311	.0307	.0303
30	10	.312	.0184	.0180	.0177	.0173	.0170	.0167	.0163	.0160	.0157	.0153	.0150
30	ST	.375	.0221	.0218	.0214	.0211	.0208	.0204	.0201	.0197	.0194	.0191	.0187
30		.438	.0259	.0255	.0252	.0249	.0245	.0242	.0238	.0235	.0231	.0228	.0225
30	20 XS	.500	.0296	.0293	.0289	.0286	.0282	.0279	.0275	.0272	.0269	.0265	.0262
30		.562	.0333	.0330	.0326	.0323	.0320	.0316	.0313	.0309	.0306	.0302	.0299
30	30	.625	.0371	.0368	.0364	.0361	.0358	.0354	.0351	.0347	.0344	.0340	.0337
34	ST	.375	.0195	.0192	.0189	.0186	.0183	.0180	.0177	.0174	.0171	.0168	.0165
34	XS	.500	.0261	.0258	.0255	.0252	.0249	.0246	.0243	.0240	.0237	.0234	.0231
36	ST	.375	.0184	.0181	.0178	.0175	.0173	.0170	.0167	.0164	.0161	.0159	.0156
36	XS	.500	.0246	.0243	.0240	.0238	.0235	.0232	.0229	.0226	.0223	.0220	.0218
42	ST	.375	.0157	.0155	.0153	.0150	.0148	.0145	.0143	.0141	.0138	.0136	.0133
42	XS	.500	.0211	.0208	.0206	.0203	.0201	.0198	.0196	.0194	.0191	.0189	.0186
48	ST	.375	.0138	.0136	.0133	.0131	.0129	.0127	.0125	.0123	.0121	.0119	.0117
48	XS	.500	.0184	.0182	.0180	.0178	.0175	.0173	.0171	.0169	.0167	.0165	.0163

Table 7-3
Continued

NUM-INAL PIPE SIZE	SCHEDULE NUMBER AND/OR WEIGHT	WALL THICK-NESS	CORROSION ALLOWANCE-INCHES									Y=0.5
			0.055	0.060	0.065	0.070	0.075	0.080	0.085	0.90	0.095	0.100
1/8	10S	.049	0.0000									
1/8	40 ST 40S	.068	.0225									
1/8	80 ST 80S	.095	.1493	.1211	.0937	.0670	.0409	.0156				
1/4	10S	.065	.0070									
1/4	40 ST 40S	.088	.0849	.0650	.0455	.0263	.0074					
1/4	80 ST 80S	.119	.2002	.1780	.1562	.1349	.1140	.0935	.0734	.0537	.0344	.0154
3/8	10S	.065	.0056									
3/8	40 ST 40S	.091	.0757	.0599	.0443	.0289	.0138					
3/8	80 ST 80S	.126	.1783	.1609	.1437	.1268	.1102	.0938	.0777	.0619	.0462	.0308
1/2	10S	.083	.0429	.0305	.0183	.0063						
1/2	40 ST 40S	.109	.1010	.0879	.0750	.0623	.0497	.0373	.0250	.0129	.0009	
1/2	80 ST 80S	.147	.1921	.1779	.1639	.1501	.1364	.1229	.1096	.0964	.0834	.0706
1/2	160	.187	.2970	.2814	.2661	.2509	.2359	.2211	.2065	.1921	.1779	.1639
1/2	XX	.294	.6343	.6138	.5936	.5737	.5542	.5349	.5159	.4972	.4788	.4606
3/4	5S	.065	.0036									
3/4	10S	.083	.0341	.0243	.0146	.0050						
3/4	40S	.113	.0872	.0769	.0667	.0566	.0465	.0366	.0268	.0170	.0074	
3/4	80S	.154	.1644	.1533	.1423	.1314	.1207	.1100	.0995	.0890	.0787	.0685
3/4		.188	.2329	.2210	.2094	.1978	.1864	.1750	.1638	.1527	.1418	.1309
3/4	160	.218	.2970	.2845	.2721	.2599	.2478	.2358	.2240	.2123	.2007	.1892
3/4	XX	.308	.5135	.4985	.4837	.4691	.4547	.4404	.4263	.4124	.3986	.3850
1	5S	.065	.0029									
1	10S	.109	.0634	.0553	.0473	.0394	.0315	.0237	.0159	.0082	.0006	
1	40 ST 40S	.133	.0979	.0896	.0813	.0731	.0650	.0569	.0489	.0409	.0330	.0252
1	80 ST 80S	.179	.1675	.1586	.1498	.1410	.1324	.1238	.1152	.1067	.0983	.0900
1		.219	.2319	.2225	.2131	.2038	.1946	.1855	.1765	.1675	.1586	.1498
1	160	.250	.2845	.2746	.2648	.2551	.2455	.2359	.2265	.2171	.2078	.1985
1	XXO	.358	.4888	.4770	.4654	.4539	.4425	.4312	.4201	.4090	.3980	.3871
11/4	5S	.065	.0023									
11/4	10S	.109	.0499	.0435	.0373	.0310	.0249	.0187	.0126	.0065	.0005	
11/4	40 ST 40S	.140	.0848	.0782	.0718	.0653	.0589	.0526	.0462	.0399	.0337	.0275
11/4	80 ST 80S	.191	.1449	.1380	.1311	.1243	.1175	.1108	.1041	.0974	.0908	.0843
11/4	160	.250	.2189	.2115	.2041	.1969	.1896	.1824	.1753	.1682	.1611	.1541
11/4	XX	.382	.4045	.3958	.3872	.3786	.3702	.3617	.3534	.3450	.3368	.3286

Table 7-3
Continued

NOMINAL PIPE SIZE	SCHEDULE NUMBER AND/OR WEIGHT	WALL THICKNESS	CORROSION ALLOWANCE-INCHES									Y=0.5
			0.055	0.060	0.065	0.070	0.075	0.080	0.085	0.90	0.095	0.100
11/2	5S	.065	.0020									
11/2	10S	.109	.0434	.0379	.0325	.0271	.0217	.0163	.0110	.0057	.0004	
11/2	40 ST 40S	.145	.0786	.0730	.0673	.0617	.0561	.0506	.0451	.0396	.0341	.0287
11/2	80 ST 80S	.200	.1348	.1289	.1229	.1170	.1111	.1053	.0994	.0937	.0879	.0822
11/2	160	.281	.2234	.2169	.2104	.2040	.1976	.1913	.1850	.1787	.1725	.1663
11/2	XX	.400	.3676	.3602	.3529	.3457	.3385	.3313	.3242	.3171	.3100	.3030
2	5S	.065	.0016									
2	10S	.109	.0346	.0302	.0259	.0216	.0173	.0130	.0088	.0045	.0003	
2	40 ST 40S	.154	.0695	.0650	.0605	.0561	.0516	.0472	.0428	.0384	.0340	.0297
2		.167	.0798	.0753	.0707	.0662	.0617	.0573	.0528	.0484	.0440	.0396
2		.188	.0967	.0921	.0875	.0829	.0783	.0738	.0693	.0648	.0603	.0558
2	80 ST 80S	.218	.1212	.1165	.1118	.1071	.1025	.0978	.0932	.0886	.0840	.0795
2		.250	.1481	.1433	.1384	.1336	.1289	.1241	.1194	.1146	.1099	.1053
2		.312	.2021	.1970	.1920	.1869	.1819	.1769	.1719	.1670	.1620	.1571
2	160	.343	.2302	.2250	.2198	.2146	.2094	.2043	.1992	.1941	.1891	.1840
2	XX	.436	.3188	.3131	.3075	.3019	.2964	.2908	.2853	.2798	.2744	.2689
21/2	5S	.083	.0123	.0088	.0053	.0018						
21/2	10S	.120	.0354	.0318	.0282	.0246	.0211	.0175	.0140	.0105	.0070	.0035
21/2	40 ST 40S	.203	.0891	.0853	.0815	.0778	.0740	.0703	.0666	.0629	.0592	.0555
21/2		.217	.0984	.0946	.0908	.0870	.0832	.0795	.0757	.0720	.0683	.0645
21/2	80 ST 805	.276	.1387	.1348	.1308	.1269	.1229	.1190	.1151	.1113	.1074	.1035
21/2	160	.375	.2099	.2057	.2015	.1973	.1931	.1889	.1848	.1806	.1765	.1724
21/2	XX	.552	.3498	.3450	.3403	.3355	.3308	.3261	.3214	.3167	.3120	.3074
3	5S	.083	.0101	.0072	.0044	.0015						
3	10S	.120	.0290	.0260	.0231	.0202	.0173	.0144	.0115	.0086	.0057	.0029
3		.125	.0316	.0286	.0257	.0228	.0198	.0169	.0140	.0111	.0082	.0054
3		.148	.0435	.0405	.0375	.0346	.0316	.0287	.0258	.0228	.0199	.0170
3		.188	.0646	.0616	.0585	.0555	.0525	.0495	.0465	.0435	.0405	.0375
3	40 ST 40S	.216	.0796	.0765	.0735	.0704	.0673	.0643	.0612	.0582	.0552	.0522
3		.241	.0932	.0901	.0870	.0839	.0808	.0777	.0746	.0715	.0685	.0654
3		.254	.1004	.0972	.0941	.0910	.0878	.0847	.0816	.0785	.0755	.0724
3		.289	.1198	.1166	.1134	.1103	.1071	.1039	.1008	.0976	.0945	.0913
3	80 XS 805	.300	.1260	.1228	.1196	.1164	.1132	.1100	.1068	.1037	.1005	.0974
3		.312	.1328	.1296	.1264	.1231	.1199	.1167	.1135	.1103	.1072	.1040
3		.406	.1877	.1843	.1809	.1775	.1741	.1707	.1674	.1640	.1607	.1573

Table 7-3
Continued

NOMINAL PIPE SIZE	SCHEDULE NUMBER AND/OR WEIGHT	WALL THICKNESS	CORROSION ALLOWANCE-INCHES									Y=0.5
			0.055	0.060	0.065	0.070	0.075	0.080	0.085	0.90	0.095	0.100
3	160	.438	.2070	.2035	.2000	.1966	.1932	.1897	.1863	.1829	.1795	.1761
3	XX	.600	.3102	.3064	.3026	.2989	.2951	.2913	.2876	.2838	.2801	.2764
31/2	5S	.083	.0089	.0063	.0038	.0013						
31/2	10S	.120	.0253	.0228	.0202	.0177	.0151	.0126	.0101	.0075	.0050	.0025
31/2		.128	.0289	.0263	.0238	.0212	.0187	.0161	.0136	.0111	.0085	.0060
31/2		.134	.0316	.0290	.0265	.0239	.0214	.0188	.0163	.0137	.0112	.0087
31/2		.148	.0380	.0354	.0328	.0302	.0276	.0251	.0225	.0199	.0174	.0149
31/2		.188	.0563	.0537	.0510	.0484	.0458	.0432	.0406	.0380	.0354	.0328
31/2	40 ST 40S	.226	.0740	.0713	.0687	.0660	.0633	.0607	.0580	.0554	.0527	.0501
31/2		.281	.1002	.0975	.0947	.0920	.0893	.0865	.0838	.0811	.0784	.0757
31/2	80 XS 805	.318	.1182	.1154	.1126	.1098	.1071	.1043	.1015	.0988	.0960	.0933
31/2		.344	.1311	.1282	.1254	.1226	.1198	.1170	.1142	.1114	.1086	.1058
31/2		.469	.1950	.1920	.1890	.1860	.1830	.1801	.1771	.1741	.1712	.1682
31/2		.636	.2867	.2834	.2802	.2769	.2737	.2705	.2673	.2640	.2608	.2577
4	5S	.083	.0079	.0056	.0034	.0012						
4	10S	.120	.0225	.0202	.0179	.0157	.0134	.0112	.0089	.0067	.0045	.0022
4		.128	.0257	.0234	.0211	.0188	.0166	.0143	.0121	.0098	.0076	.0053
4		.134	.0281	.0258	.0235	.0212	.0190	.0167	.0144	.0122	.0099	.0077
4		.142	.0313	.0290	.0267	.0244	.0221	.0199	.0176	.0153	.0131	.0108
4		.165	.0405	.0382	.0359	.0336	.0313	.0290	.0267	.0245	.0222	.0199
4		.188	.0499	.0475	.0452	.0429	.0406	.0383	.0360	.0337	.0314	.0291
4		.205	.0568	.0545	.0522	.0498	.0475	.0452	.0428	.0405	.0382	.0359
4	40 ST40S	.237	.0701	.0677	.0653	.0630	.0606	.0583	.0559	.0536	.0512	.0489
4		.250	.0755	.0731	.0708	.0684	.0660	.0636	.0613	.0589	.0566	.0542
4		.271	.0844	.0819	.0795	.0771	.0747	.0724	.0700	.0676	.0652	.0629
4		.281	.0886	.0862	.0838	.0813	.0789	.0765	.0742	.0718	.0694	.0670
4		.300	.0967	.0942	.0918	.0894	.0870	.0845	.0821	.0797	.0773	.0749
4		.312	.1018	.0994	.0969	.0945	.0921	.0896	.0872	.0848	.0824	.0800
4	80 XS 80S	.337	.1126	.1101	.1077	.1052	.1027	.1003	.0978	.0954	.0930	.0905
4		.375	.1292	.1267	.1242	.1217	.1192	.1167	.1142	.1117	.1093	.1068
4	120	.438	.1574	.1548	.1522	.1496	.1471	.1445	.1420	.1394	.1369	.1343
4		.500	.1858	.1831	.1805	.1779	.1752	.1726	.1700	.1674	.1648	.1622
4	160	.531	.2003	.1976	.1949	.1922	.1896	.1869	.1843	.1816	.1790	.1763
4	XX	.674	.2697	.2669	.2640	.2612	.2583	.2555	.2527	.2499	.2471	.2442
5	5S	.109	.0146	.0128	.0110	.0092	.0074	.0055	.0037	.0019	.0001	
5	10S	.134	.0226	.0208	.0190	.0171	.0153	.0135	.0117	.0098	.0080	.0062

Table 7-3
Continued

NOMINAL PIPE SIZE	SCHEDULE NUMBER AND/OR WEIGHT	WALL THICKNESS	CORROSION ALLOWANCE-INCHES									Y=0.5
			0.055	0.060	0.065	0.070	0.075	0.080	0.085	0.90	0.095	0.100
5	40 ST 40S	.258	.0633	.0614	.0595	.0576	.0557	.0538	.0519	.0500	.0481	.0463
5		.352	.0953	.0933	.0914	.0894	.0874	.0855	.0835	.0816	.0796	.0777
5	80 XS 80S	.375	.1033	.1013	.0993	.0973	.0953	.0934	.0914	.0894	.0875	.0855
5		.438	.1254	.1234	.1214	.1193	.1173	.1153	.1133	.1113	.1093	.1073
5	120	.500	.1477	.1456	.1435	.1415	.1394	.1374	.1353	.1333	.1312	.1292
5	160	.625	.1940	.1918	.1897	.1875	.1854	.1832	.1811	.1790	.1768	.1747
5	XX	.750	.2424	.2401	.2378	.2356	.2334	.2311	.2289	.2266	.2244	.2222
6	5S	.109	.0123	.0107	.0092	.0077	.0062	.0047	.0031	.0016	.0001	
6	10S	.134	.0190	.0174	.0159	.0144	.0128	.0113	.0098	.0083	.0067	.0052
6		.169	.0284	.0269	.0253	.0238	.0222	.0207	.0192	.0176	.0161	.0146
6		.180	.0314	.0299	.0283	.0268	.0252	.0237	.0221	.0206	.0190	.0175
6		.188	.0336	.0321	.0305	.0289	.0274	.0258	.0243	.0227	.0212	.0197
6		.219	.0421	.0405	.0390	.0374	.0358	.0343	.0327	.0312	.0296	.0280
6		.250	.0507	.0491	.0475	.0459	.0444	.0428	.0412	.0396	.0381	.0365
6		.277	.0582	.0566	.0550	.0534	.0518	.0503	.0487	.0471	.0455	.0439
6	40 ST 40S	.280	.0591	.0575	.0559	.0543	.0527	.0511	.0495	.0479	.0463	.0448
6		.375	.0860	.0844	.0827	.0811	.0795	.0778	.0762	.0746	.0729	.0713
6	80 XS 805	.432	.1025	.1008	.0992	.0975	.0959	.0942	.0925	.0909	.0892	.0876
6		.500	.1225	.1208	.1192	.1175	.1158	.1141	.1124	.1107	.1090	.1074
6	120	.562	.1412	.1394	.1377	.1360	.1343	.1325	.1308	.1291	.1274	.1257
6	160	.718	.1894	.1876	.1858	.1840	.1822	.1804	.1786	.1769	.1751	.1733
6	XX	.864	.2367	.2348	.2329	.2310	.2291	.2273	.2254	.2235	.2217	.2198
8	5S	.109	.0094	.0082	.0071	.0059	.0047	.0036	.0024	.0012	.0001	
8	10S	.148	.0174	.0162	.0151	.0139	.0127	.0115	.0104	.0092	.0080	.0069
8		.158	.0195	.0183	.0171	.0160	.0148	.0136	.0124	.0113	.0101	.0089
8		.165	.0209	.0198	.0186	.0174	.0162	.0150	.0139	.0127	.0115	.0103
8		.188	.0257	.0245	.0233	.0222	.0210	.0198	.0186	.0174	.0162	.0151
8		.203	.0288	.0277	.0265	.0253	.0241	.0229	.0217	.0205	.0193	.0182
8		.219	.0322	.0310	.0298	.0286	.0274	.0262	.0250	.0238	.0227	.0215
8		.238	.0362	.0350	.0338	.0326	.0314	.0302	.0290	.0278	.0266	.0254
8	20	.250	.0387	.0375	.0363	.0351	.0339	.0327	.0315	.0303	.0291	.0279
8	30	.277	.0444	.0432	.0420	.0408	.0396	.0384	.0372	.0360	.0348	.0336
8	40 ST 40S	.322	.0540	.0528	.0516	.0503	.0491	.0479	.0467	.0455	.0443	.0431
8		.344	.0587	.0575	.0563	.0550	.0538	.0526	.0514	.0502	.0489	.0477
8		.352	.0604	.0592	.0580	.0568	.0555	.0543	.0531	.0519	.0506	.0494
8		.375	.0654	.0642	.0629	.0617	.0605	.0592	.0580	.0568	.0556	.0543

Table 7-3
Continued

NOMINAL PIPE SIZE	SCHEDULE NUMBER AND/OR WEIGHT	WALL THICKNESS	CORROSION ALLOWANCE-INCHES Y=0.5									
			0.055	0.060	0.065	0.070	0.075	0.080	0.085	0.90	0.095	0.100
8	60	.406	.0721	.0709	.0696	.0684	.0672	.0659	.0647	.0635	.0622	.0610
8		.469	.0859	.0847	.0834	.0822	.0809	.0797	.0784	.0772	.0759	.0747
8	80 XS 80S	.500	.0928	.0915	.0903	.0890	.0877	.0865	.0852	.0840	.0827	.0814
8	100	.593	.1137	.1124	.1111	.1098	.1085	.1072	.1059	.1047	.1034	.1021
8		.625	.1210	.1197	.1184	.1171	.1158	.1145	.1132	.1119	.1106	.1093
8	120	.718	.1424	.1411	.1397	.1384	.1371	.1358	.1344	.1331	.1318	.1305
8	140	.812	.1645	.1631	.1618	.1604	.1591	.1577	.1564	.1550	.1537	.1523
8	XX	.875	.1796	.1782	.1768	.1755	.1741	.1727	.1713	.1700	.1686	.1673
8	160	.906	.1871	.1857	.1843	.1829	.1815	.1802	.1788	.1774	.1760	.1747
10	5S	.134	.0116	.0107	.0098	.0088	.0079	.0070	.0060	.0051	.0041	.0032
10	10S	.165	.0168	.0158	.0149	.0139	.0130	.0120	.0111	.0102	.0092	.0083
10		.188	.0206	.0196	.0187	.0177	.0168	.0158	.0149	.0140	.0130	.0121
10		.203	.0231	.0221	.0212	.0202	.0193	.0183	.0174	.0164	.0155	.0145
10		.219	.0257	.0248	.0238	.0229	.0219	.0210	.0200	.0191	.0181	.0172
10	20	.250	.0309	.0300	.0290	.0281	.0271	.0262	.0252	.0242	.0233	.0223
10		.279	.0358	.0349	.0339	.0329	.0320	.0310	.0300	.0291	.0281	.0272
10	30	.307	.0405	.0396	.0386	.0376	.0367	.0357	.0348	.0338	.0328	.0319
10		.348	.0475	.0465	.0456	.0446	.0436	.0427	.0417	.0407	.0398	.0388
10	40 ST 40S	.365	.0504	.0494	.0485	.0475	.0465	.0455	.0446	.0436	.0426	.0417
10		.395	.0556	.0546	.0536	.0526	.0516	.0507	.0497	.0487	.0477	.0468
10	60 XS 80S	.500	.0738	.0728	.0718	.0708	.0698	.0688	.0678	.0668	.0658	.0648
10		.531	.0792	.0782	.0772	.0762	.0752	.0742	.0732	.0722	.0712	.0702
10	80	.593	.0902	.0892	.0882	.0872	.0861	.0851	.0841	.0831	.0821	.0811
10	100	.718	.1127	.1116	.1106	.1095	.1085	.1075	.1064	.1054	.1044	.1034
10		.750	.1185	.1174	.1164	.1154	.1143	.1133	.1122	.1112	.1102	.1091
10	120	.843	.1356	.1346	.1335	.1324	.1314	.1303	.1293	.1282	.1272	.1261
10	140	1.000	.1652	.1641	.1630	.1619	.1608	.1597	.1586	.1576	.1565	.1554
10		1.062	.1770	.1759	.1748	.1737	.1726	.1716	.1705	.1694	.1683	.1672
10	160	1.125	.1893	.1882	.1870	.1859	.1848	.1837	.1826	.1815	.1804	.1793
12	5S	.156	.0129	.0121	.0113	.0105	.0097	.0089	.0081	.0073	.0065	.0057
12	10S	.180	.0162	.0154	.0146	.0138	.0130	.0122	.0114	.0106	.0099	.0091
12		.203	.0194	.0186	.0178	.0170	.0162	.0154	.0146	.0138	.0130	.0123
12		.219	.0217	.0209	.0201	.0193	.0185	.0177	.0169	.0161	.0153	.0145
12		.238	.0243	.0235	.0227	.0219	.0211	.0203	.0195	.0187	.0179	.0171
12	20	.250	.0260	.0252	.0244	.0236	.0228	.0220	.0212	.0204	.0196	.0188
12		.279	.0301	.0293	.0285	.0277	.0269	.0261	.0253	.0245	.0237	.0229

Table 7-3
Continued

NOMINAL PIPE SIZE	SCHEDULE NUMBER AND/OR WEIGHT	WALL THICKNESS	CORROSION ALLOWANCE-INCHES									Y=0.5
			0.055	0.060	0.065	0.070	0.075	0.080	0.085	0.90	0.095	0.100
12		.300	.0331	.0323	.0315	.0307	.0299	.0290	.0282	.0274	.0266	.0258
12	30	.330	.0374	.0365	.0357	.0349	.0341	.0333	.0325	.0317	.0309	.0301
12		.344	.0393	.0385	.0377	.0369	.0361	.0353	.0345	.0337	.0328	.0320
12	ST 40S	.375	.0438	.0430	.0421	.0413	.0405	.0397	.0389	.0381	.0372	.0364
12	40	.406	.0482	.0474	.0466	.0458	.0449	.0441	.0433	.0425	.0417	.0409
12		.438	.0529	.0520	.0512	.0504	.0496	.0487	.0479	.0471	.0463	.0454
12	XS 80S	.500	.0619	.0610	.0602	.0594	.0585	.0577	.0569	.0560	.0552	.0544
12	60	.562	.0709	.0701	.0693	.0684	.0676	.0667	.0659	.0651	.0642	.0634
12		.625	.0803	.0794	.0786	.0777	.0769	.0760	.0752	.0743	.0735	.0726
12	80	.687	.0895	.0886	.0878	.0869	.0861	.0852	.0844	.0835	.0827	.0818
12	100	.843	.1131	.1123	.1114	.1105	.1096	.1088	.1079	.1070	.1062	.1053
12		.875	.1181	.1172	.1163	.1154	.1145	.1137	.1128	.1119	.1110	.1102
12	120	1.000	.1375	.1366	.1357	.1348	.1339	.1330	.1321	.1312	.1303	.1294
12	140	1.125	.1572	.1563	.1554	.1545	.1536	.1527	.1518	.1509	.1500	.1491
12		1.219	.1724	.1714	.1705	.1696	.1687	.1677	.1668	.1659	.1650	.1641
12	160	1.312	.1875	.1866	.1857	.1847	.1838	.1828	.1819	.1810	.1800	.1791
14		.188	.0158	.0150	.0143	.0136	.0129	.0121	.0114	.0107	.0100	.0093
14		.220	.0198	.0191	.0184	.0177	.0169	.0162	.0155	.0148	.0140	.0133
14		.238	.0221	.0214	.0207	.0199	.0192	.0185	.0178	.0170	.0163	.0156
14	10	.250	.0237	.0229	.0222	.0215	.0207	.0200	.0193	.0186	.0178	.0171
14	20	.312	.0316	.0309	.0302	.0294	.0287	.0280	.0272	.0265	.0258	.0250
14	30ST	.375	.0398	.0391	.0383	.0376	.0368	.0361	.0353	.0346	.0339	.0331
14		.406	.0438	.0431	.0423	.0416	.0409	.0401	.0394	.0386	.0379	.0371
14	40	.438	.0480	.0473	.0465	.0458	.0450	.0443	.0435	.0428	.0420	.0413
14		.469	.0521	.0513	.0506	.0498	.0491	.0483	.0476	.0468	.0461	.0453
14	XS	.500	.0562	.0554	.0547	.0539	.0532	.0524	.0517	.0509	.0502	.0494
14	60	.593	.0685	.0678	.0670	.0662	.0655	.0647	.0640	.0632	.0624	.0617
14		.625	.0728	.0721	.0713	.0705	.0698	.0690	.0682	.0675	.0667	.0659
14		.656	.0770	.0762	.0755	.0747	.0739	.0732	.0724	.0716	.0709	.0701
14	80	.750	.0897	.0890	.0882	.0874	.0866	.0859	.0851	.0843	.0835	.0828
14	100	.937	.1156	.1148	.1140	.1132	.1124	.1116	.1108	.1100	.1092	.1084
14	120	1.093	.1376	.1368	.1360	.1352	.1344	.1336	.1327	.1319	.1311	.1303
14	140	1.250	.1603	.1595	.1586	.1578	.1570	.1561	.1553	.1545	.1536	.1528
14		1.344	.1741	.1732	.1724	.1716	.1707	.1699	.1690	.1682	.1674	.1665
14	160	1.406	.1833	.1824	.1816	.1807	.1799	.1790	.1782	.1773	.1765	.1756
16		.188	.0138	.0131	.0125	.0119	.0113	.0106	.0100	.0094	.0087	.0081

Table 7-3
Continued

NOMINAL PIPE SIZE	SCHEDULE NUMBER AND/OR WEIGHT	WALL THICKNESS	CORROSION ALLOWANCE-INCHES									Y=0.5
			0.055	0.060	0.065	0.070	0.075	0.080	0.085	0.90	0.095	0.100
16		.238	.0193	.0187	.0181	.0174	.0168	.0162	.0155	.0149	.0143	.0136
16	10	.250	.0207	.0200	.0194	.0188	.0181	.0175	.0169	.0162	.0156	.0150
16		.281	.0241	.0235	.0229	.0222	.0216	.0210	.0203	.0197	.0190	.0184
16	20	.312	.0276	.0270	.0263	.0257	.0251	.0244	.0238	.0231	.0225	.0219
16		.344	.0312	.0306	.0299	.0293	.0287	.0280	.0274	.0267	.0261	.0254
16	30 ST	.375	.0347	.0341	.0334	.0328	.0321	.0315	.0309	.0302	.0296	.0289
16		.406	.0382	.0376	.0370	.0363	.0357	.0350	.0344	.0337	.0331	.0324
16		.438	.0419	.0412	.0406	.0399	.0393	.0386	.0380	.0373	.0367	.0360
16		.469	.0454	.0448	.0441	.0435	.0428	.0422	.0415	.0409	.0402	.0396
16	40 XS	.500	.0490	.0483	.0477	.0470	.0464	.0457	.0451	.0444	.0437	.0431
16		.531	.0525	.0519	.0512	.0506	.0499	.0493	.0486	.0480	.0473	.0466
16	60	.656	.0670	.0664	.0657	.0650	.0644	.0637	.0631	.0624	.0617	.0611
16		.688	.0708	.0701	.0695	.0688	.0681	.0675	.0668	.0661	.0654	.0648
16		.750	.0781	.0774	.0767	.0761	.0754	.0747	.0741	.0734	.0727	.0720
16	80	.843	.0891	.0884	.0878	.0871	.0864	.0857	.0850	.0844	.0837	.0830
16	100	1.031	.1118	.1111	.1104	.1097	.1090	.1083	.1076	.1069	.1063	.1056
16	120	1.218	.1349	.1342	.1334	.1327	.1320	.1313	.1306	.1299	.1292	.1285
16	140	1.438	.1626	.1619	.1612	.1604	.1597	.1590	.1583	.1575	.1568	.1561
16		1.500	.1706	.1699	.1691	.1684	.1677	.1669	.1662	.1655	.1647	.1640
16	160	1.593	.1826	.1819	.1812	.1804	.1797	.1789	.1782	.1774	.1767	.1760
18	10	.250	.0184	.0178	.0172	.0167	.0161	.0155	.0150	.0144	.0138	.0133
18	20	.312	.0245	.0240	.0234	.0228	.0222	.0217	.0211	.0205	.0200	.0194
18	ST	.375	.0308	.0302	.0297	.0291	.0285	.0280	.0274	.0268	.0262	.0257
18	30	.438	.0371	.0366	.0360	.0354	.0348	.0343	.0337	.0331	.0325	.0320
18	XS	.500	.0434	.0428	.0423	.0417	.0411	.0405	.0399	.0394	.0388	.0382
18	40	.562	.0497	.0492	.0486	.0480	.0474	.0468	.0462	.0457	.0451	.0445
18		.594	.0530	.0524	.0518	.0513	.0507	.0501	.0495	.0489	.0483	.0478
18		.625	.0562	.0556	.0550	.0544	.0538	.0533	.0527	.0521	.0515	.0509
18		.719	.0659	.0653	.0647	.0641	.0635	.0629	.0623	.0618	.0612	.0606
18	60	.750	.0691	.0685	.0679	.0673	.0667	.0661	.0656	.0650	.0644	.0638
18		.812	.0756	.0750	.0744	.0738	.0732	.0726	.0720	.0714	.0708	.0702
18	80	.937	.0888	.0882	.0875	.0869	.0863	.0857	.0851	.0845	.0839	.0833
18	100	1.156	.1122	.1116	.1110	.1104	.1098	.1091	.1085	.1079	.1073	.1067
18	120	1.375	.1363	.1356	.1350	.1344	.1337	.1331	.1325	.1318	.1312	.1306
18	140	1.562	.1572	.1566	.1559	.1553	.1546	.1540	.1533	.1527	.1520	.1514
18		1.688	.1716	.1709	.1702	.1696	.1689	.1683	.1676	.1670	.1663	.1657

Table 7-3
Continued

NOMINAL PIPE SIZE	SCHEDULE NUMBER AND/OR WEIGHT	WALL THICKNESS	CORROSION ALLOWANCE-INCHES									Y=0.5
			0.055	0.060	0.065	0.070	0.075	0.080	0.085	0.90	0.095	0.100
18	160	1.781	.1823	.1816	.1809	.1803	.1796	.1790	.1783	.1776	.1770	.1763
20	10	.250	.0165	.0160	.0155	.0150	.0145	.0140	.0135	.0130	.0125	.0119
20		.312	.0220	.0215	.0210	.0205	.0200	.0195	.0190	.0185	.0180	.0175
20	20 ST	.375	.0277	.0272	.0267	.0261	.0256	.0251	.0246	.0241	.0236	.0231
20		.438	.0334	.0329	.0323	.0318	.0313	.0308	.0303	.0298	.0292	.0287
20	30 XS	.500	.0390	.0385	.0380	.0374	.0369	.0364	.0359	.0354	.0348	.0343
20		.562	.0447	.0441	.0436	.0431	.0426	.0420	.0415	.0410	.0405	.0400
20	40	.593	.0475	.0470	.0464	.0459	.0454	.0449	.0443	.0438	.0433	.0428
20		.625	.0504	.0499	.0494	.0489	.0483	.0478	.0473	.0468	.0462	.0457
20	60	.812	.0678	.0672	.0667	.0662	.0656	.0651	.0646	.0640	.0635	.0630
20		.875	.0737	.0731	.0726	.0721	.0715	.0710	.0705	.0699	.0694	.0689
20		.906	.0766	.0761	.0755	.0750	.0744	.0739	.0734	.0728	.0723	.0718
20	80	1.031	.0885	.0879	.0874	.0868	.0863	.0857	.0852	.0846	.0841	.0836
20		1.250	.1096	.1090	.1085	.1079	.1073	.1068	.1062	.1057	.1051	.1046
20	100	1.281	.1126	.1120	.1115	.1109	.1104	.1098	.1092	.1087	.1081	.1076
20	120	1.500	.1342	.1336	.1330	.1325	.1319	.1313	.1308	.1302	.1296	.1291
20	140	1.750	.1594	.1588	.1582	.1576	.1571	.1565	.1559	.1553	.1547	.1542
20		1.844	.1690	.1684	.1678	.1673	.1667	.1661	.1655	.1649	.1643	.1637
20	160	1.968	.1819	.1813	.1807	.1801	.1795	.1789	.1783	.1777	.1771	.1765
22	LG	.250	.0150	.0145	.0141	.0136	.0132	.0127	.0122	.0118	.0113	.0109
22	ST	.375	.0251	.0247	.0242	.0237	.0233	.0228	.0223	.0219	.0214	.0210
22	XS	.500	.0354	.0349	.0344	.0340	.0335	.0330	.0326	.0321	.0316	.0312
24	10	.250	.0137	.0133	.0129	.0125	.0121	.0116	.0112	.0108	.0104	.0099
24		.312	.0183	.0179	.0175	.0171	.0166	.0162	.0158	.0154	.0149	.0145
24	20 ST	.375	.0230	.0226	.0222	.0217	.0213	.0209	.0205	.0200	.0196	.0192
24		.438	.0277	.0273	.0269	.0264	.0260	.0256	.0252	.0247	.0243	.0239
24	XS	.500	.0324	.0320	.0315	.0311	.0307	.0302	.0298	.0294	.0290	.0285
24	30	.562	.0371	.0366	.0362	.0358	.0353	.0349	.0345	.0340	.0336	.0332
24		.625	.0418	.0414	.0410	.0405	.0401	.0397	.0392	.0388	.0384	.0379
24	40	.687	.0466	.0461	.0457	.0453	.0448	.0444	.0440	.0435	.0431	.0427
24		.750	.0514	.0510	.0505	.0501	.0496	.0492	.0488	.0483	.0479	.0475
24	60	.968	.0683	.0678	.0674	.0669	.0665	.0660	.0656	.0651	.0647	.0642
24		1.031	.0732	.0727	.0723	.0718	.0714	.0709	.0705	.0700	.0696	.0692
24	80	1.218	.0879	.0875	.0870	.0866	.0861	.0857	.0852	.0848	.0843	.0839
24	100	1.531	.1131	.1126	.1122	.1117	.1112	.1108	.1103	.1099	.1094	.1089

Table 7-3
Continued

NOMINAL PIPE SIZE	SCHEDULE NUMBER AND/OR WEIGHT	WALL THICKNESS	CORROSION ALLOWANCE-INCHES Y=0.5									
			0.055	0.060	0.065	0.070	0.075	0.080	0.085	0.90	0.095	0.100
24	120	1.812	.1362	.1358	.1353	.1348	.1343	.1339	.1334	.1329	.1324	.1320
24	140	2.062	.1572	.1567	.1563	.1558	.1553	.1548	.1543	.1538	.1534	.1529
24		2.188	.1680	.1675	.1670	.1665	.1660	.1655	.1650	.1646	.1641	.1636
24	160	2.343	.1813	.1808	.1803	.1798	.1794	.1789	.1784	.1779	.1774	.1769
26	ST	.375	.0212	.0208	.0204	.0201	.0197	.0193	.0189	.0185	.0181	.0177
26	XS	.500	.0299	.0295	.0291	.0287	.0283	.0279	.0275	.0271	.0267	.0263
30	10	.312	.0146	.0143	.0140	.0136	.0133	.0129	.0126	.0123	.0119	.0116
30	ST	.375	.0184	.0180	.0177	.0174	.0170	.0167	.0163	.0160	.0157	.0153
30		.438	.0221	.0218	.0214	.0211	.0208	.0204	.0201	.0197	.0194	.0191
30	20 XS	.500	.0258	.0255	.0251	.0248	.0245	.0241	.0238	.0234	.0231	.0228
30		.562	.0295	.0292	.0289	.0285	.0282	.0278	.0275	.0271	.0268	.0265
30	30	.625	.0333	.0330	.0326	.0323	.0320	.0316	.0313	.0309	.0306	.0302
34	ST	.375	.0162	.0159	.0156	.0153	.0150	.0147	.0144	.0141	.0138	.0135
34	XS	.500	.0228	.0225	.0222	.0219	.0216	.0213	.0210	.0207	.0204	.0201
36	ST	.375	.0153	.0150	.0147	.0144	.0142	.0139	.0136	.0133	.0130	.0128
36	XS	.500	.0215	.0212	.0209	.0206	.0203	.0201	.0198	.0195	.0192	.0189
42	ST	.375	.0131	.0128	.0126	.0124	.0121	.0119	.0116	.0114	.0112	.0109
42	XS	.500	.0184	.0181	.0179	.0177	.0174	.0172	.0169	.0167	.0164	.0162
48	ST	.375	.0114	.0112	.0110	.0108	.0106	.0104	.0102	.0100	.0098	.0096
48	XS	.500	.0161	.0159	.0156	.0154	.0152	.0150	.0148	.0146	.0144	.0142

Table 7-4
Pressure/Stress Ratios Where Y = 0.7

NOMINAL PIPE SIZE	SCHEDULE NUMBER AND/OR WEIGHT	WALL THICKNESS	CORROSION ALLOWANCE-INCHES Y=0.7										
			0.000	0.005	0.010	0.015	0.020	0.025	0.030	0.035	0.040	0.045	0.050
1/8	10S	.049	.2486	.2152	.1832	.1523	.1227	.0941	.0665	.0400	.0143		
1/8	40 ST 40S	.068	.3699	.3316	.2949	.2597	.2259	.1934	.1622	.1322	.1033	.0754	.0485
1/8	80 ST 80S	.095	.5760	.5285	.4833	.4400	.3987	.3592	.3214	.2851	.2503	.2169	.1847
1/4	10S	.065	.2471	.2220	.1976	.1740	.1510	.1287	.1070	.0859	.0654	.0454	.0259
1/4	40 ST 40S	.088	.3563	.3279	.3003	.2736	.2477	.2226	.1982	.1746	.1516	.1292	.1075
1/4	80 ST 80S	.119	.5283	.4941	.4611	.4293	.3985	.3687	.3398	.3119	.2849	.2586	.2332
3/8	10S	.065	.1911	.1722	.1538	.1359	.1183	.1011	.0843	.0679	.0518	.0361	.0207
3/8	40 ST 40S	.091	.2826	.2616	.2411	.2211	.2016	.1825	.1639	.1457	.1279	.1105	.0935
3/8	80 ST 80S	.126	.4235	.3989	.3750	.3517	.3290	.3068	.2853	.2642	.2436	.2236	.2040
1/2	10S	.083	.1967	.1815	.1665	.1518	.1373	.1232	.1092	.0956	.0821	.0689	.0560
1/2	40 ST 40S	.109	.2700	.2533	.2370	.2210	.2052	.1898	.1747	.1598	.1453	.1309	.1169
1/2	80 ST 80S	.147	.3898	.3707	.3520	.3337	.3158	.2982	.2810	.2641	.2476	.2314	.2154
1/2	160	.187	.5357	.5134	.4917	.4704	.4496	.4292	.4093	.3898	.3707	.3520	.3337
1/2	XX	.294	1.0722	1.0363	1.0013	.9674	.9343	.9022	.8709	.8405	.8109	.7820	.7538
3/4	5S	.065	.1172	.1062	.0952	.0845	.0739	.0634	.0531	.0429	.0329	.0230	.0132
3/4	10S	.083	.1532	.1416	.1302	.1189	.1078	.0969	.0861	.0755	.0650	.0546	.0444
3/4	40S	.113	.2169	.2044	.1920	.1799	.1679	.1561	.1445	.1330	.1217	.1106	.0996
3/4	80S	.154	.3129	.2988	.2850	.2714	.2581	.2449	.2319	.2191	.2066	.1942	.1820
3/4		.188	.4014	.3859	.3706	.3557	.3409	.3264	.3122	.2981	.2843	.2708	.2574
3/4	160	.218	.4873	.4703	.4536	.4372	.4211	.4053	.3897	.3744	.3594	.3446	.3300
3/4	XX	.308	.8012	.7783	.7558	.7337	.7121	.6910	.6702	.6499	.6299	.6103	.5911
1	5S	.065	.0921	.0835	.0750	.0667	.0584	.0502	.0421	.0341	.0261	.0183	.0105
1	10S	.109	.1615	.1521	.1428	.1337	.1246	.1157	.1069	.0981	.0895	.0810	.0725
1	40 ST 40S	.133	.2020	.1922	.1824	.1728	.1633	.1539	.1447	.1355	.1264	.1175	.1086
1	80 ST 80S	.179	.2859	.2750	.2643	.2536	.2432	.2328	.2226	.2125	.2025	.1927	.1829
1		.219	.3661	.3542	.3425	.3308	.3194	.3081	.2969	.2859	.2750	.2643	.2536
1	160	.250	.4337	.4209	.4082	.3957	.3834	.3713	.3593	.3474	.3358	.3242	.3129
1	XXO	.358	.7148	.6978	.6811	.6647	.6485	.6325	.6168	.6013	.5861	.5711	.5563
11/4	5S	.065	.0720	.0654	.0588	.0523	.0459	.0395	.0331	.0269	.0206	.0145	.0083
11/4	10S	.109	.1250	.1179	.1108	.1039	.0970	.0901	.0834	.0766	.0700	.0634	.0568
11/4	40 ST 40S	.140	.1646	.1571	.1498	.1424	.1352	.1280	.1209	.1138	.1068	.0999	.0930
11/4	80 ST 80S	.191	.2344	.2263	.2182	.2103	.2024	.1946	.1868	.1791	.1716	.1640	.1566
11/4	160	.250	.3232	.3142	.3052	.2964	.2877	.2790	.2705	.2620	.2536	.2453	.2371
11/4	XX	.382	.5608	.5492	.5377	.5264	.5151	.5041	.4931	.4823	.4715	.4609	.4505

Table 7-4
Continued

NOMINAL PIPE SIZE	SCHEDULE NUMBER AND/OR WEIGHT	WALL THICKNESS	CORROSION ALLOWANCE-INCHES									Y=0.7	
			0.000	0.005	0.010	0.015	0.020	0.025	0.030	0.035	0.040	0.045	0.050
11/2	5S	.065	.0625	.0568	.0511	.0455	.0399	.0344	.0289	.0234	.0180	.0126	.0073
11/2	10S	.109	.1080	.1019	.0959	.0899	.0840	.0781	.0723	.0665	.0608	.0551	.0494
11/2	40 ST 40S	.145	.1473	.1409	.1346	.1283	.1221	.1159	.1098	.1037	.0977	.0917	.0858
11/2	80 ST 80S	.200	.2115	.2046	.1977	.1909	.1842	.1775	.1709	.1643	.1578	.1513	.1449
11/2	160	.281	.3161	.3083	.3005	.2928	.2852	.2777	.2702	.2628	.2555	.2482	.2410
11/2	XX	.400	.4965	.4869	.4775	.4682	.4590	.4498	.4408	.4318	.4229	.4141	.4054
2	5S	.065	.0496	.0451	.0406	.0362	.0317	.0274	.0230	.0187	.0144	.0101	.0058
2	10S	.109	.0851	.0804	.0757	.0711	.0664	.0618	.0573	.0527	.0482	.0437	.0393
2	40 ST 40S	.154	.1233	.1183	.1134	.1085	.1036	.0988	.0940	.0892	.0845	.0798	.0751
2		.167	.1347	.1295	.1246	.1197	.1147	.1098	.1050	.1001	.0953	.0906	.0858
2		.188	.1534	.1483	.1431	.1381	.1330	.1280	.1230	.1181	.1131	.1083	.1034
2	80 ST 80S	.218	.1810	.1757	.1704	.1651	.1599	.1547	.1495	.1444	.1393	.1343	.1292
2		.250	.2115	.2059	.2005	.1950	.1896	.1842	.1788	.1735	.1683	.1630	.1578
2		.312	.2740	.2680	.2621	.2562	.2504	.2446	.2388	.2331	.2275	.2218	.2162
2	160	.343	.3071	.3009	.2947	.2886	.2826	.2765	.2706	.2646	.2587	.2529	.2471
2	XX	.436	.4145	.4075	.4006	.3937	.3869	.3801	.3734	.3667	.3601	.3535	.3470
21/2	5S	.083	.0524	.0486	.0449	.0412	.0376	.0339	.0303	.0267	.0231	.0195	.0159
21/2	10S	.120	.0770	.0731	.0693	.0655	.0617	.0579	.0542	.0504	.0467	.0430	.0393
21/2	40 ST 40S	.203	.1353	.1311	.1270	.1229	.1188	.1147	.1106	.1066	.1026	.0986	.0947
21/2		.217	.1455	.1413	.1371	.1330	.1288	.1247	.1206	.1165	.1125	.1084	.1044
21/2	80 ST 805	.276	.1904	.1859	.1815	.1771	.1727	.1684	.1640	.1597	.1554	.1512	.1469
21/2	160	.375	.2717	.2668	.2619	.2570	.2522	.2474	.2426	.2379	.2331	.2285	.2238
21/2	XX	.552	.4393	.4334	.4275	.4217	.4158	.4101	.4043	.3986	.3929	.3873	.3817
3	5S	.083	.0427	.0397	.0367	.0337	.0307	.0277	.0248	.0218	.0189	.0160	.0130
3	10S	.120	.0626	.0595	.0564	.0533	.0503	.0472	.0442	.0412	.0381	.0351	.0321
3		.125	.0654	.0622	.0591	.0560	.0530	.0499	.0468	.0438	.0408	.0378	.0348
3		.148	.0780	.0749	.0717	.0686	.0654	.0623	.0592	.0561	.0530	.0500	.0469
3		.188	.1006	.0974	.0941	.0909	.0876	.0844	.0812	.0780	.0749	.0717	.0686
3	40 ST 40S	.216	.1168	.1135	.1102	.1069	.1036	.1003	.0970	.0938	.0905	.0873	.0841
3		.241	.1316	.1282	.1248	.1214	.1181	.1147	.1114	.1081	.1048	.1015	.0983
3		.254	.1394	.1360	.1325	.1291	.1257	.1224	.1190	.1157	.1123	.1090	.1057
3		.289	.1608	.1572	.1537	.1502	.1467	.1433	.1398	.1364	.1330	.1296	.1262
3	80 XS 805	.300	.1676	.1640	.1605	.1570	.1535	.1500	.1465	.1430	.1396	.1361	.1327
3		.312	.1751	.1715	.1680	.1644	.1608	.1573	.1538	.1503	.1468	.1434	.1399
3		.406	.2366	.2328	.2289	.2251	.2212	.2174	.2137	.2099	.2061	.2024	.1987

Table 7-4
Continued

NOMINAL PIPE SIZE	SCHEDULE NUMBER AND/OR WEIGHT	WALL THICKNESS	CORROSION ALLOWANCE-INCHES									Y=0.7	
			0.000	0.005	0.010	0.015	0.020	0.025	0.030	0.035	0.040	0.045	0.050
3	160	.438	.2587	.2547	.2507	.2468	.2429	.2390	.2351	.2312	.2274	.2235	.2197
3	XX	.600	.3797	.3752	.3706	.3661	.3616	.3571	.3527	.3483	.3438	.3395	.3351
31/2	5S	.083	.0373	.0346	.0320	.0294	.0268	.0242	.0216	.0191	.0165	.0139	.0114
31/2	10S	.120	.0545	.0518	.0491	.0465	.0438	.0412	.0385	.0359	.0333	.0306	.0280
31/2		.128	.0583	.0556	.0529	.0502	.0475	.0449	.0422	.0396	.0369	.0343	.0317
31/2		.134	.0611	.0584	.0557	.0530	.0503	.0477	.0450	.0423	.0397	.0371	.0344
31/2		.148	.0678	.0651	.0624	.0596	.0569	.0542	.0515	.0489	.0462	.0435	.0409
31/2		.188	.0873	.0845	.0817	.0789	.0761	.0733	.0706	.0678	.0651	.0624	.0596
31/2	40 ST 40S	.226	.1062	.1033	.1005	.0976	.0948	.0919	.0891	.0863	.0835	.0807	.0779
31/2		.281	.1345	.1315	.1286	.1256	.1226	.1197	.1168	.1138	.1109	.1080	.1051
31/2	80 XS 805	.318	.1541	.1511	.1480	.1450	.1420	.1389	.1359	.1329	.1300	.1270	.1240
31/2		.344	.1682	.1651	.1620	.1589	.1558	.1528	.1497	.1467	.1436	.1406	.1376
31/2		.469	.2396	.2362	.2328	.2294	.2261	.2227	.2194	.2161	.2128	.2095	.2062
31/2		.636	.3456	.3417	.3379	.3341	.3303	.3265	.3227	.3190	.3152	.3115	.3078
4	5S	.083	.0330	.0307	.0284	.0261	.0238	.0215	.0192	.0169	.0146	.0124	.0101
4	10S	.120	.0482	.0459	.0435	.0412	.0388	.0365	.0341	.0318	.0295	.0272	.0249
4		.128	.0516	.0492	.0468	.0445	.0421	.0397	.0374	.0351	.0327	.0304	.0281
4		.134	.0541	.0517	.0493	.0469	.0446	.0422	.0399	.0375	.0352	.0328	.0305
4		.142	.0574	.0550	.0526	.0503	.0479	.0455	.0432	.0408	.0385	.0361	.0338
4		.165	.0672	.0648	.0623	.0599	.0575	.0551	.0527	.0503	.0479	.0456	.0432
4		.188	.0771	.0746	.0721	.0697	.0672	.0648	.0624	.0600	.0576	.0552	.0528
4		.205	.0844	.0819	.0795	.0770	.0745	.0721	.0696	.0672	.0648	.0623	.0599
4	40 ST40S	.237	.0985	.0960	.0935	.0909	.0884	.0859	.0834	.0810	.0785	.0760	.0735
4		.250	.1043	.1018	.0992	.0967	.0942	.0916	.0891	.0866	.0841	.0816	.0792
4		.271	.1138	.1112	.1086	.1061	.1035	.1009	.0984	.0959	.0933	.0908	.0883
4		.281	.1183	.1157	.1131	.1106	.1080	.1054	.1029	.1003	.0978	.0952	.0927
4		.300	.1270	.1244	.1218	.1192	.1166	.1140	.1114	.1088	.1062	.1037	.1011
4		.312	.1326	.1299	.1273	.1247	.1221	.1194	.1168	.1142	.1116	.1091	.1065
4	80 XS 80S	.337	.1443	.1416	.1389	.1363	.1336	.1309	.1283	.1257	.1230	.1204	.1178
4		.375	.1624	.1597	.1569	.1542	.1515	.1488	.1460	.1434	.1407	.1380	.1353
4	120	.438	.1934	.1905	.1877	.1848	.1820	.1792	.1764	.1736	.1708	.1680	.1652
4		.500	.2251	.2221	.2191	.2162	.2133	.2103	.2074	.2045	.2016	.1987	.1958
4	160	.531	.2414	.2384	.2353	.2323	.2293	.2263	.2234	.2204	.2174	.2145	.2116
4	XX	.674	.3210	.3177	.3144	.3111	.3078	.3045	.3012	.2980	.2947	.2915	.2883
5	5S	.109	.0351	.0332	.0314	.0295	.0276	.0258	.0239	.0220	.0202	.0183	.0165
5	10S	.134	.0434	.0415	.0396	.0377	.0358	.0340	.0321	.0302	.0283	.0265	.0246

Table 7-4
Continued

NOM-INAL PIPE SIZE	SCHEDULE NUMBER AND/OR WEIGHT	WALL THICK-NESS	CORROSION ALLOWANCE-INCHES									Y=0.7	
			0.000	0.005	0.010	0.015	0.020	0.025	0.030	0.035	0.040	0.045	0.050
5	40 ST 40S	.258	.0860	.0840	.0820	.0800	.0780	.0760	.0740	.0720	.0701	.0681	.0661
5		.352	.1200	.1179	.1158	.1137	.1116	.1095	.1075	.1054	.1033	.1013	.0992
5	80 XS 80S	.375	.1286	.1265	.1243	.1222	.1201	.1180	.1159	.1138	.1117	.1096	.1075
5		.438	.1525	.1503	.1481	.1459	.1437	.1416	.1394	.1372	.1351	.1329	.1308
5	120	.500	.1767	.1745	.1722	.1700	.1677	.1655	.1632	.1610	.1588	.1566	.1544
5	160	.625	.2280	.2256	.2232	.2208	.2184	.2160	.2136	.2112	.2089	.2065	.2042
5	XX	.750	.2826	.2800	.2775	.2749	.2724	.2698	.2673	.2647	.2622	.2597	.2572
6	5S	.109	.0294	.0278	.0262	.0247	.0231	.0216	.0200	.0185	.0169	.0154	.0138
6	10S	.134	.0363	.0347	.0331	.0315	.0300	.0284	.0268	.0253	.0237	.0221	.0206
6		.169	.0461	.0445	.0429	.0413	.0397	.0381	.0365	.0349	.0333	.0317	.0302
6		.180	.0492	.0476	.0460	.0444	.0428	.0412	.0396	.0380	.0364	.0348	.0332
6		.188	.0514	.0498	.0482	.0466	.0450	.0434	.0418	.0402	.0386	.0370	.0354
6		.219	.0603	.0587	.0570	.0554	.0538	.0521	.0505	.0489	.0473	.0457	.0441
6		.250	.0692	.0676	.0659	.0643	.0626	.0610	.0593	.0577	.0561	.0545	.0528
6		.277	.0771	.0754	.0738	.0721	.0704	.0688	.0671	.0655	.0638	.0622	.0605
6	40 ST 40S	.280	.0780	.0763	.0747	.0730	.0713	.0697	.0680	.0663	.0647	.0630	.0614
6		.375	.1064	.1047	.1030	.1012	.0995	.0978	.0961	.0943	.0926	.0909	.0892
6	80 XS 805	.432	.1240	.1222	.1205	.1187	.1169	.1152	.1134	.1116	.1099	.1081	.1064
6		.500	.1455	.1437	.1419	.1401	.1382	.1364	.1346	.1328	.1310	.1292	.1274
6	120	.562	.1657	.1638	.1619	.1600	.1582	.1563	.1545	.1526	.1508	.1489	.1471
6	160	.718	.2187	.2167	.2147	.2127	.2107	.2087	.2067	.2048	.2028	.2008	.1989
6	XX	.864	.2716	.2695	.2674	.2652	.2631	.2610	.2589	.2568	.2547	.2526	.2505
8	5S	.109	.0225	.0213	.0201	.0189	.0177	.0165	.0153	.0141	.0130	.0118	.0106
8	10S	.148	.0307	.0295	.0283	.0271	.0259	.0247	.0235	.0223	.0211	.0199	.0187
8		.158	.0328	.0316	.0304	.0292	.0280	.0268	.0256	.0244	.0232	.0220	.0208
8		.165	.0343	.0331	.0319	.0306	.0294	.0282	.0270	.0258	.0246	.0234	.0222
8		.188	.0392	.0380	.0367	.0355	.0343	.0331	.0319	.0307	.0295	.0283	.0271
8		.203	.0424	.0412	.0400	.0387	.0375	.0363	.0351	.0339	.0326	.0314	.0302
8		.219	.0459	.0446	.0434	.0422	.0409	.0397	.0385	.0373	.0360	.0348	.0336
8		.238	.0500	.0487	.0475	.0463	.0450	.0438	.0426	.0413	.0401	.0389	.0377
8	20	.250	.0526	.0513	.0501	.0489	.0476	.0464	.0452	.0439	.0427	.0415	.0402
8	30	.277	.0585	.0572	.0560	.0547	.0535	.0522	.0510	.0498	.0485	.0473	.0460
8	40 ST 40S	.322	.0685	.0672	.0659	.0647	.0634	.0621	.0609	.0596	.0583	.0571	.0558
8		.344	.0734	.0721	.0708	.0695	.0683	.0670	.0657	.0645	.0632	.0619	.0607
8		.352	.0752	.0739	.0726	.0713	.0701	.0688	.0675	.0662	.0650	.0637	.0624
8		.375	.0804	.0791	.0778	.0765	.0752	.0739	.0726	.0714	.0701	.0688	.0675

Table 7-4
Continued

NOMINAL PIPE SIZE	SCHEDULE NUMBER AND/OR WEIGHT	WALL THICK-NESS	CORROSION ALLOWANCE-INCHES Y=0.7										
			0.000	0.005	0.010	0.015	0.020	0.025	0.030	0.035	0.040	0.045	0.050
8	60	.406	.0874	.0861	.0848	.0835	.0822	.0809	.0796	.0783	.0770	.0758	.0745
8		.469	.1020	.1006	.0993	.0980	.0966	.0953	.0940	.0927	.0914	.0901	.0888
8	80 XS 80S	.500	.1092	.1079	.1065	.1052	.1038	.1025	.1012	.0999	.0985	.0972	.0959
8	100	.593	.1314	.1300	.1286	.1272	.1259	.1245	.1231	.1218	.1204	.1190	.1177
8		.625	.1392	.1378	.1364	.1350	.1336	.1322	.1308	.1295	.1281	.1267	.1253
8	120	.718	.1622	.1608	.1594	.1579	.1565	.1551	.1536	.1522	.1508	.1494	.1480
8	140	.812	.1862	.1848	.1833	.1818	.1803	.1789	.1774	.1759	.1745	.1730	.1716
8	XX	.875	.2027	.2012	.1997	.1982	.1967	.1952	.1937	.1922	.1907	.1892	.1878
8	160	.906	.2110	.2094	.2079	.2064	.2049	.2034	.2019	.2004	.1988	.1973	.1958
10	5S	.134	.0222	.0212	.0202	.0193	.0183	.0174	.0164	.0155	.0145	.0136	.0126
10	10S	.165	.0274	.0264	.0254	.0245	.0235	.0226	.0216	.0206	.0197	.0187	.0178
10		.188	.0313	.0303	.0293	.0284	.0274	.0264	.0255	.0245	.0235	.0226	.0216
10		.203	.0338	.0329	.0319	.0309	.0299	.0290	.0280	.0270	.0261	.0251	.0241
10		.219	.0366	.0356	.0346	.0336	.0327	.0317	.0307	.0297	.0288	.0278	.0268
10	20	.250	.0419	.0409	.0399	.0389	.0380	.0370	.0360	.0350	.0340	.0331	.0321
10		.279	.0469	.0459	.0449	.0439	.0430	.0420	.0410	.0400	.0390	.0380	.0371
10	30	.307	.0518	.0508	.0498	.0488	.0478	.0468	.0458	.0448	.0438	.0429	.0419
10		.348	.0590	.0580	.0570	.0560	.0550	.0540	.0530	.0520	.0510	.0500	.0490
10	40 ST 40S	.365	.0620	.0610	.0600	.0590	.0580	.0570	.0559	.0549	.0539	.0529	.0519
10		.395	.0673	.0663	.0653	.0643	.0633	.0623	.0612	.0602	.0592	.0582	.0572
10	60 XS 80S	.500	.0863	.0853	.0842	.0832	.0821	.0811	.0801	.0790	.0780	.0770	.0759
10		.531	.0920	.0910	.0899	.0889	.0878	.0868	.0857	.0847	.0836	.0826	.0815
10	80	.593	.1035	.1025	.1014	.1003	.0993	.0982	.0971	.0961	.0950	.0940	.0929
10	100	.718	.1273	.1262	.1251	.1240	.1229	.1218	.1207	.1196	.1185	.1174	.1163
10		.750	.1335	.1324	.1313	.1302	.1291	.1280	.1269	.1258	.1247	.1236	.1225
10	120	.843	.1518	.1507	.1495	.1484	.1473	.1461	.1450	.1439	.1428	.1416	.1405
10	140	1.000	.1837	.1825	.1814	.1802	.1790	.1778	.1766	.1755	.1743	.1731	.1720
10		1.062	.1967	.1955	.1943	.1931	.1919	.1907	.1895	.1883	.1871	.1859	.1847
10	160	1.125	.2101	.2088	.2076	.2064	.2052	.2040	.2028	.2015	.2003	.1991	.1979
12	5S	.156	.0217	.0209	.0201	.0193	.0185	.0177	.0169	.0161	.0153	.0145	.0137
12	10S	.180	.0251	.0243	.0235	.0227	.0219	.0211	.0203	.0195	.0187	.0179	.0171
12		.203	.0284	.0276	.0268	.0260	.0252	.0243	.0235	.0227	.0219	.0211	.0203
12		.219	.0307	.0299	.0291	.0283	.0274	.0266	.0258	.0250	.0242	.0234	.0226
12		.238	.0334	.0326	.0318	.0310	.0302	.0293	.0285	.0277	.0269	.0261	.0253
12	20	.250	.0352	.0343	.0335	.0327	.0319	.0311	.0302	.0294	.0286	.0278	.0270
12		.279	.0393	.0385	.0377	.0369	.0360	.0352	.0344	.0336	.0328	.0319	.0311

Table 7-4
Continued

NOMINAL PIPE SIZE	SCHEDULE NUMBER AND/OR WEIGHT	WALL THICKNESS	CORROSION ALLOWANCE-INCHES Y=0.7										
			0.000	0.005	0.010	0.015	0.020	0.025	0.030	0.035	0.040	0.045	0.050
12		.300	.0424	.0416	.0407	.0399	.0391	.0383	.0374	.0366	.0358	.0350	.0341
12	30	.330	.0468	.0459	.0451	.0443	.0434	.0426	.0418	.0409	.0401	.0393	.0385
12		.344	.0488	.0480	.0472	.0463	.0455	.0446	.0438	.0430	.0421	.0413	.0405
12	ST 40S	.375	.0534	.0526	.0517	.0509	.0500	.0492	.0483	.0475	.0467	.0458	.0450
12	40	.406	.0580	.0571	.0563	.0554	.0546	.0538	.0529	.0521	.0512	.0504	.0495
12		.438	.0628	.0619	.0611	.0602	.0593	.0585	.0576	.0568	.0560	.0551	.0543
12	XS 80S	.500	.0721	.0712	.0704	.0695	.0686	.0678	.0669	.0661	.0652	.0643	.0635
12	60	.562	.0815	.0807	.0798	.0789	.0780	.0772	.0763	.0754	.0746	.0737	.0728
12		.625	.0913	.0904	.0895	.0886	.0877	.0868	.0860	.0851	.0842	.0833	.0824
12	80	.687	.1010	.1001	.0992	.0983	.0974	.0965	.0956	.0947	.0938	.0929	.0920
12	100	.843	.1259	.1250	.1240	.1231	.1222	.1213	.1204	.1194	.1185	.1176	.1167
12		.875	.1311	.1302	.1293	.1283	.1274	.1265	.1255	.1246	.1237	.1228	.1218
12	120	1.000	.1518	.1509	.1499	.1490	.1480	.1471	.1461	.1452	.1442	.1433	.1423
12	140	1.125	.1731	.1721	.1712	.1702	.1692	.1682	.1672	.1663	.1653	.1643	.1633
12		1.219	.1895	.1885	.1875	.1865	.1855	.1845	.1835	.1825	.1815	.1805	.1795
12	160	1.312	.2061	.2050	.2040	.2030	.2020	.2009	.1999	.1989	.1979	.1969	.1958
14		.188	.0239	.0232	.0224	.0217	.0209	.0202	.0195	.0187	.0180	.0173	.0165
14		.220	.0280	.0273	.0266	.0258	.0251	.0243	.0236	.0229	.0221	.0214	.0207
14		.238	.0304	.0296	.0289	.0282	.0274	.0267	.0259	.0252	.0244	.0237	.0230
14	10	.250	.0319	.0312	.0305	.0297	.0290	.0282	.0275	.0267	.0260	.0253	.0245
14	20	.312	.0401	.0393	.0386	.0378	.0371	.0363	.0356	.0348	.0341	.0333	.0326
14	30ST	.375	.0485	.0477	.0469	.0462	.0454	.0447	.0439	.0431	.0424	.0416	.0409
14		.406	.0526	.0519	.0511	.0503	.0496	.0488	.0480	.0473	.0465	.0457	.0450
14	40	.438	.0569	.0562	.0554	.0546	.0538	.0531	.0523	.0515	.0508	.0500	.0492
14		.469	.0611	.0604	.0596	.0588	.0580	.0573	.0565	.0557	.0549	.0542	.0534
14	XS	.500	.0654	.0646	.0638	.0630	.0622	.0615	.0607	.0599	.0591	.0584	.0576
14	60	.593	.0782	.0774	.0766	.0758	.0750	.0742	.0734	.0726	.0719	.0711	.0703
14		.625	.0826	.0818	.0810	.0803	.0795	.0787	.0779	.0771	.0763	.0755	.0747
14		.656	.0870	.0862	.0854	.0846	.0838	.0830	.0822	.0814	.0806	.0798	.0790
14	80	.750	.1003	.0995	.0987	.0979	.0971	.0963	.0954	.0946	.0938	.0930	.0922
14	100	.937	.1276	.1267	.1259	.1250	.1242	.1234	.1225	.1217	.1208	.1200	.1192
14	120	1.093	.1511	.1502	.1493	.1485	.1476	.1467	.1459	.1450	.1441	.1433	.1424
14	140	1.250	.1754	.1745	.1736	.1727	.1718	.1709	.1701	.1692	.1683	.1674	.1665
14		1.344	.1904	.1895	.1886	.1876	.1867	.1858	.1849	.1840	.1831	.1822	.1813
14	160	1.406	.2004	.1995	.1985	.1976	.1967	.1958	.1949	.1939	.1930	.1921	.1912
16		.188	.0209	.0202	.0196	.0189	.0183	.0177	.0170	.0164	.0157	.0151	.0145

Table 7-4
Continued

NOMINAL PIPE SIZE	SCHEDULE NUMBER AND/OR WEIGHT	WALL THICKNESS	CORROSION ALLOWANCE-INCHES Y=0.7										
			0.000	0.005	0.010	0.015	0.020	0.025	0.030	0.035	0.040	0.045	0.050
16		.238	.0265	.0259	.0252	.0246	.0239	.0233	.0226	.0220	.0213	.0207	.0201
16	10	.250	.0279	.0272	.0266	.0259	.0253	.0246	.0240	.0233	.0227	.0221	.0214
16		.281	.0314	.0308	.0301	.0295	.0288	.0282	.0275	.0269	.0262	.0256	.0249
16	20	.312	.0350	.0343	.0336	.0330	.0323	.0317	.0310	.0304	.0297	.0291	.0284
16		.344	.0386	.0380	.0373	.0367	.0360	.0354	.0347	.0340	.0334	.0327	.0321
16	30 ST	.375	.0422	.0416	.0409	.0402	.0396	.0389	.0383	.0376	.0369	.0363	.0356
16		.406	.0458	.0452	.0445	.0438	.0432	.0425	.0418	.0412	.0405	.0399	.0392
16		.438	.0496	.0489	.0482	.0476	.0469	.0462	.0456	.0449	.0442	.0436	.0429
16		.469	.0532	.0525	.0519	.0512	.0505	.0499	.0492	.0485	.0478	.0472	.0465
16	40 XS	.500	.0569	.0562	.0555	.0548	.0542	.0535	.0528	.0521	.0515	.0508	.0501
16		.531	.0605	.0599	.0592	.0585	.0578	.0572	.0565	.0558	.0551	.0545	.0538
16	60	.656	.0755	.0749	.0742	.0735	.0728	.0721	.0714	.0707	.0700	.0693	.0686
16		.688	.0794	.0787	.0780	.0773	.0767	.0760	.0753	.0746	.0739	.0732	.0725
16		.750	.0870	.0863	.0856	.0849	.0842	.0835	.0828	.0821	.0814	.0807	.0800
16	80	.843	.0986	.0979	.0971	.0964	.0957	.0950	.0943	.0936	.0929	.0922	.0915
16	100	1.031	.1224	.1217	.1210	.1202	.1195	.1188	.1180	.1173	.1166	.1158	.1151
16	120	1.218	.1469	.1462	.1454	.1446	.1439	.1431	.1424	.1416	.1409	.1401	.1394
16	140	1.438	.1767	.1760	.1752	.1744	.1736	.1728	.1720	.1712	.1705	.1697	.1689
16		1.500	.1853	.1846	.1838	.1830	.1822	.1814	.1806	.1798	.1790	.1782	.1774
16	160	1.593	.1984	.1976	.1968	.1960	.1952	.1944	.1936	.1928	.1920	.1912	.1904
18	10	.250	.0247	.0242	.0236	.0230	.0224	.0219	.0213	.0207	.0201	.0196	.0190
18	20	.312	.0310	.0304	.0298	.0293	.0287	.0281	.0275	.0269	.0264	.0258	.0252
18	ST	.375	.0374	.0368	.0362	.0357	.0351	.0345	.0339	.0333	.0327	.0322	.0316
18	30	.438	.0439	.0433	.0427	.0421	.0415	.0409	.0404	.0398	.0392	.0386	.0380
18	XS	.500	.0503	.0497	.0491	.0485	.0479	.0474	.0468	.0462	.0456	.0450	.0444
18	40	.562	.0568	.0562	.0556	.0550	.0544	.0538	.0532	.0526	.0520	.0514	.0508
18		.594	.0602	.0596	.0590	.0584	.0578	.0572	.0566	.0560	.0554	.0548	.0542
18		.625	.0635	.0629	.0623	.0616	.0610	.0604	.0598	.0592	.0586	.0580	.0574
18		.719	.0735	.0729	.0723	.0717	.0710	.0704	.0698	.0692	.0686	.0680	.0674
18	60	.750	.0768	.0762	.0756	.0750	.0744	.0738	.0731	.0725	.0719	.0713	.0707
18		.812	.0836	.0829	.0823	.0817	.0811	.0805	.0798	.0792	.0786	.0780	.0774
18	80	.937	.0973	.0967	.0960	.0954	.0948	.0941	.0935	.0929	.0922	.0916	.0910
18	100	1.156	.1220	.1213	.1207	.1200	.1194	.1187	.1181	.1174	.1168	.1161	.1155
18	120	1.375	.1475	.1468	.1461	.1455	.1448	.1441	.1434	.1428	.1421	.1414	.1407
18	140	1.562	.1699	.1692	.1685	.1678	.1671	.1665	.1658	.1651	.1644	.1637	.1630
18		1.688	.1854	.1847	.1840	.1833	.1826	.1819	.1812	.1805	.1798	.1791	.1784

Table 7-4
Continued

NOMINAL PIPE SIZE	SCHEDULE NUMBER AND/OR WEIGHT	WALL THICKNESS	CORROSION ALLOWANCE-INCHES										Y=0.7
			0.000	0.005	0.010	0.015	0.020	0.025	0.030	0.035	0.040	0.045	0.050
18	160	1.781	.1970	.1963	.1956	.1949	.1942	.1934	.1927	.1920	.1913	.1906	.1899
20	10	.250	.0222	.0217	.0212	.0207	.0202	.0196	.0191	.0186	.0181	.0176	.0171
20		.312	.0278	.0273	.0268	.0263	.0258	.0252	.0247	.0242	.0237	.0232	.0227
20	20 ST	.375	.0336	.0331	.0325	.0320	.0315	.0310	.0304	.0299	.0294	.0289	.0284
20		.438	.0394	.0389	.0383	.0378	.0373	.0367	.0362	.0357	.0352	.0346	.0341
20	30 XS	.500	.0451	.0446	.0441	.0435	.0430	.0425	.0419	.0414	.0409	.0404	.0398
20		.562	.0509	.0504	.0499	.0493	.0488	.0483	.0477	.0472	.0467	.0461	.0456
20	40	.593	.0538	.0533	.0528	.0522	.0517	.0512	.0506	.0501	.0495	.0490	.0485
20		.625	.0569	.0563	.0558	.0552	.0547	.0542	.0536	.0531	.0526	.0520	.0515
20	60	.812	.0748	.0742	.0737	.0731	.0726	.0720	.0715	.0709	.0704	.0698	.0693
20		.875	.0809	.0803	.0798	.0792	.0787	.0781	.0776	.0770	.0764	.0759	.0753
20		.906	.0839	.0834	.0828	.0823	.0817	.0811	.0806	.0800	.0795	.0789	.0783
20	80	1.031	.0963	.0957	.0952	.0946	.0940	.0935	.0929	.0923	.0917	.0912	.0906
20		1.250	.1184	.1179	.1173	.1167	.1161	.1155	.1149	.1143	.1138	.1132	.1126
20	100	1.281	.1216	.1210	.1205	.1199	.1193	.1187	.1181	.1175	.1169	.1163	.1158
20	120	1.500	.1445	.1439	.1433	.1427	.1421	.1415	.1409	.1403	.1397	.1391	.1385
20	140	1.750	.1715	.1709	.1703	.1696	.1690	.1684	.1678	.1671	.1665	.1659	.1653
20		1.844	.1819	.1813	.1806	.1800	.1794	.1787	.1781	.1775	.1768	.1762	.1756
20	160	1.968	.1958	.1952	.1945	.1939	.1932	.1926	.1919	.1913	.1906	.1900	.1894
22	LG	.250	.0202	.0197	.0192	.0188	.0183	.0178	.0174	.0169	.0164	.0160	.0155
22	ST	.375	.0305	.0300	.0295	.0290	.0286	.0281	.0276	.0272	.0267	.0262	.0257
22	XS	.500	.0409	.0404	.0400	.0395	.0390	.0385	.0380	.0376	.0371	.0366	.0361
24	10	.250	.0185	.0180	.0176	.0172	.0168	.0163	.0159	.0155	.0151	.0146	.0142
24		.312	.0231	.0227	.0223	.0218	.0214	.0210	.0205	.0201	.0197	.0193	.0188
24	20 ST	.375	.0279	.0274	.0270	.0266	.0261	.0257	.0253	.0249	.0244	.0240	.0236
24		.438	.0327	.0322	.0318	.0314	.0309	.0305	.0301	.0296	.0292	.0288	.0283
24	XS	.500	.0374	.0370	.0365	.0361	.0357	.0352	.0348	.0343	.0339	.0335	.0330
24	30	.562	.0422	.0417	.0413	.0409	.0404	.0400	.0395	.0391	.0387	.0382	.0378
24		.625	.0471	.0466	.0462	.0457	.0453	.0449	.0444	.0440	.0435	.0431	.0426
24	40	.687	.0519	.0515	.0510	.0506	.0501	.0497	.0492	.0488	.0483	.0479	.0475
24		.750	.0569	.0564	.0560	.0555	.0551	.0546	.0542	.0537	.0533	.0528	.0524
24	60	.968	.0743	.0738	.0733	.0729	.0724	.0720	.0715	.0710	.0706	.0701	.0697
24		1.031	.0794	.0789	.0784	.0780	.0775	.0770	.0766	.0761	.0756	.0752	.0747
24	80	1.218	.0947	.0942	.0938	.0933	.0928	.0923	.0919	.0914	.0909	.0904	.0900
24	100	1.531	.1211	.1206	.1201	.1196	.1191	.1187	.1182	.1177	.1172	.1167	.1162

Table 7-4
Continued

NOMINAL PIPE SIZE	SCHEDULE NUMBER AND/OR WEIGHT	WALL THICKNESS	CORROSION ALLOWANCE-INCHES Y=0.7										
			0.000	0.005	0.010	0.015	0.020	0.025	0.030	0.035	0.040	0.045	0.050
24	120	1.812	.1456	.1451	.1446	.1441	.1436	.1431	.1426	.1421	.1416	.1411	.1405
24	140	2.062	.1680	.1675	.1670	.1665	.1660	.1654	.1649	.1644	.1639	.1634	.1629
24		2.188	.1796	.1791	.1785	.1780	.1775	.1770	.1764	.1759	.1754	.1749	.1743
24	160	2.343	.1941	.1935	.1930	.1924	.1919	.1914	.1908	.1903	.1898	.1892	.1887
26	ST	.375	.0257	.0253	.0249	.0245	.0241	.0237	.0233	.0229	.0225	.0221	.0217
26	XS	.500	.0345	.0341	.0337	.0333	.0329	.0325	.0320	.0316	.0312	.0308	.0304
30	10	.312	.0184	.0181	.0178	.0174	.0171	.0167	.0164	.0160	.0157	.0154	.0150
30	ST	.375	.0222	.0219	.0215	.0212	.0208	.0205	.0202	.0198	.0195	.0191	.0188
30		.438	.0260	.0257	.0253	.0250	.0246	.0243	.0239	.0236	.0233	.0229	.0226
30	20 XS	.500	.0298	.0294	.0291	.0287	.0284	.0280	.0277	.0273	.0270	.0267	.0263
30		.562	.0336	.0332	.0329	.0325	.0322	.0318	.0315	.0311	.0308	.0304	.0301
30	30	.625	.0374	.0371	.0367	.0364	.0360	.0357	.0353	.0350	.0346	.0343	.0339
34	ST	.375	.0196	.0193	.0190	.0187	.0184	.0181	.0178	.0175	.0172	.0169	.0165
34	XS	.500	.0262	.0259	.0256	.0253	.0250	.0247	.0244	.0241	.0238	.0235	.0232
36	ST	.375	.0185	.0182	.0179	.0176	.0173	.0170	.0168	.0165	.0162	.0159	.0156
36	XS	.500	.0247	.0244	.0242	.0239	.0236	.0233	.0230	.0227	.0224	.0221	.0219
42	ST	.375	.0158	.0156	.0153	.0151	.0148	.0146	.0143	.0141	.0139	.0136	.0134
42	XS	.500	.0211	.0209	.0207	.0204	.0202	.0199	.0197	.0194	.0192	.0189	.0187
48	ST	.375	.0138	.0136	.0134	.0132	.0130	.0127	.0125	.0123	.0121	.0119	.0117
48	XS	.500	.0185	.0183	.0180	.0178	.0176	.0174	.0172	.0170	.0168	.0165	.0163

Table 7-4
Continued

NOMINAL PIPE SIZE	SCHEDULE NUMBER AND/OR WEIGHT	WALL THICKNESS	CORROSION ALLOWANCE-INCHES									Y=0.7
			0.055	0.060	0.065	0.070	0.075	0.080	0.085	0.90	0.095	0.100
1/8	10S	.049	0.0000									
1/8	40 ST 40S	.068	.0226									
1/8	80 ST 80S	.095	.1538	.1241	.0955	.0679	.0413	.0156				
1/4	10S	.065	.0070									
1/4	40 ST 40S	.088	.0864	.0659	.0459	.0264	.0074					
1/4	80 ST 80S	.119	.2085	.1845	.1613	.1387	.1167	.0953	.0745	.0543	.0346	.0154
3/8	10S	.065	.0056									
3/8	40 ST 40S	.091	.0769	.0606	.0447	.0291	.0138					
3/8	80 ST 80S	.126	.1849	.1662	.1480	.1301	.1127	.0956	.0789	.0626	.0467	.0310
1/2	10S	.083	.0432	.0307	.0184	.0063						
1/2	40 ST 40S	.109	.1031	.0895	.0762	.0631	.0502	.0376	.0251	.0129	.0009	
1/2	80 ST 80S	.147	.1998	.1845	.1695	.1547	.1402	.1260	.1120	.0983	.0848	.0716
1/2	160	.187	.3158	.2982	.2810	.2641	.2476	.2314	.2154	.1998	.1845	.1695
1/2	XX	.294	.7264	.6997	.6736	.6481	.6232	.5990	.5753	.5521	.5295	.5074
3/4	5S	.065	.0036									
3/4	10S	.083	.0344	.0245	.0147	.0050						
3/4	40S	.113	.0888	.0781	.0676	.0572	.0470	.0369	.0269	.0171	.0074	
3/4	80S	.154	.1700	.1581	.1465	.1350	.1237	.1125	.1015	.0906	.0800	.0694
3/4		.188	.2442	.2313	.2185	.2059	.1936	.1814	.1694	.1576	.1459	.1344
3/4	160	.218	.3157	.3016	.2878	.2741	.2607	.2475	.2345	.2217	.2091	.1967
3/4	XX	.308	.5722	.5537	.5356	.5177	.5002	.4830	.4661	.4495	.4332	.4171
1	5S	.065	.0029									
1	10S	.109	.0642	.0559	.0477	.0397	.0317	.0238	.0160	.0082	.0006	
1	40 ST 40S	.133	.0999	.0912	.0827	.0742	.0658	.0576	.0494	.0413	.0333	.0253
1	80 ST 80S	.179	.1733	.1638	.1544	.1451	.1360	.1269	.1179	.1091	.1003	.0916
1		.219	.2432	.2328	.2226	.2125	.2025	.1927	.1829	.1733	.1638	.1544
1	160	.250	.3016	.2906	.2796	.2688	.2581	.2476	.2372	.2269	.2168	.2067
1	XXO	.358	.5417	.5274	.5132	.4993	.4855	.4720	.4586	.4454	.4324	.4196
11/4	5S	.065	.0023									
11/4	10S	.109	.0504	.0439	.0376	.0312	.0250	.0188	.0126	.0065	.0005	
11/4	40 ST 40S	.140	.0862	.0795	.0728	.0662	.0596	.0531	.0467	.0403	.0339	.0276
11/4	80 ST 80S	.191	.1492	.1419	.1346	.1275	.1203	.1133	.1063	.0994	.0925	.0857
11/4	160	.250	.2289	.2208	.2128	.2049	.1971	.1893	.1816	.1740	.1665	.1590
11/4	XX	.382	.4401	.4298	.4197	.4097	.3998	.3899	.3802	.3706	.3611	.3517

Table 7-4
Continued

NOMINAL PIPE SIZE	SCHEDULE NUMBER AND/OR WEIGHT	WALL THICKNESS	CORROSION ALLOWANCE-INCHES									Y=0.7
			0.055	0.060	0.065	0.070	0.075	0.080	0.085	0.90	0.095	0.100
11/2	5S	.065	.0020									
11/2	10S	.109	.0438	.0382	.0327	.0272	.0218	.0164	.0110	.0057	.0004	
11/2	40 ST 40S	.145	.0799	.0740	.0682	.0625	.0568	.0511	.0455	.0399	.0344	.0289
11/2	80 ST 80S	.200	.1386	.1323	.1260	.1198	.1136	.1075	.1015	.0955	.0895	.0836
11/2	160	.281	.2338	.2267	.2197	.2127	.2058	.1989	.1921	.1854	.1787	.1720
11/2	XX	.400	.3968	.3882	.3797	.3714	.3630	.3548	.3466	.3385	.3305	.3226
2	5S	.065	.0016									
2	10S	.109	.0348	.0304	.0260	.0217	.0174	.0131	.0088	.0045	.0003	
2	40 ST 40S	.154	.0705	.0658	.0613	.0567	.0522	.0476	.0432	.0387	.0343	.0299
2		.167	.0811	.0764	.0717	.0671	.0625	.0579	.0534	.0489	.0444	.0399
2		.188	.0986	.0938	.0890	.0843	.0796	.0749	.0702	.0656	.0610	.0565
2	80 ST 80S	.218	.1243	.1193	.1144	.1095	.1046	.0998	.0950	.0902	.0855	.0807
2		.250	.1526	.1475	.1424	.1373	.1323	.1272	.1223	.1173	.1124	.1075
2		.312	.2106	.2051	.1996	.1942	.1888	.1834	.1780	.1727	.1675	.1622
2	160	.343	.2413	.2356	.2299	.2242	.2186	.2130	.2075	.2020	.1965	.1911
2	XX	.436	.3405	.3340	.3277	.3213	.3150	.3088	.3026	.2964	.2903	.2842
21/2	5S	.083	.0124	.0088	.0053	.0018						
21/2	10S	.120	.0357	.0320	.0284	.0248	.0212	.0176	.0140	.0105	.0070	.0035
21/2	40 ST 40S	.203	.0907	.0868	.0829	.0790	.0751	.0713	.0675	.0637	.0599	.0561
21/2		.217	.1004	.0964	.0925	.0886	.0846	.0808	.0769	.0730	.0692	.0654
21/2	80 ST 805	.276	.1427	.1385	.1343	.1302	.1260	.1219	.1179	.1138	.1097	.1057
21/2	160	.375	.2191	.2145	.2099	.2054	.2008	.1963	.1918	.1874	.1829	.1785
21/2	XX	.552	.3761	.3706	.3651	.3596	.3542	.3488	.3434	.3381	.3328	.3275
3	5S	.083	.0101	.0073	.0044	.0015						
3	10S	.120	.0292	.0262	.0232	.0203	.0174	.0144	.0115	.0086	.0057	.0029
3		.125	.0318	.0288	.0258	.0229	.0199	.0170	.0141	.0112	.0083	.0054
3		.148	.0439	.0408	.0378	.0348	.0318	.0289	.0259	.0229	.0200	.0171
3		.188	.0654	.0623	.0592	.0561	.0530	.0500	.0469	.0439	.0408	.0378
3	40 ST 40S	.216	.0809	.0777	.0746	.0714	.0683	.0651	.0620	.0589	.0558	.0527
3		.241	.0950	.0918	.0885	.0853	.0821	.0789	.0757	.0726	.0694	.0663
3		.254	.1024	.0991	.0959	.0926	.0894	.0862	.0830	.0798	.0766	.0734
3		.289	.1228	.1194	.1161	.1127	.1094	.1061	.1028	.0996	.0963	.0930
3	80 XS 805	.300	.1293	.1259	.1225	.1192	.1158	.1125	.1092	.1059	.1026	.0993
3		.312	.1365	.1331	.1296	.1263	.1229	.1195	.1162	.1128	.1095	.1062
3		.406	.1950	.1913	.1876	.1840	.1804	.1767	.1731	.1696	.1660	.1624

Table 7-4
Continued

NOMINAL PIPE SIZE	SCHEDULE NUMBER AND/OR WEIGHT	WALL THICKNESS	CORROSION ALLOWANCE-INCHES									Y=0.7
			0.055	0.060	0.065	0.070	0.075	0.080	0.085	0.90	0.095	0.100
3	160	.438	.2159	.2121	.2084	.2046	.2009	.1972	.1935	.1898	.1862	.1825
3	XX	.600	.3308	.3264	.3221	.3178	.3136	.3094	.3051	.3009	.2968	.2926
31/2	5S	.083	.0089	.0063	.0038	.0013						
31/2	10S	.120	.0254	.0229	.0203	.0177	.0152	.0126	.0101	.0075	.0050	.0025
31/2		.128	.0291	.0265	.0239	.0213	.0187	.0162	.0136	.0111	.0086	.0060
31/2		.134	.0318	.0292	.0266	.0240	.0214	.0189	.0163	.0138	.0112	.0087
31/2		.148	.0382	.0356	.0330	.0304	.0278	.0252	.0226	.0200	.0175	.0149
31/2		.188	.0569	.0542	.0515	.0489	.0462	.0435	.0409	.0382	.0356	.0330
31/2	40 ST 40S	.226	.0751	.0724	.0696	.0669	.0641	.0614	.0587	.0560	.0533	.0506
31/2		.281	.1023	.0994	.0965	.0937	.0909	.0880	.0852	.0824	.0796	.0769
31/2	80 XS 80S	.318	.1211	.1182	.1152	.1123	.1094	.1065	.1036	.1008	.0979	.0951
31/2		.344	.1346	.1316	.1286	.1257	.1227	.1198	.1168	.1139	.1110	.1081
31/2		.469	.2029	.1997	.1964	.1932	.1900	.1868	.1836	.1804	.1773	.1741
31/2		.636	.3041	.3005	.2968	.2932	.2895	.2859	.2823	.2788	.2752	.2717
4	5S	.083	.0079	.0056	.0034	.0012						
4	10S	.120	.0226	.0203	.0180	.0157	.0135	.0112	.0089	.0067	.0045	.0022
4		.128	.0258	.0235	.0212	.0189	.0166	.0144	.0121	.0098	.0076	.0054
4		.134	.0282	.0259	.0236	.0213	.0190	.0167	.0145	.0122	.0100	.0077
4		.142	.0315	.0291	.0268	.0245	.0222	.0199	.0177	.0154	.0131	.0109
4		.165	.0409	.0385	.0362	.0338	.0315	.0292	.0269	.0246	.0223	.0200
4		.188	.0504	.0480	.0456	.0433	.0409	.0386	.0362	.0339	.0316	.0293
4		.205	.0575	.0551	.0527	.0503	.0479	.0456	.0432	.0409	.0385	.0362
4	40 ST40S	.237	.0711	.0686	.0662	.0638	.0614	.0589	.0565	.0541	.0518	.0494
4		.250	.0767	.0742	.0718	.0693	.0669	.0644	.0620	.0596	.0572	.0548
4		.271	.0858	.0833	.0808	.0784	.0759	.0734	.0710	.0685	.0661	.0637
4		.281	.0902	.0877	.0852	.0827	.0802	.0777	.0753	.0728	.0704	.0679
4		.300	.0986	.0961	.0935	.0910	.0885	.0860	.0835	.0810	.0785	.0761
4		.312	.1039	.1014	.0988	.0963	.0938	.0913	.0887	.0862	.0837	.0813
4	80 XS 80S	.337	.1152	.1126	.1100	.1075	.1049	.1023	.0998	.0973	.0947	.0922
4		.375	.1327	.1300	.1274	.1247	.1221	.1195	.1169	.1143	.1117	.1091
4	120	.438	.1625	.1597	.1570	.1543	.1515	.1488	.1461	.1434	.1407	.1381
4		.500	.1930	.1901	.1873	.1844	.1816	.1788	.1760	.1732	.1704	.1676
4	160	.531	.2086	.2057	.2028	.1999	.1971	.1942	.1913	.1885	.1856	.1828
4	XX	.674	.2851	.2819	.2787	.2756	.2724	.2693	.2661	.2630	.2599	.2568
5	5S	.109	.0147	.0128	.0110	.0092	.0074	.0055	.0037	.0019	.0001	
5	10S	.134	.0227	.0209	.0190	.0172	.0154	.0135	.0117	.0099	.0080	.0062

Table 7-4
Continued

NOMINAL PIPE SIZE	SCHEDULE NUMBER AND/OR WEIGHT	WALL THICKNESS	CORROSION ALLOWANCE-INCHES									Y=0.7
			0.055	0.060	0.065	0.070	0.075	0.080	0.085	0.90	0.095	0.100
5	40 ST 40S	.258	.0641	.0622	.0602	.0583	.0563	.0544	.0525	.0505	.0486	.0467
5		.352	.0971	.0951	.0931	.0910	.0890	.0870	.0849	.0829	.0809	.0789
5	80 XS 80S	.375	.1054	.1034	.1013	.0992	.0972	.0951	.0931	.0911	.0890	.0870
5		.438	.1286	.1265	.1244	.1223	.1201	.1180	.1159	.1138	.1117	.1096
5	120	.500	.1522	.1500	.1478	.1456	.1434	.1412	.1391	.1369	.1347	.1326
5	160	.625	.2018	.1995	.1972	.1948	.1925	.1902	.1879	.1856	.1833	.1810
5	XX	.750	.2547	.2522	.2497	.2472	.2448	.2423	.2399	.2374	.2350	.2325
6	5S	.109	.0123	.0108	.0092	.0077	.0062	.0047	.0031	.0016	.0001	
6	10S	.134	.0190	.0175	.0159	.0144	.0129	.0113	.0098	.0083	.0067	.0052
6		.169	.0286	.0270	.0255	.0239	.0223	.0208	.0192	.0177	.0161	.0146
6		.180	.0316	.0301	.0285	.0269	.0253	.0238	.0222	.0207	.0191	.0176
6		.188	.0338	.0323	.0307	.0291	.0275	.0260	.0244	.0229	.0213	.0197
6		.219	.0425	.0409	.0393	.0377	.0361	.0345	.0329	.0314	.0298	.0282
6		.250	.0512	.0496	.0480	.0464	.0448	.0432	.0416	.0400	.0384	.0368
6		.277	.0589	.0573	.0556	.0540	.0524	.0508	.0491	.0475	.0459	.0443
6	40 ST 40S	.280	.0598	.0581	.0565	.0549	.0532	.0516	.0500	.0484	.0468	.0452
6		.375	.0875	.0858	.0841	.0824	.0807	.0791	.0774	.0757	.0740	.0724
6	80 XS 805	.432	.1047	.1029	.1012	.0995	.0977	.0960	.0943	.0926	.0909	.0892
6		.500	.1256	.1238	.1221	.1203	.1185	.1167	.1150	.1132	.1115	.1097
6	120	.562	.1453	.1434	.1416	.1398	.1380	.1361	.1343	.1325	.1307	.1289
6	160	.718	.1969	.1950	.1930	.1911	.1891	.1872	.1853	.1833	.1814	.1795
6	XX	.864	.2484	.2463	.2443	.2422	.2401	.2381	.2360	.2340	.2319	.2299
8	5S	.109	.0094	.0083	.0071	.0059	.0047	.0036	.0024	.0012	.0001	
8	10S	.148	.0175	.0163	.0151	.0139	.0128	.0116	.0104	.0092	.0080	.0069
8		.158	.0196	.0184	.0172	.0160	.0148	.0136	.0125	.0113	.0101	.0089
8		.165	.0210	.0198	.0186	.0175	.0163	.0151	.0139	.0127	.0115	.0104
8		.188	.0259	.0247	.0235	.0223	.0211	.0199	.0187	.0175	.0163	.0151
8		.203	.0290	.0278	.0266	.0254	.0242	.0230	.0218	.0206	.0194	.0182
8		.219	.0324	.0312	.0300	.0288	.0276	.0264	.0252	.0240	.0228	.0216
8		.238	.0364	.0352	.0340	.0328	.0316	.0304	.0292	.0280	.0268	.0256
8	20	.250	.0390	.0378	.0366	.0353	.0341	.0329	.0317	.0305	.0293	.0281
8	30	.277	.0448	.0436	.0423	.0411	.0399	.0387	.0374	.0362	.0350	.0338
8	40 ST 40S	.322	.0546	.0533	.0521	.0508	.0496	.0484	.0471	.0459	.0447	.0434
8		.344	.0594	.0582	.0569	.0557	.0544	.0532	.0519	.0507	.0494	.0482
8		.352	.0612	.0599	.0587	.0574	.0562	.0549	.0537	.0524	.0512	.0499
8		.375	.0663	.0650	.0637	.0625	.0612	.0600	.0587	.0574	.0562	.0549

Table 7-4
Continued

NOMINAL PIPE SIZE	SCHEDULE NUMBER AND/OR WEIGHT	WALL THICKNESS	CORROSION ALLOWANCE-INCHES									Y=0.7
			0.055	0.060	0.065	0.070	0.075	0.080	0.085	0.90	0.095	0.100
8	60	.406	.0732	.0719	.0706	.0694	.0681	.0668	.0655	.0643	.0630	.0617
8		.469	.0875	.0861	.0848	.0835	.0822	.0809	.0797	.0784	.0771	.0758
8	80 XS 80S	.500	.0946	.0933	.0919	.0906	.0893	.0880	.0867	.0854	.0841	.0828
8	100	.593	.1163	.1150	.1136	.1123	.1109	.1096	.1082	.1069	.1056	.1042
8		.625	.1240	.1226	.1212	.1199	.1185	.1171	.1158	.1144	.1131	.1117
8	120	.718	.1466	.1452	.1438	.1423	.1409	.1395	.1382	.1368	.1354	.1340
8	140	.812	.1701	.1686	.1672	.1658	.1643	.1629	.1614	.1600	.1586	.1571
8	XX	.875	.1863	.1848	.1833	.1818	.1804	.1789	.1774	.1760	.1745	.1730
8	160	.906	.1943	.1929	.1914	.1899	.1884	.1869	.1854	.1839	.1825	.1810
10	5S	.134	.0117	.0107	.0098	.0088	.0079	.0070	.0060	.0051	.0042	.0032
10	10S	.165	.0168	.0159	.0149	.0140	.0130	.0121	.0111	.0102	.0092	.0083
10		.188	.0207	.0197	.0188	.0178	.0168	.0159	.0149	.0140	.0130	.0121
10		.203	.0232	.0222	.0213	.0203	.0194	.0184	.0174	.0165	.0155	.0146
10		.219	.0259	.0249	.0240	.0230	.0220	.0211	.0201	.0192	.0182	.0173
10	20	.250	.0311	.0302	.0292	.0282	.0273	.0263	.0253	.0244	.0234	.0224
10		.279	.0361	.0351	.0341	.0331	.0322	.0312	.0302	.0293	.0283	.0273
10	30	.307	.0409	.0399	.0389	.0379	.0370	.0360	.0350	.0340	.0330	.0321
10		.348	.0480	.0470	.0460	.0450	.0440	.0430	.0420	.0411	.0401	.0391
10	40 ST 40S	.365	.0509	.0499	.0489	.0480	.0470	.0460	.0450	.0440	.0430	.0420
10		.395	.0562	.0552	.0542	.0532	.0522	.0512	.0502	.0492	.0482	.0472
10	60 XS 80S	.500	.0749	.0739	.0728	.0718	.0708	.0698	.0687	.0677	.0667	.0657
10		.531	.0805	.0795	.0784	.0774	.0764	.0753	.0743	.0733	.0722	.0712
10	80	.593	.0919	.0908	.0897	.0887	.0876	.0866	.0856	.0845	.0835	.0824
10	100	.718	.1153	.1142	.1131	.1120	.1109	.1098	.1088	.1077	.1066	.1055
10		.750	.1214	.1203	.1192	.1181	.1170	.1159	.1148	.1137	.1127	.1116
10	120	.843	.1394	.1383	.1372	.1360	.1349	.1338	.1327	.1316	.1305	.1294
10	140	1.000	.1708	.1696	.1685	.1673	.1661	.1650	.1638	.1627	.1615	.1604
10		1.062	.1835	.1824	.1812	.1800	.1788	.1776	.1765	.1753	.1741	.1730
10	160	1.125	.1967	.1955	.1943	.1931	.1919	.1907	.1895	.1883	.1871	.1860
12	5S	.156	.0129	.0121	.0113	.0105	.0097	.0089	.0081	.0073	.0065	.0057
12	10S	.180	.0163	.0155	.0147	.0139	.0131	.0123	.0115	.0107	.0099	.0091
12		.203	.0195	.0187	.0179	.0171	.0163	.0155	.0147	.0139	.0131	.0123
12		.219	.0218	.0209	.0201	.0193	.0185	.0177	.0169	.0161	.0153	.0145
12		.238	.0245	.0236	.0228	.0220	.0212	.0204	.0196	.0188	.0180	.0172
12	20	.250	.0262	.0253	.0245	.0237	.0229	.0221	.0213	.0205	.0197	.0189
12		.279	.0303	.0295	.0287	.0278	.0270	.0262	.0254	.0246	.0238	.0230

Table 7-4
Continued

NOMINAL PIPE SIZE	SCHEDULE NUMBER AND/OR WEIGHT	WALL THICKNESS	CORROSION ALLOWANCE-INCHES Y=0.7									
			0.055	0.060	0.065	0.070	0.075	0.080	0.085	0.90	0.095	0.100
12		.300	.0333	.0325	.0317	.0308	.0300	.0292	.0284	.0276	.0268	.0260
12	30	.330	.0376	.0368	.0360	.0352	.0343	.0335	.0327	.0319	.0311	.0302
12		.344	.0397	.0388	.0380	.0372	.0364	.0355	.0347	.0339	.0331	.0322
12	ST 40S	.375	.0442	.0433	.0425	.0417	.0408	.0400	.0392	.0384	.0375	.0367
12	40	.406	.0487	.0479	.0470	.0462	.0454	.0445	.0437	.0429	.0420	.0412
12		.438	.0534	.0526	.0517	.0509	.0500	.0492	.0484	.0475	.0467	.0459
12	XS 80S	.500	.0626	.0618	.0609	.0601	.0592	.0584	.0575	.0567	.0558	.0550
12	60	.562	.0720	.0711	.0702	.0694	.0685	.0676	.0668	.0659	.0651	.0642
12		.625	.0816	.0807	.0798	.0789	.0781	.0772	.0763	.0755	.0746	.0737
12	80	.687	.0911	.0902	.0894	.0885	.0876	.0867	.0858	.0849	.0841	.0832
12	100	.843	.1158	.1148	.1139	.1130	.1121	.1112	.1103	.1094	.1085	.1075
12		.875	.1209	.1200	.1191	.1181	.1172	.1163	.1154	.1145	.1136	.1126
12	120	1.000	.1414	.1404	.1395	.1385	.1376	.1366	.1357	.1348	.1338	.1329
12	140	1.125	.1624	.1614	.1604	.1594	.1585	.1575	.1565	.1556	.1546	.1536
12		1.219	.1785	.1775	.1765	.1755	.1746	.1736	.1726	.1716	.1706	.1696
12	160	1.312	.1948	.1938	.1928	.1918	.1908	.1898	.1888	.1878	.1868	.1858
14		.188	.0158	.0151	.0144	.0136	.0129	.0122	.0114	.0107	.0100	.0093
14		.220	.0199	.0192	.0184	.0177	.0170	.0163	.0155	.0148	.0141	.0133
14		.238	.0222	.0215	.0208	.0200	.0193	.0186	.0178	.0171	.0164	.0156
14	10	.250	.0238	.0230	.0223	.0216	.0208	.0201	.0194	.0186	.0179	.0172
14	20	.312	.0318	.0311	.0303	.0296	.0289	.0281	.0274	.0266	.0259	.0251
14	30ST	.375	.0401	.0394	.0386	.0379	.0371	.0363	.0356	.0348	.0341	.0334
14		.406	.0442	.0435	.0427	.0419	.0412	.0404	.0397	.0389	.0382	.0374
14	40	.438	.0485	.0477	.0470	.0462	.0454	.0447	.0439	.0432	.0424	.0416
14		.469	.0526	.0519	.0511	.0503	.0496	.0488	.0480	.0473	.0465	.0458
14	XS	.500	.0568	.0560	.0553	.0545	.0537	.0530	.0522	.0514	.0507	.0499
14	60	.593	.0695	.0687	.0679	.0671	.0664	.0656	.0648	.0640	.0632	.0625
14		.625	.0739	.0731	.0723	.0715	.0707	.0700	.0692	.0684	.0676	.0668
14		.656	.0782	.0774	.0766	.0758	.0750	.0742	.0734	.0727	.0719	.0711
14	80	.750	.0914	.0906	.0898	.0890	.0882	.0874	.0866	.0857	.0849	.0841
14	100	.937	.1183	.1175	.1166	.1158	.1150	.1141	.1133	.1125	.1116	.1108
14	120	1.093	.1415	.1407	.1398	.1389	.1381	.1372	.1364	.1355	.1347	.1338
14	140	1.250	.1656	.1647	.1638	.1629	.1620	.1612	.1603	.1594	.1585	.1576
14		1.344	.1804	.1795	.1786	.1776	.1767	.1758	.1749	.1740	.1731	.1722
14	160	1.406	.1903	.1893	.1884	.1875	.1866	.1857	.1848	.1839	.1829	.1820
16		.188	.0138	.0132	.0125	.0119	.0113	.0106	.0100	.0094	.0087	.0081

Table 7-4
Continued

NOMINAL PIPE SIZE	SCHEDULE NUMBER AND/OR WEIGHT	WALL THICKNESS	CORROSION ALLOWANCE-INCHES									Y=0.7
			0.055	0.060	0.065	0.070	0.075	0.080	0.085	0.90	0.095	0.100
16		.238	.0194	.0188	.0181	.0175	.0169	.0162	.0156	.0149	.0143	.0137
16	10	.250	.0208	.0201	.0195	.0188	.0182	.0176	.0169	.0163	.0156	.0150
16		.281	.0243	.0236	.0230	.0223	.0217	.0210	.0204	.0198	.0191	.0185
16	20	.312	.0278	.0271	.0265	.0258	.0252	.0245	.0239	.0232	.0226	.0220
16		.344	.0314	.0308	.0301	.0295	.0288	.0282	.0275	.0269	.0262	.0256
16	30 ST	.375	.0350	.0343	.0337	.0330	.0324	.0317	.0311	.0304	.0297	.0291
16		.406	.0385	.0379	.0372	.0366	.0359	.0353	.0346	.0339	.0333	.0326
16		.438	.0422	.0416	.0409	.0403	.0396	.0389	.0383	.0376	.0370	.0363
16		.469	.0458	.0452	.0445	.0439	.0432	.0425	.0419	.0412	.0405	.0399
16	40 XS	.500	.0495	.0488	.0481	.0475	.0468	.0461	.0455	.0448	.0441	.0435
16		.531	.0531	.0524	.0518	.0511	.0504	.0498	.0491	.0484	.0477	.0471
16	60	.656	.0680	.0673	.0666	.0659	.0652	.0645	.0639	.0632	.0625	.0618
16		.688	.0718	.0711	.0704	.0697	.0691	.0684	.0677	.0670	.0663	.0656
16		.750	.0793	.0786	.0779	.0772	.0765	.0759	.0752	.0745	.0738	.0731
16	80	.843	.0907	.0900	.0893	.0886	.0879	.0872	.0865	.0858	.0851	.0844
16	100	1.031	.1144	.1136	.1129	.1122	.1115	.1107	.1100	.1093	.1086	.1078
16	120	1.218	.1386	.1378	.1371	.1363	.1356	.1348	.1341	.1334	.1326	.1319
16	140	1.438	.1681	.1673	.1665	.1658	.1650	.1642	.1634	.1627	.1619	.1611
16		1.500	.1766	.1758	.1750	.1743	.1735	.1727	.1719	.1711	.1703	.1696
16	160	1.593	.1896	.1888	.1880	.1872	.1864	.1856	.1848	.1840	.1832	.1824
18	10	.250	.0184	.0179	.0173	.0167	.0162	.0156	.0150	.0145	.0139	.0133
18	20	.312	.0246	.0241	.0235	.0229	.0223	.0218	.0212	.0206	.0201	.0195
18	ST	.375	.0310	.0304	.0298	.0293	.0287	.0281	.0275	.0270	.0264	.0258
18	30	.438	.0374	.0368	.0363	.0357	.0351	.0345	.0339	.0333	.0328	.0322
18	XS	.500	.0438	.0432	.0426	.0420	.0414	.0409	.0403	.0397	.0391	.0385
18	40	.562	.0502	.0496	.0490	.0485	.0479	.0473	.0467	.0461	.0455	.0449
18		.594	.0536	.0530	.0524	.0518	.0512	.0506	.0500	.0494	.0488	.0482
18		.625	.0568	.0562	.0556	.0550	.0544	.0538	.0532	.0526	.0520	.0514
18		.719	.0668	.0662	.0656	.0649	.0643	.0637	.0631	.0625	.0619	.0613
18	60	.750	.0701	.0695	.0689	.0683	.0676	.0670	.0664	.0658	.0652	.0646
18		.812	.0767	.0761	.0755	.0749	.0743	.0737	.0731	.0724	.0718	.0712
18	80	.937	.0904	.0897	.0891	.0885	.0879	.0872	.0866	.0860	.0854	.0847
18	100	1.156	.1148	.1142	.1135	.1129	.1122	.1116	.1109	.1103	.1096	.1090
18	120	1.375	.1401	.1394	.1387	.1381	.1374	.1367	.1361	.1354	.1347	.1341
18	140	1.562	.1623	.1616	.1609	.1602	.1596	.1589	.1582	.1575	.1568	.1561
18		1.688	.1776	.1769	.1762	.1755	.1748	.1741	.1734	.1727	.1720	.1714

Table 7-4
Continued

NOM-INAL PIPE SIZE	SCHEDULE NUMBER AND/OR WEIGHT	WALL THICK-NESS	CORROSION ALLOWANCE-INCHES									Y=0,7
			0,055	0,060	0,065	0,070	0,075	0,080	0,085	0,90	0,095	0.100
18	160	1,781	.1892	.1884	.1877	.1870	.1863	.1856	.1849	.1842	.1835	.1828
20	10	.250	.0166	.0161	.0155	.0150	.0145	.0140	.0135	.0130	.0125	.0120
20		.312	.0221	.0216	.0211	.0206	.0201	.0196	.0191	.0185	.0180	.0175
20	20 ST	.375	.0278	.0273	.0268	.0263	.0258	.0253	.0247	.0242	.0237	.0232
20		.438	.0336	.0331	.0326	.0320	.0315	.0310	.0305	.0299	.0294	.0289
20	30 XS	.500	.0393	.0388	.0382	.0377	.0372	.0367	.0361	.0356	.0351	.0346
20		.562	.0451	.0445	.0440	.0435	.0429	.0424	.0419	.0413	.0408	.0403
20	40	.593	.0479	.0474	.0469	.0463	.0458	.0453	.0447	.0442	.0437	.0432
20		.625	.0509	.0504	.0499	.0493	.0488	.0483	.0477	.0472	.0467	.0461
20	60	.812	.0687	.0682	.0676	.0671	.0665	.0660	.0654	.0649	.0643	.0638
20		.875	.0748	.0742	.0737	.0731	.0726	.0720	.0715	.0709	.0704	.0698
20		.906	.0778	.0772	.0767	.0761	.0756	.0750	.0745	.0739	.0734	.0728
20	80	1.031	.0901	.0895	.0889	.0884	.0878	.0872	.0867	.0861	.0855	.0850
20		1.250	.1120	.1114	.1109	.1103	.1097	.1091	.1085	.1080	.1074	.1068
20	100	1.281	.1152	.1146	.1140	.1134	.1128	.1123	.1117	.1111	.1105	.1099
20	120	1.500	.1379	.1373	.1367	.1361	.1355	.1349	.1343	.1337	.1331	.1325
20	140	1,750	.1646	.1640	.1634	.1628	.1622	.1615	.1609	.1603	.1597	.1591
20		1.844	.1749	.1743	.1737	.1730	.1724	.1718	.1712	.1705	.1699	.1693
20	160	1.968	.1887	.1881	.1874	.1868	.1862	.1855	.1849	.1842	.1836	.1830
22	LG	.250	.0150	.0146	.0141	.0137	.0132	.0127	.0123	.0118	.0113	.0109
22	ST	.375	.0253	.0248	.0243	.0239	.0234	.0229	.0224	.0220	.0215	.0210
22	XS	.500	.0356	.0352	.0347	.0342	.0337	.0333	.0328	.0323	.0318	.0314
24	10	.250	.0138	.0134	.0129	.0125	.0121	.0117	.0112	.0108	.0104	.0100
24		.312	.0184	.0180	.0175	.0171	.0167	.0163	.0158	.0154	.0150	.0146
24	20 ST	.375	.0231	.0227	.0223	.0218	.0214	.0210	.0206	.0201	.0197	.0193
24		.438	.0279	.0275	.0270	.0266	.0262	.0257	.0253	.0249	.0244	.0240
24	XS	.500	.0326	.0322	.0317	.0313	.0309	.0304	.0300	.0296	.0291	.0287
24	30	.562	.0373	.0369	.0365	.0360	.0356	.0352	.0347	.0343	.0338	.0334
24		.625	.0422	.0418	.0413	.0409	.0404	.0400	.0396	.0391	.0387	.0382
24	40	.687	.0470	.0466	.0461	.0457	.0452	.0448	.0443	.0439	.0435	.0430
24		.750	.0519	.0515	.0510	.0506	.0501	.0497	.0492	.0488	.0484	.0479
24	60	.968	.0692	.0687	.0683	.0678	.0674	.0669	.0665	.0660	.0655	.0651
24		1.031	.0743	.0738	.0733	.0729	.0724	.0720	.0715	.0710	.0706	.0701
24	80	1.218	.0895	.0890	.0886	.0881	.0876	.0872	.0867	.0862	.0858	.0853
24	100	1.531	.1157	.1152	.1148	.1143	.1138	.1133	.1128	.1123	.1118	.1114

Table 7-4
Continued

NOMINAL PIPE SIZE	SCHEDULE NUMBER AND/OR WEIGHT	WALL THICKNESS	CORROSION ALLOWANCE-INCHES									Y=0.7
			0.055	0.060	0.065	0.070	0.075	0.080	0.085	0.90	0.095	0.100
24	120	1.812	.1400	.1395	.1390	.1385	.1380	.1375	.1370	.1365	.1360	.1355
24	140	2.062	.1623	.1618	.1613	.1608	.1603	.1598	.1592	.1587	.1582	.1577
24		2.188	.1738	.1733	.1728	.1722	.1717	.1712	.1707	.1702	.1696	.1691
24	160	2.343	.1882	.1876	.1871	.1866	.1860	.1855	.1850	.1844	.1839	.1834
26	ST	.375	.0213	.0209	.0205	.0201	.0197	.0193	.0190	.0186	.0182	.0178
26	XS	.500	.0300	.0296	.0292	.0288	.0284	.0280	.0276	.0272	.0268	.0264
30	10	.312	.0147	.0143	.0140	.0137	.0133	.0130	.0126	.0123	.0120	.0116
30	ST	.375	.0184	.0181	.0178	.0174	.0171	.0167	.0164	.0161	.0157	.0154
30		.438	.0222	.0219	.0215	.0212	.0208	.0205	.0202	.0198	.0195	.0191
30	20 XS	.500	.0260	.0256	.0253	.0249	.0246	.0242	.0239	.0235	.0232	.0229
30		.562	.0297	.0294	.0290	.0287	.0283	.0280	.0276	.0273	.0269	.0266
30	30	.625	.0336	.0332	.0329	.0325	.0322	.0318	.0315	.0311	.0308	.0304
34	ST	.375	.0162	.0159	.0156	.0153	.0150	.0147	.0144	.0141	.0138	.0135
34	XS	.500	.0229	.0226	.0223	.0219	.0216	.0213	.0210	.0207	.0204	.0201
36	ST	.375	.0153	.0151	.0148	.0145	.0142	.0139	.0136	.0134	.0131	.0128
36	XS	.500	.0216	.0213	.0210	.0207	.0204	.0201	.0199	.0196	.0193	.0190
42	ST	.375	.0131	.0129	.0126	.0124	.0122	.0119	.0117	.0114	.0112	.0109
42	XS	.500	.0184	.0182	.0180	.0177	.0175	.0172	.0170	.0167	.0165	.0163
48	ST	.375	.0115	.0113	.0110	.0108	.0106	.0104	.0102	.0100	.0098	.0096
48	XS	.500	.0161	.0159	.0157	.0155	.0153	.0151	.0148	.0146	.0144	.0142

Tables are presented for four values of y:

$y = 0$	(Barlow)	(Table 7-1)
$y = 0.4$	(Modified lame)	(Table 7-2)
$y = 0.5$	(Average diameter)	(Table 7-3)
$y = 0.7$	(Creep)	(Table 7-4)

Instructions and Examples

Example 1: Determining Allowable Working Pressure

Determine the maximum allowable working pressure in accordance with the ASME Boiler and Pressure Vessel Code, Section VIII Division 1, 1977, for a 10-in., schedule 80 steam line, A106 Grade B materials, operating at 750°F.

Solution:

1. List known information about the pipe.

Size:	10-in. nom. (10.750 O.D.)
Weight (or schedule no.):	Schedule 80
Wall thickness $= 7/8\ t_{nom}$:	.593 nom. (.518 min.)
Material:	A106 Grade B
Code section:	ASME, Section VIII Division 1, 1983
Operating temperature:	750°F
Corrosion allowance:	0 (The 1983 ASME Code formula does not include allowance for corrosion, therefore, it is the responsibility of the designer to adjust the wall thickness where corrosive conditions exist.)

2. Obtain from 1983 ASME Code the allowable stress:

$S = 12{,}900$ psi

3. The following two solutions can be used to determine the maximum allowable working pressure permissible.

- Using the design formula from the ASME Code, Section VIII, Division 1, 1983, and the symbol definitions contained therein:

$$P = \frac{S\,E\,t}{R + 0.6t}$$

$S = 12{,}900$ psi

$E = 1.00$ (See the 1983 ASME Code on joint efficiencies)

$t = t_{min}$ .518 in.

$R =$ Inside radius or $\frac{D_o}{2} - t_{min}$

$$P = \frac{(12{,}900)\ (1)\ (.518)}{4.857 + (.6)\ (.518)}$$

$$P = \frac{6{,}682}{5.167} = 1{,}293 \text{ psi}$$

- A simpler, quicker method is to obtain the applicable P/S ratio from the pressure/stress ratio table listing $Y = 0.4$ (Table 7-2).

Note: In the ASME Code, Section VIII, 1983, formula:

$$R = \frac{D_o}{2} - t_{min}$$

$$\text{thus } P = \frac{S\,E\,t}{R + 0.6t}$$

$$P/S = \frac{E\,t}{R + 0.6t}$$

$$E = 1.0$$

$$P/S = \frac{t}{\frac{D_o}{2} - t + 0.6t}$$

$$P/S = \frac{2t}{D_o - 2t + 1.2t}$$

$$P/S = \frac{2t}{D_o - 0.8t}$$

thus, y in the basic ASME formula

$$P/S = \frac{2\ (t_m - A)}{D - 2y\ (t_m - A)}$$

must equal 0.4

With the allowable stress(s) obtained from the ASME Code, Section VIII, Division 1, 1983, (12,900 psi) and the P/S ratio obtained from Table 7-2 (.1004)

$$P = S \times P/S$$

$$P = 12{,}900 \times .1004 = 1{,}295 \text{ psi}$$

Example 2: Determining Stress or Required Yield Strength

Determine the stress or required yield strength in accordance with the ANSI Code B31.8, 1982, on gas transmission and distribution piping systems for a 12-in., schedule 60, gas line, A106 Grade B materials, operating at 1,100 psi at 250°F.

Solutions:

1. List known information about the pipe:

Size:	12 in. nom. (12,750 O.D.)
Weight (or schedule no.):	Schedule 60
Wall thickness:	.562 nom.
Material:	A106 Grade B
Code section:	ANSI Code B31.8, 1982
Operating temperature:	250°F
Operating pressure, P:	1,100 psi
Corrosion allowance:	0

2. Obtain from the Code section on gas transmission:

Minimum yield strength	= 35,000 psi
Y factor	= 0
Design factor (F) for Type C construction	= 0.5

The following two solutions can be used to find the stress or required yield strength.

- Using the design formula from the ANSI Code B31.8, 1982, and the symbol definitions contained therein:

$$P = \frac{2ST}{D} \times F \times E \times T$$

$$S = \frac{P\,D}{2tFET}$$

$P = 1{,}100$

$D = 12.75$

$t_{(nom)} = .562$

$F = .5$

$E = 1.0$

$T = 1.0$

$$S = \frac{(1{,}100)\ (12.75)}{(2)\ (.562)\ (.5)\ (1)\ (1)}$$

$$S = \frac{14{,}025}{.562} = 24{,}955 \text{ psi}$$

Since the stress or required yield strength of 24,955 psi is less than the minimum yield strength of 35,000 psi for A106 Grade B pipe, the pipe correctly meets Code requirements.

- A simpler, quicker method is to obtain from Table 7-1 where y = 0, the applicable P/S ratio, and then multiply to determine the stress or required yield strength.

P/S ratio = .0771

Because we are using a construction factor of .5 from the ANSI Code B31.8 and because this Code is based on nominal wall, we must use the .5 factor and an 8/7 factor in the following formula along with our P/S ratio.

S = P − P/S (8/7) (.5)

S = 1,100 − .0771 (8/7) (.5) = 24,967 psi

Example 3: Determining Wall Thickness Required

In accordance with the ANSI Code B31.1.0, 1983, for power piping, determine the pipe wall thickness required for a 6-in. steam line, A106 Grade B pipe, operating at 900 psi at 750°F at maximum allowable stress, with a corrosion allowance of .050 in.

Solutions:

1. List known information about the pipe:

Size:	6 in. (6.625 O.D.)
Material:	A106 Grade B
Code section:	ANSI Code B31.1.0, 1983
Operating temperature:	750°F
Operating pressure, P:	900 psi
Corrosion allowance, C:	.050

2. Obtain from the ANSI Code section on power piping (1983) the allowable stress:

S = 13,000 psi
y factor = 0.4

The following two solutions can be used to find the required wall thickness.

- Using the design formula from ANSI Code B31.1.0 and the symbol definitions contained therein:

$$t_m = \frac{P\,D_o}{2(SE + Py)} + A$$

$P = 900$

$D_o = 6.625$

$S = 13,000$

$E = 1.0$

$y = .4$

$A = 0$

$$t_m = \frac{(900)\,(6.625)}{2\,[13,000 + (900)\,(.4)]}$$

$$t_m = \frac{5,962.5}{26,720} = .223$$

The nominal wall, T_{nom}, is equal to .223 − 87½% .223 × 8/7 = .254. Because the ANSI Code B31.1.0 design formula makes no allowance for corrosion and/or erosion, the corrosion allowance determined by the designer must be added to the nominal wall calculated. Therefore T_{nom} = .254 + .050 = .304.

Then, refer to Chapter 10 "Properties of Pipe" to determine the next thicker commercially available pipe, which is schedule 60, having a nominal wall thickness of .375.

- A simpler, quicker method is to calculate the minimum required P/S ratio by dividing P by S:

P/S = 900 = 13,000 = .0692

Using Table 7-2 (where y = 0.4) across from the 6-in. nominal pipe size under the column for .050 in. corrosion allowance, pick the pipe wall thickness having a P/S ratio equal to or greater than that just calculated. This value is .0869. Therefore, t_{nom} = .375 based on a P/S ratio of .0869 as shown in the table should be used.

Note: Interpolation: For values of C and y intermediate to those shown in the tables, linear interpolation may be used.

Note: Special calculations: Only the three most important uses for the P/S values have been illustrated. Those who would like to examine all of the uses are reminded that the tables may be employed to indicate the effect of operating temperature, corrosion allowance, material, and pipe size.

Branch Reinforcement

The various ANSI piping codes give formulae for the reinforcement of nozzle openings in two respects:

1. The *pressure* area cut by the opening must be replaced by reinforcing the area within a prescribed zone around the opening.
2. The welds which attach the reinforcement to the pipe must meet certain (essentially shear strength) requirements. The Petroleum Refinery Piping Code B31.3 (1980) gives detailed requirements in Section 304.3.3. The Power Piping Code B31.1 (1983) refers to Section 104.3.1 for a detailed description of this nozzle reinforcement design and calculation. For convenience, reprinted here is ANSI Code B31.3, Section 304.3.3 in Figure 7-1.

Section 304.3.3 of the ANSI Code B31.3—Reinforcement of Welded-Branch Connections

Additional reinforcement is required when it is not provided inherently in the components of the branch connection. This paragraph gives rules governing the pressure design of such branch connections for cases where the angle between the axes of the branch and of the run is between 45 and 90 degrees, inclusive.

Notation

The notations described below are used in the pressure design of branch connections. The notations are illustrated in Figure 7-2. Note the use of subscripts b for branch and h for run. Note also that Figure 7-1 does not indicate details for construction or welding.

B = Angle between axes of branch and run, degrees
b = Subscript referring to branch
c = Corrosion allowance, in.
D_o = Outside diameter of pipe, in.
d_1 = Actual corroded length removed from run pipe, in.
= $[D_{ob} - 2(T_b - c)]/\sin B$
= d_1 or $[T_b - c) + (T_h - c) + d_1/^2]$ whichever is greater, but in any case not more than D_{oh}
h = Subscript referring to run or header
L_4 = Altitude of reinforcement zone outside of run pipe, in.
= $2.5\ (\bar{T}_h - c)$ or $2.5\ (T_b - c) + t_e$, whichever is lesser
t_e = Nominal thickness of reinforcing ring or saddle, in.
T = Actual thickness of pipe, in. (by actual measurement, or minimum thickness permissible under purchase specification)
$\bar{T}$ = Nominal thickness of pipe, in.
t = Pressure design thickness of pipe according to the appropriate wall thickness equation or procedure in 304.1 in. When the branch does not intersect the longitudinal weld of the run, the stress value for seamless pipe, of comparable grade, may be used in determining t for the purpose of reinforcement calculation only. When the branch does intersect the longitudinal weld of the run, the weld joint factor of the run shall enter the calculation. When the branch contains a weld, the weld joint factor of the branch shall enter the calculation.

Required Area

The quantity $(t_h d_1)\ (2 - \sin B)$ is known as the required area; in the case of right-angle nozzles, the required area becomes $t_h d_1$ square inches. The branch connection must be designed so that the reinforcement area defined in 304.3.3 (c) is not less than the required area.

Reinforcement Area

The reinforcement area shall be the sum of the following two areas.

1. The area lying within the reinforcement zone [defined in 304.3.3 (d)] resulting from any excess thickness available in the main run pipe wall and branch pipe wall over that required by the proper wall thickness equations, i.e., the thicknesses $T_h - t_h - c$ and $T_b - t_b - c$ multiplied by appropriate lengths. Any line having a thickness greater than that required for corrosion allowance and for pressure and other loading considerations will occasionally be in service until the excess thickness is also corroded away. If this is the basis of the design, the excess thickness cannot be used for reinforcement of pipe-to-pipe branch connections.
2. The area of all other metal within the reinforcement zone (defined in Section 304.3.3 (d)) provided by weld and other reinforcement metal properly attached to the run of branch. In computing areas of weld metal deposits, the minimum dimensions required shall be used unless a definite procedure is employed to instruct the welder to provide specific larger dimensions, in which case the latter dimensions may be used in calculations.

Portions of the reinforcement area may be composed of materials other than those of the main run pipe, but if the allowable stress of these materials is less than that for the

BRANCH REINFORCEMENT

304.1.2 Straight Pipe Under Internal Pressure

(a) For metallic pipe, the internal pressure design thickness (t) shall be not less than calculated by the following Equation 3, if t is less than $D_o/4$:

$$t = \frac{PD_o}{2(SE + PY)} \text{ or } t = \frac{Pd}{2(SE + PY\text{-}P)} \ldots\ldots (3)$$

Table 304.1.1
Values of Y for Ferrous Materials

Temperature Degree °F	900 & Below	950	1000	1050	1100	1150 & Above
Ferritic Steels	0.4	0.5	0.7	0.7	0.7	0.7
Austenitic Steels	0.4	0.4	0.4	0.4	0.5	0.7

DESIGN CONDITIONS: .... psig .... °F

	HEADER		BRANCH	
Nominal Size				
Outside Diameter	D_{oh}		D_{ob}	
Nominal Wall	$\bar{T}_h$		$\bar{T}_b$	
Actual or min. Wall	T_h		T_b	
Material Spec. ASTM				
Allowable Stress	S_h		S_b	
Joint Efficiency	E_h		E_b	
Y Coefficient	Y_h		Y_b	
Mech./Corr. Allow.	C_h		C_b	
Intersection Angle	β		β	

REQUIRED THICKNESS OF HEADER AND BRANCH:

$$t_h = \frac{PD_oh}{2S_hE_h + 2YhP} = \frac{\ldots\ldots\ldots \times \ldots\ldots\ldots}{2 \times \ldots\ldots\ldots \times \ldots\ldots\ldots + 2 \times \ldots\ldots\ldots \times \ldots\ldots\ldots} = \ldots\ldots\ldots$$

$$t_b = \frac{PD_cb}{2S_bE_b + 2Y_bP} = \frac{\ldots\ldots\ldots \times \ldots\ldots\ldots}{2 \times \ldots\ldots\ldots \times \ldots\ldots\ldots + 2 \times \ldots\ldots\ldots \times \ldots\ldots\ldots} = \ldots\ldots\ldots$$

LIMITS OF REINFORCEMENT:

$$d_1 = \frac{D_ob - 2(T_b - C_b)}{\sin\beta} = \frac{\ldots\ldots\ldots - 2 \times (\ldots\ldots\ldots - \ldots\ldots\ldots)}{\ldots\ldots\ldots} = \ldots\ldots\ldots$$

$d_2 = d_1$ or $= (T_b - C_b) + (T_h - C_h) + 0.5d_1 = (\ldots\ldots\ldots - \ldots\ldots\ldots) + (\ldots\ldots\ldots - \ldots\ldots\ldots) + 0.5 \times \ldots\ldots\ldots = \ldots\ldots\ldots$

Select larger of the values, but not to exceed D_{oh} $d_2 = \ldots\ldots\ldots$

$L_4 = 2.5(\bar{T}_h - C_h) = 2.5(\ldots\ldots\ldots - \ldots\ldots\ldots)$ or $= 2.5(\bar{T}_b - C_b) + t_e = 2.5(\ldots\ldots\ldots - \ldots\ldots\ldots) + \ldots\ldots\ldots$

Select lesser of the values ($t_e = 0$ if pad or saddle is not used) $L_4 = \ldots\ldots\ldots$

REQUIRED AND AVAILABLE REINFORCEMENT AREA:

Area $= t_hd_1 = \ldots\ldots\ldots \times \ldots\ldots\ldots = \ldots\ldots\ldots$ sq. in. required.

$A_1 = (2d_2 - d_1)(T_h - t_h - C_h) = (2 \times \ldots\ldots\ldots - \ldots\ldots\ldots)(\ldots\ldots\ldots - \ldots\ldots\ldots - \ldots\ldots\ldots) = \ldots\ldots\ldots$

$A_2 = 2L_4(T_b - t_b - C_b) = 2 \times \ldots\ldots\ldots(\ldots\ldots\ldots - \ldots\ldots\ldots - \ldots\ldots\ldots) = \ldots\ldots\ldots$

$A_3 = t_f^2 = (\ldots\ldots\ldots)^2 = \ldots\ldots\ldots$

$A_1 + A_2 + A_3 = \ldots\ldots\ldots + \ldots\ldots\ldots + \ldots\ldots\ldots = \ldots\ldots\ldots$ sq. in. available.

Area A $- (A_1 + A_2 + A_3) = \ldots\ldots\ldots - \ldots\ldots\ldots = \ldots\ldots\ldots$ sq. in. of area in pad required - A_4

$A_4 \div 2 =$ sq. in. of pad on each side of nozzle $= \ldots\ldots\ldots \div 2 = \ldots\ldots\ldots$

$$\frac{A_4 \div 2}{t_e} = L = \ldots\ldots\ldots \div \ldots\ldots\ldots = \ldots\ldots\ldots$$

QED use pad $t_e = \ldots\ldots\ldots \times L = \ldots\ldots\ldots$

Figure 7-1. Reproduction of ANSI/ASME Code B31.3, Section 304.3.3 giving detailed requirements for branch reinforcement.

main run pipe, the corresponding calculated area must be reduced in the ratio of the allowable stress values before being counted toward the reinforcement area. No additional credit shall be taken for materials having higher allowable stress values than for the main run pipe.

Reinforcement Zone

The reinforcement zone is a parallelogram whose length shall extend a distance d_2 on each side of the centerline of the branch pipe and whose width shall start at the inside surface of the main run pipe (in its corroded condition) and extend to the distance L_4 from the outside surface of the main run pipe measured perpendicular to this outside surface. (See Section 304.3.3(c) (1)).

Sample Calculations for Branch Reinforcement

Example 7-1

An NPS 8 run (header) in an oil piping system has an NPS 5 branch at right angles (Figure 7-3). Both pipes are Schedule 40 API 5L Grade A seamless. The design conditions are 300 psig at 400°F. The fillet welds at the crotch are minimum size in accordance with Section 327.4.4. A corrosion allowance of 0.10 in. is specified. Is additional reinforcement necessary?

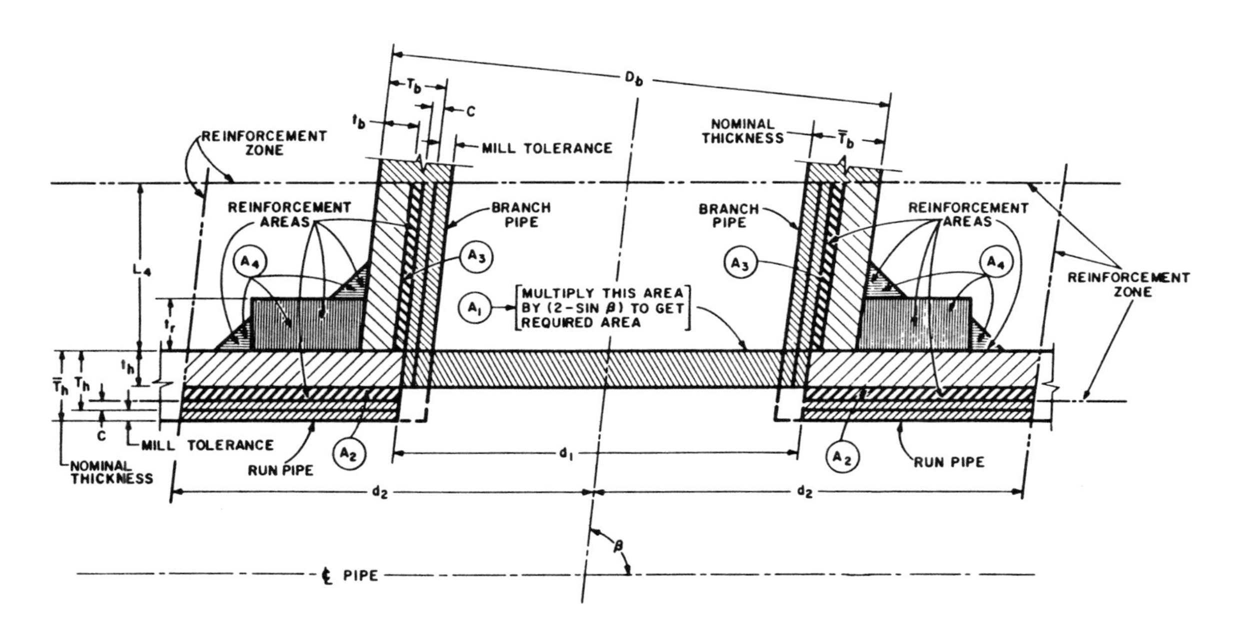

Figure 7-2. This figure illustrates the nomenclature used in ANSI Code B31.3, Section 304.3.3, 1980. It does not indicate complete welding details or a preferred method of construction. (Reprinted courtesy of the American Society of Mechanical Engineers.)

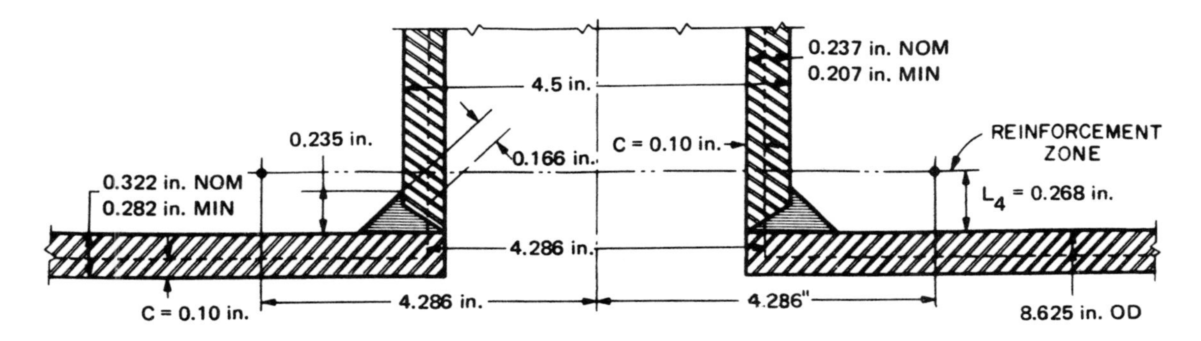

Figure 7-3. Figure of branch reinforcement for use in Example 7-1.

Solution

$SE = 16.0$ ksi.
$T_h = (0.322)\ (0.875) = 0.282$ in.
$T_b = (0.237)\ (0.875) = 0.207$ in.
$L_4 = 2.5(0.282 - 0.1) = 0.455$ in., or
$2.5(0.207 - 0.1) + 0 = 0.268$ in., whichever is less
$L_4 = 0.268$ in.
$d_1 = [4.5 - 2(0.207 - 0.1)]/\sin(90°) = 4.286$ in.

$$d_2 = (0.207 - 0.1) + (0.282 - 0.1) + \frac{4.286}{2}$$

$= 2.432$ in. or d_1, whichever is greater
$d_2 = 4.286$ in.

$$t_h = \frac{(300)\ (8.625)}{(2)\ (16{,}000) + (2)\ (0.4)\ (300)} = 0.080 \text{ in.}$$

$$t_b = \frac{(300)\ (4.500)}{(2)\ (16{,}000) + (2)\ (0.4)\ (300)} = 0.042 \text{ in.}$$

$t_c = 0.7\ (0.237) = 0.166$ in., or
$= 0.25$, whichever is less
$t_c = 0.166$ in.

$$\text{Minimum leg dimension of fillet weld} = \frac{0.166}{0.707} = 0.235 \text{ in.}$$

Thus, the required area, $A_1 = (0.080)\ (4.286)\ [2 - \sin(90°)] = 0.343$ sq. in.

The reinforcement area:
In run wall; $A_2 = (4.286)\ (0.282 - 0.08 - 0.10) = 0.437$ sq in.
In branch wall, $A_3 = (2)\ (0.268)\ [(0.207 - 0.042) - 0.10] = 0.035$ sq in.
In branch welds, $A_4 = (2)\ (1/2)\ (0.235)^2 = 0.055$ sq in.
The total reinforcement area $= 0.527$ sq in.

This is more than 0.343 sq in. so that no additional reinforcement is required to sustain the internal pressure.

8

Design Criteria for Allowable Loads, Moments, and Stresses

Design Criteria for Pumps with Steel Nozzles and Casings

API Code 610: Steel Pump Force, Moment, and Stress Limitations

The following criteria apply for pumps with 12-in. discharge nozzles or smaller. The forces contained herein are considered minimum criteria and should be adjusted where the vendor has experimental or test data permitting larger reactions. The vendor must submit comparable criteria for pump cases constructed of cast iron.

Suction and discharge nozzles should be designed to withstand forces and moments from the thermal expansion or contraction of piping. Piping reactions should be computed in conformance with ANSI Code B31.1 or ANSI Code B31.3 for pressure piping and should be designed within the limiting criteria set by this standard. The modulus of elasticity must be adjusted for the operating temperature condition.

Each nozzle should be capable of withstanding double the forces and amounts listed in Table 8-1 applied simulta-

Table 8-1
Nozzle Loadings

Force/Moment	Nominal Size of Nozzle Flange (in.) ≤ 2	3	4	6	8	10	12	14[b]	16[b]
Each top nozzle									
F_x	160	240	320	560	850	1,200	1,500	1,600	1,900
F_y (compression)	200	300	400	700	1,100	1,500	1,800	2,000	2,300
F_y (tension)	100	150	200	350	530	750	920	1,000	1,200
F_z	130	200	260	460	700	1,000	1,200	1,300	1,500
Each side nozzle									
F_x	160	240	320	560	850	1,200	1,500	1,600	1,900
F_y	130	200	260	460	700	1,000	1,200	1,300	1,500
F_z	200	300	400	700	1,100	1,500	1,800	2,000	2,300
Each end nozzle									
F_x	200	300	400	700	1,100	1,500	1,800	2,000	2,300
F_y	130	200	260	460	700	1,000	1,200	1,300	1,500
F_z	160	240	320	560	850	1,200	1,500	1,600	1,900
Each nozzle									
M_x	340	700	980	1,700	2,600	3,700	4,500	4,700	5,400
M_y	260	530	740	1,300	1,900	2,800	3,400	3,500	4,000
M_z	170	350	500	870	1,300	1,800	2,200	2,300	2,700

F = Force, lb
M = Moment ft-lb
x = Axis parallel to shaft
y = Vertical 90° to shaft
z = Horizontal 90° to shaft

Reproduced from Centrifugal Pumps for General Refinery Services, *Sixth Edition, 1981, Standard 610 Table 2. Reprinted courtesy of the American Petroleum Institute.*

neously to the pump through each nozzle, in addition to internal pressure, without causing an internal rub or adversely affecting the operation of the pumps or seal.

The baseplate and pedestal support assembly should be adequate to limit the shaft displacement, when measured at the coupling, to a maximum of 0.005 in. in any direction when subjected to the loads shown in Table 8-1. These loads represent the total effect of all external mechanical forces that may be applied to a fully grouted pump base. They are to be applied to the pump through the suction and/or discharge nozzle (see Figure 8-1):

For purposes of evaluating computed piping-imposed external moments and forces, these forces be transferred from both suction and discharge flanges to the intersection of the X, Y, and Z axes. An algebraic summation should then be made for comparison with the moment limitation just given. The vendor should submit alternative criteria for pumps larger than 12 in.

Because a particular nozzle on a pump will not always be subjected to the maximum allowable resultant force and moment simultaneously, an increase in either the resultant applied force or the resultant applied moment may be made if the following limitations can be satisfied at that nozzle:

$$(F_a/F_r) + (M_a/M_r) \leqslant 2, \quad F_a/F_r \leqslant 2, \text{ and } M_a/M_r \leqslant C$$

where
- C = 2, for nozzles 6 in. and smaller
- C = $(D + 6)/D$, for nozzles 8 in. and larger
- M_a = resultant applied moment at the nozzle, ft-lb
- F_a = resultant applied force at the nozzle, lb
- M_r = resultant moment (from Table 8-2), ft-lb
- F_r = resultant force (from Table 8-2) lb
- D = nominal diameter of nozzle flange, in.

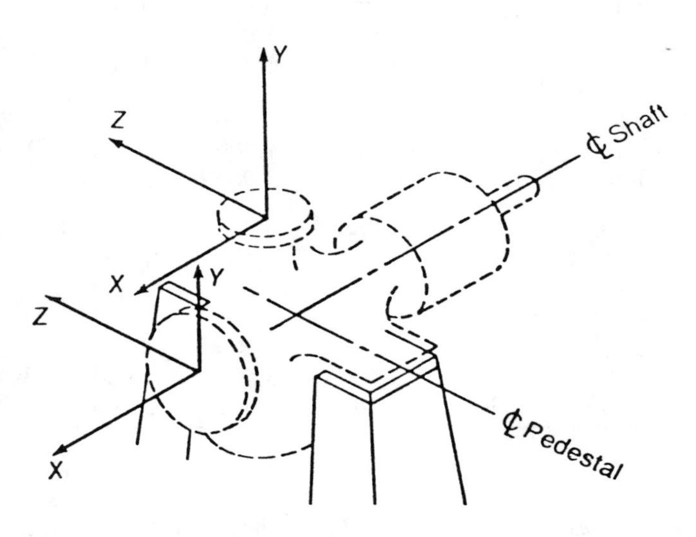

Figure 8-1. Pump coordinate system.

The resultant applied force or moment may be increased up to double the values in Table 8-2 if the maximum combined limit on the installed equipment is not exceeded. This limit is determined by the summation of the forces and moments from Table 8-2 on both nozzles simultaneously, taken about a point defined by the intersection of the axis of the shaft and the centerline of the pedestals.

For heavy-duty baseplates the total applied resultant forces and moments on the suction and discharge nozzles should not be more than twice the equivalent of those given in Table 8-1. For applied resultant forces and moments that are greater than these, allowable values shall be mutually agreed upon by the purchaser and the vendor.

Design Criteria for Pumps with Cast Iron or Aluminum Nozzles and Casings

Aluminum Pump Force, Moment, and Stress Limitations

The following criteria apply for pumps with 4-in. or smaller discharge nozzles (suction nozzles may be larger). The forces contained herein are considered minimum criteria and should be adjusted where the vendor has experimental or test data permitting larger reactions.

Suction and discharge nozzles should be designed to withstand forces and moments from the thermal expansion or contraction of piping. Piping reactions shall be computed in conformance with the petroleum refinery piping code for pressure piping ANSI Code B31.3, Section 319, and should be designed within the limiting criteria set by this standard. The modulus of elasticity should be adjusted for the operating temperature condition.

Table 8-2
Suggested Allowable Resultant Forces and Moments (For Vendor's Standard Baseplates)

Resultant Force/Moment	Nominal Size of Nozzle Flange (in.) 2	3	4	6	8	10	12[a]
F_r	430	640	860	1,500	2,300	2,700	2,900
M_r	690	1,400	2,000	3,500	5,200	6,600	8,200

Each nozzle should be capable of withstanding forces from external piping determined by the following formulas:

- Suction nozzles:

$F_{rs} \leqslant 1.6w \leqslant 50D$

- Discharge nozzles:

$F_{rd} \leqslant (2w - F_{rs}) \leqslant 50D$

- Top suction and top discharge nozzles are further limited by:

F_{rs} and $F_{rd} = (F_x^2 + F_z^2)^{1/2}$

and for suction nozzles

$F_{xs} \leqslant 1.3w \leqslant 40D$
F_{ys} (in compression) $\leqslant 1.2w \leqslant 50D$
F_{ys} (in tension) $\leqslant 25D$
$F_{zs} \leqslant w \leqslant 35D$

and for discharge nozzles

$F_{xd} \leqslant (1.8w \pm F_{xs}) \leqslant 40D$
F_{yd} (in compression) $\leqslant (2w \pm F_{ys}) \leqslant 50D$
F_{yd} (in tension) $\leqslant 0.5w < 25D$
$F_{zd} \leqslant (w \pm F_{zs}) \leqslant 35D$

- End suction and top discharge pumps are further limited by:

$F_{rs} = (F_{zs}^2 + F_{ys}^2)^{1/2}$

and

$F_{rd} = (F_{xd}^2 + F_{zd}^2)^{1/2}$

and for suction nozzles

$F_{xs} \leqslant 1.2w \leqslant 50D$
$F_{ys} \leqslant 0.6w \leqslant 35D$
$F_{zs} \leqslant w \leqslant 40D$

and for discharge nozzles

$F_{xd} \leqslant (1.8w \pm F_{xs}) \leqslant 40D$
F_{yd} (in compression) $\leqslant 2w \pm F_{ys} \leqslant 50D$
F_{yd} (in tension) $\leqslant 0.5w \leqslant 25D$
$F_{zd} \leqslant (w \pm F_{zs}) \leqslant 35D$

Limit tension and compression forces to 500 lb

where F = Force, lb
r = Resultant of forces
x = Axis parallel to shaft
y = Vertical 90° to shaft
z = Horizontal 90° to shaft
W = Weight of pump only, lb
D = Diameter, nominal diameter
d = Discharge or exhaust
S = Suction or intake

F_r is the resultant shear force in the plane of any specific flange face.

Each suction and discharge nozzle should be designed to withstand the forces described for the specific configuration. Unit stresses in each nozzle should be limited to: one-third of the allowable hot stresses for pipe sizes $\leqslant 4$ in.; one-half of the allowable hot stresses for pipe sizes > 4 in.; as shown in ANSI Codes B31.1 and B31.3.

The baseplate and pedestal support assembly on pumps having a discharge nozzle of 4 in. should be adequate to limit the shaft displacement, when measured at the coupling, to a maximum of 0.005 in. in any direction when subjected to the following loads. These loads represent the total effect of all external mechanical forces that may be applied to a fully grouted pump base. They are to be applied to the pump through the suction and/or discharge nozzle.

$M_x = 3.0\ W^*$ ft-lb
$M_y = 2.0\ W^*$ ft-lb
$M_z = 1.5\ W^*$ ft-lb
M_x = Moment in Y-Z plane
M_y = Moment in X-Z plane
M_z = Moment in X-Y plane
W = Weight of pump only, lb

For purpose of evaluating computed piping-imposed external moments and forces, they should be transferred from both suction and discharge flanges to the intersection of the X, Y and Z axes. An algebraic summation should then be made for comparison with the moment limitation just given.

The vendor must submit alternative criteria for pumps having a discharge flange of 4 in. NPS. It is suggested that these criteria be developed as a result of tests.

* Minimum W is 500 lb in these computations.

Design Criteria for Turbine Drivers with Steel Nozzles and Casings

Steel Turbines Force, Moment, and Stress Limitations

At the operating temperature, using the hot modulus "E," resultant bending moments are permissible up to a value that would cause a bending stress of $S_h/4$ in a connection having a section modulus equal to the connecting piping for the same size where the connection is 4 in. IPS or larger. On smaller size connections a stress of $S_h/3$ is permitted. (S_h is as defined by ANSI Code B31.1 or ANSI Code B31.3 (current issue) for the material of construction.)

The resultant shear force at the face of the flange and any individual component may not exceed 2,000 lb. The resultant forces and individual components are limited further as follows:

- Individual components:

$$F_x \leqslant 1.3w \leqslant 160D$$
$$F_y \leqslant .6w \leqslant 130D$$
$$F_z \leqslant w \leqslant 160D$$

- Resultant components:

Algebraic summation of $F_{rx} \leqslant 1.6w$
Algebraic summation of $F_{ry} \leqslant w$
Algebraic summation of $F_{rz} \leqslant 1.6w$

- Combined resultant:

$$(F_{rx})^2 + F_{ry}{}^2 + F_{rz}{}^2)^{1/2} \leqslant 2w$$

Use up to 100% cold spring and satisfy the operating condition only.

The total resultant force and total resultant moment imposed on the turbine at any connection must not exceed the following:

$$F = \frac{(500D_c - M)}{3}$$

where F = Resultant force (lb), including pressure forces where unrestrained expansion joints are used at the connection, except on vertical exhausts

M = Resultant moment, ft-lb

D_o = Pipe size of the connection (IPS) up to 8 in. in diameter. For sizes greater than this use $D_c = (16 + \text{IPS})/3$ in.

The combined resultants of the forces and moments of the inlets, extraction, and exhaust connections, resolved at the centerlines of the exhaust connection and shaft must not exceed the following two conditions:

$$F_r = \frac{(250\ D_r - M_r)}{2}$$

where F_r = Combined resultant of inlet, extraction, and exhaust forces, lb

M_r = Combined resultant of inlet, extraction, and exhaust moments and moments resulting from forces, ft-lb

D_r = Diameter (in.) of a circular opening equal to the total areas of the inlet, extraction and exhaust openings up to a value of 9 in. in diameter. For values beyond this, use $D_r = (18 + \text{equivalent diameter})/3$ in.

Components of these resultants should not exceed:

$$F_{rx} \leqslant 50\ D_r,\ M_{xr} \leqslant 250D_r$$
$$F_{yr} \leqslant 125\ D_r,\ M_{yr} \leqslant 125D_r$$
$$F_{zr} \leqslant 100\ D_r,\ M_{zr} \leqslant 125D_r$$

Vertical Exhaust Connection

For installation of turbines with a vertical exhaust and an unrestrained expansion joint at the exhaust, an additional amount of force caused by pressure loading is allowed. (The additional force referred to is perpendicular to the face of the exhaust flange and central.) For this type of application, calculate the vertical force component on the exhaust connection, excluding pressure loading, and compare with the value of 1/6 the pressure loading on the exhaust. Use the larger of these two numbers for a vertical force component on exhaust connections in making the calculations just outlined.

The force caused by the pressure loading on the exhaust is allowed in addition to the values established by the preceding up to a maximum value of vertical force (lb) on the exhaust connection (including pressure loading) of 15½ times the exhaust area (in.^{2}).

These values of allowable force and moment pertain to the turbine structure only. They do not pertain to the forces and moments in the connecting piping, flange, and flange bolting that should not exceed the allowable stress as defined by applicable codes and regulatory bodies. (See Figure 8-2.)

Design Criteria for Turbine Drivers with Cast Iron or Aluminum Nozzles and Casings

Cast Iron or Aluminum Turbine Force, Moment and Stress Limitations

At the operating temperature, using the hot modulus "E," resultant bending moments are permissible up to a value which would cause a bending stress of $S_h/4$ in a connection having a section modulus equal to the connecting piping for the same size where the connection is 4 in. IPS or larger. On smaller size connections a stress of $S_h/3$ is permitted. (S_h is as defined by ANSI Code B31.1 or ANSI Code B31.3 (current issue) for the material of construction.)

The resultant shear force at the face of the flange and any individual component should not exceed 500 lb. The resultant forces and individual components will be limited further as follows:

- Individual components:

$$F_x \leqslant 1.3w \leqslant 40D$$
$$F_y \leqslant .6w \leqslant 35D$$
$$F_z \leqslant w \leqslant 40D$$

- Resultant components:

Algebraic summation of $F_{rx} \leqslant 1.6w$
Algebraic summation of $F_{ry} \leqslant w$
Algebraic summation of $F_{rz} \leqslant 1.6w$

- Combined resultant:

$$(F_{rx}^2 + F_{ry}^2 + F_{rz}^2)^{1/2} \leqslant 2w$$

Use cold spring, but comply to these limitations in both operating and installed conditions.

The total resultant force and total resultant moment imposed on the turbine at any connection must not exceed the following:

$$F \leqslant \frac{(500D_c - M)}{3}$$

where F = Resultant force (lb), including pressure forces where unrestrained expansion joints are used at the connection, except on vertical exhausts
M = Resultant moment, ft-lb
D_c = Pipe size of the connection (IPS) up to an 8-in. diameter. For sizes greater than this use a $D_c = (16 + \text{IPS})/3$ in.

The combined resultants of the forces and moments of the inlet, extraction, and exhaust connections, resolved at the centerlines of the exhaust connections must not exceed the following two conditions.

1. $F_r \leqslant \dfrac{(250\ D_r - M_r)}{2}$

where F_r = Combined resultant of inlet, extraction, and exhaust forces, lb
M_r = Combined resultant of inlet, extraction, and exhaust moments and moments resulting from forces, ft-lb

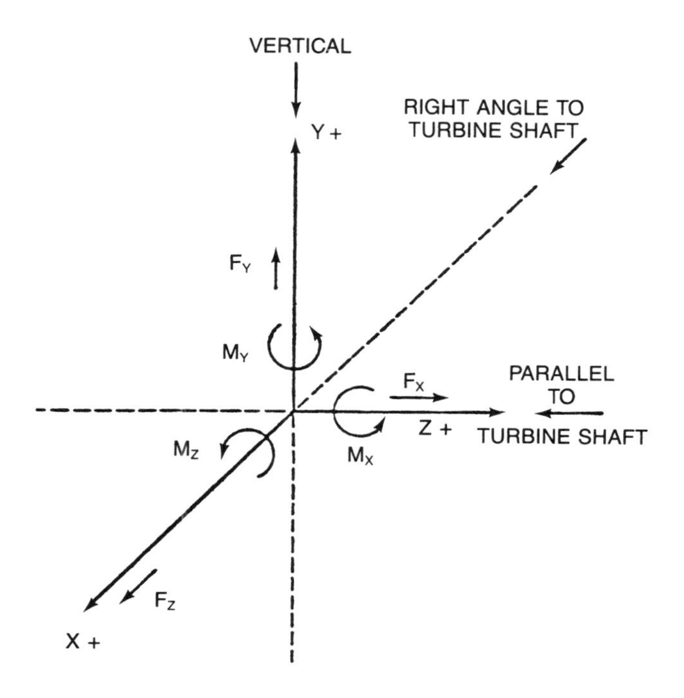

Figure 8-2. Turbine coordinate system.

D_r = Diameter (in.) of a circular opening equal to the total areas of the inlet, extraction, and exhaust openings up to a value of 9 in. in diameter. For values beyond this, use D_r (18 + equivalent diameter)/3 in.

2. Components of these resultants should not exceed:

F_{xr} 50 D_r, $\leqslant M_{xr} \leqslant$ 250 D_r
F_{yr} 125 D_r, $\leqslant M_{yr} \leqslant$ 125 D_r
F_{zr} 100 D_r, $\leqslant M_{zr} \leqslant$ 125 D_r

Design Criteria for Compressors with Steel Nozzles and Casings

Centrifugal Steel Compressor Force, Moment, and Stress Limitations

At the operating temperature, using the hot modulus "E," resultant bending moments are permissible up to a value that would cause a bending stress of $S_h/4$ in a connection having a section modulus equal to the connecting piping for the same size where the connection is 4 in. IPS or larger. On smaller-size connections a stress of $S_h/3$ is permitted. (S_h is as defined by ANSI Code B31.1 or ANSI Code B31.3 (current issue) for the material of construction.)

The resultant shear force at the face of the flange and any individual component should not exceed 2,000 lb. The resultant forces and individual components will be limited further as follows:

- Individual components:

$F_x \leqslant 1.3w \leqslant 160D$
$F_y \leqslant .6w \leqslant 130D$
$F_z \leqslant 1.0w \leqslant 160D$

- Resultant components:

Algebraic summation of $F_{rx} \leqslant 1.6w$
Algebraic summation of $F_{ry} \leqslant w$
Algebraic summation of $F_{rz} \leqslant 1.6w$

- Combined resultant:

$(F_{rx}^2 + F_{ry}^2 + F_{rz}^2)^{1/2} \leqslant 2w$

Use 100% cold spring and satisfy the operating condition only.

The total resultant force and total resultant moment imposed on the compressor at any connection must not exceed the following:

$$F \leqslant \frac{(925D_c - M)}{3}$$

where F = Resultant force (lb), including pressure forces where unrestrained expansion joints are used at the connection.
M = Resultant moment, ft-lb
D_c = Pipe size of the connection (IPS) up to 8 inches in diameter. For sizes greater than this use D_c = (16 + IPS)/3 in.

The combined resultants of the forces and moments of the suction interstage and discharge connections, resolved at the centerlines of the discharge connection must not exceed the following two conditions.

1. $F_r \leqslant \frac{(463\ D_r - M_r)}{2}$

where F_r = Combined resultant of suction, interstage and discharge forces, lb
M_r = Combined resultant of suction, interstage and discharge moments resulting from forces, ft-lb
D_r = Diameter (in.) of a circular opening equal to the total areas of the suction, interstage, and discharge openings up to a value of 9 in. in diameter. For values beyond this, use D_r = (18 + equivalent diameter)/3 in.

2. Components of these resultants should not exceed:

$F_{xr} \leqslant$ 92 D_r, $M_{xr} \leqslant$ 460 D_r
$F_{yr} \leqslant$ 230 D_r, $M_{yr} \leqslant$ 230 D_r
$F_{zr} \leqslant$ 185 D_r, $M_{zr} \leqslant$ 230 D_r

Design Criteria for Compressors with Cast Iron or Aluminum Nozzles and Casings

Cast Iron Compressor Force, Moment, and Stress Limitations

At the operating temperature, using the hot modulus, "E," resultant bending moments are permissible up to a value that would cause a bending stress of $S_h/4$ in a connection having a section modulus equal to the connecting piping for the same size where the connection is 4 in. IPS or larger. On smaller-size connections a stress of $S_h/3$ is permitted. (S_h is defined by ANSI Code B31.1 or ANSI Code B31.3 (current issue) for the material of construction.)

The resultant shear force at the face of the flange and any individual component shall not exceed 500 lb. The resultant forces and individual components are limited further as follows:

- Individual components:

$$F_x \leqslant 1.3w \leqslant 40D$$
$$F_y \leqslant .6w \leqslant 35D$$
$$F_z \leqslant w \leqslant 40D$$

- Resultant components:

Algebraic summation of $F_{rx} \leqslant 1.6w$
Algebraic summation of $F_{ry} \leqslant 1.0w$
Algebraic summation of $F_{rz} \leqslant 1.6w$

- Combined resultant:

$$(F_{rx}^2 + F_{ry}^2 + F_{rz}^2)^{1/2} \leqslant 2w$$

Use cold spring, but comply to these limitations in both operating and installed conditions.

The total resultant force and total resultant moment imposed on the turbine at any connection must not exceed the following:

$$F \leqslant \frac{(500D_c - M)}{3}$$

where F = Resultant force (lb), including pressure forces where unrestrained expansion joints are used at the connection, except on vertical exhausts
M = Resultant moment, ft-lb
D_c = Pipe size of the connection (IPS) up to 8 in. in diameter. For sizes greater than this use a $D_c = (16 + IPS)/3$ in.

The combined resultants of the forces and moments of the inlet, extraction, and exhaust connections, resolved at the centerlines of the exhaust connection must not exceed the following two conditions.

1. $F_r \leqslant \dfrac{(250\ D_r - M_r)}{2}$

where F_r = Combined resultant of suction, interstage and discharge forces, lb
M_r = Combined resultant of suction, interstage, and discharge forces, lb
D_r = Diameter (in.) of a circular opening equal to the total areas of the suction, interstage, and discharge openings up to a value of 9 in. in diameter. For values beyond this use D_r = (18 + equivalent diameter)/3 in.

2. Components of these resultants should not exceed:

$$F_{rx} \leqslant 92\ D_r,\ M_{rx} \leqslant 460\ D_r$$
$$F_{ry} \leqslant 230\ D_r,\ M_{ry} \leqslant 230\ D_r$$
$$F_{rz} \leqslant 185\ D_r,\ M_{rz} \leqslant 230\ D_r$$

API Code 661 Design Criteria for Air-Cooled Heat Exchangers

Each nozzle in the corroded condition must be capable of withstanding the moments and forces defined in Table 8-3.

The design of each fixed header, of the fixed header to sideframe connection, and of other support members should be such that no damage will occur due to the simultaneous application of the following design total nozzle loadings on a single header:

Moments, ft-lb			Forces, lb		
M_x	M_y	M_z	F_x	F_y	F_z
3,000	4,000	2,000	1,500	3,000	2,500

This recognizes that the application of these moments and forces will cause movement and that this movement will tend to reduce the actual loads.

Table 8-3
Allowable External Forces and Moments for Air-Cooled Heat Exchangers

Nozzle Size, NPS Inches	Moments ft-lb M_x	M_y	M_z	Forces, lb F_x	F_y	F_z
1½	50	70	50	100	150	100
2	70	120	70	150	200	150
3	200	300	200	300	250	300
4	400	600	400	500	400	500
6	1,050	1,500	800	600	750	750
8	1,500	3,000	1,100	850	2,000	1,200
10	2,000	3,000	1,250	1,000	2,000	1,500
12	2,500	3,000	1,500	1,250	2,000	2,000
14	3,000	3,500	1,750	1,500	2,500	2,500

For the direction of loads see Figure 8-3.

The total of all nozzle loads on one multibundle bay should not exceed three times that allowed for a single header.

The maximum allowable moments and forces for floating headers are a matter of agreement between the purchaser and the vendor.

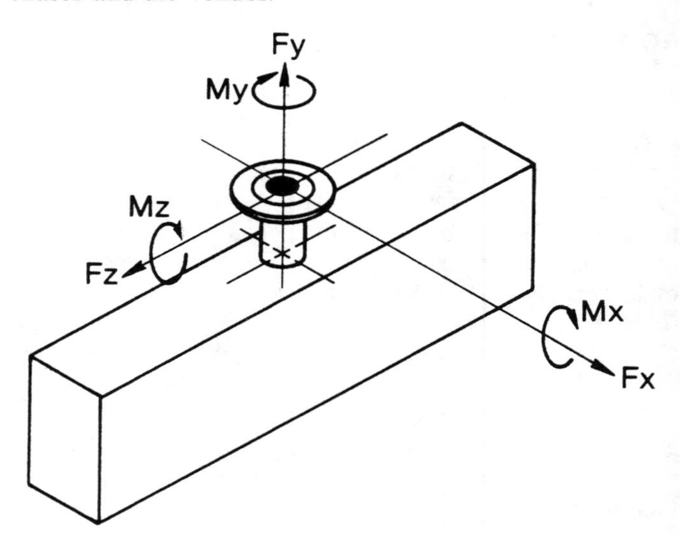

Figure 8-3. The direction of the loads defined in Table 8-3. Reproduced from *Air-Cooled Heat Exchangers for General Refinery Services,* Second Edition, 1978, Standard 661, Figure 8. Reprinted courtesy of the American Petroleum Institute.

9

Simplified Solutions for Pipe Stress

These tables are developed as a tool for the piping stress engineer or the piping designer by which he can quickly evaluate a proposed layout before he proceeds with his design work.

It is important for the reader to understand that the tables presented herein do not compose a rigorous solution to the pipe stress problem. Computer calculations must be made for borderline cases. The tables are approximate values only for two-anchor problems.

Example Problem 9-1

Consider the piping arrangement in Figure 9-1.

Size:	8 in.
Schedule:	Sch 40
Material:	A-53 Grade B
O.D.:	8.625 in.
Temperature:	600°F
Coefficient of thermal expansion:	.046 in./ft

The expansion for the 20-ft leg is X = .92 in., and the expansion for the 10-ft is X = .46 in. By inspection, it can readily be seen that the smaller expansion will deflect the longer leg more easily than the larger expansion will the shorter leg.

To develop Tables 9-1 and 9-2, a guided cantilever formula has been used to calculate stresses. If we observe our Example Problem 9-1 for an expansion of X = .92 in., the required offset is about 13 ft for a stress of 15,000 psi (See Table 9-1) and 23 ft for a stress of 5,000 psi (See Table 9-2). If Point A is attached to a piece of rotating equipment, you will need to have about 23 ft to make the system more flexible. If the system is attached to a piece of nonrotating equipment, a 13-ft offset will be sufficient.

To find the thermal forces Table 9-3 is to be used, which shows forces for a unit reflection with various lengths of offset.

Note that in identifying pipe sizes the tables show wall thickness and moment of inertia as well as O.D. All forces are calculated from the formula:

$$F = 6\ EI/1728\ L^3 \text{ (guided cantilever)}$$

where F = Force, lb (= Expansion, 1 in.)
E = Young's modulus of elasticity, (30×10^6 psi)
I = Moment of inertia of pipe, $in.^4$
L = Length of the shorter leg, ft

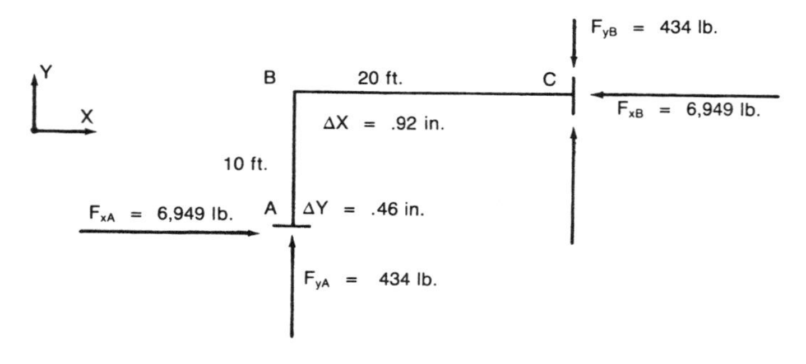

Figure 9-1. Diagram for Example Problem 9-1.

(Text continued on page 291.)

Table 9-1
Lengths of Offset Required to Safely Absorb Various Expansions for Piping Between Two Solid Anchors (Stress Limit is 15,000 psi)

Pipe O.D. (in.)	Length (ft) Required to Absorb Expansion Δ (in.)											
	0.1	0.2	0.3	0.4	0.5	0.6	0.7	0.8	0.9	1.0	1.1	1.2
1.3	1.6	2.3	2.8	3.2	3.6	4.0	4.3	4.6	4.9	5.2	5.4	5.6
1.9	1.9	2.8	3.4	3.9	4.4	4.8	5.2	5.6	5.9	6.2	6.5	6.8
2.3	2.1	3.0	3.7	4.3	4.8	5.3	5.7	6.1	6.5	6.9	7.2	7.5
3.5	2.6	3.8	4.6	5.3	6.0	6.6	7.1	7.6	8.0	8.5	8.9	9.3
4.5	3.0	4.3	5.2	6.1	6.8	7.4	8.0	8.6	9.1	9.6	10.1	10.5
5.5	3.3	4.7	5.8	6.7	7.5	8.2	8.9	9.5	10.1	10.6	11.2	11.7
6.6	3.7	5.2	6.4	7.4	8.2	9.0	9.8	10.4	11.1	11.7	12.2	12.8
8.6	4.2	5.9	7.3	8.4	9.4	10.3	11.1	11.9	12.6	13.3	14.0	14.6
10.7	4.7	6.6	8.1	9.4	10.5	11.5	12.4	13.3	14.1	14.9	15.6	16.3
12.7	5.1	7.2	8.9	10.2	11.4	12.5	13.5	14.5	15.4	16.2	17.0	17.8
14.0	5.3	7.6	9.3	10.7	12.0	13.2	14.2	15.2	16.1	17.0	17.8	18.6
16.0	5.7	8.1	9.9	11.5	12.8	14.1	15.2	16.3	17.3	18.2	19.1	19.9
18.0	6.1	8.6	10.5	12.2	13.6	14.9	16.1	17.3	18.3	19.3	20.2	21.1
20.0	6.4	9.1	11.1	12.8	14.4	15.7	17.0	18.2	19.3	20.3	21.3	22.3
24.0	7.0	9.9	12.2	14.1	15.7	17.3	18.6	19.9	21.1	22.3	23.4	24.4
30.0	7.8	11.1	13.6	15.7	17.6	19.3	20.8	22.3	23.6	24.9	26.1	27.3
36.0	8.6	12.2	14.9	17.3	19.3	21.1	22.8	24.4	25.9	27.3	28.6	29.9
42.0	9.3	13.2	16.1	18.6	20.8	22.8	24.7	26.4	28.0	29.5	30.9	32.3
48.0	9.9	14.1	17.3	19.9	22.3	24.4	26.4	28.2	29.9	31.5	33.1	34.6
54.0	10.5	14.9	18.3	21.1	23.6	25.9	28.0	29.9	31.7	33.5	35.1	36.7

Pipe O.D. (in.)	Length (ft) Required to Absorb Expansion Δ (in.)											
	1.5	2.0	2.5	3.0	3.5	4.0	4.5	5.0	5.5	6.0	6.5	7.0
1.3	6.3	7.3	8.2	9.0	9.7	10.4	11.0	11.6	12.1	12.7	13.2	13.7
1.9	7.6	8.8	9.9	10.8	11.7	12.5	13.3	14.0	14.7	15.3	16.0	16.6
2.3	8.4	9.7	10.9	11.9	12.9	13.8	14.6	15.4	16.2	16.9	17.6	18.2
3.5	10.4	12.0	13.4	14.7	15.9	17.0	18.0	19.0	20.0	20.8	21.7	22.5
4.5	11.8	13.6	15.2	16.7	18.0	19.3	20.5	21.6	22.6	23.6	24.6	25.5
5.5	13.0	15.1	16.9	18.5	20.0	21.3	22.6	23.9	25.0	26.1	27.2	28.2
6.6	14.3	16.5	18.5	20.2	21.9	23.4	24.8	26.1	27.4	28.6	29.8	30.9
8.6	16.3	18.9	21.1	23.1	25.0	26.7	28.3	29.9	31.3	32.7	34.0	35.3
10.7	18.2	21.0	23.5	25.8	27.9	29.8	31.6	33.3	34.9	36.5	38.0	39.4
12.7	19.9	22.9	25.6	28.1	30.4	32.5	34.4	36.3	38.1	39.8	41.4	43.0
14.0	20.8	24.1	26.9	29.5	31.9	34.1	36.1	38.1	40.0	41.7	43.5	45.1
16.0	22.3	25.7	28.8	31.5	34.1	36.4	38.6	40.7	42.7	44.6	46.5	48.2
18.0	23.6	27.3	30.5	33.5	36.1	38.6	41.0	43.2	45.3	47.3	49.3	51.1
20.0	24.9	28.8	32.2	35.3	38.1	40.7	43.2	45.6	47.8	49.9	52.0	53.9
24.0	27.3	31.5	35.3	38.6	41.7	44.6	47.3	49.9	52.3	54.7	56.9	59.1
30.0	30.5	35.3	39.4	43.2	46.7	49.9	52.9	55.8	58.6	61.1	63.6	66.0
36.0	33.5	38.6	43.2	47.3	51.1	54.7	58.0	61.1	64.1	67.0	69.7	72.3
42.0	36.1	41.7	46.7	51.1	55.2	59.1	62.6	66.0	69.3	72.3	75.3	78.1
48.0	38.6	44.6	49.9	54.7	59.1	63.1	67.0	70.6	74.1	77.3	80.5	83.5
54.0	41.0	47.3	52.9	58.0	62.6	67.0	71.0	74.9	78.5	82.0	85.4	88.6

Table 9-2
Lengths of Offset Required to Safely Absorb Various Expansions for Piping Connected to Rotating Equipment (Stress Limit is 5,000 psi)

Pipe O.D. (in.)	Length (ft) Required to Absorb Expansion Δ (in.)											
	0.1	0.2	0.3	0.4	0.5	0.6	0.7	0.8	0.9	1.0	1.1	1.2
1.3	2.8	4.0	4.9	5.6	6.3	6.9	7.5	8.0	8.5	9.0	9.4	9.8
1.9	3.4	4.8	5.9	6.8	7.6	8.4	9.1	9.7	10.3	10.8	11.4	11.9
2.3	3.7	5.3	6.5	7.5	8.4	9.2	10.0	10.7	11.3	11.9	12.5	13.1
3.5	4.6	6.6	8.0	9.3	10.4	11.4	12.3	13.2	14.0	14.7	15.4	16.1
4.5	5.2	7.4	9.1	10.5	11.8	12.9	14.0	14.9	15.8	16.7	17.5	18.3
5.5	5.8	8.2	10.1	11.7	13.0	14.3	15.4	16.5	17.5	18.5	19.4	20.2
6.6	6.4	9.0	11.1	12.8	14.3	15.7	16.9	18.1	19.2	20.2	21.2	22.2
8.6	7.3	10.3	12.6	14.6	16.3	17.9	19.3	20.7	21.9	23.1	24.2	25.3
10.7	8.1	11.5	14.1	16.3	18.2	20.0	21.6	23.1	24.5	25.8	27.1	28.3
12.7	8.9	12.5	15.4	17.8	19.9	21.8	23.5	25.1	26.7	28.1	29.5	30.8
14.0	9.3	13.2	16.1	18.6	20.8	22.8	24.7	26.4	28.0	29.5	30.9	32.3
16.0	9.9	14.1	17.3	19.9	22.3	24.4	26.4	28.2	29.9	31.5	33.1	34.6
18.0	10.5	14.9	18.3	21.1	23.6	25.9	28.0	29.9	31.7	33.5	35.1	36.7
20.0	11.1	15.7	19.3	22.3	24.9	27.3	29.5	31.5	33.5	35.3	37.0	38.6
24.0	12.2	17.3	21.1	24.4	27.3	29.9	32.3	34.6	36.7	38.6	40.5	42.3
30.0	13.6	19.3	23.6	27.3	30.5	33.5	36.1	38.6	41.0	43.2	45.3	47.3
36.0	14.9	21.1	25.9	29.9	33.5	36.7	39.6	42.3	44.9	47.3	49.7	51.9
42.0	16.1	22.8	28.0	32.3	36.1	39.6	42.8	45.7	48.5	51.1	53.6	56.0
48.0	17.3	24.4	29.9	34.6	38.6	42.3	45.7	48.9	51.9	54.7	57.3	59.9
54.0	18.3	25.9	31.7	36.7	41.0	44.9	48.5	51.9	55.0	58.0	60.8	63.5

Pipe O.D. (in.)	Length (ft) Required to Absorb Expansion Δ (in.)											
	1.5	2.0	2.5	3.0	3.5	4.0	4.5	5.0	5.5	6.0	6.4	7.0
1.3	11.0	12.7	14.2	15.6	16.8	18.0	19.1	20.1	21.1	22.0	22.9	23.8
1.9	13.3	15.3	17.2	18.8	20.3	21.7	23.0	24.3	25.5	26.6	27.7	28.8
2.3	14.6	16.9	18.9	20.7	22.4	23.9	25.4	26.7	28.0	29.3	30.5	31.6
3.5	18.0	20.8	23.3	25.5	27.6	29.5	31.3	33.0	34.6	36.1	37.6	39.0
4.5	20.5	23.6	26.4	29.0	31.3	33.5	35.5	37.4	39.2	41.0	42.7	44.3
5.5	22.6	26.1	29.2	32.0	34.6	37.0	39.2	41.4	43.4	45.3	47.2	49.0
6.6	24.8	28.6	32.0	35.1	37.9	40.5	43.0	45.3	47.5	49.7	51.7	53.6
8.6	28.3	32.7	36.6	40.1	43.3	46.3	49.1	51.7	54.3	56.7	59.0	61.2
10.7	31.6	36.5	40.8	44.7	48.3	51.6	54.8	57.7	60.5	63.2	65.8	68.3
12.7	34.4	39.8	44.5	48.7	52.6	56.3	59.7	62.9	66.0	68.9	71.7	74.4
14.0	36.1	41.7	46.7	51.1	55.2	59.1	62.6	66.0	69.3	72.3	75.3	78.1
16.0	38.6	44.6	49.9	54.7	59.1	63.1	67.0	70.6	74.1	77.3	80.5	83.5
18.0	41.0	47.3	52.9	58.0	62.6	67.0	71.0	74.9	78.5	82.0	85.4	88.6
20.0	43.2	49.9	55.8	61.1	66.0	70.6	74.9	78.9	82.8	86.5	90.0	93.4
24.0	47.3	54.7	61.1	67.0	72.3	77.3	82.0	86.5	90.7	94.7	98.6	102.3
30.0	52.9	61.1	68.4	74.9	80.9	86.5	91.7	96.7	101.4	105.9	110.3	114.4
36.0	58.0	67.0	74.9	82.0	88.6	94.7	100.5	105.9	111.1	116.0	120.8	125.3
42.0	62.6	72.3	80.9	88.6	95.7	102.3	108.5	114.4	120.0	125.3	130.5	135.4
48.0	67.0	77.3	86.5	94.7	102.3	109.4	116.0	122.3	128.3	134.0	139.5	144.7
54.0	71.0	82.0	91.7	100.5	108.5	116.0	123.1	129.7	136.1	142.1	147.9	153.5

Table 9-3
Force (lb/in.) of Expansion for L-Shaped Pipe (No Elbow)

2.375 TO 12.75 IN. SCH. 5S PIPE

OFF- SET FT	2.375 0.065 0.310	3.500 0.083 1.300	4.500 0.083 2.800	5.563 0.109 6.940	6.625 0.109 11.840	8.625 0.109 26.440	10.750 0.134 62.960	12.750 0.156 122.380
2	4,100	16,942	36,586	90,457	154,237	344,274	819,889	--
3	1,213	5,020	10,840	26,802	45,700	102,007	242,930	472,180
4	513	2,118	4,573	11,307	19,280	43,034	102,486	199,201
5	262	1,084	2,341	5,789	9,871	22,034	52,473	101,991
6	152	627	1,355	3,350	5,712	12,751	30,366	59,022
7	96	395	853	2,110	3,597	8,030	19,123	37,169
8	64	265	572	1,413	2,410	5,379	12,811	24,900
9	45	186	401	993	1,693	3,778	8,997	17,488
10	33	136	293	724	1,234	2,754	6,559	12,749
11	25	102	220	544	927	2,069	4,928	9,578
12	19	78	169	419	714	1,594	3,796	7,378
13	15	62	133	329	562	1,254	2,985	5,803
14	12	49	107	264	450	1,004	2,390	4,646
15	10	40	87	214	366	816	1,943	3,777
16	8	33	71	177	301	672	1,601	3,113
17	7	28	60	147	251	561	1,335	2,595
18	6	23	50	124	212	472	1,125	2,186
19	5	20	43	106	180	402	956	1,859
20	4	17	37	90	154	344	820	1,594
21	4	15	32	78	133	297	708	1,377
22	3	13	27	68	116	259	616	1,197
23	3	11	24	59	101	226	539	1,048
24	2	10	21	52	89	199	474	922
25	2	9	19	46	79	176	420	816
26	2	8	17	41	70	157	373	725
27	2	7	15	37	63	140	333	648
28	1	6	13	33	56	125	299	581
29	1	6	12	30	51	113	269	523
30	1	5	11	27	46	102	243	472
31	1	5	10	24	41	92	220	428
32	1	4	9	22	38	84	200	389
33	1	4	8	20	34	77	183	355
34	1	3	7	18	31	70	167	324
35	1	3	7	17	29	64	153	297
36	1	3	6	16	26	59	141	273
37	1	3	6	14	24	54	129	252
38	1	2	5	13	22	50	120	232
39	1	2	5	12	21	46	111	215
40	1	2	5	11	19	43	102	199
41	0	2	4	10	18	40	95	185

FIRST 3 LINES ARE O.D., WALL THICKNESS, AND MOMENT OF INERTIA.

Table 9-3
Continued

14 TO 30 IN. SCH. 5S PIPE

OFF-	14.000	16.000	18.000	20.000	24.000	30.000
SET	0.156	0.169	0.165	0.188	0.218	0.250
FT	162.560	263.340	367.620	574.170	1151.590	2585.180
8	33,074	53,577	74,793	116,815	234,292	525,957
9	23,229	37,629	52,529	82,043	164,551	369,396
10	16,934	27,432	38,294	59,809	119,957	269,290
11	12,723	20,610	28,771	44,936	90,126	202,322
12	9,800	15,875	22,161	34,612	69,420	155,839
13	7,708	12,486	17,430	27,223	54,601	122,572
14	6,171	9,997	13,955	21,796	43,716	98,138
15	5,017	8,128	11,346	17,721	35,543	79,790
16	4,134	6,697	9,349	14,602	29,286	65,745
17	3,447	5,583	7,794	12,174	24,416	54,812
18	2,904	4,704	6,566	10,255	20,569	46,175
19	2,469	3,999	5,583	8,720	17,489	39,261
20	2,117	3,429	4,787	7,476	14,995	33,661
21	1,829	2,962	4,135	6,458	12,953	29,078
22	1,590	2,576	3,596	5,617	11,266	25,290
23	1,392	2,255	3,147	4,916	9,859	22,133
24	1,225	1,984	2,770	4,326	8,677	19,480
25	1,084	1,756	2,451	3,828	7,677	17,235
26	963	1,561	2,179	3,403	6,825	15,321
27	860	1,394	1,946	3,039	6,094	13,681
28	771	1,250	1,744	2,725	5,465	12,267
29	694	1,125	1,570	2,452	4,919	11,041
30	627	1,016	1,418	2,215	4,443	9,974
31	568	921	1,285	2,008	4,027	9,039
32	517	837	1,169	1,825	3,661	8,218
33	471	763	1,066	1,664	3,338	7,493
34	431	698	974	1,522	3,052	6,851
35	395	640	893	1,395	2,798	6,281
36	363	588	821	1,282	2,571	5,772
37	334	542	756	1,181	2,368	5,316
38	309	500	698	1,090	2,186	4,908
39	285	462	646	1,008	2,022	4,540
40	265	429	598	935	1,874	4,208
41	246	398	556	868	1,741	3,907
42	229	370	517	807	1,619	3,635
43	213	345	482	752	1,509	3,387
44	199	322	450	702	1,408	3,161
45	186	301	420	656	1,316	2,955
46	174	282	393	614	1,232	2,767
47	163	264	369	576	1,155	2,594

FIRST 3 LINES ARE O.D., WALL THICKNESS, AND MOMENT OF INERTIA.

Table 9-3
Continued

2.375 TO 12.75 IN. SCH. 10S PIPE

OFF- SET FT	2.375 0.109 0.490	3.500 0.120 1.820	4.500 0.120 3.960	5.563 0.134 8.420	6.625 0.134 14.390	8.625 0.148 35.410	10.750 0.165 76.860	12.750 0.180 140.410
2	6,500	23,723	51,597	109,705	187,466	461,125	--	--
3	1,926	7,029	15,288	32,505	55,546	136,630	296,542	541,741
4	812	2,965	6,450	13,713	23,433	57,641	125,104	228,547
5	416	1,518	3,302	7,021	11,998	29,512	64,053	117,016
6	241	879	1,911	4,063	6,943	17,079	37,068	67,718
7	152	553	1,203	2,559	4,372	10,755	23,343	42,644
8	102	371	806	1,714	2,929	7,205	15,638	28,568
9	71	260	566	1,204	2,057	5,060	10,983	20,064
10	52	190	413	878	1,500	3,689	8,007	14,627
11	39	143	310	659	1,127	2,772	6,016	10,989
12	30	110	239	508	868	2,135	4,633	8,465
13	24	86	188	399	683	1,679	3,644	6,658
14	19	69	150	320	547	1,344	2,918	5,331
15	15	56	122	260	444	1,093	2,372	4,334
16	13	46	101	214	366	901	1,955	3,571
17	11	39	84	179	305	751	1,630	2,977
18	9	33	71	150	257	633	1,373	2,508
19	8	28	60	128	219	538	1,167	2,133
20	6	24	52	110	187	461	1,001	1,828
21	6	20	45	95	162	398	865	1,579
22	5	18	39	82	141	346	752	1,374
23	4	16	34	72	123	303	658	1,202
24	4	14	30	63	108	267	579	1,058
25	3	12	26	56	96	236	512	936
26	3	11	23	50	85	210	456	832
27	3	10	21	45	76	187	407	743
28	2	9	19	40	68	168	365	666
29	2	8	17	36	61	151	328	600
30	2	7	15	33	56	137	297	542
31	2	6	14	29	50	124	269	491
32	2	6	13	27	46	113	244	446
33	1	5	11	24	42	103	223	407
34	1	5	11	22	38	94	204	372
35	1	4	10	20	35	86	187	341
36	1	4	9	19	32	79	172	314
37	1	4	8	17	30	73	158	289
38	1	3	8	16	27	67	146	267
39	1	3	7	15	25	62	135	247
40	1	3	6	14	23	58	125	229
41	1	3	6	13	22	54	116	212

FIRST 3 LINES ARE O.D., WALL THICKNESS, AND MOMENT OF INERTIA.

Table 9-3
Continued

14 TO 30 IN. SCH. 10S PIPE

OFF- SET FT	14.000 0.188 194.560	16.000 0.188 291.900	18.000 0.188 417.250	20.000 0.218 662.790	24.000 0.250 1315.340	30.000 0.312 3206.310
8	39,585	59,388	84,891	134,846	267,607	652,326
9	27,802	41,710	59,622	94,707	187,949	458,149
10	20,267	30,407	43,464	69,041	137,015	333,991
11	15,227	22,845	32,655	51,872	102,941	250,932
12	11,729	17,596	25,153	39,954	79,291	193,282
13	9,225	13,840	19,783	31,425	62,365	152,021
14	7,386	11,081	15,840	25,161	49,933	121,717
15	6,005	9,009	12,878	20,457	40,597	98,960
16	4,948	7,424	10,611	16,856	33,451	81,541
17	4,125	6,189	8,847	14,053	27,888	67,981
18	3,475	5,214	7,453	11,838	23,494	57,269
19	2,955	4,433	6,337	10,066	19,976	48,694
20	2,533	3,801	5,433	8,630	17,127	41,749
21	2,188	3,283	4,693	7,455	14,795	36,064
22	1,903	2,856	4,082	6,484	12,868	31,367
23	1,666	2,499	3,572	5,674	11,261	27,451
24	1,466	2,200	3,144	4,994	9,911	24,160
25	1,297	1,946	2,782	4,419	8,769	21,375
26	1,153	1,730	2,473	3,928	7,796	19,003
27	1,030	1,545	2,208	3,508	6,961	16,968
28	923	1,385	1,980	3,145	6,242	15,215
29	831	1,247	1,782	2,831	5,618	13,694
30	751	1,126	1,610	2,557	5,075	12,370
31	680	1,021	1,459	2,318	4,599	11,211
32	619	928	1,326	2,107	4,181	10,193
33	564	846	1,209	1,921	3,813	9,294
34	516	774	1,106	1,757	3,486	8,498
35	473	709	1,014	1,610	3,196	7,790
36	434	652	932	1,480	2,937	7,159
37	400	600	858	1,363	2,705	6,594
38	369	554	792	1,258	2,497	6,087
39	342	513	733	1,164	2,310	5,630
40	317	475	679	1,079	2,141	5,219
41	294	441	631	1,002	1,988	4,846
42	274	410	587	932	1,849	4,508
43	255	382	547	868	1,723	4,201
44	238	357	510	810	1,608	3,921
45	222	334	477	758	1,504	3,665
46	208	312	447	709	1,408	3,431
47	195	293	419	665	1,320	3,217

FIRST 3 LINES ARE O.D., WALL THICKNESS, AND MOMENT OF INERTIA.

Table 9-3
Continued

14 TO 30 IN. SCH. 10 PIPE

OFF-SET FT	14.000 0.250 255.300	16.000 0.250 383.660	18.000 0.250 549.133	20.000 0.250 756.430	24.000 0.250 1315.340	30.000 0.312 3206.310
2	--	--	--	--	--	--
3	984,955	--	--	--	--	--
4	415,528	624,453	893,779	--	--	--
5	212,750	319,720	457,615	630,361	--	--
6	123,119	185,023	264,823	364,792	634,328	--
7	77,533	116,516	166,769	229,724	399,460	973,734
8	51,941	78,057	111,722	153,897	267,607	652,326
9	36,480	54,822	78,466	108,087	187,949	458,149
10	26,594	39,965	57,202	78,795	137,015	333,991
11	19,980	30,026	42,977	59,200	102,941	250,932
12	15,390	23,128	33,103	45,599	79,291	193,282
13	12,105	18,191	26,036	35,865	62,365	152,021
14	9,692	14,565	20,846	28,715	49,933	121,717
15	7,880	11,841	16,949	23,347	40,597	98,960
16	6,493	9,757	13,965	19,237	33,451	81,541
17	5,413	8,135	11,643	16,038	27,888	67,981
18	4,560	6.853	9,808	13,511	23,494	57,269
19	3,877	5,827	8,340	11,488	19,976	48,694
20	3,324	4,996	7,150	9,849	17,127	41,749
21	2,872	4,315	6,177	8,508	14,795	36,064
22	2,498	3,753	5,372	7,400	12,868	31,367
23	2,186	3,285	4,701	6,476	11,261	27,451
24	1,924	2,891	4,138	5,700	9,911	24,160
25	1,702	2,558	3,661	5,043	8,769	21,375
26	1,513	2,274	3,255	4,483	7,796	19,003
27	1,351	2,030	2,906	4,003	6,961	16,968
28	1,211	1,821	2,606	3,589	6,242	15,215
29	1,090	1,639	2,345	3,231	5.618	13,694
30	985	1,480	2,119	2,918	5,075	12,370
31	893	1,342	1,920	2,645	4,599	11,211
32	812	1,220	1,746	2,405	4,181	10,193
33	740	1.112	1,592	2,193	3.813	9,294
34	677	1,017	1,455	2,005	3,486	8,498
35	620	932	1,334	1,838	3,196	7,790
36	570	857	1,226	1,689	2,937	7,159
37	525	789	1,129	1,556	2,705	6,594
38	485	728	1,042	1,436	2,497	6,087
39	448	674	964	1,328	2,310	5,630
40	416	624	894	1.231	2,141	5,219
41	386	580	830	1,143	1,988	4,846

FIRST 3 LINES ARE O.D., WALL THICKNESS, AND MOMENT OF INERTIA.

Table 9-3
Continued

2.375 TO 12.75 IN. SCH. 40 PIPE

OFF- SET FT	2.375 0.154 0.660	3.500 0.216 3.010	4.500 0.237 7.230	5.563 0.258 15.160	6.625 0.280 28.140	8.625 0.322 72.480	10.750 0.365 160.730	12.750 0.406 300.200
2	8,669	39,286	94,175	197,424	366,435	943,871	--	--
3	2,568	11,640	27,904	58,496	108,573	279,665	620,117	--
4	1,084	4,911	11,772	24,678	45,804	117,984	261,612	488,521
5	555	2,514	6,027	12,635	23,452	60,408	133,945	250,174
6	321	1,455	3,488	7,312	13,572	34,958	77,515	144,777
7	202	916	2,196	4,605	8,547	22,014	48,814	91,171
8	135	614	1,471	3,085	5,726	14,748	32,701	61,078
9	95	431	1,033	2,167	4,021	10,358	22,967	42,897
10	69	314	753	1,579	2,931	7,551	16,743	31,272
11	52	236	566	1,187	2,202	5,673	12,579	23,495
12	40	182	436	914	1,696	4,370	9,689	18,097
13	32	143	343	719	1,334	3,437	7,621	14,234
14	25	115	275	576	1,068	2,752	6,102	11,376
15	21	93	223	468	869	2,237	4,961	9,266
16	17	77	184	386	716	1,843	4,088	7,635
17	14	64	153	321	597	1,537	3,408	6,365
18	12	54	129	271	503	1,295	2,871	5,362
19	10	46	110	230	427	1,101	2,441	4,559
20	9	39	94	197	366	944	2,093	3,909
21	7	34	81	171	317	815	1,808	3,377
22	7	30	71	148	275	709	1,572	2,937
23	6	26	62	130	241	621	1,376	2,570
24	5	23	54	114	212	546	1,211	2,262
25	4	20	48	101	188	483	1,072	2,001
26	4	18	43	90	167	430	953	1,779
27	4	16	38	80	149	384	851	1,589
28	3	14	34	72	134	344	763	1,425
29	3	13	31	65	120	310	687	1,282
30	3	12	28	58	109	280	620	1,158
31	2	11	25	53	98	253	562	1,050
32	2	10	23	48	89	230	511	954
33	2	9	21	44	82	210	466	870
34	2	8	19	40	75	192	426	796
35	2	7	18	37	68	176	391	729
36	1	7	16	34	63	162	359	670
37	1	6	15	31	58	149	331	617
38	1	6	14	29	53	138	305	570
39	1	5	13	27	49	127	282	527
40	1	5	12	25	46	118	262	489
41	1	5	11	23	43	110	243	454

FIRST 3 LINES ARE O.D., WALL THICKNESS, AND MOMENT OF INERTIA.

Table 9-3
Continued

14 TO 24 IN. SCH. 40 PIPE

OFF- SET FT	14.000	16.000	18.000	20.000	24.000
	0.438	0.500	0.562	0.593	0.687
	429.490	731.940	1171.480	1703.700	3421.270
8	87,381	148,914	238,340	346,621	696,061
9	61,370	104,587	167,394	243,443	488,866
10	44,739	76,244	122,030	177,470	356,383
11	33,613	57,283	91,683	133,336	267,756
12	25,891	44,123	70,619	102,702	206,240
13	20,364	34,704	55,544	80,778	162,213
14	16,304	27,786	44,472	64,676	129,877
15	13,256	22,591	36,157	52,584	105,595
16	10,923	18,614	29,792	43,328	87,008
17	9,106	15,519	24,838	36,122	72,539
18	7,671	13,073	20,924	30,430	61,108
19	6,523	11,116	17,791	25,874	51,958
20	5,592	9,530	15,254	22,184	44,548
21	4,831	8,233	13,177	19,163	38,482
22	4,202	7,160	11,460	16,667	33,469
23	3,677	6,266	10,030	14,586	29,291
24	3,236	5,515	8,827	12,838	25,780
25	2,863	4,880	7,810	11,358	22,809
26	2,545	4,338	6,943	10,097	20,277
27	2,273	3,874	6,200	9,016	18,106
28	2,038	3,473	5,559	8,084	16,235
29	1,834	3,126	5,003	7,277	14,612
30	1,657	2,824	4,520	6,573	13,199
31	1,502	2,559	4,096	5,957	11,963
32	1,365	2,327	3,724	5,416	10,876
33	1,245	2,122	3,396	4,938	9,917
34	1,138	1,940	3,105	4,515	9,067
35	1,043	1,778	2,846	4,139	8,312
36	959	1,634	2,616	3,804	7,639
37	883	1,505	2,409	3,504	7,036
38	815	1,389	2,224	3,234	6,495
39	754	1,285	2,057	2,992	6,008
40	699	1,191	1,907	2,773	5,568
41	649	1,106	1,771	2,575	5,171
42	604	1,029	1,647	2,395	4,810
43	563	959	1,535	2,232	4,482
44	525	895	1,433	2,083	4,184
45	491	837	1,339	1,948	3,911
46	460	783	1,254	1,823	3,661
47	431	734	1,175	1,709	3,433

FIRST 3 LINES ARE O.D., WALL THICKNESS, AND MOMENT OF INERTIA.

Table 9-3
Continued

2.375 TO 12.75 IN. SCH. STD PIPE

OFF-SET FT	2.375 0.154 0.660	3.500 0.216 3.010	4.500 0.237 7.230	5.563 0.258 15.160	6.625 0.280 28.140	8.625 0.322 72.480	10.750 0.365 160.730	12.750 0.375 279.330
2	8,669	39,286	94,175	197,424	366,435	943,871	--	--
3	2,569	11,640	27,904	58,496	108,573	279,665	620,117	--
4	1,084	4,911	11,772	24,678	45,804	117,984	261,612	454,647
5	555	2,514	6,027	12,635	23,452	60,408	133,945	232,779
6	321	1,455	3,488	7,312	13,572	34,958	77,515	134,710
7	202	916	2,196	4,605	8,547	22,014	48,814	84,832
8	135	614	1,471	3,085	5,726	14,748	32,701	56,831
9	95	431	1,033	2,167	4,021	10,358	22,967	39,914
10	69	314	753	1,579	2,931	7,551	16,743	29,097
11	52	236	566	1,187	2,202	5,673	12,579	21,861
12	40	182	436	914	1,696	4,370	9,689	16,839
13	32	143	343	719	1,334	3,437	7,621	13,244
14	25	115	275	576	1,068	2,752	6,102	10,604
15	21	93	223	468	869	2,237	4,961	8,621
16	17	77	184	386	716	1,843	4,088	7,104
17	14	64	153	321	597	1,537	3,408	5,923
18	12	54	129	271	503	1,295	2,871	4,989
19	10	46	110	230	427	1,101	2,441	4,242
20	9	39	94	197	366	944	2,093	3,637
21	7	34	81	171	317	815	1,808	3,142
22	7	30	71	148	275	709	1,572	2,733
23	6	26	62	130	241	621	1,376	2,392
24	5	23	54	114	212	546	1,211	2,105
25	4	20	48	101	188	483	1,072	1,862
26	4	18	43	90	167	430	953	1,656
27	4	16	38	80	149	384	851	1,478
28	3	14	34	72	134	344	763	1,326
29	3	13	31	65	120	310	687	1,193
30	3	12	28	58	109	280	620	1,078
31	2	11	25	53	98	253	562	977
32	2	10	23	48	89	230	511	888
33	2	9	21	44	82	210	466	810
34	2	8	19	40	75	192	426	740
35	2	7	18	37	68	176	391	679
36	1	7	16	34	63	162	359	624
37	1	6	15	31	58	149	331	574
38	1	6	14	29	53	138	305	530
39	1	5	13	27	49	127	282	491
40	1	5	12	25	46	118	262	455
41	1	5	11	23	43	110	243	422

FIRST 3 LINES ARE O.D., WALL THICKNESS, AND MOMENT OF INERTIA.

Table 9-3
Continued

14 TO 42 IN. SCH. STD PIPE

OFF- SET FT	14.000 0.375 372.760	16.000 0.375 562.080	18.000 0.375 806.630	20.000 0.375 1113.470	24.000 0.375 1942.290	30.000 0.375 3829.440	36.000 0.375 6658.910	42.000 0.375 10621.600
8	75,838	114,356	164,110	226,536	395,162	779,103	--	--
9	53,264	80,316	115,259	159,104	277,535	547,189	951,492	--
10	38,829	58,550	84,024	115,987	202,323	398,901	693,637	--
11	29,173	43,990	63,129	87,142	152,008	299,700	521,140	831,266
12	22,471	33,883	48,625	67,122	117,085	230,845	401,411	640,286
13	17,674	26,650	38,245	52,793	92,090	181,566	315,720	503,602
14	14,151	21,338	30,621	42,269	73,733	145,372	252,783	403,212
15	11,505	17,348	24,896	34,366	59,947	118,193	205,522	327,826
16	9,480	14,295	20,514	28,317	49,395	97,388	169,345	270,121
17	7,903	11,917	17,102	23,608	41,181	81,193	141,184	225,201
18	6,658	10,040	14,407	19,888	34,692	68,399	118,936	189,714
19	5,661	8,536	12,250	16,910	29,497	58,157	101,128	161,308
20	4,854	7,319	10,503	14,498	25,290	49,863	86,705	138,302
21	4,193	6,322	9,073	12,524	21,847	43,073	74,899	119,470
22	3,647	5,499	7,891	10,893	19,001	37,462	65,143	103,908
23	3,191	4,812	6,906	9,533	16,629	32,785	57,010	90,936
24	2,809	4,235	6,078	8,390	14,636	28.856	50,176	80,036
25	2,485	3,747	5.378	7.423	12,949	25,530	44,393	70,811
26	2,209	3,331	4,781	6,599	11,511	22,696	39,465	62,950
27	1,973	2,975	4,269	5,893	10,279	20,266	35,240	56,212
28	1,769	2,667	3,828	5,284	9,217	18,171	31,598	50,402
29	1,592	2,401	3,445	4,756	8,296	16,356	28,441	45,365
30	1,438	2,169	3,112	4,296	7,493	14,774	25,690	40,978
31	1,303	1,965	2,820	3,893	6,791	13,390	23,283	37,139
32	1,185	1,787	2,564	3,540	6,174	12,173	21,168	33,765
33	1,080	1,629	2,338	3,227	5,630	11,100	19,301	30,788
34	988	1,490	2,138	2,951	5,148	10,149	17,648	28,150
35	906	1,366	1.960	2,705	4,719	9,304	16,178	25,806
36	832	1,255	1,801	2,486	4,336	8,550	14,867	23,714
37	767	1,156	1,659	2,290	3,994	7,875	13,694	21,843
38	708	1,067	1,531	2,114	3,687	7,270	12,641	20,164
39	655	987	1,416	1,955	3,411	6,725	11,693	18,652
40	607	915	1,313	1,812	3,161	6.233	10,838	17,288
41	563	850	1,219	1,683	2,936	5,788	10,064	16,053
42	524	790	1,134	1,566	2,731	5,384	9,362	14.934
43	486	736	1,057	1.459	2,545	5,017	8,724	13,916
44	456	687	986	1,362	2,375	4,683	8,143	12,989
45	426	643	922	1,273	2.220	4,378	7,612	12,142
46	399	602	863	1,192	2,079	4,098	7,126	11,367
47	374	564	809	1,117	1.949	3,842	6,681	10,657

FIRST 3 LINES ARE O.D., WALL THICKNESS, AND MOMENT OF INERTIA.

Table 9-3
Continued

2.375 TO 12.75 IN. SCH. 40S PIPE

OFF-SET FT	2.375	3.500	4.500	5.563	6.625	8.625	10.750	12.750
	0.154	0.216	0.237	0.258	0.280	0.322	0.365	0.375
	0.660	3.010	7.230	15.160	28.140	72.480	160.730	279.330
2	8,669	39,286	94,175	197,424	366,435	943,871	--	--
3	2,568	11,640	27.904	58,496	108,573	279,665	620.117	--
4	1,084	4,911	11,772	24,678	45,804	117,784	261,612	454.647
5	555	2,514	6,027	12,635	23,452	60,408	133,945	232,779
6	321	1,455	3,488	7,312	13,572	34,958	77,515	134,710
7	202	916	2,196	4,605	8,547	22,014	48,814	84,832
8	135	614	1,471	3,085	5,726	14,748	32,701	56,831
9	95	431	1,033	2,167	4,021	10,358	22,967	39,914
10	69	314	753	1,579	2,931	7,551	16,743	29,097
11	52	236	566	1,187	2,202	5,673	12,579	21,861
12	40	182	436	914	1,696	4,370	9,689	16,839
13	32	143	343	719	1,334	3.437	7,621	13,244
14	25	115	275	576	1,068	2,752	6.102	10,604
15	21	93	223	468	869	2,237	4.961	8,621
16	17	77	184	386	716	1,843	4,088	7,104
17	14	64	153	321	597	1,537	3,408	5,923
18	12	54	129	271	503	1,295	2,871	4.989
19	10	46	110	230	427	1,101	2.441	4,242
20	9	39	94	197	366	944	2,093	3,637
21	7	34	81	171	317	815	1,806	3,142
22	7	30	71	148	275	709	1.572	2.733
23	6	26	62	130	241	621	1,376	2,392
24	5	23	54	114	212	546	1,211	2,105
25	4	20	48	101	188	483	1,072	1,862
26	4	18	43	90	167	430	953	1,656
27	4	16	38	80	149	384	851	1,478
28	3	14	34	72	134	344	763	1,326
29	3	13	31	65	120	310	687	1,193
30	3	12	28	58	109	280	620	1,078
31	2	11	25	53	98	253	562	977
32	2	10	23	48	89	230	511	888
33	2	9	21	44	82	210	466	810
34	2	8	19	40	75	192	426	740
35	2	7	18	37	68	176	391	679
36	1	7	16	34	63	162	359	624
37	1	6	15	31	58	149	331	574
38	1	6	14	29	53	138	305	530
39	1	5	13	27	49	127	282	491
40	1	5	12	25	46	118	262	455
41	1	5	11	23	43	110	243	422

FIRST 3 LINES ARE O.D., WALL THICKNESS, AND MOMENT OF INERTIA.

Table 9-3
Continued

2.375 TO 12.75 IN. SCH. XS PIPE

OFF-	2.375	3.500	4.500	5.563	6.625	8.625	10.750	12.750
SET	0.218	0.300	0.337	0.375	0.432	0.500	0.500	0.500
FT	0.860	3.890	9.610	20.670	40.490	105.710	211.950	361.540
2	11,301	50,707	125,137	269,149	527,222	--	--	--
3	3,348	15,024	37,078	79,748	156,214	407,856	817,709	--
4	1,413	6,338	15,642	33,644	65,903	172,064	344,971	588,450
5	723	3,245	8,009	17,226	33,742	88,097	176,625	301,287
6	419	1,878	4,635	9,968	19,527	50,982	102,214	174,356
7	264	1,183	2,919	6,278	12,297	32,105	64,368	109,798
8	177	792	1,955	4,205	8,238	21,508	43,121	73,556
9	124	556	1,373	2,954	5,786	15,106	30,286	51,661
10	90	406	1,001	2,153	4,218	11,012	22,078	37,661
11	68	305	752	1,618	3,169	8,274	16,588	28,295
12	52	235	579	1,246	2,441	6,373	12,777	21,794
13	41	185	456	980	1,920	5,012	10,049	17,142
14	33	148	365	785	1,537	4,013	8,046	13,725
15	27	120	297	638	1,250	3,263	6,542	11,159
16	22	99	244	526	1,030	2,689	5,390	9,195
17	18	83	204	438	858	2,241	4,494	7,666
18	16	70	172	369	723	1,888	3,786	6,458
19	13	59	146	314	615	1,605	3,219	5,491
20	11	51	125	269	527	1,377	2,760	4,708
21	10	44	108	233	455	1,189	2,384	4,067
22	8	38	94	202	396	1,034	2,073	3,537
23	7	33	82	177	347	905	1,815	3,095
24	7	29	72	156	305	797	1,597	2,724
25	6	26	64	138	270	705	1,413	2,410
26	5	23	57	123	240	627	1,256	2,143
27	5	21	51	109	214	559	1,122	1,913
28	4	18	46	98	192	502	1,006	1,716
29	4	17	41	88	173	452	905	1,544
30	3	15	37	80	156	408	818	1,395
31	3	14	34	72	142	370	741	1,264
32	3	12	31	66	129	336	674	1,149
33	3	11	28	60	117	306	614	1,048
34	2	10	25	55	107	280	562	958
35	2	9	23	50	98	257	515	878
36	2	9	21	46	90	236	473	807
37	2	8	20	43	83	217	436	744
38	2	7	18	39	77	201	402	686
39	2	7	17	36	71	186	372	635
40	1	6	16	34	66	172	345	588
41	1	5	15	31	61	160	320	546

FIRST 3 LINES ARE O.D., WALL THICKNESS, AND MOMENT OF INERTIA.

Table 9-3
Continued

14 TO 42 IN. SCH. XS PIPE

OFF-SET FT	14.000	16.000	18.000	20.000	24.000	30.000	36.000	42.000
	0.500	0.500	0.500	0.500	0.500	0.500	0.500	0.500
	483.750	731.940	1053.170	1456.860	2549.350	5042.200	8786.200	14035.800
8	98,420	148,914	214,268	296,400	518,667	--	--	--
9	69,124	104,587	150,487	208,171	364,277	720.480	--	--
10	50,391	76,244	109,705	151,757	265,558	525,230	915,229	--
11	37,860	57,283	82,423	114,017	199,517	394,613	687,625	--
12	29,162	44,123	63,487	87,822	153,679	303,953	529.647	846.101
13	22.936	34,704	49,934	69,075	120,873	239,067	416,581	665.481
14	18,364	27,786	39,980	55,305	96,778	191,410	333,538	532,822
15	14,931	22,591	32,505	44,965	78,684	155,624	271,179	433,204
16	12,303	18,614	26,783	37,050	64,833	128,230	223,445	356,949
17	10,257	15,519	22,330	30,889	54,052	106,906	186,287	297,591
18	8,640	13,073	18,811	26,021	45,535	90,060	156,932	250,697
19	7,347	11,116	15,994	22,125	38,717	76,575	133,435	213,160
20	6,299	9,530	13,713	18,970	33,195	65,654	114,404	182,758
21	5,441	8,233	11,846	16,387	28,675	56,714	98,826	157,873
22	4,732	7,160	10,303	14,252	24,940	49,327	85,953	137,309
23	4,142	6,266	9,017	12,473	21,826	43,168	75,222	120,166
24	3,645	5,515	7,936	10,978	19,210	37,994	66,205	105,763
25	3,225	4,890	7,021	9,712	16,996	33,615	58,575	93,572
26	2,867	4,338	6,242	8,634	15,109	29,883	52,073	83,165
27	2,560	3,874	5,574	7,710	13,492	26,684	46,498	74,280
28	2,296	3,473	4,998	6,913	12,097	23,926	41,692	66,603
29	2,066	3,126	4,498	6,222	10,888	21,536	37,526	59,948
30	1,866	2,824	4,063	5,621	9,835	19,453	33,897	54,150
31	1.691	2,559	3,682	5,094	8,914	17,630	30,722	49,077
32	1,538	2,327	3,348	4,631	8,104	16,029	27,931	44,619
33	1,402	2,122	3,053	4,223	7,390	14,615	25,468	40,684
34	1,282	1,940	2,791	3,861	6,757	13,363	23,286	37,199
35	1,175	1,778	2,559	3,540	6,194	12,250	21,346	34,101
36	1,080	1,634	2,351	3,253	5,692	11,258	19,617	31,337
37	995	1,505	2,166	2,996	5,243	10,369	18,069	28,864
38	918	1,389	1,999	2,766	4,840	9,572	16,679	26,645
39	849	1,285	1,849	2,558	4,477	8,854	15,429	24,647
40	787	1,191	1,714	2,371	4,149	8,207	14,300	22,845
41	731	1,106	1,592	2,202	3,853	7,621	13,279	21,214
42	680	1,029	1,481	2,048	3,584	7,089	12,353	19,734
43	634	959	1,380	1,909	3.340	6,606	11,511	18,389
44	592	895	1.288	1,782	3,117	6,166	10,744	17,164
45	553	837	1,204	1,665	2,914	5.764	10,044	16,045
46	518	783	1,127	1,559	2,728	5,396	9,403	15,021
47	485	734	1,057	1,462	2,558	5.059	8,815	14,082

FIRST 3 LINES ARE O.D., WALL THICKNESS, AND MOMENT OF INERTIA.

Table 9-3
Continued

8.625 TO 24 IN. SCH. 60 PIPE

OFF-SET FT	8.625 0.406 88.730	10.750 0.500 211.950	12.750 0.562 400.420	14.000 0.593 562.280	16.000 0.656 932.330	18.000 0.750 1514.630	20.000 0.812 2256.740	24.000 0.968 4652.610
2	--	--	--	--	--	--	--	--
3	342,347	817,709	--	--	--	--	--	--
4	144,428	344,971	651,725	915,181	--	--	--	--
5	73,947	176,625	333,683	468,573	776,947	--	--	--
6	42,793	102,214	193,104	271,165	449,622	730,439	--	--
7	26,949	64,368	121,605	170,763	283,144	459,985	685,357	--
8	18,053	43,121	81,466	114,398	189,684	308,154	459,136	946,576
9	12,680	30,286	57,216	80,345	133,221	216,426	322,466	664,811
10	9,243	22,078	41,710	58,572	97,118	157,775	235,077	484,647
11	6,945	16,588	31,338	44,006	72,966	118,538	176,617	364,123
12	5,349	12,777	24,138	33,896	56,203	91,305	136,040	280,467
13	4,207	10,049	18,985	26,660	44,205	71,814	106,999	220,595
14	3,369	8,046	15,201	21,345	35,393	57,498	85,670	176,621
15	2,739	6,542	12,359	17,355	28,776	46,748	69,653	143,599
16	2,257	5,390	10,183	14,300	23,711	38,519	57,392	118,322
17	1,881	4,494	8,490	11,922	19,768	32,114	47,848	98,646
18	1,585	3,786	7,152	10,043	16,653	27,053	40,308	83,101
19	1,348	3,219	6.081	8,539	14,159	23,003	34,273	70,659
20	1,155	2,760	5,214	7,321	12,140	19,722	29,385	60,581
21	998	2,384	4,504	6,325	10,487	17,036	25,384	52,332
22	868	2,073	3,917	5,501	9,121	14,817	22,077	45,515
23	760	1,815	3,428	4,814	7,982	12,967	19,321	39,833
24	669	1,597	3,017	4,237	7,025	11,413	17,005	35,058
25	592	1,413	2,669	3,749	6,216	10,098	15,045	31,017
26	526	1,256	2,373	3,332	5,526	8,977	13,375	27,574
27	470	1,122	2,119	2,976	4,934	8,016	11,943	24,623
28	421	1,006	1,900	2,668	4,424	7,187	10,709	22,078
29	379	905	1,710	2,402	3,982	6,469	9,639	19,872
30	342	818	1,545	2,169	3,597	5,844	8,707	17,950
31	310	741	1,400	1,966	3,260	5,296	7,891	16,268
32	282	674	1,273	1,787	2,964	4,815	7,174	14,790
33	257	614	1,161	1,630	2,702	4,390	6,541	13,486
34	235	562	1,061	1,490	2,471	4,014	5,981	12,331
35	216	515	973	1,366	2,265	3,680	5,483	11,304
36	198	473	894	1,255	2,082	3,382	5,039	10,388
37	182	436	823	1,156	1,917	3,115	4,641	9,568
38	168	402	760	1,067	1,770	2,875	4,284	8,832
39	156	372	703	987	1,637	2,660	3,963	8,170
40	144	345	652	915	1,517	2,465	3,673	7,573
41	134	320	605	850	1,409	2,289	3,411	7,032

FIRST 3 LINES ARE O.D., WALL THICKNESS, AND MOMENT OF INERTIA.

Table 9-3
Continued

2.375 TO 12.75 IN. SCH. 80 PIPE

OFF-SET FT	2.375 0.218 0.860	3.500 0.300 3.890	4.500 0.337 9.610	5.563 0.375 20.670	6.625 0.432 40.490	8.625 0.500 105.710	10.750 0.593 244.840	12.750 0.687 475.100
2	11,301	50,707	125,137	269,149	527,222	--	--	--
3	3,348	15,024	37,078	79,748	156,214	407.856	944,613	--
4	1,413	6.338	15,642	33,644	65,903	172,064	398,508	773,282
5	723	3,245	8,009	17,226	33,742	88,097	204,036	395,920
6	419	1,878	4,635	9,968	19,527	50,982	118,077	229,120
7	264	1.183	2,919	6,278	12,297	32,105	74,357	144,286
8	177	792	1,955	4,205	8,238	21,508	49,814	96,660
9	124	556	1,373	2,954	5,786	15,106	34,986	67,888
10	90	406	1,001	2,153	4,218	11,012	25,505	49,490
11	68	305	752	1,618	3,169	8,274	19,162	37,183
12	52	235	579	1,246	2,441	6,373	14,760	28,640
13	41	185	456	980	1,920	5,012	11,609	22,526
14	33	148	365	785	1,537	4,013	9,295	18,036
15	27	120	297	638	1,250	3,263	7,557	14,664
16	22	99	244	526	1,030	2,689	6,227	12,083
17	18	83	204	438	858	2,241	5,191	10,073
18	16	70	172	369	723	1,888	4,373	8,486
19	13	59	146	314	615	1,605	3,718	7,215
20	11	51	125	269	527	1,377	3,188	6,186
21	10	44	108	233	455	1,189	2,754	5,344
22	8	38	94	202	396	1,034	2,395	4,648
23	7	33	82	177	347	905	2,096	4,068
24	7	29	72	156	305	797	1,845	3,580
25	6	26	64	138	270	705	1,632	3,167
26	5	23	57	123	240	627	1,451	2,816
27	5	21	51	109	214	559	1,296	2,514
28	4	18	46	98	192	502	1,162	2,254
29	4	17	41	88	173	452	1,046	2,029
30	3	15	37	80	156	408	945	1,833
31	3	14	34	72	142	370	856	1,661
32	3	12	31	66	129	336	773	1,510
33	3	11	28	60	117	306	710	1,377
34	2	10	25	55	107	280	649	1,259
35	2	9	23	50	98	257	595	1,154
36	2	9	21	46	90	236	547	1,061
37	2	8	20	43	83	217	504	977
38	2	7	18	39	77	201	465	902
39	2	7	17	36	71	186	430	834
40	1	6	16	34	66	172	399	773
41	1	6	15	31	61	160	370	718

FIRST 3 LINES ARE O.D., WALL THICKNESS, AND MOMENT OF INERTIA.

Table 9-3
Continued

14 TO 24 IN. SCH. 80 PIPE

OFF- SET FT	14.000 0.750 687.310	16.000 0.843 1156.290	18.000 0.937 1833.460	20.000 1.031 2771.610	24.000 1.218 5671.820
8	139,835	235,249	373,020	563,887	--
9	98,211	165,223	261,984	396,036	810,445
10	71,596	120,447	190,986	288,710	590,815
11	53,791	90,494	143,491	216,912	443,888
12	41,433	69,703	110,524	167,078	341,907
13	32,588	54,824	86,930	131,411	268,919
14	26,092	43,895	69,601	105,215	215,311
15	21,214	35,688	56,589	85,544	175,056
16	17,479	29,406	46,628	70,486	144,242
17	14,573	24,516	38,874	58,764	120,255
18	12,276	20,653	32,748	49,504	101,306
19	10,438	17,560	27,845	42,092	86,137
20	8,949	15,056	23,873	36,089	73,852
21	7,731	13,006	20,623	31,175	63,796
22	6,724	11,312	17,936	27,114	55,486
23	5,884	9,900	15,697	23,729	48,559
24	5,179	8,713	13,816	20,885	42,738
25	4,582	7,709	12,223	18,477	37,812
26	4,073	6,853	10,866	16,426	33,615
27	3,637	6,119	9,703	14,668	30,016
28	3,261	5,487	8,700	13,152	26,914
29	2,936	4,939	7,831	11,838	24,225
30	2,652	4,461	7,074	10,693	21,882
31	2,453	4,043	6,411	9,691	19,832
32	2,185	3,676	5,828	8,811	18,030
33	1,992	3,352	5,314	8,034	16,440
34	1,822	3,065	4,859	7,346	15,032
35	1,670	2,809	4,454	6,734	13,780
36	1,535	2,582	4,093	6,188	12,663
37	1,413	2,378	3,770	5,700	11,664
38	1,305	2,195	3,481	5,262	10,767
39	1,207	2,031	3,220	4,867	9,960
40	1,119	1,882	2,984	4,511	9,231
41	1,039	1,748	2,771	4,189	8,572
42	966	1,626	2,578	3,897	7,974
43	900	1,515	2,402	3,631	7,431
44	840	1,414	2,242	3,389	6,936
45	786	1,322	2,096	3,168	6,484
46	736	1,237	1,962	2,966	6,070
47	690	1,160	1,840	2,781	5,691

FIRST 3 LINES ARE O.D., WALL THICKNESS, AND MOMENT OF INERTIA.

Table 9-3
Continued

2.375 TO 12.75 IN. SCH. 80S PIPE

OFF- SET FT	2.375 0.218 0.860	3.500 0.300 3.890	4.500 0.337 9.610	5.563 0.375 20.670	6.625 0.432 40.490	8.625 0.500 105.710	10.750 0.500 211.950	12.750 0.500 361.540
2	11,301	50,707	125,137	269,149	527,222	--	--	--
3	3,348	15,024	37,078	79,748	156,214	407,856	817,709	--
4	1,413	6,338	15,642	33,644	65,903	172,064	344,971	588,450
5	723	3,245	8,009	17,226	33,742	88,097	176,625	301,287
6	419	1,878	4,635	9,968	19,527	50,982	102,214	174,356
7	264	1,183	2,919	6,278	12,297	32,105	64,368	109,798
8	177	792	1,955	4,205	8,238	21,508	43,121	73,556
9	124	556	1,373	2,954	5,786	15,106	30,286	51,661
10	90	406	1,001	2,153	4,218	11,012	22,078	37,661
11	68	305	752	1,618	3,169	8,274	16,588	28,295
12	52	235	579	1,246	2,441	6,373	12,777	21,794
13	41	185	456	980	1,920	5,012	10,049	17,142
14	33	148	365	785	1,537	4,013	8,046	13,725
15	27	120	297	638	1,250	3,263	6,542	11,159
16	22	99	244	526	1,030	2,689	5,390	9,195
17	18	83	204	438	858	2,241	4,494	7,666
18	16	70	172	369	723	1,888	3,786	6,458
19	13	59	146	314	615	1,605	3,219	5,491
20	11	51	125	269	527	1,377	2,760	4,708
21	10	44	108	233	455	1,189	2,384	4,067
22	8	38	94	202	396	1,034	2,073	3,537
23	7	33	82	177	347	905	1,815	3,095
24	7	29	72	156	305	797	1,597	2,724
25	6	26	64	138	270	705	1,413	2,410
26	5	23	57	123	240	627	1,256	2,143
27	5	21	51	109	214	559	1,122	1,913
28	4	18	46	98	192	502	1,006	1,716
29	4	17	41	88	173	452	905	1,544
30	3	15	37	80	156	408	818	1,395
31	3	14	34	72	142	370	741	1,264
32	3	12	31	66	129	336	674	1,149
33	3	11	28	60	117	306	614	1,048
34	2	10	25	55	107	280	562	958
35	2	9	23	50	98	257	515	878
36	2	9	21	46	90	236	473	807
37	2	8	20	43	83	217	436	744
38	2	7	18	39	77	201	402	686
39	2	7	17	36	71	186	372	635
40	1	6	16	34	66	172	345	588
41	1	6	15	31	61	160	320	546

FIRST 3 LINES ARE O.D., WALL THICKNESS, AND MOMENT OF INERTIA.

Table 9-3
Continued

2.375 TO 8.625 IN. SCH. XXS PIPE

OFF-	2.375	3.500	4.500	5.563	6.625	8.625
SET	0.436	0.600	0.674	0.750	0.864	0.875
FT	1.310	5.990	15.280	33.630	66.330	161.980
2	17,074	78,027	199,006	437,953	863,706	--
3	5,059	23,119	58,965	129,764	255,913	624,941
4	2,134	9,753	24,876	54,744	107,963	263,647
5	1,093	4,994	12,736	28,029	55,277	134,987
6	632	2,890	7,371	16,220	31,989	78,118
7	398	1,820	4,642	10,215	20,145	49,194
8	267	1,219	3,109	6,843	13,495	32,956
9	187	856	2,184	4,806	9,478	23,146
10	137	624	1,592	3,504	6,910	16,873
11	103	469	1,196	2,632	5,191	12,677
12	79	361	921	2,028	3,999	9,765
13	62	284	725	1,595	3,145	7,680
14	50	227	580	1,277	2,518	6,149
15	40	185	472	1,038	2,047	5,000
16	33	152	389	855	1,687	4,119
17	28	127	324	713	1,406	3,434
18	23	107	273	601	1,185	2,893
19	20	91	232	511	1,007	2,460
20	17	78	199	438	864	2,109
21	15	67	172	378	746	1,822
22	13	59	150	329	649	1,585
23	11	51	131	288	568	1,387
24	10	45	115	253	500	1,221
25	9	40	102	224	442	1,080
26	8	36	91	199	393	960
27	7	32	81	178	351	857
28	6	28	73	160	315	769
29	6	26	65	144	283	692
30	5	23	59	130	256	625
31	5	21	53	118	232	566
32	4	19	49	107	211	515
33	4	17	44	97	192	470
34	3	16	41	89	175	429
35	3	15	37	82	161	394
36	3	13	34	75	148	362
37	3	12	31	69	136	333
38	2	11	29	64	126	308
39	2	11	27	59	116	284
40	2	10	25	55	108	264
41	2	9	23	51	100	245

FIRST 3 LINES ARE O.D., WALL THICKNESS, AND MOMENT OF INERTIA.

Table 9-3
Continued

8.625 TO 24 IN. SCH. 100 PIPE

FF-	8.625	10.750	12.750	14.000	16.000	18.000	20.000	24.000
SET	0.593	0.718	0.843	0.937	1.031	1.156	1.281	1.531
FT	121.320	286.130	561.650	824.430	1364.430	2179.680	3315.010	6851.690
2	--	--	--	--	--	--	--	--
3	468,071	--	--	--	--	--	--	--
4	197,467	465,709	914,144	--	--	--	--	--
5	101,103	238,443	468,042	687,030	--	--	--	--
6	58,509	137,988	270,858	397,587	658,002	--	--	--
7	36,845	86,896	170,569	250,375	414,369	661,955	--	--
8	24,683	58,214	114,268	167,732	277,595	443,458	674,443	--
9	17,336	40,885	80,254	117,804	194,964	311,455	473,683	979,037
10	12,638	29,805	58,505	85,879	142,128	227,051	345,315	713,718
11	9,495	22,393	43,956	64,522	106,783	170,587	259,440	536,227
12	7,314	17,248	33,857	49,698	82,250	131,395	199,835	413,031
13	5,752	13,566	26,630	39,089	64,692	103,346	157,175	324,860
14	4,606	10,862	21,321	31,297	51,796	82,744	125,844	260.101
15	3,745	8.831	17,335	25,446	42,112	67,274	102,315	211,472
16	3,085	7,277	14,284	20,966	34,699	55,432	84,305	174,248
17	2,572	6,067	11,908	17,480	28,929	46,214	70,286	145,271
18	2,167	5,111	10,032	14,725	24,370	38,932	59,210	122,380
19	1,843	4,345	8,530	12,521	20,721	33,103	50,345	104,056
20	1,580	3,726	7,313	10,735	17,766	28,381	43,164	89,215
21	1.365	3,218	6,317	9,273	15,347	24,517	37,287	77,067
22	1,187	2,799	5,494	8,065	13,348	21.323	32,430	67,028
23	1,039	2,450	4,809	7,058	11,681	18,661	28.381	58,660
24	914	2,156	4.232	6,212	10,281	16,424	24.979	51,629
25	809	1.908	3,744	5,496	9,096	14,531	22.100	45,678
26	719	1,696	3,329	4,886	8,087	12,918	19,647	40.608
27	642	1,514	2,972	4,363	7,221	11,535	17.544	36,261
28	576	1,358	2.665	3,912	6,475	10,343	15,730	32,513
29	518	1,222	2,399	3,521	5,828	9,310	14,159	29,264
30	468	1,104	2,167	3,181	5.264	8.409	12,739	26.434
31	424	1,000	1,964	2,883	4,771	7,621	11,591	23,958
32	386	910	1,785	2,621	4,337	6,929	10,538	21,731
33	352	829	1,628	2,390	3,955	6,318	9,609	19,860
34	322	758	1,489	2,185	3,616	5,777	8,786	18.159
35	295	695	1,365	2,003	3,315	5,296	8,054	16.646
36	271	639	1,234	1,841	3,046	4,866	7,401	15.297
37	249	588	1.155	1,695	2,806	4,482	6,817	14,090
38	230	543	1,066	1,565	2,590	4,138	6,293	13,007
39	213	502	986	1,448	2,396	3,828	5,821	12,032
40	197	466	914	1,342	2,221	3.548	5.396	11,152
41	183	432	849	1,246	2,062	3.294	5.010	10,356

FIRST 3 LINES ARE O.D., WALL THICKNESS, AND MOMENT OF INERTIA.

Table 9-3
Continued

4.5 TO 12.75 IN. SCH. 120 PIPE

OFF-SET FT	4.500 0.438 11.660	5.563 0.500 25.730	6.625 0.562 49.610	8.625 0.718 140.530	10.750 0.843 324.220	12.750 1.000 641.660
2	151,849	335,048	645,971	--	--	--
3	44,992	99,274	191,399	542,189	--	--
4	18,981	41,881	80,746	228,736	527,711	--
5	9,718	21,443	41,342	117,113	270,188	534,720
6	5,624	12,409	23,925	67,774	156,359	309,445
7	3,542	7,815	15,066	42,680	98,465	194,869
8	2,373	5,235	10,093	28,592	65,964	130,547
9	1,666	3,677	7,089	20,081	46,329	91,687
10	1,215	2,680	5,168	14,639	33,773	66,840
11	913	2,014	3,883	10,999	25,375	50,218
12	703	1,551	2,991	8,472	19,545	38,681
13	553	1,220	2,352	6,663	15,373	30,423
14	443	977	1,883	5,335	12,308	24,359
15	360	794	1,531	4,338	10,007	19,804
16	297	654	1,262	3,574	8,245	16,318
17	247	546	1,052	2,980	6,874	13,605
18	208	460	886	2,510	5,791	11,461
19	177	391	753	2,134	4,924	9,745
20	152	335	646	1,830	4,222	8,355
21	131	289	558	1,581	3,647	7,217
22	114	252	485	1,375	3,172	6,277
23	100	220	425	1,203	2,776	5,494
24	88	194	374	1,059	2,443	4,835
25	78	172	331	937	2,162	4,278
26	69	153	294	833	1,922	3,803
27	62	136	263	744	1,716	3,396
28	55	122	235	667	1,539	3,045
29	50	110	212	600	1,385	2,741
30	45	99	191	542	1,251	2,476
31	41	90	173	491	1,134	2,244
32	37	82	158	447	1,031	2,040
33	34	75	144	407	940	1,860
34	31	68	131	372	859	1,701
35	28	63	121	341	788	1,559
36	26	57	111	314	724	1,433
37	24	53	102	289	667	1,320
38	22	49	94	267	615	1,218
39	20	45	87	247	569	1,127
40	19	42	81	229	528	1,044
41	18	39	75	212	490	970

FIRST 3 LINES ARE O.D., WALL THICKNESS, AND MOMENT OF INERTIA.

Table 9-3
Continued

14 TO 24 IN. SCH. 120 PIPE

OFF-	14.000	16.000	18.000	20.000	24.000
SET	1.093	1.218	1.375	1.500	1.812
FT	929.520	1555.410	2498.090	3754.150	7824.550
8	189,112	316,449	508,238	763,785	--
9	132,819	222,252	356,952	536,430	--
10	96,825	162,022	260,218	391,058	815,057
11	72,746	121,730	195,505	293,807	612,365
12	56,033	93,763	150,589	226,307	471,677
13	44,072	73,747	118,442	177,996	370,987
14	35,286	59,046	94,832	142,514	297,033
15	28,689	48,007	77,102	115,869	241,498
16	23,639	39,556	63,530	95,473	198,989
17	19,708	32,978	52,965	79,597	165,898
18	16,602	27,782	44,619	67,054	139,756
19	14,117	23,622	37,938	57,014	118,830
20	12,103	20,253	32,527	48,882	101,882
21	10,455	17,495	28,098	42,226	88,010
22	9,093	15,216	24,438	36,726	76,546
23	7,958	13,317	21,387	32,141	66,989
24	7,004	11,720	18,824	28,288	58,960
25	6,197	10,369	16,654	25,028	52,164
26	5,509	9,218	14,805	22,250	46,373
27	4,919	8,232	13,220	19,868	41,409
28	4,411	7,381	11,854	17,814	37,129
29	3,970	6,643	10,669	16,034	33,419
30	3,586	6,001	9,638	14,484	30,187
31	3,250	5,439	8,735	13,127	27,359
32	2,955	4,945	7,941	11,934	24,874
33	2,694	4,509	7,241	10,882	22,680
34	2,463	4,122	6,621	9,950	20,737
35	2,258	3,779	6,069	9,121	19,010
36	2,075	3,473	5,577	8,382	17,470
37	1,912	3,199	5,137	7,720	16,091
38	1,765	2,953	4,742	7,127	14,854
39	1,632	2,731	4,387	6,592	13,740
40	1,513	2,532	4,066	6,110	12,735
41	1,405	2,351	3,776	5,674	11,826
42	1,307	2,187	3,512	5,278	11,001
43	1,218	2,038	3,273	4,919	10,251
44	1,137	1,902	3,055	4,591	9,568
45	1,063	1,778	2,856	4,291	8,944
46	995	1,665	2,673	4,018	8,374
47	933	1,561	2,506	3,767	7,850

FIRST 3 LINES ARE O.D., WALL THICKNESS, AND MOMENT OF INERTIA.

Table 9-3
Continued

8.625 TO 24 IN. SCH. 140 PIPE

OFF-SET FT	8.625 0.812 153.720	10.750 1.000 367.800	12.750 1.125 700.550	14.000 1.250 1027.190	16.000 1.438 1760.740	18.000 1.375 2498.090	20.000 1.750 4215.620	24.000 2.062 8625.000
2	--	--	--	--	--	--	--	--
3	593,062	--	--	--	--	--	--	--
4	250,198	598,642	--	--	--	--	--	--
5	128,101	306,505	583,792	856,000	--	--	--	--
6	74,133	177,375	337,843	495,370	849,125	--	--	--
7	46,684	111,700	212,752	311,953	534,726	758,652	--	--
8	31,275	74,830	142,527	208,984	358,224	508,238	857,670	--
9	21,965	52,556	100,102	146,776	251,592	356,952	602,369	--
10	16,013	38,313	72,974	107,000	183,411	260,218	439,127	898,438
11	12,031	28,785	54,826	80,391	137,799	195,505	329,923	675,010
12	9,267	22,172	42,230	61,921	106,141	150,589	254,125	519,930
13	7,288	17,439	33,215	48,703	83,482	118,442	199,876	408,939
14	5,836	13,962	26,594	38,994	66,841	94,832	160,032	327,419
15	4,744	11,352	21,622	31,704	54,344	77,102	130,112	266,204
16	3,909	9,354	17,816	26,123	44,778	63,530	107,209	219,345
17	3,259	7,798	14,853	21,779	37,332	52,965	89,381	182,870
18	2,746	6,569	12,513	18,347	31,449	44,619	75,296	154,053
19	2,335	5,586	10,639	15,600	26,740	37,938	64,022	130,987
20	2,002	4,789	9,122	13,375	22,926	32,527	54,891	112,305
21	1,729	4,137	7,880	11,554	19,805	28,098	47,417	97,013
22	1,504	3,598	6,853	10,049	17,225	24,438	41,240	84,378
23	1,316	3,149	5,998	8,794	15,074	21,387	36,092	73,842
24	1,158	2,771	5,279	7,740	13,268	18,824	31,766	64,991
25	1,025	2,452	4,670	6,848	11,738	16,654	28,104	57,500
26	911	2,180	4,152	6,088	10,435	14,805	24,984	51,117
27	814	1,947	3,707	5,436	9,318	13,220	22,310	45,645
28	729	1,745	3,324	4,874	8,355	11,854	20,004	40,927
29	657	1,571	2,992	4,387	7,520	10,669	18,005	36,838
30	593	1,419	2,703	3,963	6,793	9,638	16,264	33,275
31	538	1,286	2,450	3,592	6,157	8,735	14,740	30,158
32	489	1,169	2,227	3,265	5,597	7,941	13,401	27,418
33	446	1,066	2,031	2,977	5,104	7,241	12,219	25,000
34	407	975	1,857	2,722	4,666	6,621	11,173	22,859
35	373	894	1,702	2,496	4,278	6,069	10,242	20,955
36	343	821	1,564	2,293	3,931	5,577	9,412	19,257
37	316	756	1,441	2,112	3,621	5,137	8,669	17,737
38	292	698	1,330	1,950	3,343	4,742	8,003	16,373
39	270	646	1,230	1,804	3,092	4,387	7,403	15,146
40	250	599	1,140	1,672	2,866	4,066	6,861	14,038
41	232	556	1,059	1,553	2,661	3,776	6,371	13,036

FIRST 3 LINES ARE O.D., WALL THICKNESS, AND MOMENT OF INERTIA.

Table 9-3
Continued

2.375 TO 12.75 IN. SCH. 160 PIPE

OFF- SET FT	2.375 0.343 1.160	3.500 0.438 5.030	4.500 0.531 13.270	5.563 0.625 30.020	6.625 0.718 58.970	8.625 0.906 165.880	10.750 1.125 399.300	12.750 1.312 781.120
2	15,134	65,612	172,799	390,962	767,880	--	--	--
3	4,484	19,441	51,200	115,840	227,520	639,998	--	--
4	1,892	8,202	21,600	48,870	95,985	269,999	649,915	--
5	969	4,199	11,059	25,022	49,144	138,239	332,756	650,938
6	561	2,430	6,400	14,480	28,440	80,000	192,567	376,700
7	353	1,530	4,030	9,119	17,910	50,379	121,267	237,222
8	236	1,025	2,700	6,109	11,998	33,750	81,239	158,920
9	166	720	1,896	4,290	8,427	23,704	57,057	111,615
10	121	525	1,382	3,128	6,143	17,280	41,595	81,367
11	91	394	1,039	2,350	4,615	12,983	31,251	61,132
12	70	304	800	1,810	3,555	10,000	24,071	47,088
13	55	239	629	1,424	2,796	7,865	18,932	37,036
14	44	191	504	1,140	2,239	6,297	15,158	29,653
15	36	156	410	927	1,820	5,120	12,324	24,109
16	30	128	337	764	1,500	4,219	10,155	19,865
17	25	107	281	637	1,250	3,517	8,466	16,562
18	21	90	237	536	1,053	2,963	7,132	13,952
19	18	77	202	456	896	2,519	6,064	11,863
20	15	66	173	391	768	2,160	5,199	10,171
21	13	57	149	338	663	1,866	4,491	8,786
22	11	49	130	294	577	1,623	3,906	7,642
23	10	43	114	257	505	1,420	3,419	6,688
24	9	38	100	226	444	1,250	3,009	5,886
25	8	34	88	200	393	1,106	2,662	5,208
26	7	30	79	178	350	983	2,367	4,629
27	6	27	70	159	312	878	2,113	4,134
28	6	24	63	142	280	787	1,895	3,707
29	5	22	57	128	252	709	1,705	3,336
30	4	19	51	116	228	640	1,541	3,014
31	4	18	46	105	206	580	1,396	2,731
32	4	16	42	95	187	527	1,269	2,483
33	3	15	38	87	171	481	1,157	2,264
34	3	13	35	80	156	440	1,058	2,070
35	3	12	32	73	143	403	970	1,898
36	3	11	30	67	132	370	892	1,744
37	2	10	27	62	121	341	821	1,606
38	2	10	25	57	112	315	758	1,483
39	2	9	23	53	104	291	701	1,372
40	2	8	22	49	96	270	650	1,271
41	2	8	20	45	89	251	604	1,181

FIRST 3 LINES ARE O.D., WALL THICKNESS, AND MOMENT OF INERTIA.

Table 9-3
Continued

14 TO 24 IN. SCH. 160 PIPE

OFF-	14.000	16.000	18.000	20.000	24.000
SET	1.406	1.593	1.781	1.968	2.343
FT	1116.640	1893.530	3019.960	4585.210	9455.410
8	227,182	385,241	614,413	932,863	--
9	159,557	270,567	431,522	655,180	--
10	116,317	197,243	314,579	477,626	984,939
11	87,391	148,192	236,348	358,848	739,999
12	67,313	114,146	182,048	276,404	569,988
13	52,944	89,779	143,186	217,399	448,311
14	42,390	71,882	114,643	174,062	358,943
15	34,464	58,443	93,209	141,519	291,834
16	28,398	48,155	76,802	116,608	240,464
17	23,675	40,147	64,030	97,217	200,476
18	19,945	33,821	53,940	81,897	168,885
19	16,958	28,757	45,864	69,635	143,598
20	14,540	24,655	39,322	59,703	123,117
21	12,560	21,298	33,968	51,574	106,353
22	10,924	18,524	29,544	44,856	92,500
23	9,560	16,211	25,855	39,256	80,952
24	8,414	14,268	22,756	34,550	71,248
25	7,444	12,624	20,133	30,568	63,036
26	6,618	11,222	17,898	27,175	56,039
27	5,910	10,021	15,982	24,266	50,040
28	5,299	8,985	14,330	21,758	44,868
29	4,769	8,087	12,898	19,584	40,385
30	4,308	7,305	11,651	17,690	36,479
31	3,904	6,621	10,560	16,033	33,062
32	3,550	6,019	9,600	14,576	30,058
33	3,237	5,489	8,754	13,291	27,407
34	2,959	5,018	8,004	12,152	25,060
35	2,713	4,600	7,337	11,140	22,972
36	2,493	4,228	6,743	10,237	21,111
37	2,296	3,894	6,210	9,429	19,445
38	2,120	3,595	5,733	8,704	17,950
39	1,961	3,325	5,303	8,052	16,604
40	1,817	3,082	4,915	7,463	15,390
41	1,688	2,862	4,564	6,930	14,291
42	1,570	2,662	4,246	6,447	13,294
43	1,463	2,481	3,957	6,007	12,388
44	1,365	2,315	3,693	5,607	11,562
45	1,276	2,165	3,452	5,241	10,809
46	1,195	2,026	3,232	4,907	10,119
47	1,120	1,900	3,030	4,600	9,487

FIRST 3 LINES ARE O.D., WALL THICKNESS, AND MOMENT OF INERTIA.

For the example shown in Figure 9-1, it will take 7,552 lb for a 1-in. expansion for a 10-ft offset for Δx .9214 expansion the force F_x = 6,949 lb. For a 20-ft offset the force will be 944 lb for a 1-in. expansion, for Δy .46 in. the force F_y = 434 lb.

The nomograph in Figure 9-2 is used to size piping loops, depending on the size of the pipe and the thermal expansion between anchors. This nomograph is conservative for a refined design. An exact calculation by computer should be required.

Example Problem 9-2

What size piping loop will be required for a 300-ft straight pipeline under the following conditions:

Temperature:	400°F
O.D.:	12,750
Schedule:	Sch 140
Materials:	A-53 Grade B C.S.

Use the nomograph in Figure 9-2, and join points A, B, and C. This will show a need of a 70-ft loop (L = 70 ft).

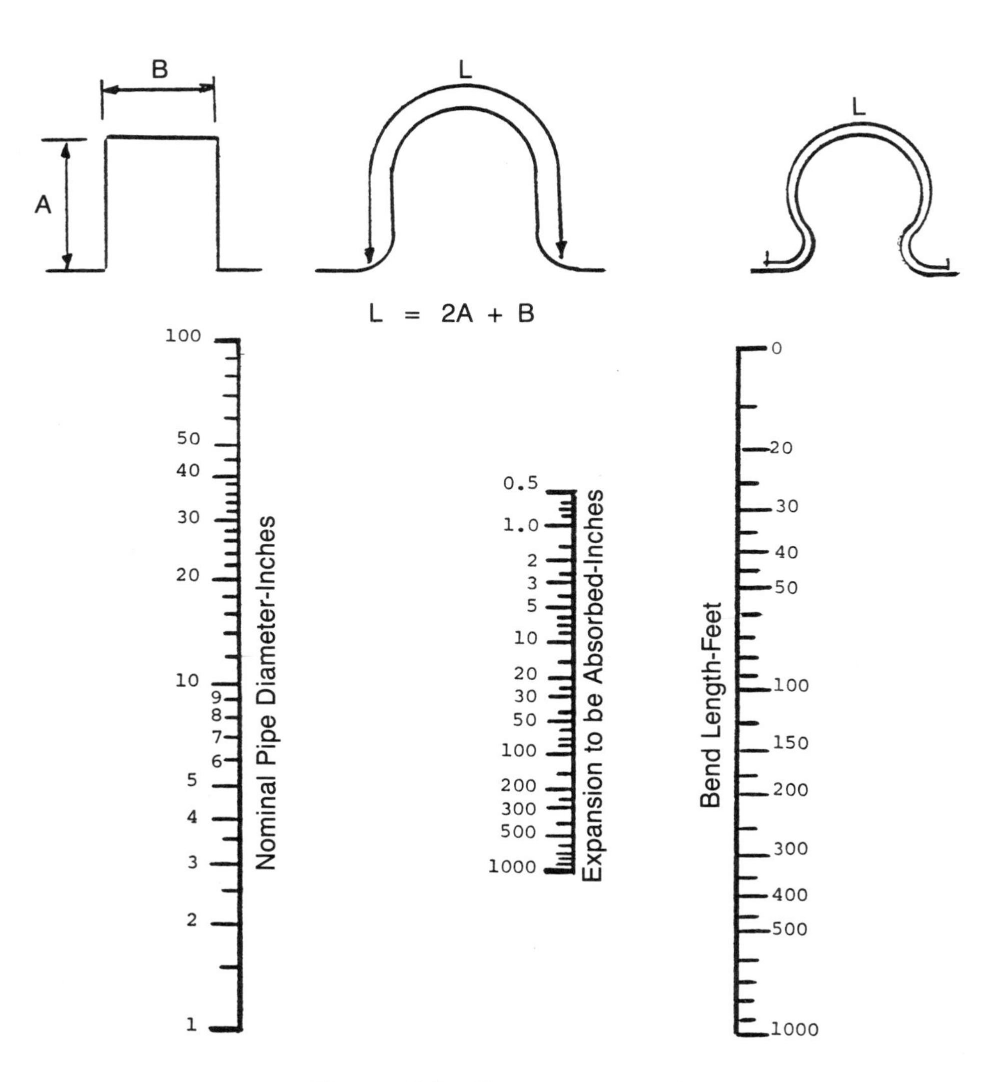

Figure 9-2. Stress nomograph.

10

Properties of Pipe

Carbon steel

$\rho_{steel} = 489.6$ lb/ft³

The following are the definitions of the terms used in the table.

Definitions

D = Outside diameter of pipe, in.
Sch = Pipe schedule, nondimensional
t = Wall thickness, in.
d = Inside diameter of pipe, in.
d^5 = Fifth power of d, $in.^5$
A_o = $D\pi/12$ = outside pipe surface, ft^2/ft (length)
A_i = $d\pi/12$ = inside pipe surface, ft^2/ft (length)
A_m = $(D^2 - d^2)\pi/4$ = metal area, $in.^2$
A_f = $d^2 \pi/4$ = flow area, $in.^2$
W = $3.4A_m$ = weight of pipe, lb/ft
W_w = $0.433\ A_f$ = weight of water in pipe, lb/ft
R_g = $(I/A)^{1/2}$ = $(D^2 + d^2)^{1/2}/4$ = radius of gyration, in.
I = $A_m R_g^2 = 0.0491\ (D^4 - d^4)$ = moment of inertia, $in.^4$
Z = $2I/D = 0.0982\ (D^4 - d^4)/D$ = section modulus = $in.^3$

Table 10-1
Properties of Pipe

D	Sch	t	d	d^5	Ao	Ai	Am	Af	W	Ww	Rg	I	Z
1/8 D=.405	10S	.049	.307	.00273	.106	.080	.055	.074	.186	.032	.1271	.0009	.0043
	40 ST 40S	.068	.269	.00141	.106	.070	.072	.057	.245	.025	.1215	.0011	.0052
	80 XS 80S	.095	.215	.00046	.106	.056	.092	.036	.314	.016	.1146	.0012	.0060
1/4 D=.540	10S	.065	.410	.01159	.141	.107	.097	.132	.330	.057	.1694	.0028	.0103
	40 ST 40S	.088	.364	.00639	.141	.095	.125	.104	.425	.045	.1628	.0033	.0123
	80 XS 80S	.119	.302	.00251	.141	.079	.157	.072	.535	.031	.1547	.0038	.0140
3/8 D=.675	10S	.065	.545	.04808	.177	.143	.124	.233	.423	.101	.2169	.0059	.0174
	40 ST 40S	.091	.493	.02912	.177	.129	.167	.191	.568	.083	.2090	.0073	.0216
	80 XS 80S	.126	.423.	.01354	.177	.111	.217	.140	.739	.061	.1991	.0086	.0255
1/2 D=.840	10S	.083	.674	.13909	.220	.176	.197	.357	.671	.154	.269	.0143	.0341
	40 ST 40S	.109	.622	:09310	.220	.163	.250	.304	.851	.132	.261	.0171	.0407
	80 XS 80S	.147	.546	.04852	.220	.143	.320	.234	1.088	.101	.250	.0201	.0478
	160	.187	.466	.02198	.220	.122	.384	.171	1.304	.074	.240	.0221	.0527
	XX	.294	.252	.00102	.220	.066	.504	.050	1.715	.022	.219	.0243	.0577

Table 10-1
Continued

D	Sch	t	d	d^5	Ao	Ai	Am	Af	W	Ww	Rg	I	Z
3/4	5S	.065	.920	.6591	.275	.241	.201	.664	.683	.288	.349	.0245	.0467
	10S	.083	.884	.5398	.275	.231	.252	.614	.857	.266	.343	.0297	.0566
	40 ST 40S	.113	.824	.3799	.275	.216	.333	.533	1.131	.231	.334	.0370	.0706
	80 XS 80S	.154	.742	.2249	.275	.194	.434	.432	1.474	.187	.321	.0448	.0853
		.188	.675	.1401	.275	.177	.508	.358	1.728	.155	.312	.0495	.0943
D = 1.050	160	.218	.614	.0873	.275	.161	.570	.296	1.937	.128	.304	.0527	.1004
	XX	.308	.434	.0154	.275	.114	.718	.148	2.441	.064	.284	.0579	.1104
1	5S	.065	1.185	2.337	.344	.310	.255	1.103	.867	.478	.443	.0500	.0760
	10S	.109	1.097	1.589	.344	.287	.413	.945	1.404	.409	.428	.0757	.1151
	40 ST 40S	.133	1.049	1.270	.344	.275	.494	.864	1.679	.374	.420	.0874	.1329
	80 XS 80S	.179	.957	.803	.344	.250	.639	.719	2.172	.311	.407	.1056	.1606
		.219	.877	.519	.344	.230	.754	.604	2.564	.262	.395	.1178	.1791
D = 1.315	160	.250	.815	.360	.344	.213	.836	.522	2.844	.226	.387	.1252	.1903
	XX	.358	.599	.077	.344	.157	1.076	.282	3.659	.122	.361	.1405	.2137
1 1/4	5S	.065	1.530	8.384	.435	.401	.326	1.839	1.108	.796	.564	.1037	.1253
	10S	.109	1.442	6.235	.434	.378	.531	1.633	1.805	.707	.550	.1605	.1934
	40 ST 40S	.140	1.380	5.005	.434	.361	.668	1.496	2.273	.648	.540	.1948	.2346
	80 XS 80S	.191	1.278	3.409	.434	.334	.881	1.283	2.997	.555	.524	.2418	.2914
D = 1.660	160	.250	1.160	2.100	.434	.304	1.107	1.057	3.765	.458	.506	.2839	.3421
	XX	.382	.896	.577	.434	.234	1.534	.630	5.215	.273	.472	.3412	.4111
1 1/2	5S	.065	1.770	17.37	.497	.463	.375	2.461	1.275	1.066	.649	.158	.166
	10S	.109	1.682	13.46	.497	.440	.613	2.222	2.085	.962	.634	.247	.260
	40 ST 40S	.145	1.610	10.82	.497	.421	.799	2.036	2.718	.882	.623	.310	.326
	80 XS 80S	.200	1.500	7.59	.497	.393	1.068	1.767	3.632	.765	.605	.391	.412
D = 1.900	160	.281	1.337	4.27	.497	.350	1.431	1.404	4.866	.608	.581	.483	.508
	XX	.400	1.100	1.61	.497	.288	1.885	.950	6.409	.411	.549	.568	.598
2	5S	.065	2.245	57.03	.622	.588	.472	3.958	1.605	1.714	.817	.315	.265
	10S	.109	2.157	46.69	.622	.565	.776	3.654	2.638	1.582	.802	.499	.420
	40 ST 40S	.154	2.067	37.73	.622	.541	1.074	3.356	3.653	1.453	.787	.666	.561
		.167	2.041	35.42	.622	.534	1.158	3.272	3.938	1.417	.783	.710	.598
		.188	2.000	32.00	.622	.524	1.288	3.142	4.381	1.360	.776	.777	.654
	80 XS 80S	.218	1.939	27.41	.622	.508	1.477	2.953	5.022	1.278	.766	.868	.731
D = 2.375		.250	1.875	23.17	.622	.491	1.669	2.761	5.674	1.196	.756	.955	.804
		.312	1.750	16.41	.622	.458	2.025	2.405	6.884	1.041	.738	1.102	.928
	160	.343	1.689	13.74	.622	.442	2.190	2.240	7.445	.970	.728	1.163	.979
	XX	.436	1.503	7.67	.622	.393	2.656	1.774	9.030	.768	.703	1.312	1.104
2 1/2	5S	.083	2.709	145.9	.753	.709	.728	5.76	2.475	2.496	.988	.711	.495
	10S	.120	2.635	127.0	.753	.690	1.039	5.45	3.531	2.361	.975	.988	.687
	40 ST 40S	.203	2.469	91.8	.753	.646	1.704	4.79	5.794	2.073	.947	1.530	1.064
		.217	2.441	86.7	.753	.639	1.812	4.68	6.160	2.026	.943	1.611	1.121
	80 XS 80S	.276	2.323	67.6	.753	.608	2.254	4.24	7.662	1.835	.924	1.925	1.339
D = 2.875	160	.375	2.125	43.3	.753	.556	2.945	3.55	10.01	1.536	.894	2.353	1.637
	XX	.552	1.771	17.4	.753	.464	4.028	2.46	13.70	1.067	.844	2.872	1.998
3	5S	.083	3.334	411.9	.916	.873	.891	8.73	3.03	3.78	1.208	1.300	.743
	10S	.120	3.260	368.2	.916	.853	1.274	8.35	4.33	3.61	1.196	1.822	1.041
		.125	3.250	362.6	.916	.851	1.325	8.30	4.51	3.59	1.194	1.890	1.080
		.148	3.204	337.6	.916	.839	1.558	8.06	5.30	3.49	1.186	2.194	1.253
D = 3.500		.188	3.124	297.6	.916	.818	1.956	7.66	6.65	3.32	1.173	2.692	1.538
	40 ST 40S	.216	3.068	271.8	.916	.803	2.228	7.39	7.58	3.20	1.164	3.018	1.724

Table 10-1
Continued

D	Sch	t	d	d^5	Ao	Ai	Am	Af	W	Ww	Rg	I	Z
(continued)		.241	3.018	250	.916	.790	2.467	7.15	8.39	3.10	1.155	3.29	1.883
		.254	2.992	240	.916	.783	2.590	7.03	8.81	3.04	1.151	3.43	1.962
		.289	2.922	213	.916	.765	2.915	6.71	9.91	2.90	1.140	3.79	2.165
3	80 XS 80S	.300	2.900	205	.916	.759	3.016	6.60	10.25	2.86	1.136	3.90	2.226
		.312	2.875	196	.916	.753	3.129	6.49	10.64	2.81	1.132	4.01	2.294
D = 3.500		.406	2.687	140	.916	.703	3.950	5.67	13.43	2.46	1.103	4.81	2.748
	160	.438	2.624	124	.916	.687	4.213	5.41	14.33	2.34	1.094	5.04	2.879
	XX	.600	2.300	64	.916	.602	5.466	4.15	18.58	1.80	1.047	5.99	3.425
	5S	.083	3.834	828	1.047	1.004	1.021	11.55	3.47	5.00	1.385	1.96	.979
	10S	.120	3.760	752	1.047	.984	1.463	11.10	4.97	4.81	1.372	2.76	1.378
		.128	3.744	736	1.047	.980	1.557	11.01	5.29	4.77	1.370	2.92	1.461
		.134	3.732	724	1.047	.977	1.628	10.94	5.53	4.74	1.368	3.04	1.522
		.148	3.704	697	1.047	.970	1.791	10.78	6.09	4.67	1.363	3.33	1.664
3½		.188	3.624	625	1.047	.949	2.251	10.31	7.65	4.47	1.349	4.10	2.050
	40 ST 40S	.226	3.548	562	1.047	.929	2.680	9.89	9.11	4.28	1.337	4.79	2.394
D = 4.000		.281	3.438	480	1.047	.900	3.283	9.28	11.16	4.02	1.319	5.71	2.855
	80 XS 80S	.318	3.364	431	1.047	.881	3.678	8.89	12.51	3.85	1.307	6.28	3.141
		.344	3.312	399	1.047	.867	3.951	8.62	13.43	3.73	1.298	6.66	3.331
		.469	3.062	269	1.047	.802	5.203	7.36	17.69	3.19	1.259	8.25	4.127
		.636	2.728	151	1.047	.714	6.721	5.84	22.85	2.53	1.210	9.85	4.925
	5S	.083	4.334	1529	1.178	1.135	1.151	14.75	3.91	6.39	1.562	2.81	1.248
	10S	.120	4.260	1403	1.178	1.115	1.651	14.25	5.61	6.17	1.549	3.96	1.762
		.128	4.244	1377	1.178	1.111	1.758	14.15	5.98	6.13	1.546	4.21	1.869
		.134	4.232	1358	1.178	1.108	1.838	14.07	6.25	6.09	1.544	4.38	1.949
		.142	4.216	1332	1.178	1.104	1.944	13.96	6.61	6.04	1.542	4.62	2.054
		.165	4.170	1261	1.178	1.092	2.247	13.66	7.64	5.91	1.534	5.29	2.350
		.188	4.124	1193	1.178	1.080	2.55	13.36	8.66	5.78	1.526	5.93	2.64
		.205	4.090	1144	1.178	1.071	2.77	13.14	9.40	5.69	1.520	6.39	2.84
	40 ST 40S	.237	4.026	1058	1.178	1.054	3.17	12.73	10.79	5.51	1.510	7.23	3.22
4		.250	4.000	1024	1.178	1.047	3.34	12.57	11.35	5.44	1.505	7.56	3.36
		.271	3.958	971	1.178	1.036	3.60	12.30	12.24	5.33	1.498	8.08	3.59
D = 4.500		.281	3.938	947	1.178	1.031	3.74	12.18	12.72	5.27	1.495	8.33	3.70
		.300	3.900	902	1.178	1.021	3.96	11.95	13.46	5.17	1.489	8.78	3.90
		.312	3.876	875	1.178	1.015	4.10	11.80	13.96	5.11	1.485	9.05	4.02
	80 XS 80S	.337	3.826	820	1.178	1.002	4.41	11.50	14.99	4.98	1.477	9.61	4.27
		.375	3.750	742	1.178	.982	4.86	11.04	16.52	4.78	1.464	10.42	4.63
	120	.438	3.624	625	1.178	.949	5.59	10.31	19.00	4.47	1.444	11.66	5.18
		.500	3.500	525	1.178	.916	6.28	9.62	21.36	4.17	1.425	12.77	5.67
	160	.531	3.438	480	1.178	.900	6.62	9.28	22.51	4.02	1.416	13.27	5.90
	XX	.674	3.152	311	1.178	.825	8.10	7.80	27.54	3.38	1.374	15.29	6.79
	5S	.109	5.345	4363	1.456	1.399	1.88	22.43	6.38	9.71	1.928	6.97	2.51
	10S	.134	5.295	4162	1.456	1.386	2.29	22.02	7.77	9.53	1.920	8.43	3.03
	40 ST 40S	.258	5.047	3275	1.456	1.321	4.30	20.01	14.62	8.66	1.878	15.17	5.45
		.352	4.859	2708	1.456	1.272	5.76	18.54	19.59	8.03	1.847	19.65	7.07
5	80 XS 80S	.375	4.813	2583	1.456	1.260	6.11	18.19	20.78	7.88	1.839	20.68	7.43
		.438	4.688	2264	1.456	1.227	7.04	17.26	23.95	7.47	1.819	23.31	8.38
D = 5.563	120	.500	4.563	1978	1.456	1.194	7.95	16.35	27.04	7.06	1.799	25.74	9.25
	160	.625	4.313	1492	1.456	1.129	9.70	14.61	32.97	6.33	1.760	30.03	10.80
	XX	.750	4.063	1107	1.456	1.064	11.34	12.97	38.55	5.61	1.722	33.64	12.10

Table 10-1
Continued

D	Sch	t	d	d^5	Ao	Ai	Am	Af	W	Ww	Rg	I	Z
6 D=6.625	5S	.109	6.407	10.80	1.734	1.677	2.23	32.2	7.58	13.96	2.304	11.84	3.58
	10S	.134	6.357	10.38	1.734	1.664	2.73	31.7	9.29	13.74	2.295	14.40	4.35
		.169	6.287	9.82	1.734	1.646	3.43	31.0	11.66	13.44	2.283	17.87	5.40
		.180	6.265	9.65	1.734	1.640	3.64	30.8	12.39	13.35	2.280	18.94	5.72
		.188	6.249	9.53	1.734	1.636	3.80	30.7	12.93	13.28	2.277	19.71	5.95
		.219	6.187	9.07	1.734	1.620	4.41	30.1	14.99	13.02	2.266	22.64	6.83
		.250	6.125	8.62	1.734	1.604	5.01	29.5	17.02	12.75	2.256	25.5	7.69
		.277	6.071	8.25	1.734	1.589	5.52	28.9	18.78	12.53	2.246	27.9	8.42
	40 ST 40S	.280	6.065	8.21	1.734	1.588	5.58	28.9	18.98	12.51	2.246	28.1	8.50
		.375	5.875	7.00	1.734	1.538	7.36	27.1	25.04	11.73	2.214	36.1	10.90
	80 XS 80S	.432	5.761	6.35	1.734	1.508	8.40	26.1	28.58	11.29	2.195	40.5	12.23
		.500	5.625	5.63	1.734	1.473	9.62	24.9	32.71	10.76	2.173	45.4	13.71
	120	.562	5.501	5.04	1.734	1.440	10.70	23.8	36.40	10.29	2.153	49.6	14.98
	160	.718	5.189	3.76	1.734	1.358	13.32	21.1	45.30	9.16	2.104	59.0	17.81
	XX	.864	4.897	2.82	1.734	1.282	15.64	18.8	53.17	8.16	2.060	66.3	20.03
8 D=8.625	5S	.109	8.407	42.0	2.258	2.201	2.92	55.5	9.91	24.04	3.01	26.4	6.13
	10S	.148	8.329	40.1	2.258	2.180	3.94	54.5	13.40	23.59	3.00	35.4	8.21
		.158	8.309	39.6	2.258	2.175	4.20	54.2	14.29	23.48	2.99	37.7	8.74
		.165	8.295	39.3	2.258	2.172	4.39	54.0	14.91	23.40	2.99	39.3	9.10
		.188	8.249	38.2	2.258	2.160	4.98	53.4	16.94	23.14	2.98	44.4	10.29
		.203	8.219	37.5	2.258	2.152	5.37	53.1	18.26	22.97	2.98	47.7	11.05
		.219	8.187	36.8	2.258	2.143	5.78	52.6	19.66	22.94	2.97	51.1	11.86
		.238	8.149	35.9	2.258	2.133	6.27	52.2	21.32	22.58	2.97	55.2	12.80
	20	.250	8.125	35.4	2.258	2.127	6.58	51.8	22.37	22.45	2.96	57.7	13.39
	30	.277	8.071	34.2	2.258	2.113	7.26	51.2	24.70	22.15	2.95	63.4	14.69
	40 ST 40S	.322	7.981	32.4	2.258	2.089	8.40	50.0	28.56	21.68	2.94	72.5	16.81
		.344	7.937	31.5	2.258	2.078	8.95	49.5	30.43	21.42	2.93	76.9	17.82
		.352	7.921	31.2	2.258	2.074	9.15	49.3	31.1	21.3	2.93	78.4	18.19
		.375	7.875	30.3	2.258	2.062	9.72	48.7	33.0	21.1	2.92	82.9	19.22
	60	.406	7.813	29.1	2.258	2.045	10.48	47.9	35.6	20.8	2.91	88.8	20.58
		.469	7.687	26.8	2.258	2.012	12.02	46.4	40.9	20.1	2.89	100.3	23.25
	80 XS 80S	.500	7.625	25.8	2.258	1.996	12.76	45.7	43.4	19.8	2.88	105.7	24.52
	100	.593	7.439	22.8	2.258	1.948	14.96	43.5	50.9	18.8	2.85	121.4	28.14
		.625	7.375	21.8	2.258	1.931	15.71	42.7	53.4	18.5	2.84	126.5	29.32
	120	.718	7.189	19.2	2.258	1.882	17.84	40.6	60.6	17.6	2.81	140.6	32.60
	140	.812	7.001	16.8	2.258	1.833	19.93	38.5	67.8	16.7	2.78	153.7	35.63
	XX	.875	6.875	15.4	2.258	1.800	21.30	37.1	72.4	16.1	2.76	162.0	37.57
	160	.906	6.813	14.7	2.258	1.784	21.97	36.5	74.7	15.8	2.75	165.9	38.48
10 D=10.750	5S	.134	10.482	127	2.81	2.74	4.47	86.3	15.2	37.4	3.75	63.0	11.72
	10S	.165	10.420	123	2.81	2.73	5.49	85.3	18.7	36.9	3.74	76.9	14.30
		.188	10.374	120	2.81	2.72	6.24	84.5	21.2	36.6	3.73	87.0	16.19
		.203	10.344	118	2.81	2.71	6.73	84.0	22.9	36.4	3.73	93.6	17.41
		.219	10.310	116	2.81	2.70	7.28	83.5	24.7	36.1	3.72	100.9	18.78
	20	.250	10.250	113	2.81	2.68	8.25	82.5	28.0	35.7	3.71	113.7	21.16
		.279	10.192	110	2.81	2.67	9.18	81.6	31.2	35.3	3.70	125.9	23.42
	30	.307	10.136	107	2.81	2.65	10.07	80.7	34.2	34.9	3.69	137.5	25.57
		.348	10.054	103	2.81	2.63	11.37	79.4	38.7	34.4	3.68	154.0	28.66
	40 ST 40S	.365	10.020	101	2.81	2.62	11.91	78.9	40.5	34.1	3.67	160.8	29.91

Table 10-1
Continued

D	Sch	t	d	d⁵	Ao	Ai	Am	Af	W	Ww	Rg	I	Z
(continued)		.395	9.960	98.0	2.81	2.61	12.85	77.9	43.7	33.7	3.66	172.5	32.1
	60 XS 80S	.500	9.750	88.1	2.81	2.55	16.10	74.7	54.7	32.3	3.63	212.0	39.4
		.531	9.687	85.3	2.81	2.54	17.06	73.7	58.0	31.9	3.62	223.4	41.6
	80	.593	9.564	80.0	2.81	2.50	18.92	71.8	64.3	31.1	3.60	244.8	45.5
10	100	.718	9.314	70.1	2.81	2.44	22.63	68.1	76.9	29.5	3.56	286.2	53.2
		.750	9.250	67.7	2.81	2.42	23.56	67.2	80.1	29.1	3.55	296.3	55.1
D = 10.750	120	.843	9.064	61.2	2.81	2.37	26.24	64.5	89.2	27.9	3.52	324.3	60.3
	140	1.000	8.750	51.3	2.81	2.29	30.63	60.1	104.1	26.0	3.47	367.9	68.4
		1.062	8.625	47.7	2.81	2.26	32.33	58.4	109.9	25.3	3.45	384.0	71.4
	160	1.125	8.500	44.4	2.81	2.23	34.02	56.7	115.7	24.6	3.43	399.4	74.3
	5S	.156	12.438	298	3.34	3.26	6.17	121.5	21.0	52.6	4.45	122.4	19.2
	10S	.180	12.390	292	3.34	3.24	7.11	120.6	24.2	52.2	4.44	140.5	22.0
		.203	12.344	287	3.34	3.23	8.00	119.7	27.2	51.8	4.44	157.5	24.7
		.219	12.312	283	3.34	3.22	8.62	119.1	29.3	51.6	4.43	169.3	26.6
		.238	12.274	279	3.34	3.21	9.36	118.3	31.8	51.2	4.42	183.2	28.7
	20	.250	12.250	276	3.34	3.21	9.82	117.9	33.4	51.0	4.42	191.9	30.1
		.279	12.192	269	3.34	3.19	10.93	116.7	37.2	50.6	4.41	212.7	33.4
		.300	12.150	265	3.34	3.18	11.73	115.9	39.9	50.2	4.40	227.5	35.7
	30	.330	12.090	258	3.34	3.17	12.88	114.8	43.8	49.7	4.39	248.5	39.0
		.344	12.062	255	3.34	3.16	13.41	114.3	45.6	49.5	4.39	258	40.5
12	ST 40S	.375	12.000	249	3.34	3.14	14.58	113.1	49.6	49.0	4.38	279	43.8
	40	.406	11.938	242	3.34	3.13	15.74	111.9	53.5	48.5	4.37	300	47.1
D = 12.750		.438	11.874	236	3.34	3.11	16.94	110.7	57.6	47.9	4.36	321	50.4
	XS 80S	.500	11.750	224	3.34	3.08	19.24	108.4	65.4	47.0	4.33	362	56.7
	60	.562	11.626	212	3.34	3.04	21.52	106.2	73.2	46.0	4.31	401	62.8
		.625	11.500	201	3.34	3.01	23.81	103.9	80.9	45.0	4.29	439	68.8
	80	.687	11.376	191	3.34	2.98	26.04	101.6	88.5	44.0	4.27	475	74.5
	100	.843	11.064	166	3.34	2.90	31.53	96.1	107.2	41.6	4.22	562	88.1
		.875	11.000	161	3.34	2.88	32.64	95.0	111.0	41.1	4.21	579	90.8
	120	1.000	10.750	144	3.34	2.81	36.91	90.8	125.5	39.3	4.17	642	100.7
	140	1.125	10.500	128	3.34	2.75	41.09	86.6	139.7	37.5	4.13	701	109.9
		1.219	10.313	117	3.34	2.70	44.14	83.5	150.1	36.2	4.10	742	116.4
	160	1.312	10.126	106	3.34	2.65	47.14	80.5	160.3	34.9	4.07	781	122.6
		.188	13.624	469	3.67	3.57	8.16	145.8	27.7	63.1	4.88	195	27.8
		.220	13.560	458	3.67	3.55	9.52	144.4	32.4	62.5	4.87	226	32.3
		.238	13.524	452	3.67	3.54	10.29	143.6	35.0	62.2	4.87	244	34.8
	10	.250	13.500	448	3.67	3.53	10.80	143.1	36.7	62.0	4.86	255	36.5
	20	.312	13.375	428	3.67	3.50	13.44	140.5	45.7	60.8	4.84	315	45.0
	30 ST	.375	13.250	408	3.67	3.47	16.05	137.9	54.6	59.7	4.82	373	53.3
14		.406	13.188	399	3.67	3.45	17.34	136.6	59.0	59.1	4.81	401	57.3
D = 14.000	40	.438	13.125	389	3.67	3.44	18.66	135.3	63.4	58.6	4.80	429	61.4
		.469	13.062	380	3.67	3.42	19.94	134.0	67.8	58.0	4.79	457	65.3
	XS	.500	13.000	371	3.67	3.40	21.21	132.7	72.1	57.5	4.78	484	69.1
	60	.593	12.814	345	3.67	3.35	24.98	129.0	84.9	55.8	4.74	562	80.3
		.625	12.750	337	3.67	3.34	26.26	127.7	89.3	55.3	4.73	589	84.1

Table 10-1
Continued

D	Sch	t	d	d^5	Ao	Ai	Am	Af	W	Ww	Rg	I	Z
(continued)		.656	12.688	329	3.67	3.32	27.50	126.4	93.5	54.8	4.72	614	87.7
	80	.750	12.500	305	3.67	3.27	31.22	122.7	106.1	53.1	4.69	687	98.2
	100	.937	12.125	262	3.67	3.17	38.47	115.5	130.8	50.0	4.63	825	117.9
14	120	1.093	11.814	230	3.67	3.09	44.32	109.6	150.7	47.5	4.58	930	132.8
	140	1.250	11.500	201	3.67	3.01	50.07	103.9	170.2	45.0	4.53	1027	146.8
D = 14.000		1.344	11.313	185	3.67	2.96	53.42	100.5	181.6	43.5	4.50	1082	154.6
	160	1.406	11.188	175	3.67	2.93	55.63	98.3	189.1	42.6	4.48	1117	159.6
		.188	15.624	931	4.19	4.09	9.34	191.7	31.8	83.0	5.59	292	36.5
		.238	15.524	902	4.19	4.06	11.78	189.3	40.1	82.0	5.57	366	45.8
	10	.250	15.500	895	4.19	4.06	12.37	188.7	42.1	81.7	5.57	384	48.0
		.281	15.438	877	4.19	4.04	13.88	187.2	47.2	81.1	5.56	429	53.6
	20	.312	15.375	859	4.19	4.02	15.40	185.7	52.4	80.4	5.55	474	59.3
		.344	15.312	842	4.19	4.01	16.92	184.1	57.5	79.7	5.54	519	64.8
	30 ST	.375	15.250	825	4.19	3.99	18.41	182.7	62.6	79.1	5.53	562	70.3
		.406	15.188	808	4.19	3.98	19.89	181.2	67.6	78.4	5.52	605	75.6
		.438	15.124	791	4.19	3.96	21.41	179.6	72.8	77.8	5.50	649	81.1
16		.469	15.062	775	4.19	3.94	22.88	178.2	77.8	77.2	5.49	691	86.3
	40 XS	.500	15.000	759	4.19	3.93	24.35	176.7	82.8	76.5	5.48	732	91.5
D = 16.000		.531	14.938	744	4.19	3.91	25.81	175.3	87.7	75.9	5.47	773	96.6
	60	.656	14.688	684	4.19	3.85	31.62	169.4	107.5	73.4	5.43	933	116.6
		.688	14.625	669	4.19	3.83	33.07	168.0	112.4	72.7	5.42	972	121.4
		.750	14.500	641	4.19	3.80	35.90	165.1	127.5	71.5	5.40	1047	130.9
	80	.843	14.314	601	4.19	3.75	40.14	160.9	136.5	69.7	5.37	1157	144.6
	100	1.031	13.938	526	4.19	3.65	48.48	152.6	164.8	66.1	5.29	1365	170.6
	120	1.218	13.564	459	4.19	3.55	56.56	144.5	192.3	62.6	5.23	1556	194.5
	140	1.438	13.124	389	4.19	3.44	65.79	135.3	223.7	58.6	5.17	1761	220.1
		1.500	13.000	371	4.19	3.40	68.33	132.7	232.3	57.5	5.15	1815	226.9
	160	1.593	12.814	345	4.19	3.35	72.10	129.0	245.1	55.8	5.12	1894	236.7
	10	.250	17.500	1641	4.71	4.58	13.94	240.5	47.4	104.1	6.28	549	61.0
	20	.312	17.375	1584	4.71	4.55	17.36	237.1	59.0	102.7	6.25	679	75.5
	ST	.375	17.250	1527	4.71	4.52	20.76	233.7	70.6	101.2	6.23	807	89.6
	30	.438	17.124	1472	4.71	4.48	24.17	230.3	82.2	99.7	6.21	932	103.6
	XS	.500	17.000	1420	4.71	4.45	27.49	227.0	93.5	98.3	6.19	1053	117.0
	40	.562	16.876	1369	4.71	4.42	30.79	223.7	104.7	96.9	6.17	1171	130.2
		.594	16.813	1344	4.71	4.40	32.46	222.0	110.4	96.1	6.16	1231	136.8
18		.625	16.750	1318	4.71	4.39	34.12	220.4	116.0	95.4	6.15	1289	143.3
		.719	16.562	1247	4.71	4.34	38.98	215.5	132.5	93.3	6.12	1458	162.0
D = 18.000	60	.750	16.500	1223	4.71	4.32	40.64	213.8	138.2	92.6	6.10	1515	168.3
		.812	16.375	1177	4.71	4.29	43.87	210.6	149.2	91.2	6.08	1624	180.5
	80	.937	16.126	1090	4.71	4.22	50.23	204.2	170.8	88.4	6.04	1834	203.8
	100	1.156	15.688	950	4.71	4.11	61.17	193.3	208.0	83.7	5.97	2180	242.2
	120	1.375	15.250	825	4.71	3.99	71.81	182.7	244.2	79.1	5.90	2498	277.6
	140	1.562	14.876	728	4.71	3.89	80.66	173.8	274.3	75.3	5.84	2750	305.5
		1.688	14.625	669	4.71	3.83	86.48	168.0	294.0	72.7	5.80	2908	323.1
	160	1.781	14.438	627	4.71	3.78	90.75	163.7	308.5	70.9	5.77	3020	335.6

Table 10-1
Continued

D	Sch	t	d	d^5	Ao	Ai	Am	Af	W	Ww	Rg	I	Z
20 D = 20.000	10	.250	19.500	2.82	5.24	5.11	15.51	298.6	52.7	129.3	6.98	757	75.7
		.312	19.375	2.73	5.24	5.07	19.36	294.8	65.8	127.6	6.96	938	93.8
	20 ST	.375	19.250	2.64	5.24	5.04	23.12	291.0	78.6	126.0	6.94	1114	111.4
		.438	19.124	2.56	5.24	5.01	26.9	287.2	91.5	124.4	6.92	1289	128.9
	30 XS	.500	19.000	2.48	5.24	4.97	30.6	283.5	104.1	122.8	6.90	1457	145.7
		.562	18.875	2.40	5.24	4.94	34.3	279.8	116.8	121.2	6.88	1624	162.4
	40	.593	18.814	2.36	5.24	4.93	36.2	278.0	122.9	120.4	6.86	1704	170.4
		.625	18.750	2.32	5.24	4.91	38.0	276.1	129.3	119.6	6.85	1787	178.7
	60	.812	18.376	2.10	5.24	4.81	48.9	265.2	166.4	114.8	6.79	2257	225.7
		.875	18.250	2.02	5.24	4.78	52.6	261.6	178.7	113.3	6.77	2409	240.9
		.906	18.188	1.99	5.24	4.76	54.3	259.8	184.8	112.5	6.76	2483	248.3
	80	1.031	17.938	1.86	5.24	4.70	61.4	252.7	208.9	109.4	6.72	2772	277.2
		1.250	17.500	1.64	5.24	4.58	73.6	240.5	250.3	104.1	6.64	3251	325.1
	100	1.281	17.438	1.61	5.24	4.57	75.3	238.8	256.1	103.4	6.63	3316	331.6
	120	1.500	17.000	1.42	5.24	4.45	87.2	227.0	296.4	98.3	6.56	3755	375.5
	140	1.750	16.500	1.22	5.24	4.32	100.3	213.8	341.1	92.6	6.48	4217	421.7
		1.844	16.313	1.16	5.24	4.27	105.2	209.0	357.5	90.5	6.45	4379	437.9
	160	1.968	16.064	1.07	5.24	4.21	111.5	202.7	379.1	87.8	6.41	4586	458.6
22 D = 22.000	10	.250	21.500	4.59	5.76	5.63	17.1	363	58.1	157.2	7.69	1010	91.8
	ST	.375	21.250	4.33	5.76	5.56	25.5	355	86.6	153.6	7.65	1490	135.4
	XS	.500	21.000	4.08	5.76	5.50	33.8	346	114.8	150.0	7.60	1953	177.5
24 D = 24.000	10	.250	23.500	7.17	6.28	6.15	18.7	434	63.4	187.8	8.40	1316	109.6
		.312	23.376	6.98	6.28	6.12	23.2	429	78.9	185.8	8.38	1629	135.8
	20 ST	.375	23.250	6.79	6.28	6.09	27.8	425	94.6	183.8	8.35	1943	161.9
		.438	23.125	6.61	6.28	6.05	32.4	420	110.1	181.9	8.33	2249	187.4
	XS	.500	23.000	6.44	6.28	6.02	36.9	415	125.5	179.9	8.31	2550	212.5
	30	.562	22.876	6.26	6.28	5.99	41.4	411	140.7	178.0	8.29	2840	237.0
		.625	22.750	6.09	6.28	5.96	45.9	406	156.0	176.0	8.27	3140	261
	40	.687	22.626	5.93	6.28	5.92	50.3	402	171.1	174.1	8.25	3420	285
		.750	22.500	5.77	6.28	5.89	54.8	398	186.3	172.2	8.22	3710	309
	60	.968	22.064	5.23	6.28	5.78	70.0	382	238.1	165.6	8.15	4653	388
		1.031	21.938	5.08	6.28	5.74	74.4	378	252.9	163.7	8.13	4920	410
	80	1.218	21.564	4.66	6.28	5.65	87.2	365	296.4	158.1	8.07	5670	473
	100	1.531	20.938	4.02	6.28	5.48	108.1	344	367.4	149.1	7.96	6852	571
	120	1.812	20.376	3.51	6.28	5.33	126.3	326	429.4	141.2	7.87	7824	652
	140	2.062	19.876	3.10	6.28	5.20	142.1	310	483.2	134.3	7.79	8630	719
		2.188	19.625	2.91	6.28	5.14	149.9	302	509.7	131.0	7.75	9010	751
	160	2.343	19.314	2.69	6.28	5.06	159.4	293	542.0	126.9	7.70	9455	788
26 D = 26.000	ST	.375	25.250	10.26	6.81	6.61	30.2	501	102.6	216.8	9.06	2479	191
	XS	.500	25.000	9.77	6.81	6.54	40.1	491	136.2	212.5	9.02	3257	250
30 D = 30.000	10	.312	29.376	21.9	7.85	7.69	29.1	678	98.9	293.5	10.50	3210	214
	ST	.375	29.250	21.4	7.85	7.66	34.9	672	118.7	291.0	10.48	3833	255
		.438	29.125	21.0	7.85	7.62	40.6	666	138.0	288.4	10.45	4434	296
	20 XS	.500	29.000	20.5	7.85	7.59	46.3	661	157.6	286.0	10.43	5040	336
		.562	28.875	20.1	7.85	7.56	52.0	655	176.8	283.6	10.41	5635	376
	30	.625	28.750	19.6	7.85	7.53	57.7	649	196.1	281.1	10.39	6230	415
34 D = 34.000	ST	.375	33.250	40.6	8.90	8.70	39.6	868	134.7	376.0	11.89	5599	329
	XS	.500	33.000	39.1	8.90	8.64	52.6	855	178.9	370.3	11.85	7383	434
36 D = 36.000	ST	.375	35.250	54.4	9.44	9.23	42.0	976	142.7	422.6	12.60	6659	370
	XS	.500	35.000	52.5	9.44	9.16	55.8	962	189.6	416.6	12.55	8786	488
42 D = 42.000	ST	.375	41.250	119.4	11.0	10.80	49.0	1336	166.7	578.7	14.72	10621	506
	XS	.500	41.000	115.9	11.0	10.73	65.2	1320	221.6	571.7	14.67	14037	668

11

Weight and Dimensions of Pipe and Components

Weight of Pipe and Components

When determining the weight of the pipe and components, several factors must be taken into consideration:

- *Weight of pipe:* Use the values for properties for carbon steel pipe as a standard. These values can be found in Chapter 10. The relative weight factors for other materials are:

Aluminum	=	0.35
Brass	=	1.12
Cast iron	=	0.91
Copper	=	1.14
Ferritic stainless steel	=	0.95
Austenitic stainless steel	=	1.02
Carbon Steel	=	1.00
Wrought iron	=	0.98
Depleted uranium	=	2.22

- *Weight of water in pipe:* See the properties of pipe in Chapter 10.

- *Weight of insulation of the pipe*

I = Insulation density, lb/ft^3
T = Insulation thickness, in.
D = Outside diameter of pipe, in.

Weight of insulation = .0218 IT (D+T) = lb/ft

Values for insulation density:

Calcium silicate	=	11 lb/ft^3
85% magnesium	=	10 to 11 lb/ft^3
Thermobestos	=	11.53 lb/ft^3
KALO	=	19–21 lb/ft^3
Diatomaceous earth	=	21 lb/ft^3
High temperature	=	24 lb/ft^3
Super-X	=	25 lb/ft^3
Poly-Urethane	=	2.3 lb/ft^3
Amosite asbestos	=	16 lb/ft^3
Foamglas	=	9 lb/ft^3
Cellular glass	=	9 lb/ft^3
Mineral wool	=	8 lb/ft^3

Tables 11-1 through 11-10 give the weight of insulation and various pipe components by size.

The following pages are tables and figures showing standard dimensions of flanges, fittings, valves, and pipe bends.

Table 11-1
Weight of Insulation
(lb/linear ft)

Pipe Size (in.)	Thickness of Insulation 1″	1½″	2″	2½″	3″	3½″	4″	4½″	5″	6″
1	.72	1.23	1.94	2.76	3.70					
1.5	.84	1.35	2.52	3.47	4.52					
2	1.01	1.71	2.53	3.48	4.42	5.59				
3	1.25	2.08	3.01	4.07	5.24	6.65				
4	1.62	2.55	3.61	4.66	6.07	7.48	9.10			
6	2.11	3.28	4.57	6.09	7.60	9.82	11.5			
8		4.13	5.64	7.85	9.48	11.5	13.8	16.0		
10		5.20	7.07	8.93	11.0	13.2	15.5	18.1		
12		6.04	8.13	10.5	12.7	15.1	17.4	20.4		
14		6.16	8.38	10.7	13.1	15.8	18.5	21.3		
16		6.90	9.33	12.0	14.6	17.5	20.5	23.6		
18		7.73	10.4	13.3	16.3	19.3	22.6	25.9		
20		8.45	11.6	14.6	17.7	21.1	24.6	28.1		
24		10.0	13.4	17.0	21.0	24.8	28.7	32.9		
26		10.4	14.1	18.0	21.9	26.0	30.2	34.6		
28		11.2	15.1	19.2	23.4	27.8	32.2	36.9	41.6	51.4
30		11.9	16.1	20.5	25.0	29.5	34.3	39.1	44.1	54.4
32		12.7	17.1	21.7	26.5	31.3	36.3	41.1	46.6	57.5
34		13.4	18.2	23.0	28.0	33.1	38.3	43.7	49.1	60.5
36		14.2	19.2	24.2	29.5	34.8	40.3	45.9	51.7	63.5
42		16.5	22.2	28.0	34.0	40.1	46.4	52.2	59.2	72.6

** The table is based on calcium silicate at 11 lb/ft^3 and must be adjusted for other materials. The table includes banding and covering weight.*

Table 11-2
Weight of Flanged Gate Valves
(lb)

Size (in.)	Rating 150#	300#	400#	600#	900#	1500#	2500#
1	31	35					
1.5	45	68	91			136	
2	55	75	115			256	
3	95	145	194		314	460	
4	140	215	270	330	430	610	
6	240	420	530	720	900	1,410	
8	400	700	940	1,220	1,560	2,600	
10	630	1,050	1,530	1,880	2,350		
12	830	1,490	2,000	2,630	3,500		
14	1,150	2,170	2,410	3,200	4,680		
16	1,580	2,800	3,500	4,230	6,500		
18	1,910	3,720		7,200			
20	2,350	4,640		9,800			
24	3,900	7,380		11,800			

Courtesy of Crane Co.

Table 11-3
Weight of Weld End Gate Valves
(lb)

Size (in.)	Rating 150#	300#	400#	600#	900#	1500#	2500#
1		20		25		80	
1.5	29	55		70		125	
2	45	60		80		190	
3	80	120		155	260	410	
4	120	170	220	270	350	520	
6	210	360	460	640	750	1,250	
8	340	590	830	1,080	1,300	1,910	
10	550	910	1,250	1,610	1,970		
12	730	1,220	1,800	2,240	3,200		
14	990	1,960	2,210	3,000	4,350		
16	1,460	2,550	3,100	4,030	6,000		
18	1,730	3,300	3,765	6,760			
20	2,200	4,350		8,950			
24	3,350	6,700		10,500			

Courtesy of Crane Co.

Table 11-4
Weight of Flanged Check (Swing) Valves
(lb)

Size	Rating						
(in.)	150#	300#	400#	600#	900#	1500#	2500#
2	34	62		70		160	
3	65	120		140	180	280	
4	100	180	200	260	340	630	
6	200	330	395	530	640	1,360	
8	390	620	680	900	1,180	2,100	
10	510	920	900	1,440	2,170		
12	775	1,290	1,250	1,970			
14	1,200	1,650					
16	1,450	2,050					
18		2,420					
20							
24							

Courtesy of Crane Co.

Table 11-5
Weight of Weld End Check (Swing) Valves
(lb)

Size	Rating						
(in.)	150#	300#	400#	600#	900#	1500#	2500#
2	25	47		55		130	
3	50	80		100	155	210	
4	100	130	190	270	240	390	
6	160	260	310	420	500	780	
8	360	510	580	740	890	1,320	
10		760	820	880			
12		1,015	1,150	1,200			
14							
16							
18							
20							
24							

Courtesy of Crane Co.

Table 11-6
Weight of Flanged Globe Valves
(lb)

Size	Rating						
(in.)	150#	300#	400#	600#	900#	1500#	2500#
2	47	79	90	115	215	215	
3	80	139	160	191	460	460	
4	140	214	233	318	490	665	
6	250	396	476	782	920	1,890	
8	420	628	820	1,224			
10	598	686					
12	824						
14							
16							
18							
20							
24							

Courtesy of Crane Co.

Table 11-7
Weight of Weld End Globe Valves
(lb)

Size	Rating						
(in.)	150#	300#	400#	600#	900#	1500#	2500#
2	34	75	78	97			
3	75	115	130	166	170	185	
4	120	179	206	272	240	285	
6	220	332	401	656	630	680	
8	363	530	900	1,100	1,140	1,370	
10	535		1,056		1,730	2,400	
12	794		1,160		2,700	3,020	
14					3,850	4,400	
16							
18							
20							
24							

Courtesy of Crane Co.

Table 11-8
Weight of Flanged Angle Valves (lb)

Size (in.)	Rating 150#	300#	400#	600#	900#	1500#	2500#
2	38						
3	70	130		160	230		
4	110	200	235	280	370		
6	210	370	385	675	1,000		
8	360	634	685	985			
10	552	1,130		1,950			
12		1,720		3,100			
14		2,350					
16							
18							
20							
24							

Courtesy of Crane Co.

Table 11-9
Weight of Weld End Angle Valves (lb)

Size (in.)	Rating 150#	300#	400#	600#	900#	1500#	2500#
2		70		130			
3		81		170			
4		155		490			
6		330					
8		530					
10		880					
12							
14							
16							
18							
20							
24							

Courtesy of Crane Co.

Table 11-10
Weights of Flanges (Including Bolts)

Size (in.)	Type	Rating 150#	300#	400#	600#	900#	1500#	2500#
2	WN	6	10	13	13	31	31	48
2	SO	6	9	11	11	32	32	48
2	BLD	5	10	12	12	31	31	49
3	WN	11	19	27	27	38	61	113
3	SO	9	17	19	19	36	60	99
3	BLD	10	20	24	24	38	61	105
4	WN	17	29	41	48	64	90	177
4	SO	15	26	32	43	66	90	158
4	BLD	19	31	39	47	67	90	164
6	WN	27	48	67	96	130	202	451
6	SO	22	45	54	95	128	202	396
6	BLD	29	56	71	101	133	197	418
8	WN	42	76	104	137	222	334	692
8	SO	33	67	82	135	207	319	601
8	BLD	48	90	115	159	232	363	649
10	WN	60	110	152	225	316	546	1,291
10	SO	51	100	117	213	293	528	1,148
10	BLD	78	146	181	267	338	599	1,248
12	WN	88	163	212	272	434	843	1,919
12	SO	72	140	164	261	388	820	1,611
12	BLD	118	209	261	341	475	928	1,775
14	WN	113	217	277	406	642	1,241	
14	SO	96	195	235	318	460	1,016	
14	BLD	142	267	354	437	574		
16	WN	108	288	351	577	785	1,597	
16	SO	185	262	310	442	559	1,297	
16	BLD	160	349	455	603	719		
18	WN	140	355	430	652	1,074	2,069	
18	SO	229	331	380	573	797	1,694	
18	BLD	196	440	572	762	1,030		
20	WN		431	535	811	1,344	2,614	
20	SO	181	378	468	733	972	2,114	
20	BLD	298	545	711	976	1,287		
24	WN	295	632	777	1,157	2,450	4,153	
24	SO	245	577	676	1,056	1,823	3,378	
24	BLD	446	841	1,355	2,442			

Courtesy of Crane Co.

Steel Butt-Welding Fittings (in.)

Courtesy of Crane Co.

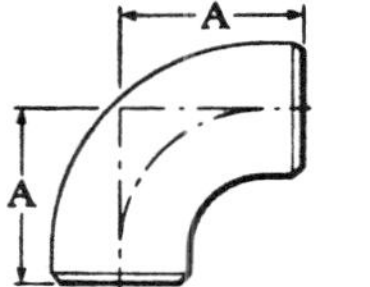

90° Long Radius Elbow
Straight or Reducing

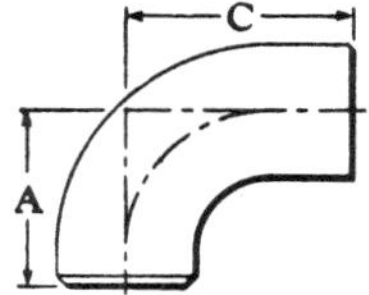
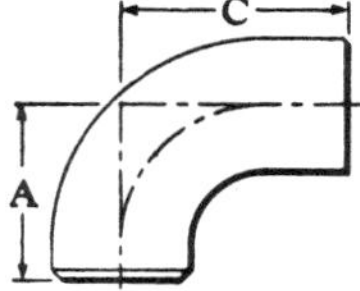

90° Long Radius Elbow with Long Tangent on One End

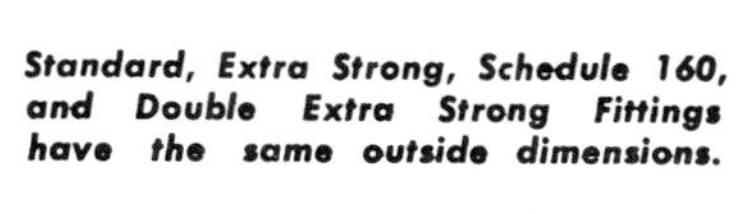

Standard, Extra Strong, Schedule 160, and Double Extra Strong Fittings have the same outside dimensions.

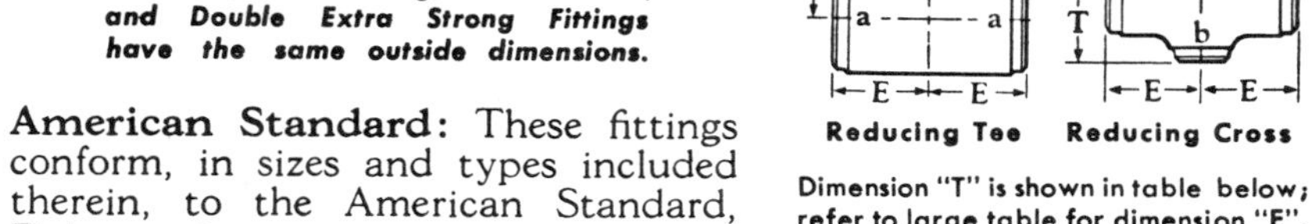

90° Short Radius Elbow

45° Long Radius Elbow

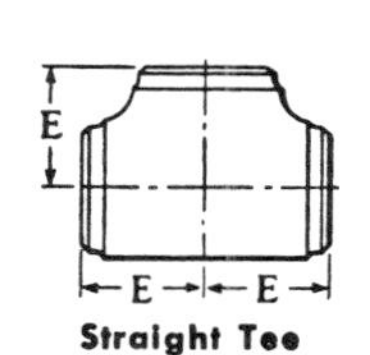

Straight Tee

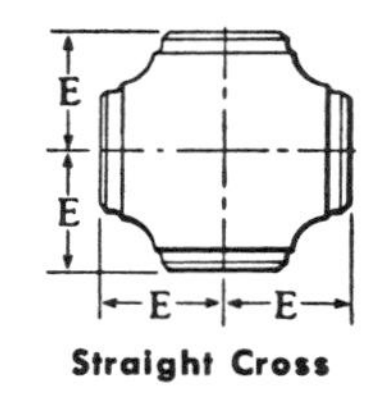

Straight Cross

American Standard: These fittings conform, in sizes and types included therein, to the American Standard, B16.9-1958; see page 293.

Thickness: Standard Fittings 12-inch and smaller are made for use with Standard pipe (heaviest weight on 8, 10, and 12-inch sizes); sizes 14-inch and larger are made for use with O.D. pipe ⅜-inch thick.

Extra Strong Fittings 12-inch and smaller are made for use with Extra Strong pipe; larger sizes are made for use with O.D. pipe ½-inch thick.

Schedule 160 Fittings are made for use with Schedule 160 pipe.

Double Extra Strong Fittings are made for use with Double Extra Strong pipe.

Cap

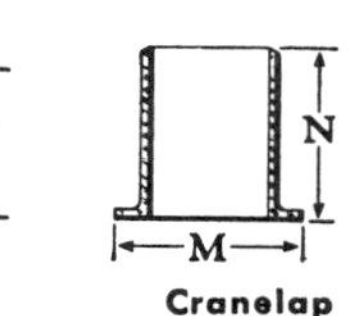

Short Radius Return Bend

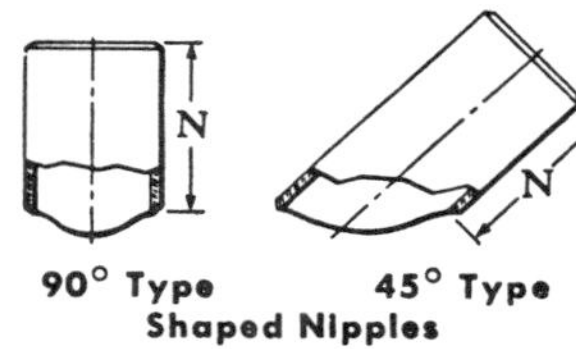

Cranelap Stub End

90° Type

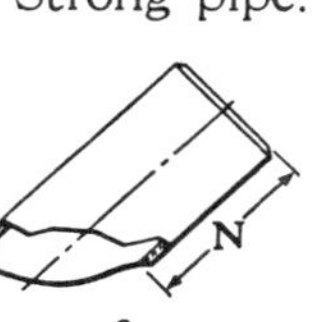

45° Type

Shaped Nipples

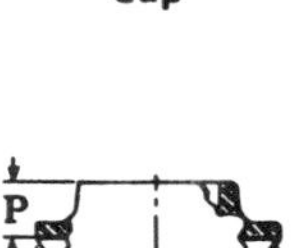

Reinforcing Welding Saddle

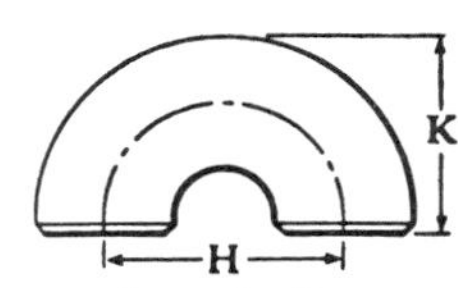

Long Radius Return Bend

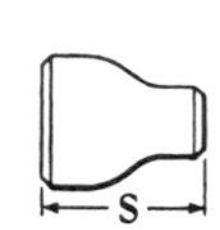

Concentric Reducer

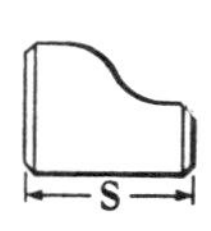

Eccentric Reducer

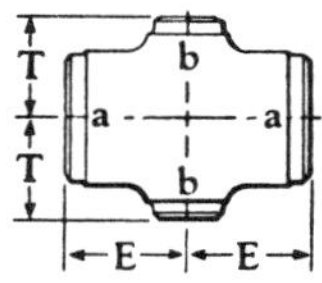

Reducing Tee Reducing Cross

Dimension "T" is shown in table below; refer to large table for dimension "E".

Size a × b	T	Size a × b	T
1 ×¾ *	1½	6×3½	5
1¼×1 *	1⅞	×3	4⅞
×¾ *	1⅞	×2½	4¾
1½×1¼*	2¼	8×6	6⅝
×1 *	2¼	×5	6⅜
×¾ *	2¼	×4	6⅛
2 ×1½	2⅜	×3½	6
×1¼	2¼	10×8	8
×1	2	×6	7⅝
×¾	1¾	×5	7½
2½×2	2¾	×4	7¼
×1½	2⅝	12×10	9½
×1¼	2½	×8	9
×1	2¼	×6	8⅝
3 ×2½	3¼	×5	8½
×2	3	14×12*	10⅝
×1½	2⅞	×10*	10⅛
×1¼	2¾	×8 *	9⅝
3½×3	3⅝	×6 *	9¼
×2½	3½	16×14*	12
×2	3¼	×12*	11⅝
×1½	3⅛	×10*	11⅛
4 ×3½	4	×8 *	10⅝
×3	3⅞	18×16*	13
×2½	3¾	×14*	13
×2	3½	×12*	12⅝
×1½	3⅜	×10*	12⅛
5 ×4	4⅝	20×18*	14½
×3½	4½	×16*	14
×3	4⅜	×14*	14
×2½	4¼	×12*	13⅝
×2	4⅛	24×20*	17
6 ×5	5⅜	×18*	16½
×4	5⅛	×16*	16

																Pipe Schedule Numbers for:	
Size	A	B	C	D	E	F	G	H	J	K	M	N	P	Q	S	Std. Ftgs.	Extra Strong
½	1½	..	..	⅝	..	..	..	3	..	1 15/16	..	..	..	..	..	40	80
¾	1⅛	..	..	7/16	1⅛*	..	..	2¼	..	1 11/16	1 11/16	4	..	..	2	40	80
1	1½	1	..	⅞	1½*	1½	2	3	1⅝	2 3/16	2	4	1	4⅛	2	40	80
1¼	1⅞	1¼	..	1	1⅞*	1½	2½	3¾	2 1/16	2¾	2½	4	1⅛	4¾	2	40	80
1½	2¼	1½	3¼	1⅛	2¼*	1½	3	4½	2 7/16	3¼	2⅞	4	1⅛	5¼	2½	40	80
2	3	2	4¼	1⅜	2½	1½	4	6	3 3/16	4 3/16	3⅝	6	1⅛	5 15/16	3	40	80
2½	3¾	2½	5	1¾	3.	1½	5	7½	3 15/16	5 3/16	4⅛	6	1⅛	6 7/16	3½	40	80
3	4½	3	5¾	2	3⅜	2	6	9	4¾	6¼	5	6	1⅛	7 9/16	3½	40	80
3½	5¼	3½	6¾	2¼	3¾	2½	..	..	..	..	5½	6	1¼	8 1/16	4	40	80
4	6	4	7½	2½	4⅛	2½	8	12	6¼	8¼	6 3/16	6	1⅜	8 9/16	4	40	80
5	7½	5	9	3⅛	4⅞	3	10	15	7¾	10 5/16	7 5/16	8	1⅜	9⅝	5	40	80
6	9	6	10¾	3¾	5⅝	3½	12	18	9 5/16	12 5/16	8½	8	1½	11¾	5½	40	80
8	12	8	13¾	5	7	4	16	24	12 5/16	16 5/16	10⅝	8	2	14¾	6	40	80
10	15	10	17	6¼	8½	5	20	30	15⅜	20⅜	12¾	10	2½	17⅞	7	40	60
12	18	12	20½	7½	10	6	24	36	18⅜	24⅜	15	10	2¾	20⅞	8	..	..
14	21	14	..	8¾	11*	6½	28	42	21	28	16¼	12	3¼	22⅛	13	30	..
16	24	16	..	10	12*	7	32	48	24	32	18½	12	3½	24⅛	14	30	40
18	27	18	..	11¼	13½*	8	36	54	27	36	21	12	4	26⅛	15	..	..
20	30	20	..	12½	15*	9	40	60	30	40	23	12	4	30⅛	20	20	30
24	36	24	..	15	17*	10½	48	72	36	48	27¼	12	4	34⅛	20	20	..

Forged Steel Flanges (in.)

Courtesy of Crane Co.

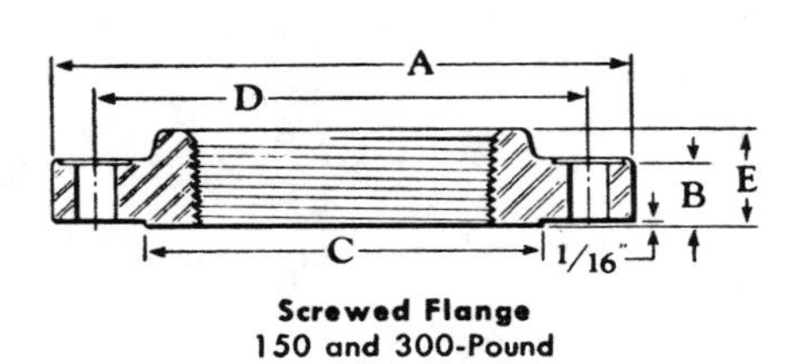

Screwed Flange
150 and 300-Pound

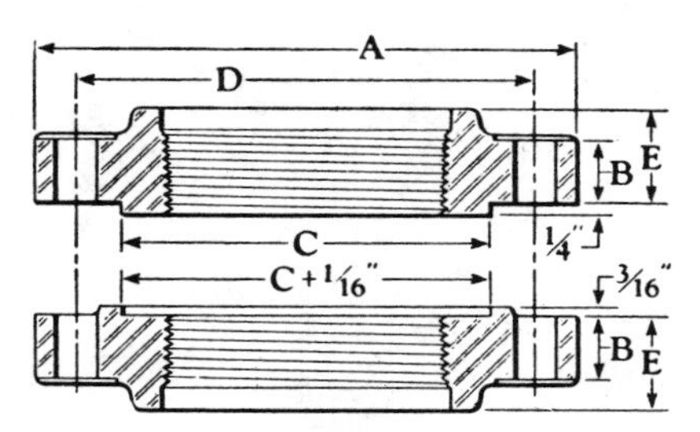

Screwed Flange
400, 600, 900, 1500, and 2500-Pound

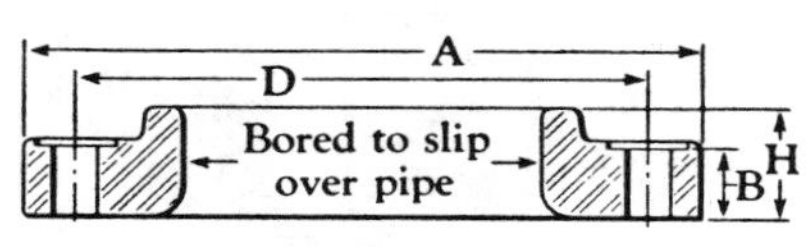

Cranelap Flange
150 and 300-Pound

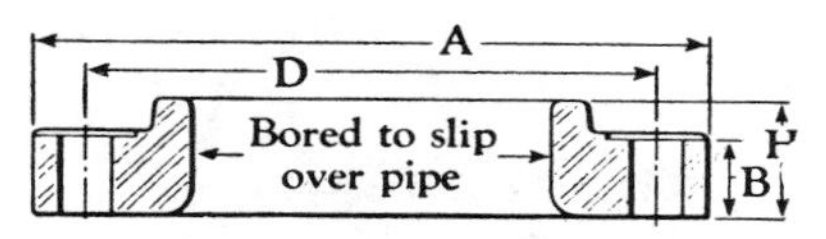

Cranelap Flange
400, 600, 900, 1500, and 2500-Pound

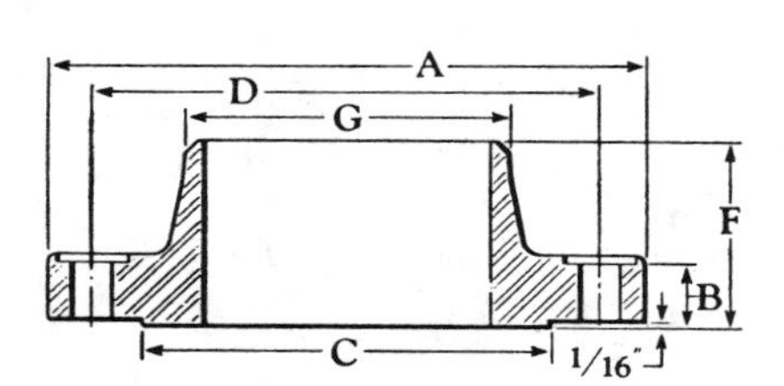

Welding Neck Flange
150 and 300-Pound

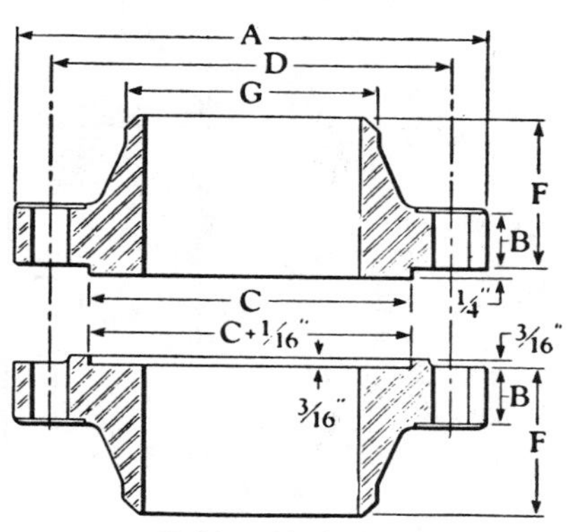

Welding Neck Flange
400, 600, 900, 1500, and 2500-Pound

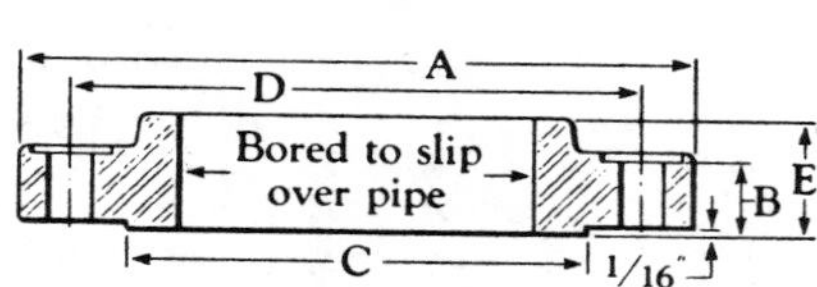

Slip-On Welding Flange
150 and 300-Pound

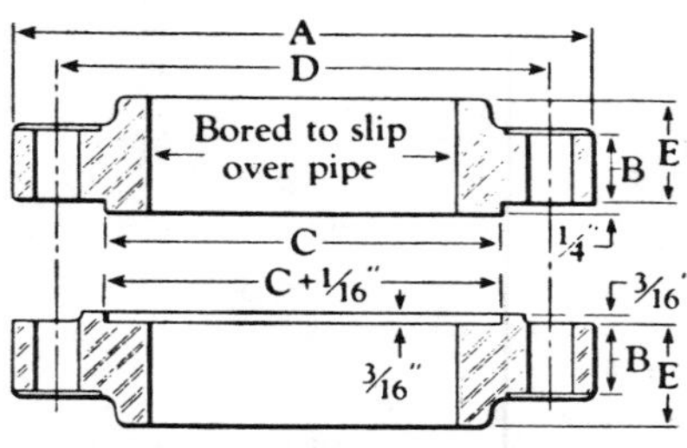

Slip-On Welding Flange
400, 600, 900, and 1500-Pound

Class	Pipe Size	A	B	C	D	Bolts No.	Bolts Dia.	E	F	G	H
150 Pound	1/2	3 1/2	7/16	1 3/8	2 3/8	4	1/2	5/8	1 7/8	0.84	5/8
	3/4	3 7/8	1/2	1 11/16	2 3/4	4	1/2	5/8	2 1/16	1.05	5/8
	1	4 1/4	9/16	2	3 1/8	4	1/2	11/16	2 3/16	1.32	11/16
	1 1/4	4 5/8	5/8	2 1/2	3 1/2	4	1/2	13/16	2 1/4	1.66	13/16
	1 1/2	5	11/16	2 7/8	3 7/8	4	1/2	7/8	2 7/16	1.90	7/8
	2	6	3/4	3 5/8	4 3/4	4	5/8	1	2 1/2	2.38	1
	2 1/2	7	7/8	4 1/8	5 1/2	4	5/8	1 1/8	2 3/4	2.88	1 1/8
	3	7 1/2	15/16	5	6	4	5/8	1 3/16	2 3/4	3.50	1 3/16
	3 1/2	8 1/2	15/16	5 1/2	7	8	5/8	1 1/4	2 13/16	4.00	1 1/4
	4	9	15/16	6 3/16	7 1/2	8	5/8	1 5/16	3	4.50	1 5/16
	5	10	15/16	7 5/16	8 1/2	8	3/4	1 7/16	3 1/2	5.56	1 7/16
	6	11	1	8 1/2	9 1/2	8	3/4	1 9/16	3 1/2	6.63	1 9/16
	8	13 1/2	1 1/8	10 5/8	11 3/4	8	3/4	1 3/4	4	8.63	1 3/4
	10	16	1 3/16	12 3/4	14 1/4	12	7/8	1 15/16	4	10.75	1 15/16
	12	19	1 1/4	15	17	12	7/8	2 3/16	4 1/2	12.75	2 3/16
	14	21	1 3/8	16 1/4	18 3/4	12	1	2 1/4	5	14.00	3 1/8
	16	23 1/2	1 7/16	18 1/2	21 1/4	16	1	2 1/2	5	16.00	3 7/16
	18	25	1 9/16	21	22 3/4	16	1 1/8	2 11/16	5 1/2	18.00	3 13/16
	20	27 1/2	1 11/16	23	25	20	1 1/8	2 7/8	5 11/16	20.00	4 1/16
	24	32	1 7/8	27 1/4	29 1/2	20	1 1/4	3 1/4	6	24.00	4 3/8
300 Pound	1/2	3 3/4	9/16	1 3/8	2 5/8	4	1/2	7/8	2 1/16	0.84	...
	3/4	4 5/8	5/8	1 11/16	3 1/4	4	5/8	1	2 1/4	1.05	1
	1	4 7/8	11/16	2	3 1/2	4	5/8	1 1/16	2 7/16	1.32	1 1/16
	1 1/4	5 1/4	3/4	2 1/2	3 7/8	4	5/8	1 1/16	2 9/16	1.66	1 1/16
	1 1/2	6 1/8	13/16	2 7/8	4 1/2	4	3/4	1 3/16	2 11/16	1.90	1 3/16
	2	6 1/2	7/8	3 5/8	5	8	5/8	1 5/16	2 3/4	2.38	1 5/16
	2 1/2	7 1/2	1	4 1/8	5 7/8	8	3/4	1 1/2	3	2.88	1 1/2
	3	8 1/4	1 1/8	5	6 5/8	8	3/4	1 11/16	3 1/8	3.50	1 11/16
	3 1/2	9	1 3/16	5 1/2	7 1/4	8	3/4	1 3/4	3 3/16	4.00	...
	4	10	1 1/4	6 3/16	7 7/8	8	3/4	1 7/8	3 3/8	4.50	1 7/8
	5	11	1 3/8	7 5/16	9 1/4	8	3/4	2	3 7/8	5.56	2
	6	12 1/2	1 7/16	8 1/2	10 5/8	12	3/4	2 1/16	3 7/8	6.63	2 1/16
	8	15	1 5/8	10 5/8	13	12	7/8	2 7/16	4 3/8	8.63	2 7/16
	10	17 1/2	1 7/8	12 3/4	15 1/4	16	1	2 5/8	4 5/8	10.75	3 3/4
	12	20 1/2	2	15	17 3/4	16	1 1/8	2 7/8	5 1/8	12.75	4
	14	23	2 1/8	16 1/4	20 1/4	20	1 1/8	3	5 5/8	14.00	4 3/8
	16	25 1/2	2 1/4	18 1/2	22 1/2	20	1 1/4	3 1/4	5 3/4	16.00	4 3/4
	18	28	2 3/8	21	24 3/4	24	1 1/4	3 1/2	6 1/4	18.00	5 1/8
	20	30 1/2	2 1/2	23	27	24	1 1/4	3 3/4	6 3/8	20.00	5 1/2
	24	36	2 3/4	27 1/4	32	24	1 1/2	4 3/16	6 5/8	24.00	6
400 Pound (For smaller sizes, use 600-Pound)	4	10	1 3/8	6 3/16	7 7/8	8	7/8	2	3 1/2	4.50	2
	5	11	1 1/2	7 5/16	9 1/4	8	7/8	2 1/8	4	5.56	2 1/8
	6	12 1/2	1 5/8	8 1/2	10 5/8	12	7/8	2 1/4	4 1/16	6.63	2 1/4
	8	15	1 7/8	10 5/8	13	12	1	2 11/16	4 5/8	8.63	2 11/16
	10	17 1/2	2 1/8	12 3/4	15 1/4	16	1 1/8	2 7/8	4 7/8	10.75	4
	12	20 1/2	2 1/4	15	17 3/4	16	1 1/4	3 1/8	5 3/8	12.75	4 1/4
	14	23	2 3/8	16 1/4	20 1/4	20	1 1/4	3 5/16	5 7/8	14.00	4 5/8
	16	25 1/2	2 1/2	18 1/2	22 1/2	20	1 3/8	3 11/16	6	16.00	5
	18	28	2 5/8	21	24 3/4	24	1 3/8	3 7/8	6 1/2	18.00	5 3/8
	20	30 1/2	2 3/4	23	27	24	1 1/2	4	6 5/8	20.00	5 3/4
	24	36	3	27 1/4	32	24	1 3/4	4 1/2	6 7/8	24.00	6 1/4

Forged Steel Flanges (in.) Continued.

Courtesy of Crane Co.

Class	Pipe Size	A	B	C	D	Bolts		E	F	G	H
						No.	Dia.				
600 Pound	½	3¾	9/16	1⅜	2⅝	4	½	⅞	2 1/16	0.84	⅞
	¾	4⅝	⅝	1 11/16	3¼	4	⅝	1	2¼	1.05	1
	1	4⅞	11/16	2	3½	4	⅝	1 1/16	2 7/16	1.32	1 1/16
	1¼	5¼	13/16	2½	3⅞	4	⅝	1⅛	2⅝	1.66	1⅛
	1½	6⅛	⅞	2⅞	4½	4	¾	1¼	2¾	1.90	1¼
	2	6½	1	3⅝	5	8	⅝	1 7/16	2⅞	2.38	1 7/16
	2½	7½	1⅛	4⅛	5⅞	8	¾	1⅝	3⅛	2.88	1⅝
	3	8¼	1¼	5	6⅝	8	¾	1 13/16	3¼	3.50	1 13/16
	4	10¾	1½	6 3/16	8½	8	⅞	2⅛	4	4.50	2⅛
	5	13	1¾	7 5/16	10½	8	1	2⅜	4½	5.56	2⅜
	6	14	1⅞	8½	11½	12	1	2⅝	4⅝	6.63	2⅝
	8	16½	2 3/16	10⅝	13¾	12	1⅛	3	5¼	8.63	3
	10	20	2½	12¾	17	16	1¼	3⅜	6	10.75	4⅜
	12	22	2⅝	15	19¼	20	1¼	3⅝	6⅛	12.75	4⅝
	14	23¾	2¾	16¼	20¾	20	1⅜	3 11/16	6½	14.00	5
	16	27	3	18½	23¾	20	1½	4 3/16	7	16.00	5½
	18	29¼	3¼	21	25¾	20	1⅝	4⅝	7¼	18.00	6
	20	32	3½	23	28½	24	1⅝	5	7½	20.00	6½
	24	37	4	27¼	33	24	1⅞	5½	8	24.00	7¼
900 Pound (For smaller sizes, use 1500 Pound)	3	9½	1½	5	7½	8	⅞	2⅛	4	3.50	2⅛
	4	11½	1¾	6 3/16	9¼	8	1⅛	2¾	4½	4.50	2¾
	5	13¾	2	7 5/16	11	8	1¼	3⅛	5	5.56	3⅛
	6	15	2 3/16	8½	12½	12	1⅛	3⅜	5½	6.63	3⅜
	8	18½	2½	10⅝	15½	12	1⅜	4	6⅜	8.63	4½
	10	21½	2¾	12¾	18½	16	1⅜	4¼	7¼	10.75	5
	12	24	3⅛	15	21	20	1⅜	4⅝	7⅞	12.75	5⅝
	14	25¼	3⅜	16¼	22	20	1½	5⅛	8⅜	14.00	6⅛
	16	27¾	3½	18½	24¼	20	1⅝	5¼	8½	16.00	6½
	18	31	4	21	27	20	1⅞	6	9	18.00	7½
	20	33¾	4¼	23	29½	20	2	6¼	9¾	20.00	8¼
	24	41	5½	27¼	35½	20	2½	8	11½	24.00	10½
1500 Pound	½	4¾	⅞	1⅜	3¼	4	¾	1¼	2⅜	0.84	1¼
	¾	5⅛	1	1 11/16	3½	4	¾	1⅜	2¾	1.05	1⅜
	1	5⅞	1⅛	2	4	4	⅞	1⅝	2⅞	1.32	1⅝
	1¼	6¼	1⅛	2½	4⅜	4	⅞	1⅝	2⅞	1.66	1⅝
	1½	7	1¼	2⅞	4⅞	4	1	1¾	3¼	1.90	1¾
	2	8½	1½	3⅝	6½	8	⅞	2¼	4	2.38	2¼
	2½	9⅝	1⅝	4⅛	7½	8	1	2½	4⅛	2.88	2½
	3	10½	1⅞	5	8	8	1⅛	2⅞	4⅝	3.50	2⅞
	4	12¼	2⅛	6 3/16	9½	8	1¼	3 9/16	4⅞	4.50	3 9/16
	5	14¾	2⅞	7 5/16	11½	8	1½	4⅛	6⅛	5.56	4⅛
	6	15½	3¼	8½	12½	12	1⅜	4 11/16	6¾	6.63	4 11/16
	8	19	3⅝	10⅝	15½	12	1⅝	5⅝	8⅜	8.63	5⅝
	10	23	4¼	12¾	19	12	1⅞	6¼	10	10.75	7
	12	26½	4⅞	15	22½	16	2	7⅛	11⅛	12.75	8⅝
	14	29½	5¼	16¼	25	16	2¼	...	11¾	14.00	9½
2500 Pound	½	5¼	1 3/16	1⅜	3½	4	¾	1 9/16	2⅞	0.84	1 9/16
	¾	5½	1¼	1 11/16	3¾	4	¾	1 11/16	3⅛	1.05	1 11/16
	1	6¼	1⅜	2	4¼	4	⅞	1⅞	3½	1.32	1⅞
	1¼	7¼	1½	2½	5⅛	4	1	2 1/16	3¾	1.66	2 1/16
	1½	8	1¾	2⅞	5¾	4	1⅛	2⅜	4⅜	1.90	2⅜
	2	9¼	2	3⅝	6¾	8	1	2¾	5	2.38	2¾
	2½	10½	2¼	4⅛	7¾	8	1⅛	3⅛	5⅝	2.88	3⅛
	3	12	2⅝	5	9	8	1¼	3⅝	6⅝	3.50	3⅝
	4	14	3	6 3/16	10¾	8	1½	4¼	7½	4.50	4¼
	5	16½	3⅝	7 5/16	12¾	8	1¾	5⅛	9	5.56	5⅛
	6	19	4¼	8½	14½	8	2	6	10¾	6.63	6
	8	21¾	5	10⅝	17¼	12	2	7	12½	8.63	7
	10	26½	6½	12¾	21¼	12	2½	9	16½	10.75	9
	12	30	7¼	15	24⅜	12	2¾	10	18¼	12.75	10

Cast Steel Wedge Gate Valves
150- to 1500-Pound Dimensions
Courtesy of Crane Co.

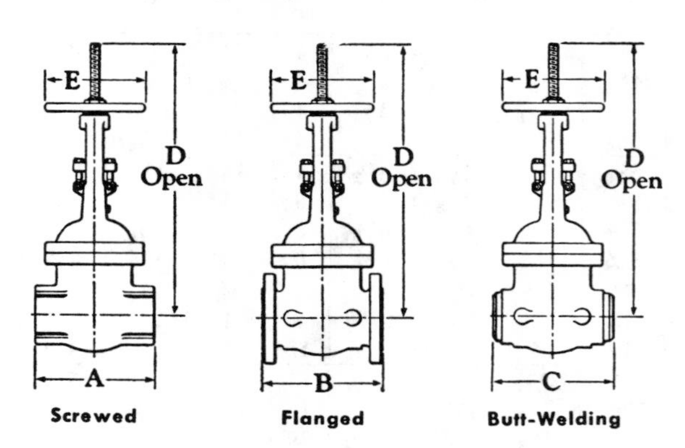

Dimensions, in Inches

Class	Size of Valve	A	B	C	D	E
150-Pound	2	6¼	7	8½	15¾	8
	2½	7	7½	9½	16½	8
	3	7⅜	8	11⅛	20¾	9
	3½	...	8½	...	23	9
	4	8	9	12	25¾	10
	5	...	10	15	30½	12
	6	...	10½	15⅞	35¼	14
	8	...	11½	16½	44	16
	10	...	13	18	52½	18
	12	...	14	19¾	60½	18
	14	...	15	22½	70¼	22
	16	...	16	24	79¾	24
	18	...	17	26	89	27
	20	...	18	28	97¼	30
	24	...	20	32	112¾	30
300-Pound	1½	...	7½	...	16¾	8
	2	7	8½	8½	18	8
	2½	8	9½	9½	19	8
	3	9	11⅛	11⅛	23¼	9
	4	11	12	12	28¼	10
	5	...	15	15	33½	12
	6	...	15⅞	15⅞	38½	14
	8	...	16½	16½	47	16
	10	...	18	18	56½	20
	12	...	19¾	19¾	64¼	20
	14	...	30	30	75¼	27
	16	...	33	33	81	27
	18	...	36	36	91½	30
	20	...	39	39	99¾	36
	24	...	45	45	120½	36
400-Pound	4	...	16	16	30¾	12
	5	...	18	18	35	14
	6	...	19½	19½	40¼	16
	8	...	23½	23½	50½	20
	10	...	26½	26½	59¾	24
	12	...	30	30	67¾	24
	14	...	32½	32½	74¾	27
	16	...	35½	35½	80¾	27

Class	Size of Valve	B	C	D	E
600-Pound	2	11½	11½	18¼	8
	2½	13	13	22¼	9
	3	14	14	25¾	10
	3½	15	...	32	14
	4	17	17	31½	14
	5	20	20	36¾	16
	6	22	22	42¾	20
	8	26	26	52¼	24
	10	31	31	62¼	27
	12	33	33	70	27
	14	35	35	77¼	30
	16	39	39	83¾	30
	18	43	43	93¾	36
	20	47	47	104½	36
	24	55	55	126	42
900-Pound	3	15	15	27¼	12
	4	18	18	31½	14
	5	22	22	36¾	16
	6	24	24	42¾	20
	8	29	29	52½	24
	10	33	33	62¼	27
	12	38	38	73½	30
	14	40½	40½	77¼	30
	16	44½	44½	85¾	36
1500-Pound	1	10	10	16	8
	1¼	11	11	16½	8
	1½	12	12	20	9
	2	14½	14½	22⅛	10
	2½	16½	16½	26⅜	12
	3	18½	18½	28	14
	4	21½	21½	33	16
	5	26½	26½	38¾	20
	6	27¾	27¾	47	24
	8	32¾	32¾	55	27

Cast Steel Globe and Angle Valves

Courtesy of Crane Co.

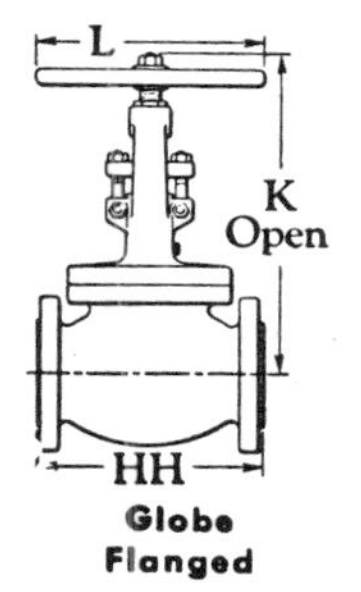

Globe Flanged

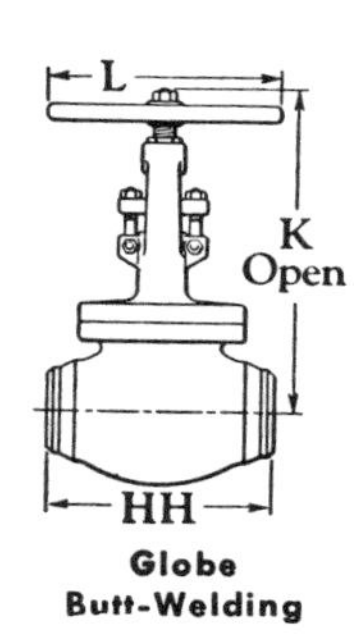

Globe Butt-Welding

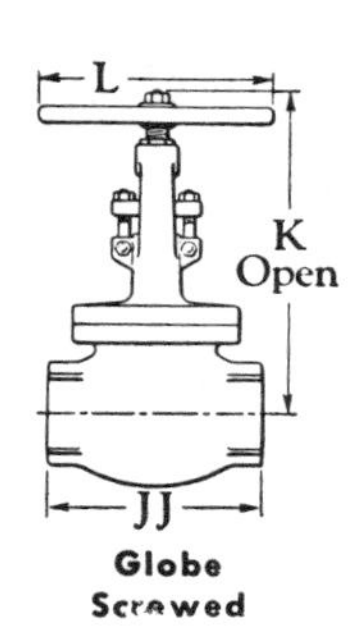

Globe Screwed

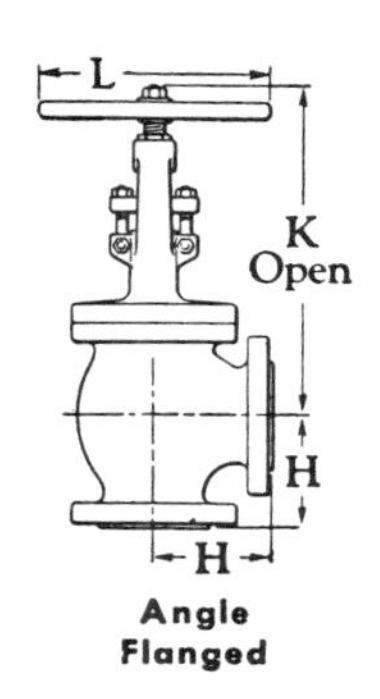

Angle Flanged

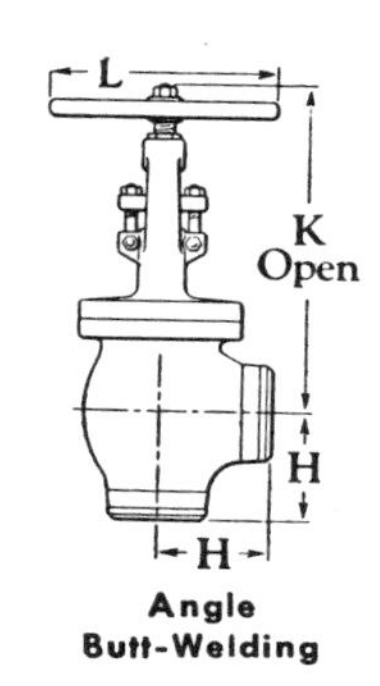

Angle Butt-Welding

Class	Size	Globe Valves						Angle Valves		All Valves
		Flanged		Butt-Welding		Screwed		Flanged or Butt-Welding†		
		HH	K	HH	K	JJ	K	H	K	L
150 Pound	2	8	13¾	8	13¾	8	13¾	4	12½	8
	2½	8½	14½	8½	14½	...	...	4¼	13	8
	3	9½	16½	9½	16½	...	...	4¾	15	9
	3½	10½	17¼	...	...	...	...	...	...	9
	4	11½	19¾	11½	19¾	...	...	5¾	17¾	10
	5	14	23	14	23	...	...	7	20¾	10
	6	16	24½	16	24½	...	...	8	21¾	12
	8	19½	26	19½	26	...	...	9¾	23½	16
300 Pound	2	10½	17¾	10½	17¾	...	...	5¼	17¾	9
	2½	11½	19	11½	19	...	...	5¾	19	10
	‡3	12½	20½	12½	20½	...	...	6¼	20½	10
	3½	13¼	22½	...	...	...	...	6⅝	22½	12
	4	14	24¾	14	24¾	...	...	7	24¾	14
	5	15¾	26½	...	...	...	...	7⅞	26½	16
	6	17½	29¾	17½	29¾	...	...	8¾	29¾	18
	8	22	36½	22	36½	...	...	11	36½	24
400 Pound	4	16	25¼	16	25¼	...	...	8	25¼	14
	5	18	28½	18	28½	...	...	9	28½	18
	6	19½	31¼	19½	31¼	...	...	9¾	31¼	20
	8	23½	38¼	23½	38¼	...	...	11¾	38¼	27
600 Pound	2	11½	19	11½	19	...	...	...	...	10
	2½	13	21¼	13	21¼	...	...	6½	21¼	12
	‡3	14	23½	14	23½	...	...	7	23½	12
	3½	15	25	...	...	...	...	7½	25	14
	4	17	27½	17	27½	...	...	8½	27½	18
	5	20	30¾	20	30¾	...	...	10	30¾	20
	6	22	35	22	35	...	...	11	35	24
900 Pound	3	15	24	15	24	...	...	7½	24	12
	4	18	29½	18	29½	...	...	9	29½	20
	6	24	37¾	24	37¾	...	...	12	37¾	27
1500 Pound	2	14½	25⅛	14½	25⅛	...	...	...	...	14
	2½	16½	28⅛	16½	28⅛	...	...	...	...	18
	3	18½	33½	18½	33½	...	...	...	...	24

Cast Steel Swing Check Valves

Courtesy of Crane Co.

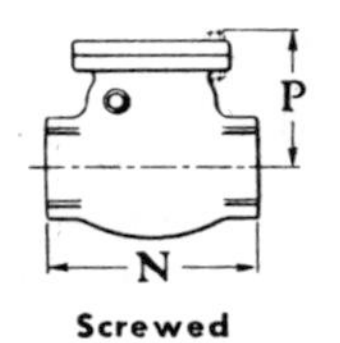

Screwed

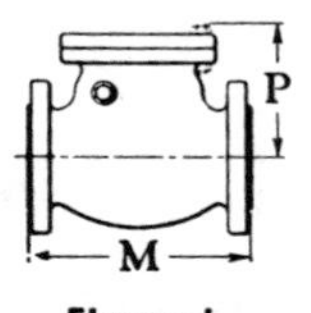

Flanged

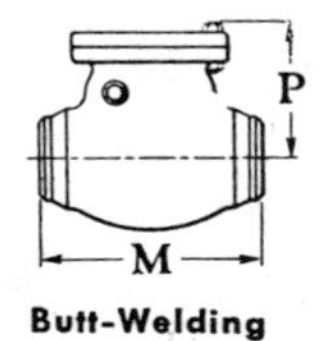

Butt-Welding

Weights and Dimensions

Pressure Class	Size	Pounds, Each			Dimensions, in Inches			
		Screwed Valves	Flanged Valves	Butt-Welding Valves	Screwed		Flanged or Butt-Welding	
	Inches		FD & SF		N	P	M	P
150 Pound	2	27	34	25	8	5	8	5
	2½	40	50	30	8½	5½	8½	5½
	3	50	65	50	9½	6	9½	6
	3½	...	94	...	...	...	10½	6½
	4	96	100	100	11½	7	11½	7
	5	...	140	120	...	...	13	8
	6	...	200	160	...	...	14	9
	8	...	390	360	...	...	19½	10¼
	10	...	510	...	...	...	24½	12⅛
	12	...	775	...	...	...	27½	13¾
	14	...	1200	...	...	...	35	on
	16	...	1450	...	...	...	39	request
300 Pound	2	40	62	47	9½	6¾	10½	6¾
	2½	70	80	60	10¾	8	11½	8
	*3	100	120	80	11¾	8½	12½	8½
	4	...	180	130	...	...	14	9¾
	5	...	250	240	...	...	15¾	10¾
	6	...	330	260	...	...	17½	11¾
	8	...	620	510	...	...	21	14
	10	...	920	760	...	...	24½	15
	12	...	1290	1015	...	...	28	16¾
400 Pound	4	...	200	190	...	...	16	10
	5	...	270	265	...	...	18	12
	6	...	395	310	...	...	19½	12½
	8	...	680	580	...	...	23½	14½
	10	...	900	820	...	...	26½	15¼
	12	...	1250	1150	...	...	30	16⅞
600 Pound	1¼	...	38	32	...	...	9	6¼
	1½	...	58	40	...	...	9½	6¾
	2	...	70	55	...	...	11½	7
	2½	...	105	70	...	...	13	8¼
	*3	...	140	100	...	...	14	9
	4	...	260	170	...	...	17	10¼
	5	...	400	300	...	...	20	12¾
	6	...	530	420	...	...	22	13½
	8	...	900	740	...	...	26	15¼
	10	...	1440	880	...	...	31	18¾
	12	...	1970	1200	...	...	33	21½
900 Pound	3	...	180	155	...	...	15	9½
	4	...	340	240	...	...	18	11
	6	...	640	500	...	...	24	13¾
	8	...	1180	890	...	...	29	16½
1500 Pound	1½	...	110	80	...	...	12	8¼
	2	...	160	130	...	...	14½	9¾
	2½	...	245	170		...	16½	10½
	3	...	280	210	...	...	18½	11¼
	4	...	630	390	...	...	21½	13¼
	5	...	950	480	...	...	26½	15¼
	6	...	1360	780	...	...	27¾	15¾
	8	...	2100	1320	...	...	32¾	18¼

Miter Welding

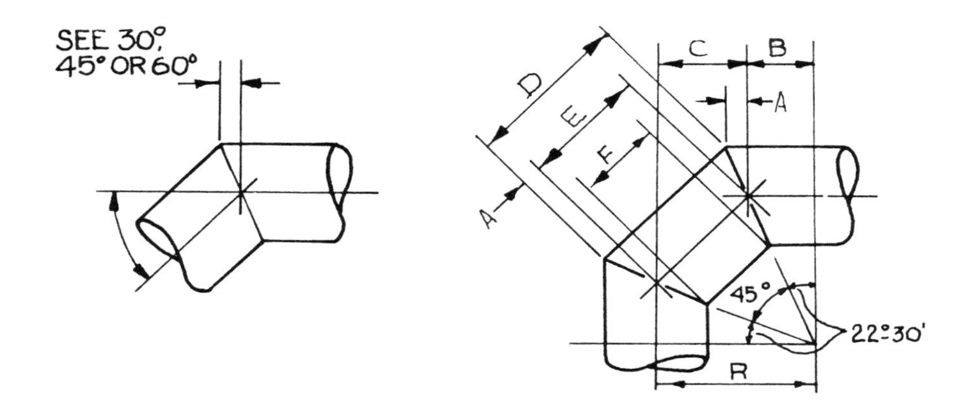

Size	30°	45°	60°	R	A	B	C	D	E	F
3	1/2	3/4	1	4-1/2	3/4	1-7/8	2-5/8	5-1/4	3-3/4	2-1/4
4	5/8	15/16	1-5/16	6	15/16	2-1/2	3-1/2	6-7/8	5	3-1/8
6	7/8	1-3/8	1-15/16	9	1-3/8	3-3/4	5-1/4	10-3/16	7-7/16	4-11/16
8	1-1/8	1-13/16	2-1/2	1 – 0	1-13/16	5	7	1 – 1-9/16	9-15/16	6-5/16
10	1-7/16	2-1/4	3-1/8	1 – 3	2-1/4	6-3/16	8-13/16	1 – 4-15/16	1 – 0-7/16	7-15/16
12	1-11/16	2-5/8	3-11/16	1 – 6	2-5/8	7-7/16	10-9/16	1 – 8-3/16	1 – 2-15/16	9-11/16
14	1-7/8	2-7/8	4-1/16	1 – 9	2-7/8	8-11/16	1 – 0-5/16	1 – 11-1/8	1 – 5-3/8	11-5/8
16	2-1/8	3-5/16	4-5/8	2 – 0	3-5/16	9-15/16	1 – 2-1/16	2 – 2-1/2	1 – 7-7/8	1 – 1-1/4
18	2-7/16	3-3/4	5-3/16	2 – 3	3-3/4	11-3/16	1 – 3-13/16	2 – 5-7/8	1 – 10-3/8	1 – 2-7/8
20	2-11/16	4-1/8	5-3/4	2 – 6	4-1/8	1 – 0-7/16	1 – 5-9/16	2 – 9-1/8	2 – 0-7/8	1 – 4-5/8
22	2-15/16	4-9/16	6-3/8	2 – 9	4-9/16	1 – 1-11/16	1 – 7-5/16	3 – 0-7/16	2 – 3-5/16	1 – 6-3/16
24	3-3/16	5	6-15/16	3 – 0	5	1 – 2-15/16	1 – 9-1/16	3 – 3-13/16	2 – 5-13/16	1 – 7-13/16
26	3-1/2	5-3/8	7-1/2	3 – 3	5-3/8	1 – 4-1/8	1 – 10-7/8	3 – 7-1/16	2 – 8-5/16	1 – 9-9/16
28	3-3/4	5-13/16	8-1/16	3 – 6	5-13/16	1 – 5-3/8	2 – 0-5/8	3 – 10-7/16	2 – 10-13/16	1 – 11-3/16
30	4	6-3/16	8-5/8	3 – 9	6-3/16	1 – 6-5/8	2 – 2-3/8	4 – 1-5/8	3 – 1-1/4	2 – 0-7/8
32	4-5/16	6-5/8	9-1/4	4 – 0	6-5/8	1 – 7-7/8	2 – 4-1/8	4 – 5	3 – 3-3/4	2 – 2-1/2
34	4-9/16	7-1/16	9-13/16	4 – 3	7-1/16	1 – 9-1/8	2 – 5-7/8	4 – 8-3/8	3 – 6-1/4	2 – 4-1/8
36	4-13/16	7-7/16	10-3/8	4 – 6	7-7/16	1 – 10-3/8	2 – 7-5/8	4 – 11-5/8	3 – 8-3/4	2 – 5-7/8
38	5-1/16	7-7/8	11	4 – 9	7-7/8	1 – 11-5/8	2 – 9-3/8	5 – 3	3 – 11-1/4	2 – 7-1/2
40	5-3/8	8-5/16	11-9/16	5 – 0	8-5/16	2 – 0-7/8	2 – 11-1/8	5 – 6-5/16	4 – 1-11/16	2 – 9-1/16
42	5-5/8	8-11/16	1 – 0-1/8	5 – 3	8-11/16	2 – 2-1/8	3 – 0-7/8	5 – 9-9/16	4 – 4-3/16	2 – 10-13/16
48	6-7/16	9-15/16	1 – 1-7/8	6 – 0	9-15/16	2 – 5-13/16	3 – 6-3/16	6 – 7-1/2	4 – 11-5/8	3 – 3-3/4
54	7-1/4	11-3/16	1 – 3-9/16	6 – 9	11-3/16	2 – 9-9/16	3 – 11-7/8	7 – 5-1/2	5 – 7-1/8	3 – 8-3/4
60	8-1/16	1 – 0-7/16	1 – 5-5/16	7 – 6	1 – 0-7/16	3 – 1-1/4	4 – 4-3/4	8 – 3-7/16	6 – 2-9/16	4 – 1-11/16
72	9-5/8	1 – 2-15/16	1 – 8-13/16	9 – 0	1 – 2-15/16	3 – 8-3/4	5 – 3-1/4	9 – 11-3/8	7 – 5-1/2	4 – 11-5/8

Source: Texas Pipe Bending Co., Inc., Houston, Texas.

Miter Welding Dimensions

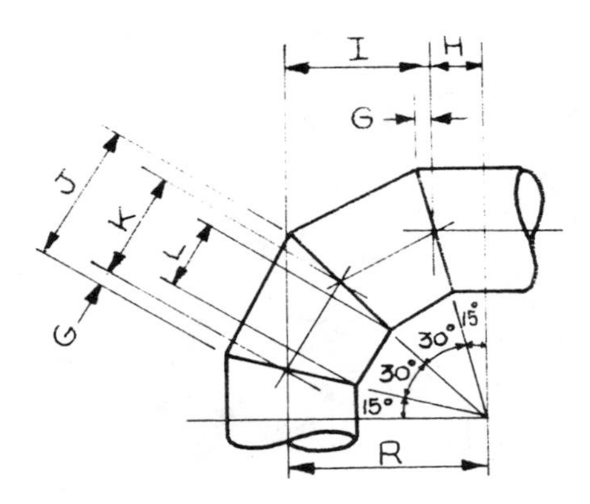

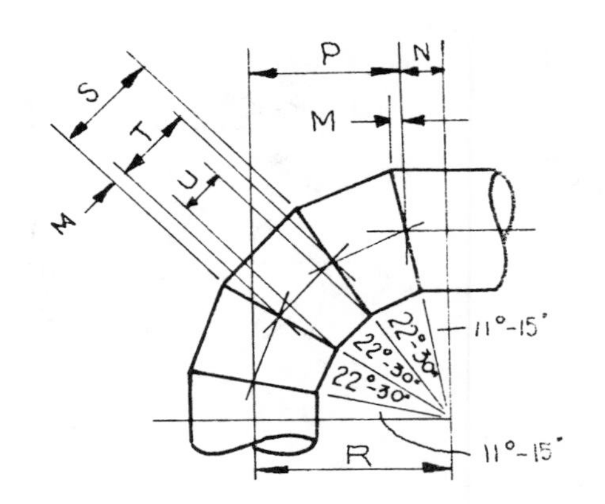

G	H	I	J	K	L	M	N	P	S	T	U
1/2	1-3/16	3-5/16	3-7/16	2-7/16	1-7/16	3/8	7/8	3-5/8	2-9/16	1-13/16	1-1/16
5/8	1-5/8	4-3/8	4-7/16	3-3/16	1-15/16	7/16	1-3/16	4-13/16	3-1/4	2-3/8	1-1/2
7/8	2-7/16	6-9/16	6-9/16	4-13/16	3-1/16	11/16	1-13/16	7-3/16	4-15/16	3-9/16	2-3/16
1-1/8	3-3/16	8-13/16	8-11/16	6-7/16	4-3/16	7/8	2-3/8	9-5/8	6-1/2	4-3/4	3
1-7/16	4	11	10-15/16	8-1/16	5-3/16	1-1/16	3	1 – 0	8-1/16	5-15/16	3-13/16
1-11/16	4-13/16	1 – 1-3/16	1 – 1	9-5/8	6-1/4	1-1/4	3-9/16	1 – 2-7/16	9-11/16	7-3/16	4-11/16
1-7/8	5-5/8	1 – 3-3/8	1 – 3	11-1/4	7-1/2	1-3/8	4-3/16	1 – 4-13/16	11-1/8	8-3/8	5-5/8
2-1/8	6-7/16	1 – 5-9/16	1 – 5-1/8	1 – 0-7/8	8-5/8	1-9/16	4-3/4	1 – 7-1/4	1 – 0-11/16	9-9/16	6-7/16
2-7/16	7-1/4	1 – 7-3/4	1 – 7-5/16	1 – 2-7/16	9-9/16	1-13/16	5-3/8	1 – 9-5/8	1 – 2-3/8	10-3/4	7-1/8
2-11/16	8-1/16	1 – 9-15/16	1 – 9-7/16	1 – 4-1/16	10-11/16	2	5-15/16	2 – 0-1/16	1 – 3-15/16	11-15/16	7-15/16
2-15/16	8-13/16	2 – 0-3/16	1 – 11-9/16	1 – 5-11/16	11-13/16	2-3/16	6-9/16	2 – 2-7/16	1 – 5-1/2	1 – 1-1/8	8-3/4
3-3/16	9-5/8	2 – 2-3/8	2 – 1-11/16	1 – 7-5/16	1 – 0-15/16	2-3/8	7-3/16	2 – 4-13/16	1 – 7-1/16	1 – 2-5/16	9-9/16
3-1/2	10-7/16	2 – 4-9/16	2 – 3-7/8	1 – 8-7/8	1 – 1-7/8	2-9/16	7-3/4	2 – 7-1/4	1 – 8-5/8	1 – 3-1/2	10-3/8
3-3/4	11-1/4	2 – 6-3/4	2 – 6	1 – 10-1/2	1 – 3	2-13/16	8-3/8	2 – 9-5/8	1 – 10-5/16	1 – 4-11/16	11-1/16
4	1 – 0-1/16	2 – 8-15/16	2 – 8-1/8	2 – 0-1/8	1 – 4-1/8	3	8-15/16	3 – 0-1/16	1 – 11-7/8	1 – 5-7/8	11-7/8
4-5/16	1 – 0-7/8	2 – 11-1/8	2 – 10-5/16	2 – 1-11/16	1 – 5-1/16	3-3/16	9-9/16	3 – 2-7/16	2 – 1-1/2	1 – 7-1/8	1 – 0-3/4
4-9/16	1 – 1-11/16	3 – 1-5/16	3 – 0-7/16	2 – 3-5/16	1 – 6-3/16	3-3/8	10-1/8	3 – 4-7/8	2 – 3-1/16	1 – 8-5/16	1 – 1-9/16
4-13/16	1 – 2-7/16	3 – 3-9/16	3 – 2-9/16	2 – 4-15/16	1 – 7-5/16	3-9/16	10-3/4	3 – 7-1/4	2 – 4-5/8	1 – 9-1/2	1 – 2-3/8
5-1/16	1 – 3-1/4	3 – 5-3/4	3 – 4-11/16	2 – 6-9/16	1 – 8-7/16	3-3/4	11-5/16	3 – 9-11/16	2 – 6-3/16	1 – 10-11/16	1 – 3-3/16
5-3/8	1 – 4-1/16	3 – 7-15/16	3 – 6-7/8	2 – 8-1/8	1 – 9-3/8	4	11-15/16	4 – 0-1/16	2 – 7-7/8	1 – 11-7/8	1 – 3-7/8
5-5/8	1 – 4-7/8	3 – 10-1/8	3 – 9	2 – 9-3/4	1 – 10-1/2	4-3/16	1 – 0-1/2	4 – 2-1/2	2 – 9-7/16	2 – 1-1/16	1 – 4-11/16
6-7/16	1 – 7-5/16	4 – 4-11/16	4 – 3-7/16	3 – 2-9/16	2 – 1-11/16	4-3/4	1 – 2-5/16	4 – 9-11/16	3 – 2-1/8	2 – 4-5/8	1 – 7-1/8
7-1/4	1 – 9-11/16	4 – 11-5/16	4 – 9-7/8	3 – 7-3/8	2 – 4-7/8	5-3/8	1 – 4-1/8	5 – 4-7/8	3 – 7	2 – 8-1/4	1 – 9-1/2
8-1/16	2 – 0-1/8	5 – 5-7/8	5 – 4-3/8	4 – 0-1/4	2 – 8-1/8	5-15/16	1 – 5-7/8	6 – 0-1/8	3 – 11-5/8	2 – 11-3/4	1 – 11-7/8
9-5/8	2 – 5	6 – 7	6 – 5-1/4	4 – 10	3 – 2-3/4	7-3/16	1 – 9-1/2	7 – 2-1/2	4 – 9-3/8	3 – 7	2 – 4-5/8

Source: Texas Pipe Bending Co., Inc., Houston, Texas

Length of Pipe in Bends
Courtesy of Crane Co.

Radius of Pipe Bends						
nches	Feet	90° Bends	180° Bends	270° Bends	360° Bends	540° Bends
1		1½″	3″	4¾″	6¼″	9½″
2		3	6¼	9½	12½	18¾
3	¼	4¾	9½	14¼	18¾	28¼
4		6¼	12½	18¾	25¼	37¾
5		7¾	15¾	23½	31½	47¼
6	½	9½	18¾	28¼	37¾	56½
7		11	22	33	44	66
8		12½	25¼	37¾	50¼	75½
9	¾	14¼	28¼	42½	56½	84¾
10		15¾	31½	47¼	62¾	94¼
11		17¼	34½	51¾	69	103¾
12	1	18¾	37¾	56½	75½	113
12.5		19¾	39¼	59	78½	117¾
14		22	44	66	88	132
15	1¼	23½	47	70¾	94¼	141¼
16		25¼	50¼	75½	100½	150¾
17.5		27½	55	82½	110	165
18	1½	28¼	56½	84¾	113	169¾
20		31½	62¾	94¼	125¾	188½
21	1¾	33	66	99	132	198
24	2	37¾	75½	113	150¾	226¼
25		39¼	78½	117¾	157	235½
30	2½	47¼	94¼	141¼	188½	282¾
32		50¼	100½	150¾	201	301½
36	3	56½	113	169½	226¼	339¼
40		62¾	125¾	188½	251¼	377
48	4	75½	150¾	226¼	301½	452½
50		78½	157	235½	314¼	471¼
56		88	176	264	351¾	527¾
60	5	94¼	188½	282¾	377	565½
64		100½	201	301½	402	603¼
70		110	220	329¾	439¾	659¾
72	6	113	226¼	339¼	452½	678½
80		125¾	251¼	377	502¾	754
84	7	132	263¾	395¾	527¾	791½
90	7½	141¼	282¾	424	565½	848¼
96	8	150¾	301½	452½	603	904¾
00		157	314¼	471¼	628¼	942½
08	9	169½	339¼	509	678½	1017¾
20	10	188½	377	565½	754	1131
32	11	207¼	414¾	622	829½	1244
44	12	226¼	452½	678½	904¾	1357¼
56	13	245	490	735¼	980¼	1470¼
68	14	263¾	527¾	791½	1055½	1583½
80	15	282¾	565½	848¼	1131	1696½
92	16	301½	603	904¾	1206¼	1809½
04	17	320½	640¾	961¼	1281¾	1922½
16	18	339¼	678½	1017¾	1357¼	2035¾
28	19	358	716¼	1074½	1432½	2148¾
40	20	377	754	1131	1508	2262

To find the length of pipe in a bend having a radius not given above, add together the length of pipe in bends whose combined radii equal the required radius.

Example: **Find length of pipe in 90° bend of 5′ 9″ radius.**

Length of pipe in 90° bend of 5′ radius = 94¼″

Length of pipe in 90° bend of 9″ radius = 14¼″

Then, length of pipe in 90° bend of 5′ 9″ radius = 108½″

Calculation of Pipe Bends

Courtesy of Crane Co.

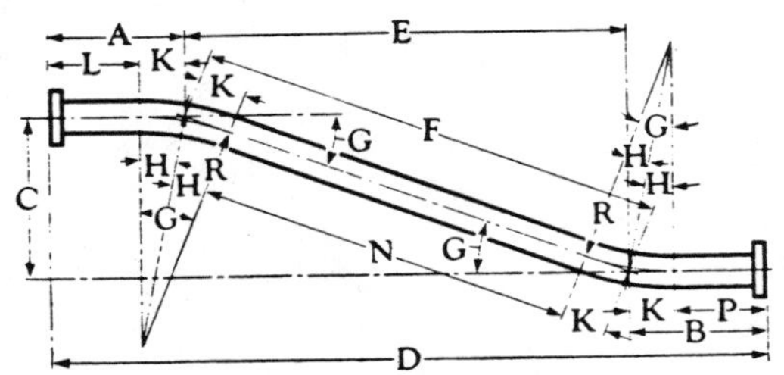

Example No. 8—**Given A, B, C, D, R**

$$E = D - A - B$$
$$F = \sqrt{E^2 + C^2}$$
$$\frac{C}{F} = \sin \angle G$$
$$\angle H = \tfrac{1}{2} \angle G$$
$$K = \tan \angle H \times R$$
$$L = A - K$$
$$P = B - K$$
$$N = F - 2K$$

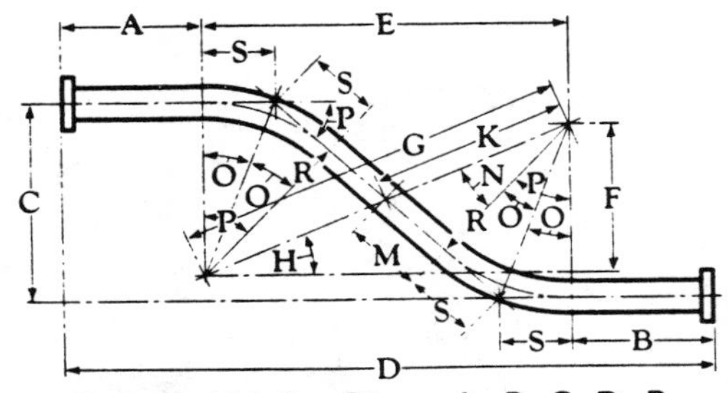

Example No. 9—**Given A, B, C, D, R**

$$E = D - A - B$$
$$F = 2R - C$$
$$G = \sqrt{E^2 + F^2}$$
$$\frac{F}{E} = \tan \angle H$$
$$K = \tfrac{1}{2} G$$
$$M = \sqrt{K^2 - R^2}$$
$$\frac{M}{K} = \sin \angle N$$
$$\angle P = 90^\circ - \angle H - \angle N$$
$$\angle O = \tfrac{1}{2} \angle P$$
$$S = \tan \angle O \times R$$

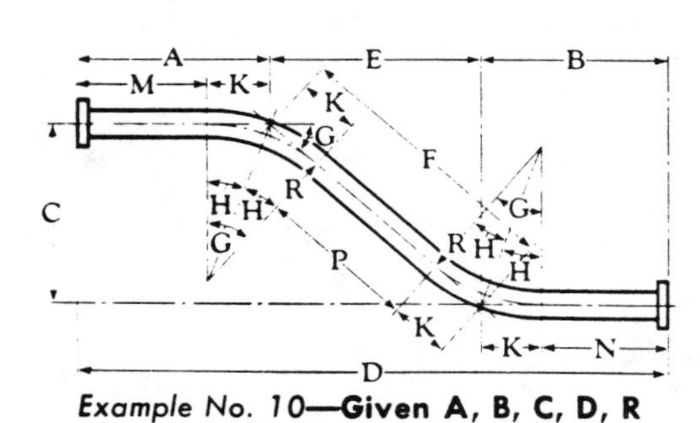

Example No. 10—**Given A, B, C, D, R**

$$E = D - A - B$$
$$F = \sqrt{C^2 + E^2}$$
$$\frac{C}{F} = \sin \angle G$$
$$\angle H = \tfrac{1}{2} \angle G$$
$$K = \tan \angle H \times R$$
$$M = A - K$$
$$N = B - K$$
$$P = F - 2K$$

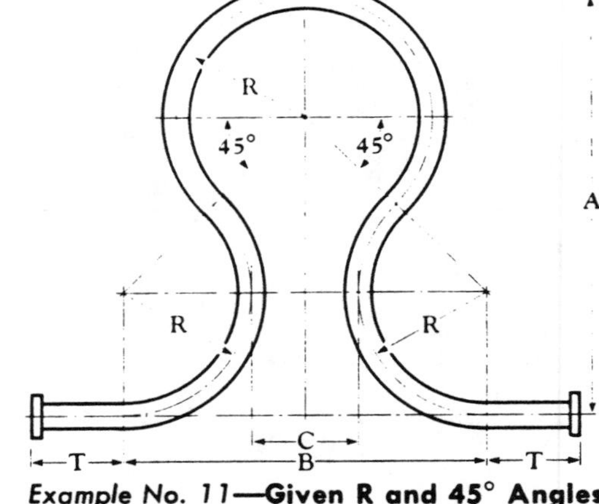

Example No. 11—**Given R and 45° Angles**

$$A = 3.414 \times R$$
$$B = 2.828 \times R$$
$$C = 0.828 \times R$$

T = Tangent

Length of pipe in bend = $9.425 \times R + 2T$

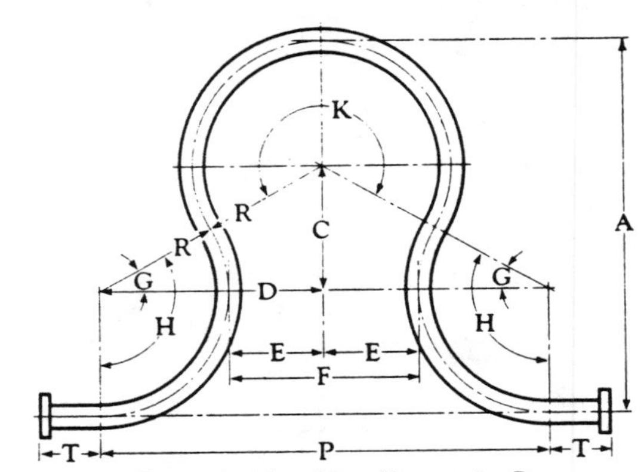

Example No. 12—**Given A, R**

$$C = A - 2R$$
$$D = \sqrt{(2R)^2 - C^2}$$
$$P = 2D$$
$$E = D - R$$
$$F = 2E$$
$$C/2R = \sin \angle G$$
$$\angle H = 90^\circ + \angle G$$
$$\angle K = 180^\circ + 2 \angle G$$

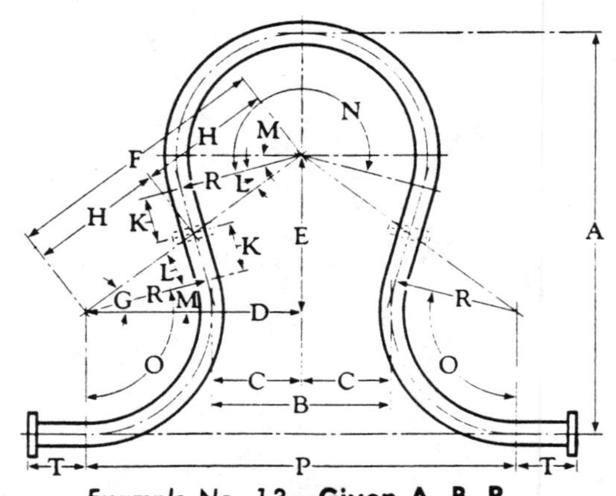

Example No. 13—**Given A, B, R**

$$C = \tfrac{1}{2} B$$
$$D = R + C$$
$$E = A - 2R$$
$$F = \sqrt{D^2 + E^2}$$
$$E/F = \sin \angle G$$
$$H = \tfrac{1}{2} F$$
$$K = \sqrt{H^2 - R^2}$$
$$K/H = \sin \angle L$$
$$\angle M = \angle G - \angle L$$
$$\angle N = 180^\circ + 2 \angle M$$
$$\angle O = 90^\circ + \angle M$$
$$P = 2D$$

Calculation of Pipe Bends

Courtesy of Crane Co.

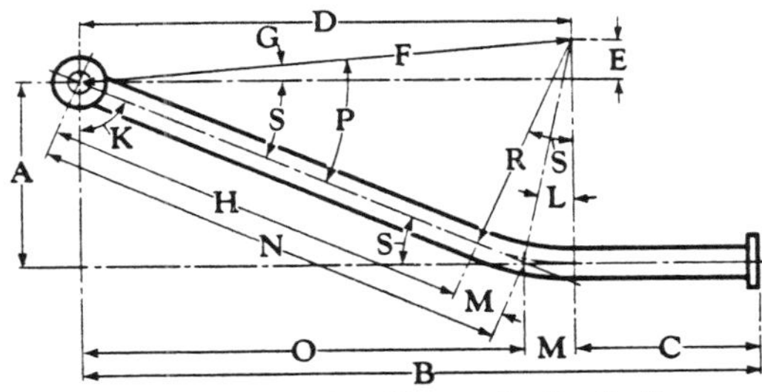

Example No. 1—**Given A, B, C, R**

$D = B - C$

$E = R - A$

$F = \sqrt{D^2 + E^2}$

$\frac{E}{F} = \sin \angle G$

$H = \sqrt{F^2 - R^2}$

$\frac{R}{F} = \sin \angle P$

$\angle S = \angle P - \angle G$

$\angle K = 90° - \angle S$

$\angle L = \frac{1}{2} \angle S$

$M = \tan \angle L \times R$

$N = H + M$

$O = B - C - M$

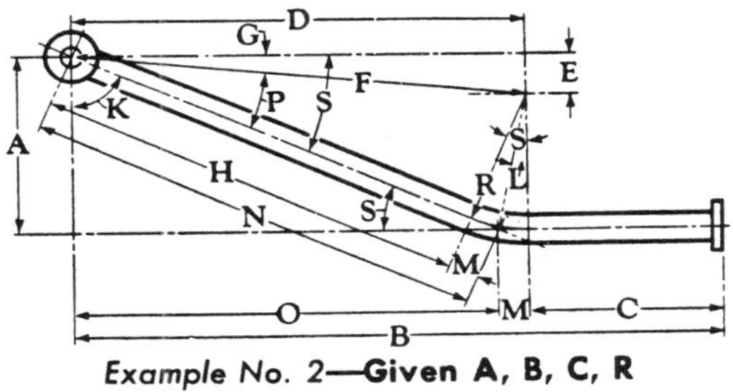

Example No. 2—**Given A, B, C, R**

$D = B - C$

$E = A - R$

$F = \sqrt{D^2 + E^2}$

$\frac{E}{F} = \sin \angle G$

$H = \sqrt{F^2 - R^2}$

$\frac{R}{F} = \sin \angle P$

$\angle S = \angle P + \angle G$

$\angle K = 90° - \angle S$

$\angle L = \frac{1}{2} \angle S$

$M = \tan \angle L \times R$

$N = H + M$

$O = B - C - M$

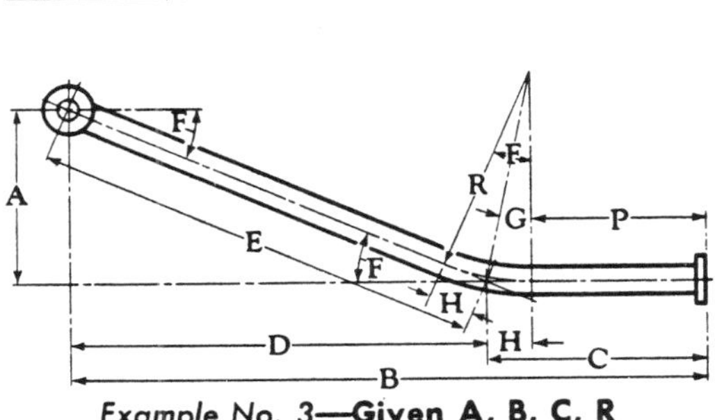

Example No. 3—**Given A, B, C, R**

$D = B - C$

$E = \sqrt{A^2 + D^2}$

$\frac{A}{E} = \sin \angle F$

$\angle G = \frac{1}{2} \angle F$

$H = \tan \angle G \times R$

$P = C - H$

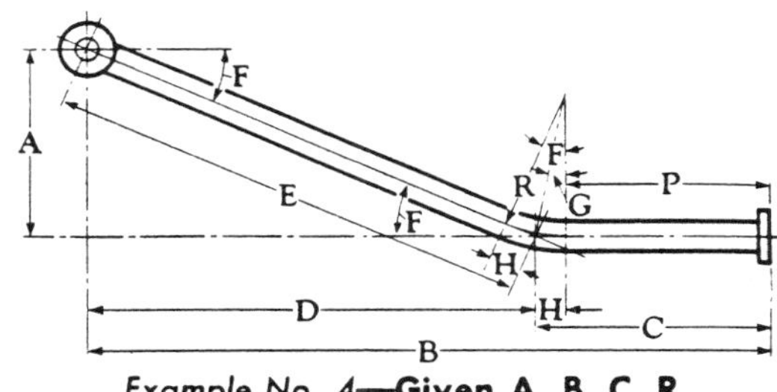

Example No. 4—**Given A, B, C, R**

$D = B - C$

$E = \sqrt{A^2 + D^2}$

$\frac{A}{E} = \sin \angle F$

$\angle G = \frac{1}{2} \angle F$

$H = \tan \angle G \times R$

$P = C - H$

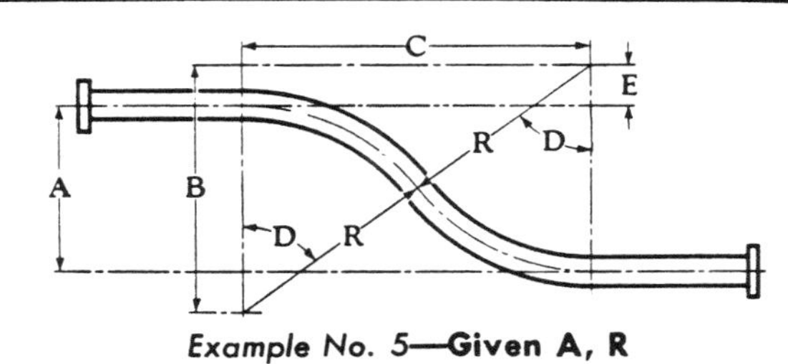

Example No. 5—**Given A, R**

$B = 2R - A$

$C = \sqrt{(2R)^2 - B^2}$

$\frac{C}{2R} = \sin \angle D$

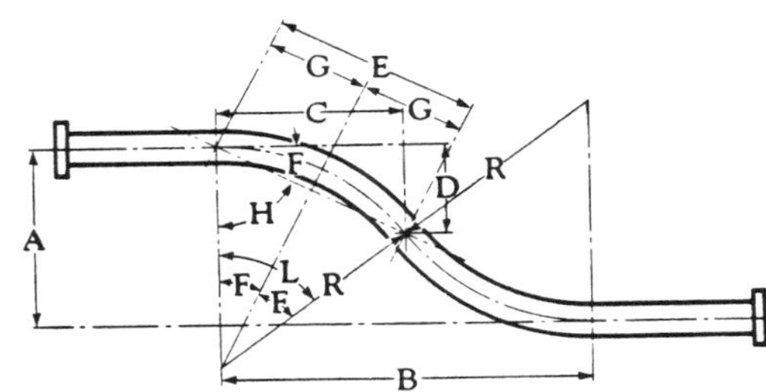

Example No. 6—**Given A, B**

$C = \frac{1}{2} B$

$D = \frac{1}{2} A$

$E = \sqrt{C^2 + D^2}$

$\frac{D}{E} = \sin \angle F$

$G = \frac{1}{2} E$

$\angle H = 90° - \angle F$

$R = \frac{A^2 + B^2}{4A}$

$L = 2F$

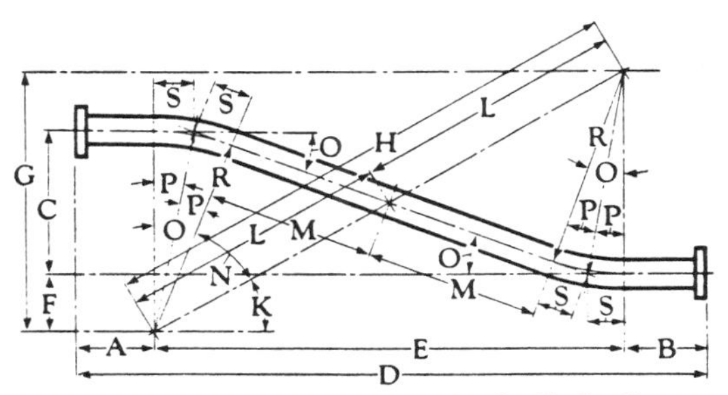

Example No. 7—**Given A, B, C, D, R**

$E = D - A - B$

$F = R - C$

$G = R + F$

$H = \sqrt{E^2 + G^2}$

$G/H = \sin \angle K$

$L = \frac{1}{2} H$

$M = \sqrt{L^2 - R^2}$

$M/L = \sin \angle N$

$\angle O = 90° - \angle K - \angle N$

$\angle P = \frac{1}{2} \angle O$

$S = \tan \angle P \times R$

12

Allowable Pipe Span Formulas and Tables

Pipe-Span Stress Limits

In order to have a workable set of pipe-span tables or to find an allowable span that will require a minimum of manual calculations, the limit for dead load stresses is set at $S_h/2$. This eliminates the need for checking the sum of the longitudinal pressure stresses plus dead load stress. (S_h = allowable stress at maximum temperature, ASA Code B31.1 and B31.3.)

The formula used to determine the maximum spans in the tables (Tables 12-1 through 12-9) is a mean between a uniformly loaded beam simply supported at both ends and a uniformly loaded beam with both ends fixed. This mean formula most nearly depicts the conditions actually existing in a refinery. (See Figure 12-1.)

By inspection, if the two moment diagrams in Figure 12-1 are superimposed, the point of the maximum bending moment will still be at mid-span.

$$\text{Mean} = M = 1/2\left(\frac{WL^2}{8} + \frac{WL^2}{24}\right)$$

A safety factor of 1.25 is required because of the discrepancy between theoretical assumption and the actual field situation.

$$M = \frac{WL^2}{12} \times \frac{5}{4} = \frac{5\ WL^2}{48}$$

In order to maintain homogeneous units, "L" must be in lb/in.; however, for ease of handling we wish to have "L" in feet and "W" in lb/ft, which we must now convert to inch units. Thus the preceding equation becomes:

$$M = \frac{5\ WL^2}{48} = \frac{60\ WL^2}{48} = \frac{5\ WL^2}{4}$$

$$S_B = \frac{M}{Z} = \frac{5\ WL^2}{4Z} = f_s$$

$$L \leqslant \sqrt{\frac{4\ Z\ f_s}{5\ W}}$$

or

$$L \leqslant \sqrt{\frac{0.8\ Z\ f_s}{W}}$$

Pipe-Span Deflection Limits

Maximum allowable pipe deflection between supports must not exceed 1 in. or 1/2 the nominal pipe diameter, whichever is the smaller. This is the basic piping practice, however, it is subject to compliance with the customer's specification.

The formula used to determine the deflections in Tables 12-1 through 12-9 is a mean between a uniformly loaded beam simply supported at both ends and a uniformly loaded beam with both ends fixed. (See Figure 12-2.)

In order to maintain homogeneous units, "L" must be in in. and "W" must be in lbs/in., however, for ease of handling we wish to have "L" in ft and "W" in lb/ft, which we must now convert to inch units. The preceding equation becomes:

$$\triangle = \frac{WL^4}{128EI} = \frac{13.5WL^4}{EI}$$

$$\triangle = \frac{13.5WL^4}{EI}$$

(Text continued on page 320.)

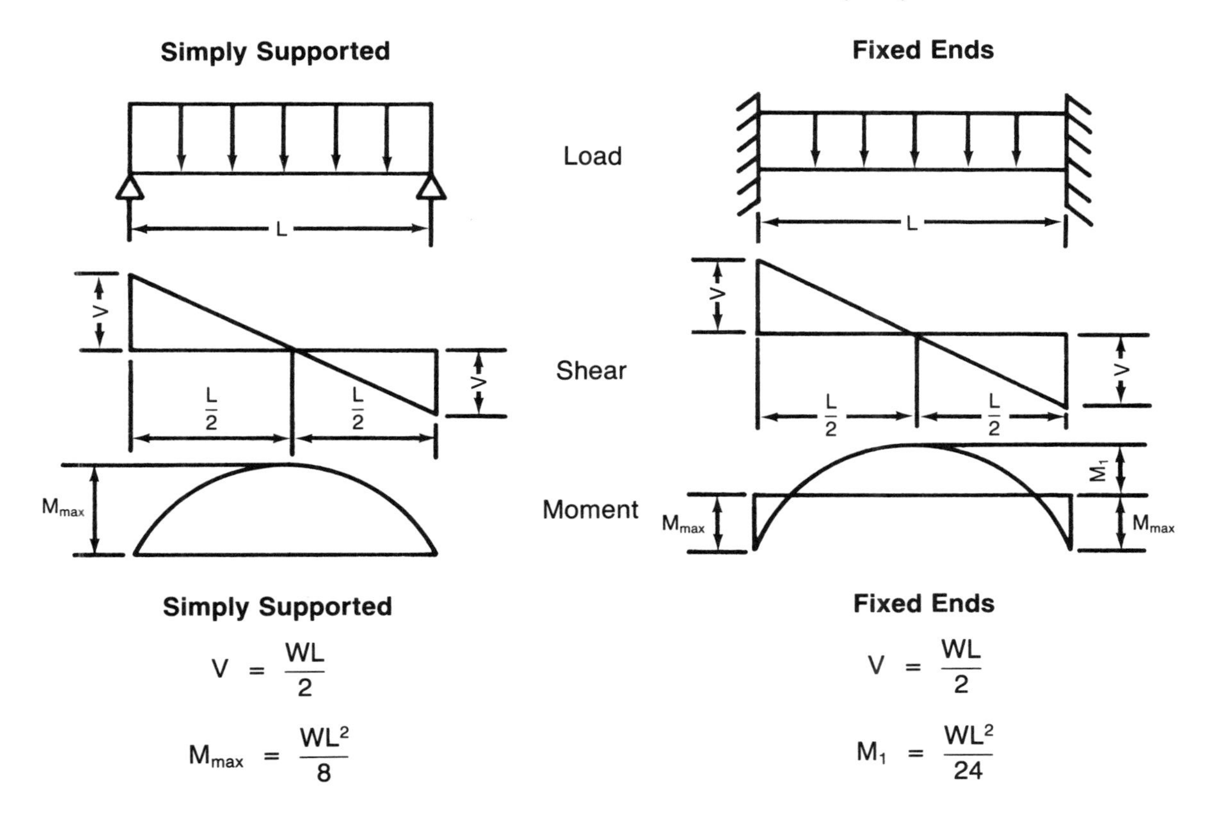

Figure 12-1. Diagram showing how stress limits are determined by figuring the mean between a uniformly loaded beam supported at both ends and a uniformly loaded beam with both ends fixed.

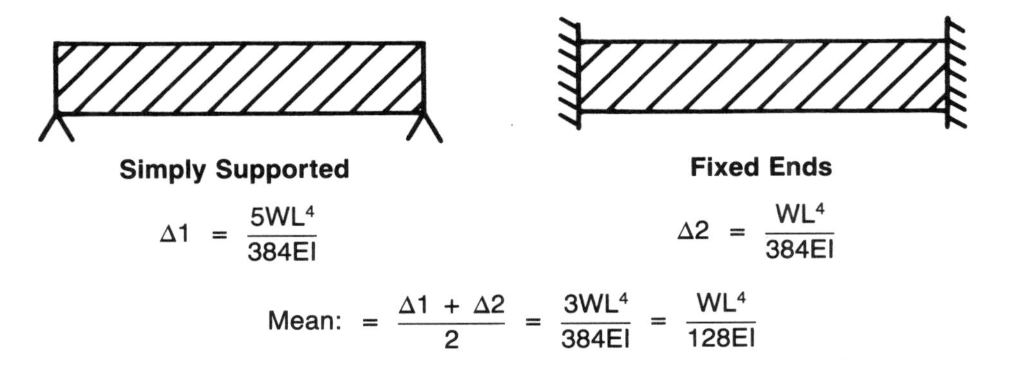

$$\Delta 1 = \frac{5WL^4}{384EI} \qquad \Delta 2 = \frac{WL^4}{384EI}$$

$$\text{Mean:} = \frac{\Delta 1 + \Delta 2}{2} = \frac{3WL^4}{384EI} = \frac{WL^4}{128EI}$$

Figure 12-2. Diagram showing how deflection limits are determined by figuring the mean between a uniformly loaded beam supported at both ends and a uniformly loaded beam with both ends fixed.

Table 12-1
Piping Spans Based on the Following Carbon Steel Materials: Seamless A53 Gr. A, A106 Gr. A, API 5L Gr. A; Welded A53 Gr. B, API 5L Gr. B, A155 C55 Class 2

		≥200°F with Water, No Insulation (f_s = 7,650 psi)				201°F–600°F with Commodity = Weight of Water, Minimum Insulation (f_s = 6,175 psi)			
Pipe Size	**SCH.**	**Maximum Span**	**Defl.**	**Recommended Span**	**Defl.**	**Maximum Span**	**Defl.**	**Recommended Span**	**Defl.**
3/4"	80	17'-6"	1-13/16"*	12'-0"	3/8"	14'-0"	7/8" *	11'-0"	3/8"
1"	80	20'-0"	1-13/16"*	14'-6"	1/2"	15'-6"	7/8" *	13'-6"	1/2"
1-1/2"	80	24'-0"	1-13/16"*	19'-0"	3/4"	19'-6"	1" *	18'-0"	3/4"
2"	40	26'-0"	1-3/4" *	23'-0"	1"	21'-0"	7/8"	20'-0"	3/4"
2"	80	26'-6"	1-3/4" *	23'-0"	1"	22'-0"	1"	21'-0"	7/8"
3"	40	31'-6"	1-3/4" *	27'-6"	1"	26'-6"	1"	25'-6"	7/8"
4"	40	34'-6"	1-4/16" *	31'-0"	1"	29'-6"	1"	27'-6"	3/4"
6"	40	40'-6"	1-1/2" *	37'-0"	1"	35'-0"	7/8"	33'-0"	3/4"
8"	40	45'-0"	1-5/16" *	41'-6"	1"	39'-6"	7/8"	39'-0"	7/8"
10"	20	45'-0"	1-1/8" *	44'-0"	1"	39'-0"	7/8"	36'-6"	9/16"
10"	40	49'-6"	1-3/8" *	46'-0"	1"	43'-0"	13/16"	40'-6"	11/16"
12"	20	47'-0"	1-3/16" *	45'-6"	1"	40'-0"	5/8"	56'-6"	1/16"
12"	STD.	52'-0"	1-1/4" *	44'-0"	1"	45'-6"	13/16"	43'-0"	11/16"
14"	10	47'-6"	1"	46'-6"	7/8"	41'-6"	5/8"	37'-6"	7/16"
14"	STD.	53'-6"	1-1/4" *	51'-0"	1"	46'-6"	3/4"	44'-0"	5/8"
16"	10	48'-6"	7/8" *	46'-6"	3/4"	42'-6"	1/2"	38'-0"	3/8"
16"	STD.	55'-0"	1-1/8" *	53'-6"	1"	48'-0"	3/4"	45'-0"	9/16"
18"	10	49'-6"	13/16"	47'-6"	11/16"	43'-6"	1/2"	39'-6"	3/8"
18"	STD.	56'-6"	1-1/16" *	55'-6"	1"	49'-6"	5/8"	45'-6"	1/2"
20"	10	50'-6"	3/4"	47'-6"	5/8"	44'-0"	1/2"	41'-0"	3/8"
20"	20	57'-6"	1"	56'-0"	7/8"	51'-0"	5/8"	47'-0"	1/2"
24"	10	51'-6"	3/4"	51'-0"	5/8"	45'-6"	7/16"	41'-6"	5/16"
24"	20	59'-6"	7/8"	57'-0"	3/4"	52'-6"	9/16"	48'-6"	7/16"
30"	58	53'-0"	9/16"	50'-0"	7/16"	46'-6"	3/8"	42'-0"	1/4"

* Exceeds maximum deflection.
Courtesy of Power Piping Company.

Table 12-2
Piping Spans Based on the Following Stainless Steel Pipe Materials: Seamless A312 TP316, A312 TP317, A430 FP316H, A376 TP317

		≥200°F with Water, No Insulation (f_s = 9,375 psi)				201°F–600°F with Commodity = Weight of Water, Minimum Insulation (f_s = 8,550 psi)			
Pipe Size	**SCH.**	**Maximum Span**	**Defl.**	**Recommended Span**	**Defl.**	**Maximum Span**	**Defl.**	**Recommended Span**	**Defl.**
3/4"	80S	19'-0"	2-5/8" *	12'-0"	3/8"	15'-6"	1-11/16"	10'6"	3/8"
1"	80S	21'-6"	2-5/8" *	14'-0"	1/2"	18'-0"	1-7/8" *	13'-0"	1/2"
1-1/2"	80S	26'-0"	2-5/8" *	19'-0"	3/4"	22'-6"	2" *	17'-6"	3/4"
2"	40S	28'-0"	2-7/16" *	22'-6"	1"	24'-6"	1-7/8" *	21'-0"	1"
3"	10S	31'-0"	2" *	26'-0"	1"	27'-0"	1-1/2" *	24'-6"	1"
3"	40S	34'-0"	2-7/16" *	27'-6"	1"	30'-6"	2" *	26'-0"	1"
4"	10S	33'-0"	1-3/4" *	29'-0"	1"	29'-6"	1-7/16"*	27'-0"	1"
4"	40S	38'-0"	2-3/8" *	31'-0"	1"	34'-6"	1-15/16" *	29'-0"	1"
6"	10S	37'-0"	1-1/2" *	33'-6"	1"	34'-0"	1-1/4" *	32'-0"	1"
6"	40S	44'-6"	2-1/4" *	36'-6"	1"	41'-0"	1-7/8"	35'-0"	1"
8"	10S	40'-6"	1-3/8" *	37'-0"	1"	36'-0"	1-1/16" *	35'-0"	15/16"
8"	20	47'-0"	1-7/8" *	40'-0"	1"	42'-6"	1-1/2" *	38'-0"	1"
10"	10S	43'-6"	1-1/4" *	41'-0"	1"	39'-6"	1-1/16" *	38'-6"	15/16"
10"	20	49'-6"	1-5/8" *	43'-6"	1"	45'-0"	1-3/8" *	41'-6"	1"
12"	10S	46'-0"	1-3/16" *	41'-0"	1"	42'-0"	1"	40'-6"	7/8"
12"	20	51'-0"	1-1/2" *	46'-0"	1"	47'-0"	1-1/4" *	44'-6"	1"
14"	10	52'-0"	1-7/16" *	47'-0"	1"	48'-0"	1-3/16" *	46'-0"	1"
14"	20	55'-6"	1-5/8" *	49'-6"	1"	51'-6"	1-3/8" *	47'-6"	1"
16"	10	63'-6"	1-5/16" *	50'-0"	1"	49'-6"	1-1/8" *	48'-0"	1"
16"	20	57'-6"	1-1/2" *	52'-0"	1"	53'-0"	1-1/4" *	50'-0"	1"
18"	10	54'-6"	1-3/16" *	52'-0"	1"	50'-6"	1"	48'-6"	7/8"
20"	10	55'-6"	1-1/8" *	54'-0"	1"	51'-6"	15/16"	49'-6"	13/16"
24"	10	57'-0"	1"	55'-0"	7/8"	53'-0"	7/8"	51'-0"	3/4"

* Exceeds maximum deflection.
Courtesy of Power Piping Company.

Table 12-3
Piping Spans Based on the Following Stainless Steel Pipe Materials: Seamless A213 TP304L, A312 TP304L, A376 TP304, A430 FP304H

		≥200°F with Water, No Insulation (f_s = 7,650 psi)				201°F–600°F with Commodity = Weight of Water, Minimum Insulation (f_s = 5,800 psi)			
Pipe Size	SCH.	Maximum Span	Defl.	Recommended Span	Defl.	Maximum Span	Defl.	Recommended Span	Defl.
3/4"	80S	18'-0"	2-1/16"	12'-0"	3/8"	12'-6"	3/4" *	10'-6"	3/8"
1"	80S	20'-0"	2-1/16"	14'-0"	1/2"	15'-0"	7/8" *	13'-0"	1/2"
1-1/2"	80S	24'-6"	2-1/16"	14'-0"	3/4"	18'-6"	7/8" *	17'-6"	3/4"
2"	40S	26'-6"	2"*	22'-6"	1"	20'-0"	13/16"	14'-0"	11/16"
2"	80S	27'-6"	2-1/16"*	23'-0"	1"	21'-0"	15/16"	20'-0"	13/16"
3"	10S	29'-0"	1-1/16"*	26'-0"	1"	22'-6"	11/16"	21'-6"	5/8"
3"	40S	32'-0"	1-15/16"	27'-6"	1"	25'-0"	7/8"	24'-0"	3/4"
4"	10S	31'-0"	1-7/16"*	29'-0"	1"	24'-0"	5/8"	23'-0"	1/2"
4"	40S	35'-6"	1-7/8"*	31'-0"	1"	28'-6"	7/8"	27'-0"	3/4"
6"	10S	35'-0"	1-1/4"*	33'-6"	1"	28'-0"	9/16"	26'-0"	7/16"
6"	40S	42'-0"	1-3/4"*	36'-6"	1"	33'-6"	13/16"	32'-0"	11/16"
8"	10S	38'-0"	1-1/8"*	37'-0"	1"	30'-0"	1/2"	28'-0"	3/8"
8"	20	44'-0"	1-1/2"*	40'-0"	1"	35'-0"	11/16"	33'-0"	9/16"
10"	10S	41'-0"	1"	39'-6"	7/8"	32'-6"	7/16"	29'-6"	5/16"
10"	20	46'-6"	1-5/16"*	43'-6"	1"	37'-0"	5/8"	35'-0"	1/2"
12"	20S	43'-6"	1-5/16"*	41'-0"	13/16"	34'-6"	7/16"	32'-6"	5/16"
12"	20	48'-6"	1-3/16"*	46'-0"	1"	38'-6"	9/16"	36'-0"	7/16"
14"	10	49'-0"	1-1/8"*	47'-0"	1"	39'-6"	9/16"	37'-0"	7/16"
14"	20	52'-6"	1-1/4"*	49'-6"	1"	42'-6"	5/8"	40'-0"	1/2"
16"	10	50'-6"	1"	48'-6"	7/8"	40'-6"	1/2"	39'-0"	3/8"
16"	20	54'-0"	1-3/16"*	52'-0"	1"	43'-6"	9/16"	41'-0"	7/16"
18"	10	51'-6"	15/16"	49'-6"	11/16"	41'-6"	7/16"	39'-6"	5/16"
20"	10	52'-0"	7/8"	50'-0"	3/4"	42'-6"	7/16"	39'-6"	5/16"
24"	10	53'-6"	3/4"	51'-0"	5/8"	43'-6"	3/8"	38'-6"	1/4"

* **Exceeds maximum deflection.**

Courtesy of Power Piping Company.

Table 12-4
Piping Spans Based on the Following Stainless Steel Pipe Materials: Seamless A213 TP304L, A312 TP304L

		≥200°F with Water, No Insulation (f_s = 7,650 psi)				201°F–600°F with Commodity = Weight of Water, Minimum Insulation (f_s = 4,500 psi)			
Pipe Size	SCH.	Maximum Span	Defl.	Recommended Span	Defl.	Maximum Span	Defl.	Recommended Span	Defl.
3/4"	80S	17'-6"	1-3/4"*	12'-0"	3/8"	11'-0"	7/16" *	10'-0"	5/16"
1"	80S	19'-6"	1-3/4"*	14'-0"	1/2"	13'-0"	1/2"	12'-0"	3/8"
1-1/2"	80S	23'-6"	1-3/4"*	19'-0"	3/4"	16'-6"	9/16"	15'-6"	5/16"
2"	40S	25'-6"	1-5/8"*	22'-6"	1"	17'-6"	1/2"	16'-6"	3/8"
2"	80S	26'-0"	1-3/4"*	23'-0"	1"	19'-0"	9/16"	17'-6"	7/16"
3"	10S	28'-0"	1-5/16"	26'-0"	1"	19'-6"	7/16"	18'-0"	5/16"
3"	40S	31'-0"	1-5/8"*	27'-6"	1"	22'-0"	9/16"	20'-0"	3/8"
4"	10S	30'-0"	1-1/4"*	29'-0"	1"	21'-6"	3/8"	19'-6"	1/4"
4"	40S	34'-0"	1-4/16"*	31'-0"	1"	25'-0"	1/2"	23'-0"	3/8"
6"	10S	33'-6"	1"	32'-6"	7/8"	24'-6"	3/8"	22'-6"	1/4"
6"	40S	40'-0"	1-1/2" *	36'-6"	1"	29'-6"	1/2"	27'-0"	3/8"
8"	10S	36'-6"	15/16"	35'-6"	13/16"	26'-0"	5/16"	24'-6"	1/4"
8"	20	42'-6"	1-1/4"*	40'-0"	1"	30'-6"	7/16"	28'-0"	5/16"
10"	10S	39'-6"	7/8"	38'-0"	3/4"	28'-6"	1/4"	26'-0"	3/16"
10"	20	44'-6"	1-1/8"*	43'-6"	1"	32'-6"	3/8"	30'-0"	1/4"
12"	10S	41'-6"	13/16"	40'-0"	11/16"	30'-6"	1/4"	28'-0"	3/16"
12"	20	46'-6"	1"	45'-0"	7/8"	34'-0"	3/8"	31'-6"	1/4"
14"	10	47'-0"	15/16"	45'-0"	11/16"	35'-0"	5/16"	32'-0"	1/4"
14"	20	50'-6"	1-1/16"*	48'-6"	15/16"	37'-0"	3/8"	34'-0"	1/4"
16"	10	48'-6"	7/8"	46'-6"	3/4"	36'-0"	5/16"	33'-0"	1/4"
16"	20	52'-0"	1"	50'-0"	7/8"	38'-6"	3/8"	35'-0"	1/4"
18"	10	49'-0"	13/16"	47'-6"	11/16"	36'-6"	1/4"	34'-0"	3/16"
20"	10	50'-0"	3/4"	48'-0"	5/8"	37'-0"	1/4"	34'-0"	3/16"
24"	10	51'-6"	11/16"	49'-6"	9/16"	38'-6"	1/4"	35'-0"	3/16"

* **Exceeds maximum deflection.**

Courtesy of Power Piping Company.

Table 12-5
Piping Spans Based on the Following Nickel Pipe Material: Seamless B161 Annealed

		≥200°F with Water, No Insulation (f_s = 4,000 psi)				201°F–450°F with Commodity = Weight of Water, Minimum Insulation (f_s = 1,000 psi)			
Pipe Size	SCH.	Maximum Span	Defl.	Recommended Span	Defl.	Maximum Span	Defl.	Recommended Span	Defl.
3/4"	80	12'-0"	1/2"	10'0"	3/8"	10'-0"	3/8"	9'-6"	3/8"
1"	80	13'-6"	1/2"	12'-6"	1/2"	12'-0"	3/8"	11'-6"	3/8"
1-1/2"	80	16'-0"	1/2"	15'-6"	1/2"	15'-0"	7/16"	14'-0"	7/16"
2"	40	17'-6"	1/2"	16'-6"	1/2"	16'-0"	3/8"	15'-0"	3/8"
2"	80	18'-0"	1/2"	16'-6"	1/2"	17'-0"	7/16"	16'-0"	7/16"
3"	40	21'-6"	1/2"	19'-6"	1/2"	20'-0"	7/16"	19'-6"	7/16"
4"	40	24'-0"	7/16"	22'-0"	7/16"	23'-0"	7/16"	22'-0"	7/16"
6"	40	28'-0"	7/16"	26'-0"	7/16"	27'-0"	3/8"	26'-0"	3/8"
8"	40	31'-6"	3/8"	29'-6"	3/8"	37'-0"	3/8"	28'-0"	3/8"
10"	20	31'-6"	5/16"	29'-6"	5/16"	38'-0"	5/16"	28'-0"	5/16"
10"	40	34'-6"	3/8"	32'-6"	3/8"	33'-0"	3/8"	31'-0"	3/8"
12"	20	32'-6"	5/16"	31'-0"	5/16"	31'-6"	1/4"	29'-0"	1/4"
12"	STD	36'-6"	3/8"	34'-6"	3/8"	35'-0"	3/8"	33'-0"	3/8"
14"	10	33'-6"	3/8"	31'-6"	5/16"	32'-0"	1/4"	30'-0"	1/4"
14"	STD	37'-0"	3/8"	35'-6"	3/8"	36'-0"	5/16"	34'-0"	5/16"
16"	10	34'-0"	1/4"	32'-6"	1/4"	33'-0"	1/4"	31'-0"	1/4"
16"	STD	33'-6"	3/16"	36'-6"	5/16"	17'-6"	5/16"	35'-6"	5/16"
18"	10	35'-0"	1/4"	33'-0"	1/4"	34'-0"	1/4"	32'-0"	1/4"
18"	STD	39'-6"	5/16"	38'-0"	5/16"	38'-6"	5/16"	37'-0"	5/16"
20"	10	35'-6"	1/4"	34'-0"	1/4"	34'-6"	1/4"	33'-0"	1/4"
20"	20	40'-6"	5/16"	39'-0"	5/16"	39'-6"	1/4"	38'-0"	1/4"
24"	10	36'-6"	3/16"	35'-0"	3/16"	35'-6"	3/16"	34'-0"	3/16"
24"	20	42'-0"	1/4"	40'-0"	1/4"	41'-0"	1/4"	39'-0"	1/4"
30"	5S	37'-6"	3/16"	36'-0"	3/16"	37'-0"	3/16"	35'-0"	3/16"

Courtesy of Power Piping Company.

Table 12-6
Piping Spans Based on the Following Aluminum Pipe Material: Seamless B241 Gr. 3003 H112

		≥200°F with Water, No Insulation (f_s = 4,000 psi)				201°F–400°F with Commodity = Weight of Water, Minimum Insulation (f_s = 1,750 psi)			
Pipe Size	SCH.	Maximum Span	Defl.	Recommended Span	Defl.	Maximum Span	Defl.	Recommended Span	Defl.
3/4"	80	12'-0"	7/16"	11'-0"	3/8"	6'-6"	1/8"	6'-6"	1/8"
1"	80	13'-0"	7/16"	13'-0"	7/16"	8'-0"	1/8"	7'-6"	1/8"
1-1/2"	80	15'-6"	3/8"	15'-0"	3/8"	10'-0"	1/8"	9'-6"	1/8"
2"	40	15'-6"	5/16"	15'-0"	5/16"	10'-6"	1/8"	10'-0"	1/8"
2"	80	17'-0"	3/8"	16'-6"	3/8"	11'-6"	1/8"	11'-0"	1/8"
3"	40	18'-6"	5/16"	18'-6"	5/16"	13'-0"	1/8"	13'-0"	1/8"
4"	40	20'-0"	5/16"	20'-0"	5/16"	14'-6"	1/8"	14'-0"	1/8"
6"	40	23'-0"	1/4"	22'-0"	1/4"	17'-0"	1/8"	16'-0"	1/8"
8"	40	25'-0"	1/4"	24'-0"	1/4"	18'-6"	1/16"	17'-6"	1/16"
10"	20	23'-6"	3/16"	22'-6"	3/16"	17'-6"	1/16"	16'-6"	1/16"
10"	40	27'-0"	1/4"	25'-0"	1/4"	20'-6"	1/16"	19'-6"	1/16"
12"	20	24'-0"	1/8"	23'-0"	1/3"	18'-0"	1/16"	17'-0"	1/16"
12"	STD	28'-0"	3/16"	25'-0"	3/8"	21'-0"	1/16"	20'-0"	1/16"
14"	10	24'-0"	1/8"	23'-0"	1/8"	18'-0"	1/16"	17'-0"	1/16"
14"	STD	28'-6"	3/16"	25'-0"	3/8"	21'-6"	1/16"	20'-6"	1/16"
16"	10	24'-0"	1/8"	23'-6"	1/8"	18'-6"	1/16"	17'-6"	1/16"
16"	STD	28'-6"	3/16"	25'-0"	3/16"	22'-0"	1/16"	21'-0"	1/16"
18"	10	24'-6"	1/8"	23'-6"	1/8"	18'-6"	1/16"	18'-0"	1/16"
18"	STD	29'-0"	1/8"	25'-0"	1/8"	22'-0"	1/16"	21'-6"	1/16"
20"	10	25'-6"	1/8"	24'-0"	1/8"	19'-0"	1/16"	18'-0"	1/16"
20"	20	29'-6"	1/8"	25'-0"	1/8"	22'-6"	1/16"	22'-0"	1/16"
24"	10	25'-0"	1/16"	24'-0"	1/16"	19'-0"	1/16"	18'-0"	1/16"
24"	20	29'-6"	1/8"	25'-0"	1/8"	23'-0"	1/16"	22'-0"	1/16"
30"	5S	25'-0"	1/16"	24'-0"	1/16"	19'-6"	1/16"	18'-6"	1/16"

Courtesy of Power Piping Company.

Table 12-7
Piping Spans Based on the Following Aluminum Pipe Material: Seamless B241 Gr. 6061 T6

Pipe Size	SCH.	≥200°F with Water, No Insulation (f_s = 3,000 psi) Maximum Span	Defl.	Recommended Span	Defl.	201°F–400°F with Commodity = Weight of Water, Minimum Insulation (f_s = 2,000 psi) Maximum Span	Defl.	Recommended Span	Defl.
3/4"	80	21'-0"	3-15/16"*	12'-0"	3/8"	10'-0"	7/16"	9'-6"	3/8"
1"	80	23'-0"	3-7/8" *	14'-0"	1/2"	11'-6"	1/2"	11'-6"	1/2"
1-1/2"	80	27'-0"	3-5/8" *	18'-0"	3/4"	14'-6"	1/2"	14'-0"	1/2"
2"	40	27'-0"	2-15/16"*	21'-0"	1"	15'-0"	7/16"	14'-0"	7/16"
3"	40	32'-6"	2-7/8" *	25'-0"	1"	19'-0"	1/2"	18'-6"	1/2"
4"	40	35'-0"	2-5/8"	28'-0"	1"	21'-6"	1/2"	20'-6"	1/2"
6"	40	40'-0"	2-1/4" *	32'-6"	1"	25'-0"	7/16"	24'-0"	7/16"
8"	40	43'-6"	2-1/16" *	36'-6"	1"	27'-0"	3/8"	26'-0"	3/8"
10"	20	40'-6"	1-1/2" *	37'-0"	1"	25'-6"	1/4"	24'-6"	1/4"
10"	40	47'-0"	1-15/16"*	40'-0"	1"	29'-6"	3/8"	28'-6"	3/8"
12"	20	41'-6"	1-1/4" *	39'-0"	1"	26'-0"	1/4"	25'-0"	1/4"
12"	STD	48'-6"	1-3/4" *	42'-6"	1"	30'-6"	5/16"	30'-0"	5/16"
14"	10	41'-6"	1-3/16" *	40'-0"	1"	26'-6"	1/4"	25'-6"	1/4"
14"	STD	49'-0"	1-5/8" *	44'-0"	1"	31'-0"	5/16"	30'-6"	5/16"
16"	10	42'-0"	1-1/16" *	41'-0"	15/16"	27'-0"	1/4"	26'-0"	1/4"
16"	STD	50'-0"	1-1/2" *	45'-6"	1"	32'-0"	5/16"	31'-0"	5/16"
18"	10	42'-6"	15/16"	41'-0"	11/16"	27'-0"	3/16"	26'-0"	3/16"
18"	STD	50'-6"	1-5/16"	47'-0"	1"	32'-6"	1/4"	31'-6"	1/4"
20"	10	42'-6"	7/8"	41'-6"	3/4"	27'-6"	3/16"	26'-6"	3/16"
20"	20	51'-0"	1-1/4" *	48'-6"	1"	33'-0"	1/4"	32'-0"	1/4"
24"	10	43'-0"	3/4"	41'-6"	5/8"	28'-0"	3/16"	27'-0"	3/16"
24"	20	51'-6"	1-1/16" *	51'-0"	1"	33'-6"	1/4"	32'-6"	1/4"
30	5S	43'-6"	5/8"	42'-0"	1/2"	28'-6"	1/8"	27'-6"	1/8"

*** Exceeds maximum deflection.**
Courtesy of Power Piping Company.

Table 12-8
Piping Spans Based on the Following Aluminum Pipe Materials: Seamless B210, B234, and B235 Gr. 6061 T4, B241 Gr. 3003 H18

Pipe Size	SCH.	≥200°F with Water, No Insulation (f_s = 4,500 psi) Maximum Span	Defl.	Recommended Span	Defl.	201°F–600°F with Commodity = Weight of Water, Minimum Insulation (f_s = 950 psi) Maximum Span	Defl.	Recommended Span	Defl.
3/4"	80	17'-0"	1-3/4" *	12'-0"	3/8"	9'-0"	5/16"	8'-6"	5/16"
1"	80	19'-0"	1-3/4" *	14'-0"	1/2"	11'-0"	3/8"	10'-6"	3/8"
1-1/2"	80	22'-0"	1-9/16"*	18'-0"	3/4"	13'-6"	7/16"	13'-6"	7/16"
2"	40	22'-0"	1-5/16"*	21'-0"	1"	14'-0"	5/16"	13'-6"	5/16"
2"	80	24'-0"	1-1/2" *	22'-0"	1"	15'-6"	7/16"	14'-6"	7/16"
3"	40	26'-6"	1-1/4" *	25'-0"	1"	18'-0"	3/8"	17'-0"	3/8"
4"	40	28'-6"	1-3/16"*	28'-0"	1"	20'-0"	3/8"	19'-0"	3/8"
6"	40	32'-6"	1"	31'-6"	7/8"	23'-6"	5/16"	22'-0"	5/16"
8"	40	35'-6"	15/16"	34'-6"	13/16"	25'-0"	5/16"	23'-6"	5/16"
10"	20	33'-0"	5/8"	31'-6"	1/2"	24'-0"	1/4"	22'-6"	1/4"
10"	40	38'-6"	7/8"	37'-0"	3/4"	27'-6"	5/16"	26'-0"	5/16"
12"	20	33'-6"	9/16"	32'-0"	7/16"	24'-6"	3/16"	23'-0"	3/16"
12"	STD	39'-6"	3/4"	37'-6"	5/8"	28'-6"	1/4"	27'-0"	1/4"
14"	10	34'-6"	1/2"	32'-6"	3/8"	24'-6"	3/16"	25'-0"	1/2"
14"	STD	40'-6"	3/4"	39'-0"	5/8"	29'-0"	1/4"	27'-6"	1/4"
16"	10	34'-6"	1/2"	32'-6"	3/8"	25'-0"	3/16"	23'-0"	3/16"
16"	STD	40'-6"	5/8"	39'-0"	9/16"	30'-0"	1/4"	27'-0"	1/4"
18"	10	34'-6"	7/16"	33'-6"	5/16"	25'-6"	1/8"	23'-6"	1/8"
18"	STD	41'-0"	5/8"	39'-6"	1/2"	30'-0"	1/4"	27'-6"	1/4"
20"	10	35'-0"	3/8"	33'-6"	1/4"	25'-6"	1/8"	24'-0"	1/8"
20"	20	41'-6"	1/2"	40'-0"	3/8"	30'-6"	3/16"	28'-0"	3/16"
24"	10	35'-0"	5/16"	33'-6"	3/16"	26'-0"	1/8"	24'-0"	1/8"
24"	20	42'-0"	7/16"	40'-0"	3/8"	31'-0"	3/16"	28'-0"	3/16"
30"	5S	35'-6"	1/4"	33'-0"	1/8"	26'-6"	1/8"	24'-6"	1/8"

*** Exceeds maximum deflection.**
Courtesy of Power Piping Company.

Table 12-9
Piping Spans Based on the Following Red Brass Pipe Material: Seamless B43

		≥200°F with Water, No Insulation (f_s = 1,500 psi)				201°F–600°F with Commodity = Weight of Water, Minimum Insulation (f_s = 4,000 psi)			
Pipe Size	SCH.	Maximum Span	Defl.	Recommended Span	Defl.	Maximum Span	Defl.	Recommended Span	Defl.
3/4"	80	12'-0"	11/16"	10'-0"	3/8"	5'-0"	1/16"	4'-6"	1/16"
1"	80	13'-6"	11/16"	11'-0"	1/2"	6'-0"	1/16"	5'-6"	1/16"
1-1/2"	80	16'-6"	11/16"	15'-0"	11/16"	7'-6"	1/16"	7'-0"	1/16"
2"	40	17'-6"	5/8"	17'-0"	5/8"	8'-0"	1/16"	7'-6"	1/16"
2"	80	18'-0"	11/16"	17'-0"	11/16"	8'-6"	1/16"	8'-0"	1/16"
3"	40	21'-6"	5/8"	20'-6"	5/8"	10'-0"	1/16"	9'-6"	1/16"
4"	40	24'-0"	5/8"	23'-0"	5/8"	11'-6"	1/16"	10'-6"	1/16"
6"	40	28'-0"	9/16"	27'-0"	9/16"	13'-6"	1/16"	12'-6"	1/16"
8"	40	31'-6"	9/16"	30'-0"	9/16"	15'-0"	1/16"	14'-0"	1/16"
10"	20	31'-6"	7/16"	30'-0"	7/16"	15'-0"	1/16"	14'-0"	1/16"
10"	40	34'-6"	1/2"	32'-6"	1/2"	16'-6"	1/16"	15'-6"	1/16"
12"	20	33'-0"	7/16"	31'-0"	7/16"	15'-6"	1/16"	15'-0"	1/16"
12"	STD	36'-6"	1/2"	34'-6"	1/2"	17'-6"	1/16"	16'-6"	1/16"
14"	10	33'-6"	3/8"	31'-6"	3/8"	16'-0"	1/16"	15'-0"	1/16"
14"	STD	37'-6"	1/2"	35'-6"	1/2"	18'-0"	1/16"	17'-0"	1/16"
16"	10	34'-6"	3/8"	32'-6"	3/8"	16'-6"	1/16"	15'-6"	1/16"
16"	STD	38'-6"	7/16"	32'-6"	7/16"	18'-6"	1/16"	18'-0"	1/16"
18"	10	35'-0"	5/16"	33'-0"	5/16"	17'-0"	1/16"	16'-0"	1/16"
18"	STD	39'-6"	7/16"	38'-0"	7/16"	19'-0"	1/16"	18'-6"	1/16"
20"	10	35'-6"	5/16"	36'-0"	5/16"	17'-0"	1/16"	16'-6"	1/16"
20"	20	40'-6"	3/8"	39'-0"	3/8"	19'-0"	1/16"	19'-0"	1/16"
24"	10	36'-6"	1/4"	35'-0"	1/4"	17'-6"	1/16"	17'-0"	1/16"
24"	20	42'-0"	3/8"	40'-0"	3/8"	20'-6"	1/16"	20'-0"	1/16"
30"	5S	37'-6"	1/4"	36'-0"	1/4"	18'-6"	1/16"	17'-6"	1/16"

Courtesy of Power Piping Company.

where S_B = Longitudinal bending stress, psi
 = Maximum deflection, in.
W = Weight of pipe, including commodity and insulation if any, lb/ft
L = Length of span, ft
E = Hot modulus of elasticity of pipe, psi
I = Moment of inertia of pipe, in.^{4}
Z = Section modulus of pipe, in.^{3}
f_s = Unit stress = $S_h/2$, psi. S_h per ASA Code B31.3

To solve for an allowable pipe span with a known deflection, use the following formula:

$$L = \sqrt[4]{\frac{EI\Delta}{13.5W}}$$

Piping Wind Loads

Wind Loads

Tables 12-10 through 12-12 can be used to calculate wind loads.

The wind pressure (P) in lb/ft^2 on a flat surface normal to the direction the wind for any given velocity (V) in miles/hr is given quite accurately by the formula

$$P = 0.004V^2$$

Table 12-11 gives the pressure per square foot on a flat surface normal to the direction of the wind for different velocities as calculated by the preceding formula.

The design wind pressure at the location of a given pipeline should be applied to the projected area of the outside of the pipe (or insulation) to determine a uniformly distributed load as follows:

$$W = \frac{(P)(C_s)(D)}{144}$$

where P = Design wind pressure, lb/ft^2
C_s = Shape factor (See Table 12-12)
D = Outside diameter of pipe (or insulation), in.
W = Wind load (lb/in) pounds per linear foot of pipe

The design wind pressure depends on the location of the vessel or stack. The U.S.A. Standard Building Code Requirements for Minimum Design Loads, in Buildings and Other Structures, A58.1-1972, and the Uniform Building Code include a table showing wind pressure at various heights, and a map where these values apply.

More tables have been developed according to wind velocity in miles/hr, wind pressure lb/ft^2, with reference to a pipe outside diameter. These tables are very useful for computer data input to model uniform wind load on piping.

Table 12-10
Official Designations of Winds

Designation	Miles per Hour
Calm	Less than 1
Light wind	1 to 7
Gentle wind	8 to 12
Moderate wind	13 to 18
Fresh wind	19 to 24
Strong wind	25 to 38
Gale	39 to 54
Whole gale	55 to 75
Hurricane	Above 75

** Beaufort Wind Scale, U.S. Weather Bureau.*

Table 12-11
Pressure per Sq Ft on a Flat Surface Normal to the Direction of the Wind

Velocity (miles/hr)	Pressure (lb/ft^2)	Corresponding To
10	0.4	Gentle wind
20	1.6	Fresh wind
30	3.6	Strong wind
40	6.4	Gale
50	10.0	Gale
60	14.4	Whole gale
80	25.6	Hurricane
100	40.0	Violent hurricanes

Table 12-12
Shape Factors

Surface	General Use	Shape Factor
Cylinder	Towers, stacks, drums, tanks, exchangers, piping, etc.	0.6
Octagon	Piers for towers and drums	0.80
Sphere	Tanks	0.60
Flat	Open signs	1.60
	Solid signs	1.40
	Closed buildings, framing, and com. parts	1.30
Prism	Frames, open-type structure	1.60 Open plan 0.80 Sec. plan 0.00 Other plan

Table 12-13
Wind Load (lb/in.)

PIPE OUTSIDE DIAMETER

Press, lb/ft^2	15	20	25	30	35	40	45	50	55
Wind Velocity Miles/HR	61	71	80	86	93	100	106	112	117
2.375	.14	.19	.24	.29	.34	.39	.44	.49	.54
3.50	.21	.29	.36	.43	.51	.58	.65	.72	.80
4.00	.25	.33	.41	.50	.58	.66	.74	.83	.91
4.500		.37	.46	.56	.65	.75	.84	.93	1.03
5.563		.46	.57	.69	.81	.92	1.04	1.15	1.27
6.625	.41	.55	.68	.82	.96	1.10	1.23	1.38	1.51
8.625	.53	.71	.89	1.07	1.25	1.44	1.61	1.79	1.97
10.750	.67	.89	1.11	1.34	1.56	1.79	2.01	2.39	1.46
12.750	.79	1.06	1.32	1.59	1.85	2.12	1.38	2.65	2.92
14	.87	1.16	1.45	1.75	2.04	2.33	2.61	2.91	3.20
16	1.00	1.33	1.66	2.00	2.33	2.67	2.99	3.33	3.66
18	1.12	1.49	1.87	2.25	2.62	3.00	3.36	3.74	4.12
20	1.25	1.66	2.08	2.50	2.91	3.34	3.74	4.16	4.58
22	1.37	1.83	2.28	2.75	3.20	3.67	4.11	4.58	5.04
24	1.50	1.99	2.49	3.00	3.45	4.00	4.48	4.99	5.45
26	1.62	2.16	2.70	3.25	3.79	4.34	4.86	5.45	5.95
28	1.75	2.33	2.91	3.50	4.08	4.67	5.23	5.83	6.41
30	1.87	2.49	3.12	3.75	4.37	5.01	5.61	6.25	6.87
32	2.00	2.66	3.32	4.00	4.66	5.34	5.98	6.66	7.33
34	2.12	2.83	3.53	4.25	4.95	5.67	6.35	7.08	7.78
36	2.25	2.99	3.74	4.50	5.24	6.01	6.73	7.49	8.24
38	2.37	3.16	3.95	4.75	5.54	6.34	7.10	7.91	8.70
40	2.50	3.33	4.16	5.00	5.83	6.68	7.48	8.33	9.16
42	2.62	3.49	4.36	5.25	6.12	7.01	7.85	8.74	9.62
44	2.75	3.66	4.57	5.50	6.41	7.34	8.22	9.16	10.08
46	2.87	3.83	4.78	5.75	6.70	7.68	8.60	9.58	10.53
48	3.00	3.99	4.99	6.00	6.99	8.01	8.97	9.99	10.99
50	3.12	4.16	5.20	6.25	7.29	8.35	9.35	10.41	11.45
52	3.25	4.33	5.40	6.50	7.58	8.68	9.72	10.83	11.91
54	3.37	4.49	5.61	6.75	7.87	9.01	10.09	11.24	12.37
56	3.50	4.66	5.82	7.00	8.16	9.35	10.47	11.66	12.82
58	3.62	4.83	6.03	7.25	8.45	9.68	10.84	12.08	13.28
60	3.75	4.99	6.24	7.50	8.74	10.02	11.22	12.49	13.74
62	3.87	5.16	6.44	7.75	9.03	10.35	11.59	12.91	14.20
64	4.00	5.33	6.65	.008	9.33	10.68	11.96	13.33	14.66
66	4.12	5.49	6.86	8.25	9.62	11.02	12.34	13.74	15.12

Table 12-13
Uniform Wind Loads (lb/in.)

PIPE OUTSIDE DIAMETER

Press, lb/ft^2	60	65	70	75	80	85	90	95	100
Wind Velocity Miles/HR	122	127	132	137	141	146	150	154	158
2.375	.59	.64	.69	.74	.79	.84	.89	.94	.98
3.50	.87	.94	1.02	1.09	1.16	1.23	1.31	1.38	1.45
4.00	1.00	1.08	1.16	1.25	1.33	1.41	1.50	1.58	1.66
4.500	1.12	1.21	1.31	1.40	1.49	1.59	1.68	1.78	1.87
6.525	1.65	1.79	1.93	2.07	2.20	2.34	2.48	2.62	2.76
8.625	2.15	2.33	2.51	2.69	2.87	3.05	3.32	3.41	3.59
10.750	2.68	2.91	3.13	3.35	3.58	3.80	4.03	4.25	4.47
12.70	3.18	3.45	3.71	3.99	4.24	4.51	4.78	5.02	5.31
14	3.50	3.79	4.08	4.37	4.66	4.95	5.25	5.54	5.83
16	4.00	4.33	4.66	5.00	5.33	5.66	6.00	6.33	6.66
18	4.50	4.87	5.25	5.62	5.99	6.37	6.75	7.12	7.50
20	5.00	5.41	5.83	6.25	6.66	7.08	7.50	7.91	8.33
22	5.50	5.95	6.41	6.87	7.33	7.79	8.25	8.70	9.16
24	6.00	6.49	7.00	7.50	7.99	8.49	9.00	9.49	10.00
26	6.50	7.048	7.54	8.12	8.66	9.20	9.75	10.29	10.83
28	7.00	7.58	8.16	8.75	9.33	9.91	10.50	11.08	11.66
30	7.50	8.12	8.75	9.37	9.99	10.62	11.25	11.87	12.50
32	8.00	8.66	9.33	10.00	10.66	11.33	12.00	12.66	13.33
34	8.50	9.20	9.91	10.62	11.33	12.03	12.75	13.45	14.16
36	9.00	9.74	10.50	11.25	11.99	12.74	13.5	14.24	15.00
39	9.50	10.29	11.08	11.87	12.66	13.45	14.25	15.04	15.83
40	10.0	10.83	11.66	12.50	13.3	14.1	14.00	15.83	16.66
42	10.5	11.37	12.25	13.12	13.99	14.87	15.75	16.62	17.50
44	11.0	11.91	12.83	13.75	14.66	15.58	16.5	17.41	18.33
46	11.5	12.45	13.41	14.37	15.33	15.28	17.25	18.20	19.16
45	12.0	12.994	14.00	15.00	15.99	16.99	18.00	18.99	20.00
50	12.5	13.54	14.58	15.62	16.66	17.70	18.75	19.79	20.83
52	13.0	14.08	15.16	16.25	17.33	18.41	19.50	20.58	21.66
54	13.5	14.62	15.75	16.87	17.99	19.12	20.25	21.37	22.50
56	14.0	15.16	16.33	17.50	18.66	19.82	21.00	22.16	23.22
58	14.5	15.70	16.91	18.12	19.33	20.53	21.75	22.95	24.16
60	15.0	16.24	17.50	18.75	19.99	21.24	22.50	23.74	25.00
62	15.5	16.78	18.08	19.37	20.66	21.95	23.25	24.53	25.83
64	16.0	17.33	18.66	20.00	21.33	22.66	24.00	25.33	26.66
66	15.5	17.87	19.25	20.62	21.99	23.27	24.75	26.12	27.50

13

Pipe Support Selection and Design

Pipe Supports

Because piping is affected by thermal expansion, supports in a piping system move thermally in different directions. Weight is supported by two kinds of supports—rigid and flexible.

- *Rigid supports* are supports in a piping system which stay fixed. They generally move thermally in two directions—horizontally and laterally, but not vertically. The weight at this point is usually supported by shoe supports, bracket supports, dummy legs, or a rigid hanger. There are hundreds of ways these supports can be designed and every company seems to have its own way. (See Figure 13-1.)

- *Flexible supports* move in all three directions. Weight is supported in this application by use of spring supports.

Spring Supports

The types of springs offered for industrial support applications can be segregated into three classifications:

- *Coil springs* are the springs most commonly used in the petrochemical industry for supporting loads. They are used almost exclusively in the construction of pre-engineered and calibrated variable- and constant-support spring hangers. They are also used in less expensive forms in the construction of hold downs, field supports, and vibration dampeners.
- *Disc springs (Bellville springs)* are seldom used in the construction of variable- or constant-support spring hangers, but are available if desired when space limitations are critical (very expensive). They have been used frequently in hold-down applications.
- *Leaf springs* have no known applications in the petrochemical industry.

Variable Spring Supports

The word "variable" in this description refers to the fact that the load-carrying capacity of the spring varies considerably as the spring is compressed or extended from a fixed reference point. In other words, as the pipe moves up, the spring is extended and the load that it exerts is decreased. The opposite effect is experienced when the pipe moves down. In either case, the force exerted must not vary when extended or compressed by more than 25% (maximum) from the calculated load.

Manufacturers offer a large variety of variable-load spring hangers with standard and nonstandard scales. (See Figure 13-2.) The scale is attached to the spring support frame and indicates the vendor's recommendation for range of load. Normally, a safety scale is provided above and below the scale. Beyond these points the unit either loses all load carrying capacity or it reaches its fully compressed position, therefore prohibiting further displacement. In every case, an attempt should be made to select a spring so that the calculated load falls in the center of the spring-scale range. The maximum deflection, which will compute to be not more than a 25% variability, can be found by dividing the full range of the spring scale, in inches, by a factor of 2.5. Where the equipment loading is sensitive or critical, larger-range scales may be beneficial in reducing the variability percentage.

Typical applications are shown in the next pages along with an explanation on how to size and how to determine the type of spring to be used. Dimensions for variable

(Text continued on page 327.)

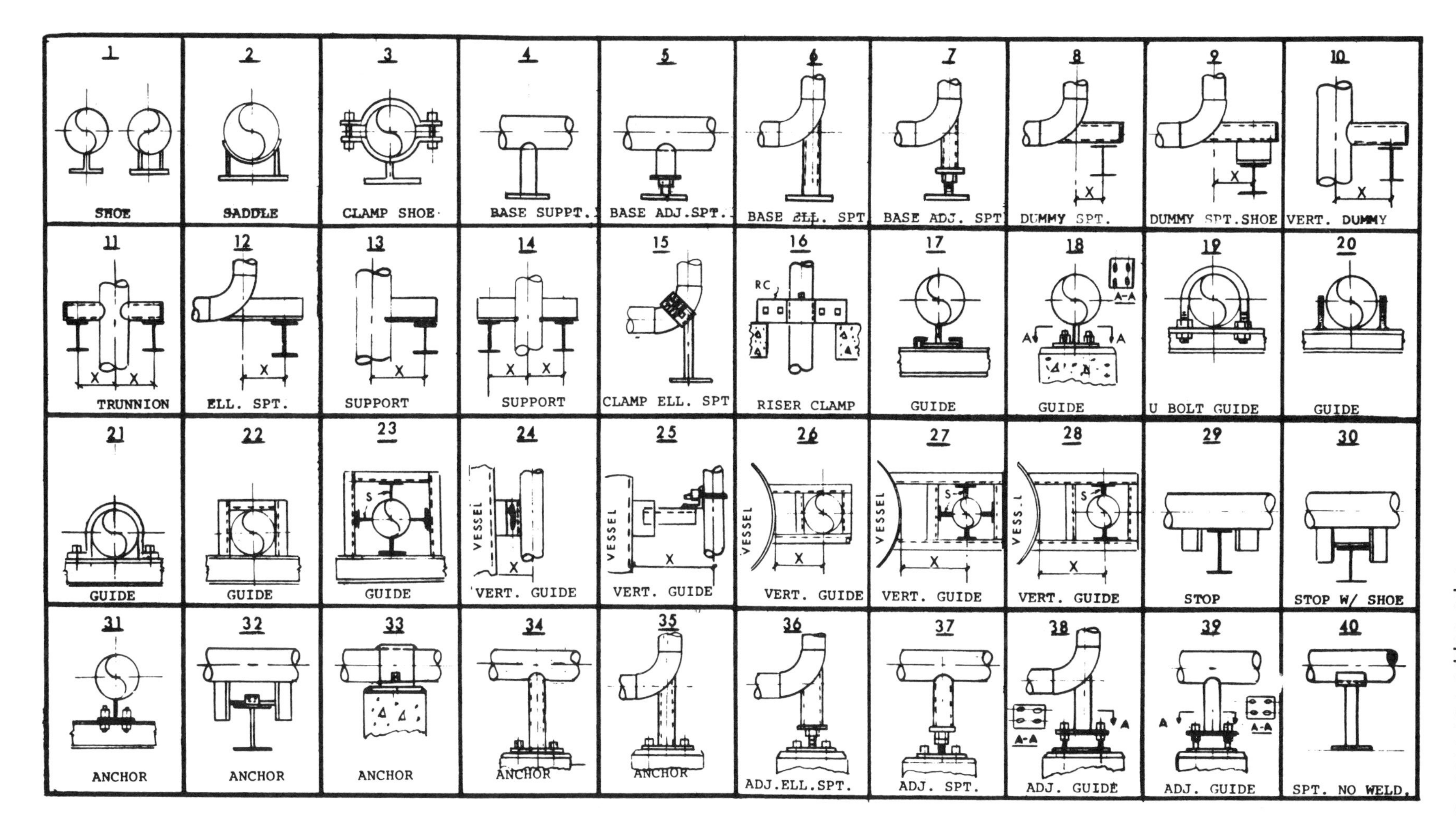

Figure 13-1. Structural supports.

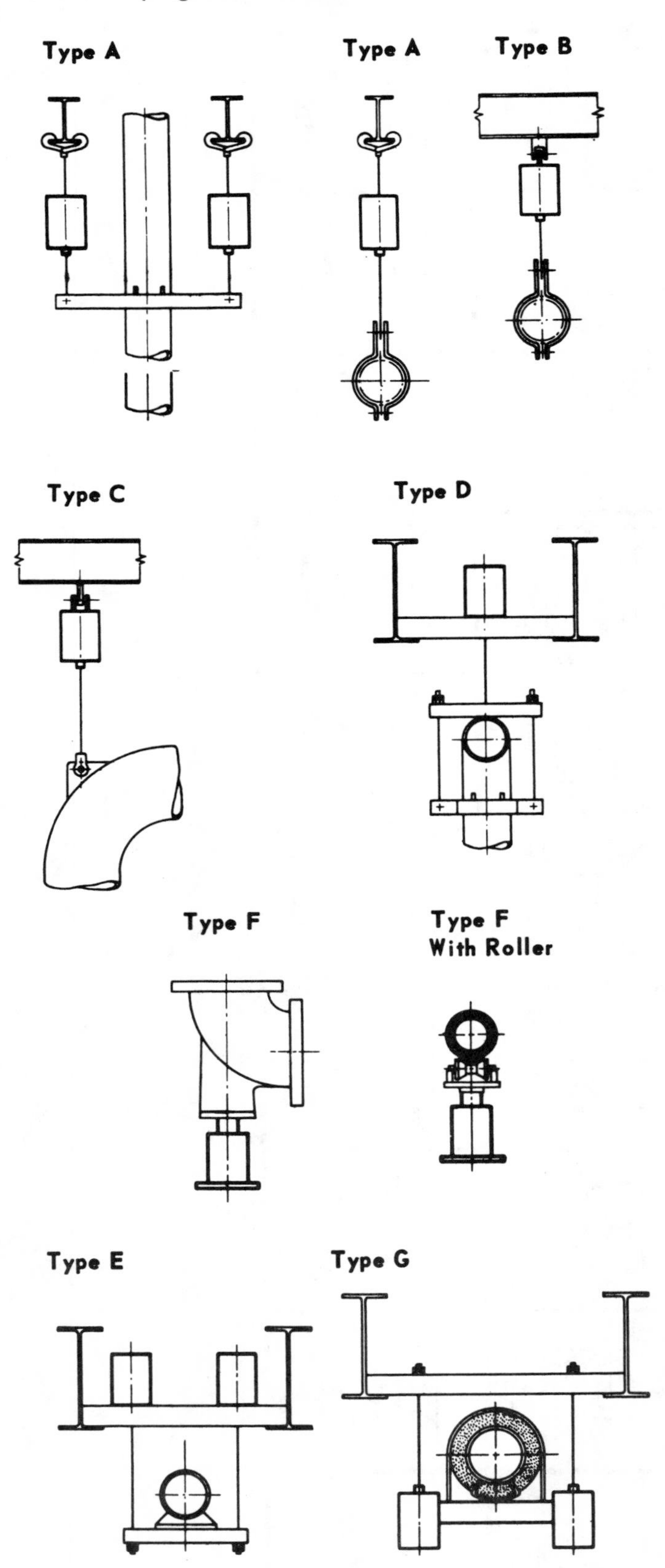

How to Determine Type: The type of variable spring hanger to be used depends upon the physical characteristics required by the suspension problem; i.e., amount of head room, whether pipe is to be supported above the spring or below the spring, etc. Consideration should be given to the seven standard types offered (see line cuts of types "A" through "G"). Special variable spring hangers can be fabricated for unusual conditions.

How to Determine Size: Complete sizing information is given above the hanger selection chart
This information is applicable to sizing hangers of all series.

It will be noted on the hanger selection charts that the total spring deflection in the casing leaves a reserve above and below the recommended working load range.

Travel Stop:

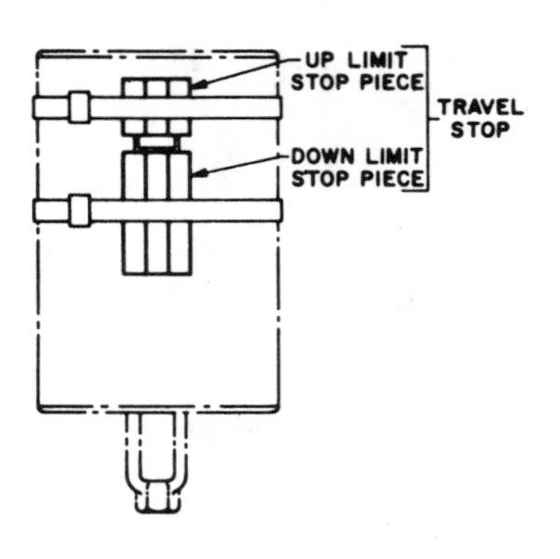

The functional design of the pre-compressed variable spring hanger permits the incorporation of a two-piece travel stop that locks the hanger spring against upward or downward movement for temporary conditions of underload or overload. The complete travel stop, the up limit stop only for cold set purposes or the down limit stop only which may be employed during erection, hydrostatic test or chemical cleanout will be furnished only when specified. The travel stop is painted red and is installed at the factory with a red "caution" tag attached calling attention that the device must be removed before the pipe line is put in service.

Figure 13-2. Variable supports. (Courtesy Support Technology and Piping Technology Products, Inc.)

springs are generally the same for all the manufacturers. That is why loading tables and dimensions that can be used for application in supporting piping have been included.

Constant Spring Supports

The word "constant" in this description implies that the spring will exert the same lifting effort as the pipe moves up and down. Actually, the spring rate in most cases is minimized by transferring the load through a series of levers so that the elongation or compression of the spring is negligible.

Constant-support spring hangers are considerably more expensive than variables and are therefore used sparingly. They are used in conjunction with large deflections where variability becomes a problem, large loads where even small variabilities are a problem, and at strain-sensitive equipment. (See Figure 13-3.)

Manufacturers offer a wide variety of load ranges, deflection ranges, and frames for their constant-support springs. Loading tables given in Tables 13-1 through 13-5 and in Figures 13-3 through 13-6, generally are the same for all the manufacturers, but dimensions are different and should be obtained from each manufacturer. (See Figure 13-7 for typical arrangements of constant supports.)

Travel Stops

All hangers have built-in stops to limit the travel at the top and bottom to a small percentage beyond the specified range. In addition, temporary stop pins are provided at the initial travel position for the purpose of hydrostatic testing and to facilitate erection. All stops are of rugged construction to withstand appreciable overloads.

It should be remembered, however, that hangers will function only when temporary stops are removed and the hangers load-rods are adjusted properly to enable the hanger to operate within the specified range of travel. An arrow traveling on a scale readily indicates the travel position at all times.

Load Adjustment

All hangers are equipped with a load-adjusting nut that permits up to a 10% increase or a 10% decrease in load-carrying capacity. However, since all hangers are carefully tested and preset in the factory to specified loads, it is recommended that no field load adjustment be made until it is accurately determined that a change is necessary. Otherwise, the proper distribution of pipe stresses in the system may be disturbed.

Standard Hangers

Load-travel data, physical design features, and dimensions are shown on the following pages, for convenience in selecting the proper type and size hangers for any specific requirement. Since the load-supporting capacity of a given size is inversely proportional to the travel function, excessive overtravel when specified may require a larger and more costly hanger size than actually needed.

Sway Brace Support

This type of support is also a spring, but is not used to take care of the weight effect. It is recommended for controlling vibration, absorbing shock loading, guiding or restraining thermal expansion, and bracing a pipe line against sway. Figure 13-8 shows different sway braces and tables for loading and sizes.

Insulated Pipe Supports and Anchors for Cryogenic Service

Cryogenic Pipe Supports and Hangers

The design of supports for piping used in cryogenic service differs from those designs used for standard piping. In this application the support is designed to avoid metal-to-metal contact of the support with the pipe. Such contact would create a heat sink whereby heat would be transferred from the ambient environmental conditions to the cold pipe through the metal support. To avoid this metal-to-metal contact, a support is manufactured from rigid polyurethane foam. Polyurethane offers both the insulating properties necessary to maintain the cryogenic temperature, and also the high strength necessary to support the pipe. Figure 13-9 illustrates a typical cryogenic support. The insulated support is normally furnished with the foam, vapor barrier, protection shield, and a galvanized cradle. These components are all adhered together into a unit that is easily installed. The saddle as shown in this figure may be removed and replaced with other types of supports such as a pipe clamp for use with rigid and spring hangers, or with graphite teflon slide plates.

The design of the polyurethane support includes the following considerations:

- Required insulation property (K-factor).
- Thickness of the insulation on the remainder of the pip-

(Text continued on page 345.)

Table 13-1
Load Table for Variable Spring Supports for Selection of Hanger Size

Load Table in Pounds: for Selection of Hanger Size

Working Range, In.					Hanger Size																							Spring Deflection, In.				
995	990	980	2680	820	00	10	20	30	40	50	60	70	80	90	100	110	120	130	140	150	160	170	180	190	200	210	220	820	2680	980	990	995
					43	63	81	105	141	189	252	336	450	600	780	1020	1350	1800	2400	3240	4500	6000	7990	10610	14100	18750	25005	0	0	0	0	0
					44	66	84	109	147	197	263	350	469	625	813	1063	1406	1875	2500	3375	4688	6250	8322	11053	14688	19531	26047					
					46	68	88	114	153	206	273	364	488	650	845	1105	1463	1950	2600	3510	4875	6500	8655	11495	15275	20313	27089					
					48	71	91	118	159	213	284	378	506	675	878	1148	1519	2025	2700	3645	5063	6750	8987	11938	15863	21094	28131					
0	0	0	0	0	50	74	95	123	165	221	294	392	525	700	910	1190	1575	2100	2800	3780	5250	7000	9320	12380	16450	21875	29173	¼	½	1	1½	2
					52	76	98	127	170	228	305	406	544	725	943	1233	1631	2175	2900	3915	5438	7250	9652	12823	17038	22656	30215					
					54	79	101	131	176	236	315	420	563	750	975	1275	1688	2250	3000	4050	5625	7500	9985	13265	17625	23438	31256					
					56	81	105	136	182	244	326	434	581	775	1008	1318	1744	2325	3100	4185	5813	7750	10317	13708	18213	24219	32298					
2	1½	1	½	¼	58	84	108	140	188	252	336	448	600	800	1040	1360	1800	2400	3200	4320	6000	8000	10650	14150	18800	25000	33340	½	1	2	3	4
					59	87	111	144	194	260	347	462	619	825	1073	1403	1856	2475	3300	4455	6188	8250	10982	14592	19388	25781	34382					
					61	89	115	149	200	268	357	476	638	850	1105	1445	1913	2550	3400	4590	6375	8500	11315	15035	19975	26563	35424					
					63	92	118	153	206	276	368	490	656	875	1138	1488	1969	2625	3500	4725	6563	8750	11647	15477	20563	27344	36466					
4	3	2	1	½	65	95	122	158	212	284	378	504	675	900	1170	1530	2025	2700	3600	4860	6750	9000	11980	15920	21150	28125	37508	¾	1½	3	4½	6
					67	97	125	162	217	291	389	518	694	925	1203	1573	2081	2775	3700	4995	6938	9250	12312	16362	21738	28906	38549					
					69	100	128	166	223	299	399	532	713	950	1235	1615	2138	2850	3800	5130	7125	9500	12645	16805	22325	29688	39591					
					71	102	132	171	229	307	410	546	731	975	1268	1658	2194	2925	3900	5265	7313	9750	12977	17247	22913	30469	40633					
6	4½	3	1½	¾	73	105	135	175	235	315	420	560	750	1000	1300	1700	2250	3000	4000	5400	7500	10000	13310	17690	23500	31250	41675	1	2	4	6	8
					74	108	138	179	241	323	431	574	769	1025	1333	1743	2306	3075	4100	5535	7688	10250	13642	18132	24088	32031	42717					
					76	110	142	184	247	331	441	588	788	1050	1365	1785	2363	3150	4200	5670	7875	10500	13975	18575	24675	32813	43759					
					78	113	145	188	253	339	452	602	806	1075	1398	1828	2419	3225	4300	5805	8063	10750	14307	19017	25263	33594	44801					
8	6	4	2	1	80	116	149	193	258	347	462	616	825	1100	1430	1870	2475	3300	4400	5940	8250	11000	14640	19460	25850	34375	45843	1¼	2½	5	7½	10
					82	118	152	197	264	354	473	630	844	1125	1463	1913	2531	3375	4500	6075	8438	11250	14972	19902	26438	35156	46885					
					84	121	155	201	270	362	483	644	863	1150	1495	1955	2588	3450	4600	6210	8625	11500	15305	20345	27025	35938	47926					
					86	123	159	206	276	370	494	658	881	1175	1528	1998	2644	3525	4700	6345	8813	11750	15637	20787	27613	36719	48968					
10	7½	3	2½	1¼	88	126	162	210	282	378	504	672	900	1200	1560	2040	2700	3600	4800	6480	9000	12000	15970	21230	28200	37500	50010	1½	3	6	9	12
					89	129	165	214	288	386	515	686	919	1225	1593	2083	2756	3675	4900	6615	9188	12250	16302	21672	28788	38281	51052					
					91	131	169	219	294	394	525	700	938	1250	1625	2125	2813	3750	5000	6750	9375	12500	16635	22115	29375	39063	52094					
					93	134	172	223	300	402	536	714	956	1275	1658	2168	2869	3825	5100	6885	9563	12750	16967	22557	29963	39844	53136					
					95	137	176	228	306	410	546	728	975	1300	1690	2210	2925	3900	5200	7020	9750	13000	17300	23000	30550	40625	54178	1¾	3½	7	10½	14

Spring Scale — lb. per in.

Series	00	10	20	30	40	50	60	70	80	90	100	110	120	130	140	150	160	170	180	190	200	210	220
820	30	42	54	70	94	126	168	224	300	400	520	680	900	1200	1600	2160	3000	4000	5320	7080	9400	12500	16670
2680	15	21	27	35	47	63	84	112	150	200	260	340	450	600	800	1080	1500	2000	2660	3540	4700	6250	8335
980	7	10	13	17	23	31	42	56	75	100	130	170	225	300	400	540	750	1000	1330	1770	2350	3125	4167
990	5	7	9	12	16	21	28	37	50	67	87	113	150	200	267	360	500	667	887	1180	1567	2083	2778
995	4	5	7	9	12		21	28	38	50	65	85	113	150	200	270	375	500	665	885	1175	1563	2034

Courtesy of Support Technology Products, Inc., and Piping Technology Products, Inc.

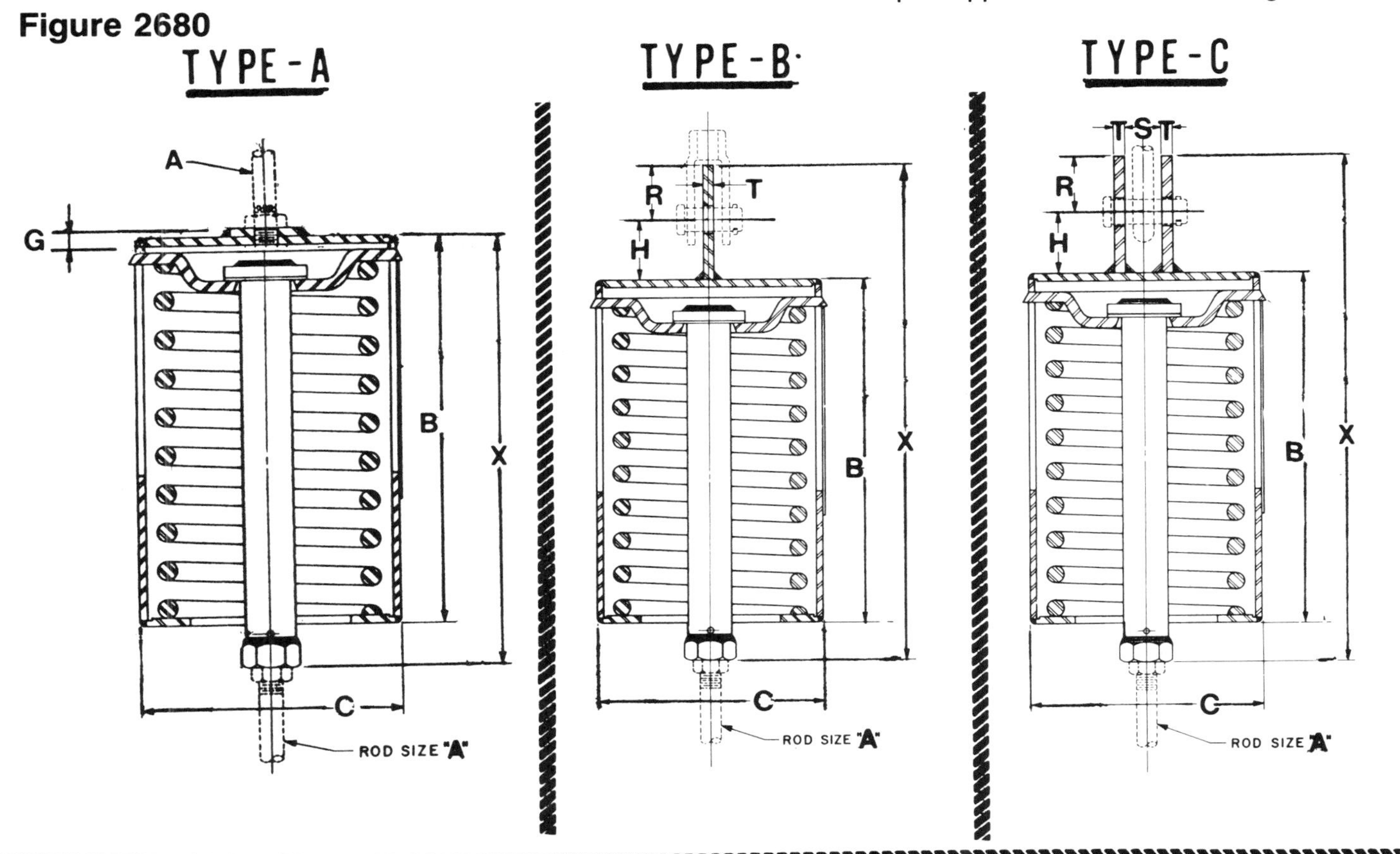

Type A springs are furnished with a threaded ushing in the top plate, providing for a simple rod ttachment for the upper connection.

Type B and C springs are furnished with one or two lugs as shown, welded to the top cap of spring.

hanger size	rated load lb	wgt (approx) each lb	rod size A	R.H. thd lgth	lug hole size	casing length B	casing diam C	thread depth G	height of pin H	shipping length X	R	clevis opening S	thickness T	loaded length X min	loaded length X max
0o	69	7	1/2	5	11/16	6 11/16	4	7/16	1 1/2	10 1/16	1 1/4	7/8	1/4	10 9/16	13 1/16
1o	100	8	1/2	5	11/16	7 9/16	4	7/16	1 1/2	10 13/16	1 1/4	7/8	1/4	11 5/16	13 13/16
2o	128	9	1/2	5	11/16	8 5/16	4	7/16	1 1/2	11 9/16	1 1/4	7/8	1/4	12 1/16	14 9/16
3o	166	12	1/2	5	11/16	7 5/16	5 9/16	7/16	1 1/2	10 13/16	1 1/4	7/8	1/4	11 5/16	13 13/16
4o	223	14	1/2	5	11/16	7 15/16	5 9/16	7/16	1 1/2	11 5/16	1 1/4	7/8	1/4	11 13/16	14 5/16
5o	299	15	1/2	5	11/16	8 5/8	5 9/16	7/16	1 1/2	12 1/8	1 1/4	7/8	1/4	12 5/8	15 1/8
6o	399	24	5/8	5	13/16	8 13/16	6 5/8	5/8	1 1/2	12 3/8	1 1/4	1 1/16	1/4	12 7/8	15 3/8
7o	532	27	5/8	5	13/16	9 3/4	6 5/8	5/8	1 1/2	13 3/8	1 1/4	1 1/16	1/4	13 7/8	16 3/8
8o	713	29	5/8	5	13/16	10 1/4	6 5/8	5/8	1 1/2	13 7/8	1 1/4	1 1/16	1/4	14 3/8	16 7/8
9o	950	56	3/4	6	15/16	10 7/8	8 5/8	1	1 1/2	14 1/2	1 1/4	1 1/4	3/8	15	17 1/2
10o	1235	62	3/4	6	15/16	12 1/8	8 5/8	1	1 1/2	15 3/4	1 1/4	1 1/4	3/8	16 1/4	18 3/4
11o	1615	56	7/8	6	1 1/8	9 15/16	8 5/8	1	2	14 7/8	1 1/4	1 7/16	3/8	15 3/8	17 7/8
12o	2138	61	1	6	1 1/4	10 9/16	8 5/8	1	2	15 7/16	1 1/2	1 5/8	1/2	15 15/16	18 7/16
13o	2850	79	1 1/8	7	1 3/8	13 1/8	8 5/8	1	3	18 7/16	1 1/2	1 13/16	1/2	18 15/16	21 7/16
14o	3800	84	1 1/8	7	1 3/8	13 1/4	8 5/8	1	3	18 7/16	1 1/2	1 13/16	1/2	18 15/16	21 7/16
15o	5130	100	1 1/4	7	1 1/2	13 3/4	8 5/8	1 3/8	3	20 11/16	2	2	5/8	21 3/16	23 11/16
16o	7125	124	1 1/2	8	1 3/4	16 1/16	8 5/8	1 3/8	3	23 15/16	2 1/2	2 3/8	3/4	24 7/16	26 15/16
17o	9500	154	1 3/4	8	2	18 1/8	8 5/8	1 3/8	3	26 3/16	2 1/2	2 5/8	3/4	26 11/16	29 3/16
18o	12645	301	2	9	2 3/8	18 1/8	12 3/4	2 1/4	4	28 1/16	3	2 7/8	3/4	28 9/16	31 1/16
19o	16805	348	2 1/4	9	2 5/8	20 3/8	12 3/4	2 1/4	4 1/2	31 3/16	3	3 1/8	3/4	31 11/16	34 3/16
20o	22325	456	2 1/2	10	2 7/8	23 5/8	12 3/4	2 1/4	4 1/2	35 11/16	4	3 3/8	1	36 3/16	38 11/16
21o	29688	528	2 3/4	10	3 1/8	26 5/16	12 3/4	2 3/4	4 1/2	38 13/16	4	3 5/8	1	39 5/16	41 13/16
22o	39591	684	3	11	3 3/8	32 3/8	12 3/4	3	5	45 11/16	4	3 7/8	1	46 3/16	48 11/16

Figure 13-3. Spring supports. (Courtesy Support Technology Products, Inc. and Piping Technology Products, Inc.)

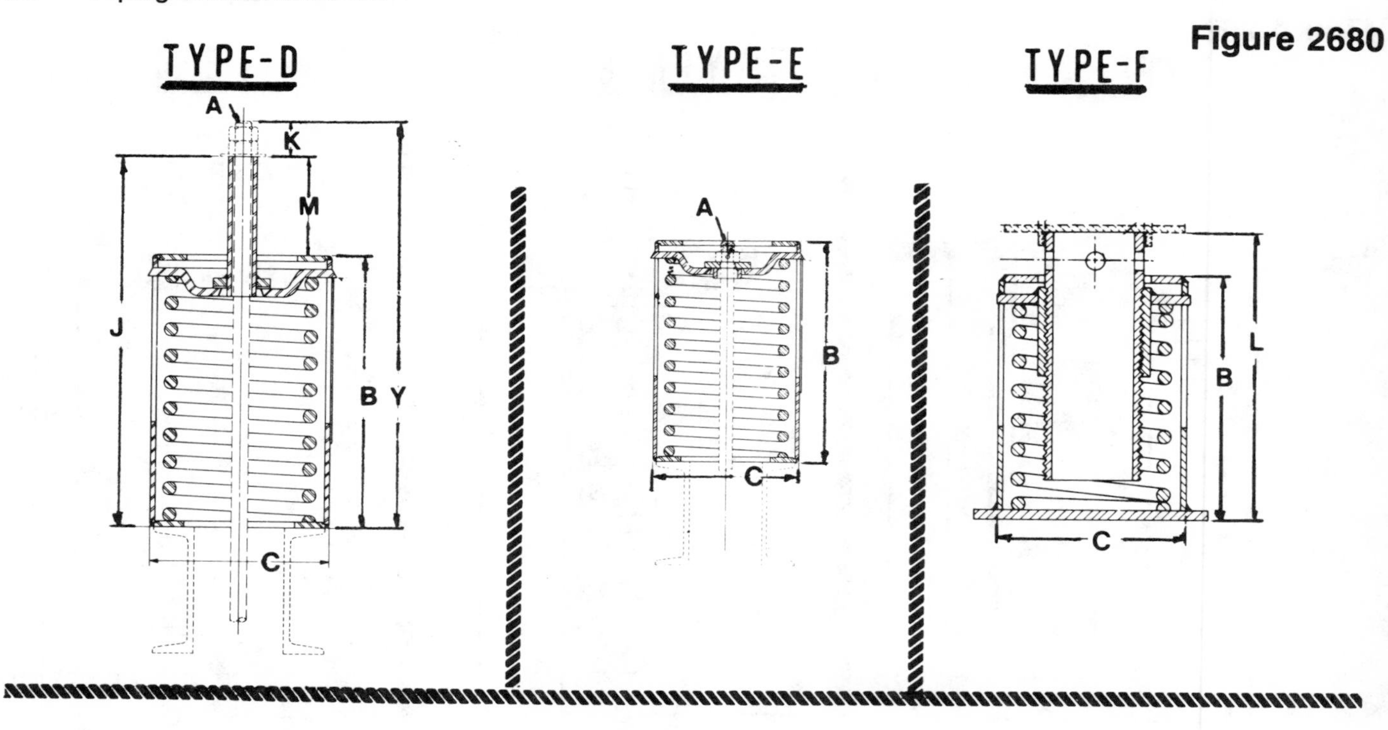

Type D spring permits adjustment from the top, by turning the nuts on the hanger rod against a piece of tubing. The tubing is securely welded to the spring cap. Type D spring is set above the supporting steel. Type E permits rod adjustment from either above or below the spring.

Type F spring assembly is designed to support piping from below, directly from the floor.

Adjustment is made by inserting a bar into holes in the load column, and turning the load column as a jack screw. The base plate is welded to the case and has four holes for fastening.

hanger size	rod size A	casing length B	casing diam C	allowance for nuts K	shipping length J	height of spacer M	rod length Y	type F: length L min	length L max	bottom flange square	bottom flange bolt circle min	bottom flange bolt circle max	bottom flange bolts	thickness bottom flange	load flange diam.
00	½	6 11/16	4	1¼	9 13/16	3⅛	11 1/16	8 3/16	10 3/16	7½	7	8¾	⅝	¼	3 13/16
10	½	7 9/16	4	1¼	10 11/16	3⅛	11 15/16	9 1/16	11 1/16	7½	7	8¾	⅝	¼	3 13/16
20	½	8 5/16	4	1¼	11 7/16	3⅛	12 11/16	9 13/16	11 13/16	7½	7	8¾	⅝	¼	3 13/16
30	½	7 5/16	5 9/16	1¼	10 7/16	3⅛	11 11/16	8 15/16	10 15/16	7½	7¾	8¾	¾	¼	5¼
40	½	7 15/16	5 9/16	1¼	11 1/16	3⅛	12 5/16	9 9/16	11 9/16	7½	7¾	8¾	¾	¼	5¼
50	½	8⅝	5 9/16	1¼	11¾	3⅛	13	10¼	12¼	7½	7¾	8¾	¾	¼	5¼
60	⅝	8 13/16	6⅝	1½	11 13/16	3	13 5/16	10 7/16	12 7/16	9	8	10⅞	¾	⅜	6 5/16
70	⅝	9¾	6⅝	1½	12¾	3	14¼	11 7/16	13 7/16	9	8	10⅞	¾	⅜	6 5/16
80	⅝	10¼	6⅝	1½	13¼	3	14¾	11⅞	13⅞	9	8	10⅞	¾	⅜	6 5/16
90	¾	10⅞	8⅝	1¾	13⅞	3	15⅝	12 7/16	14 7/16	13¼	10 9/16	16½	¾	½	8¼
100	¾	12⅛	8⅝	1¾	15⅛	3	16⅞	13 11/16	15 11/16	13¼	10 9/16	16½	¾	½	8¼
110	⅞	9 15/16	8⅝	2	12 15/16	3	14 15/16	11½	13½	13¼	10 9/16	16½	¾	½	8¼
120	1	10 9/16	8⅝	2¼	13 9/16	3	15 13/16	12⅛	14⅛	13¼	10 9/16	16½	¾	½	8¼
130	1⅛	13⅛	8⅝	2½	16⅛	3	18⅝	14 11/16	16 11/16	13¼	10 9/16	16½	¾	½	8¼
140	1⅛	13¼	8⅝	2½	16¼	3	18¾	14 13/16	16 13/16	13¼	10 9/16	16½	¾	½	8¼
150	1¼	13¾	8⅝	3	16¾	3	19¾	15 1/16	17 1/16	13¼	10 9/16	16½	¾	½	8¼
160	1½	16 1/16	8⅝	3½	19 1/16	3	22 9/16	17⅜	19⅜	13¼	10 9/16	16½	¾	½	8¼
170	1¾	18⅛	8⅝	4	21⅛	3	25⅛	19 7/16	21 7/16	13¼	10 9/16	16½	¾	½	8¼
180	2	18⅛	12¾	4 9/16	21⅛	3	25 11/16	19 1/16	21 1/16	17¼	15¾	22	¾	⅝	12½
190	2¼	20⅜	12¾	5	23⅜	3	28⅜	21 5/16	23 5/16	17¼	15¾	22	¾	⅝	12½
200	2½	23⅝	12¾	5 9/16	26⅝	3	32 3/16	24 9/16	26 9/16	17¼	15¾	22	¾	⅝	12½
210	2¾	26 5/16	12¾	6¼	29 5/16	3	35 9/16	27 5/16	29 5/16	17¼	15¾	22	¾	⅝	12½
220	3	32⅜	12¾	6⅝	35⅜	3	42	33⅜	35⅜	17¼	15¾	22	¾	⅝	12½

Figure 13-3. Continued.

Figure 2680

TYPE - G

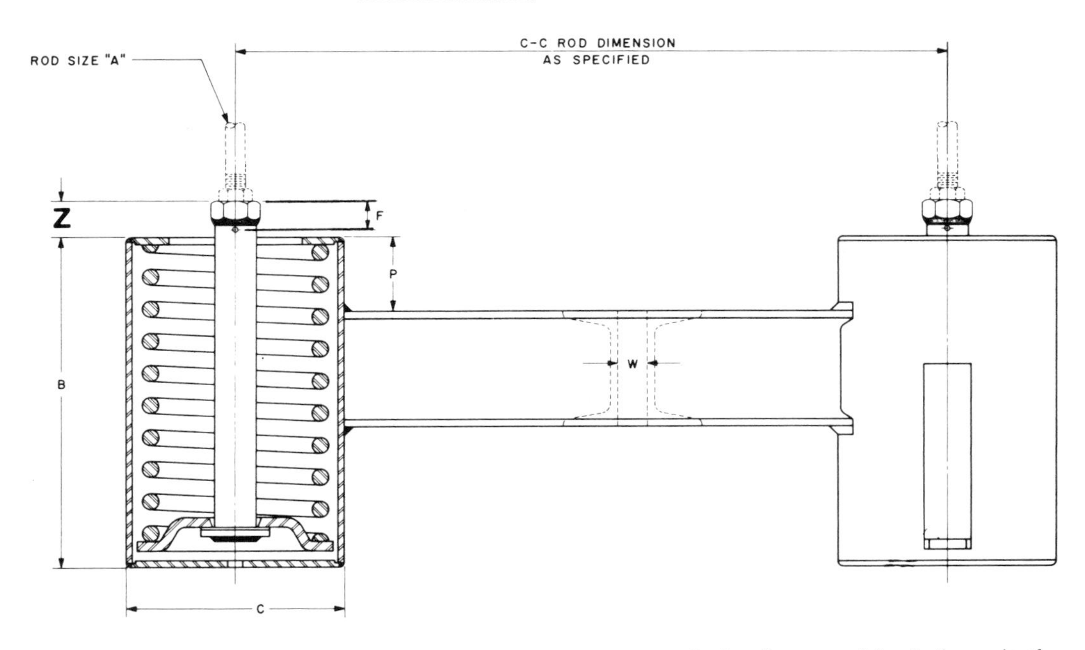

Type G trapeze type spring assembly is formed by welding two standard spring assemblies to the ends of a pair of channels. Type G assembly is especially adaptable for use where headroom is limited, to avoid interference, or to accommodate unusually heavy loads.

The assembly can be furnished with center to center dimensions, as specified by purchaser. When ordering Type G, divide the total pipe load in half to select the proper spring size. The travel range of the springs remain unchanged.

hanger size	rated load lb	wgt■ (approx) each, lb	rod size A	casing length B	casing diameter C	min thread engagement F	space between channels W	P	Z
00	138	28	1/2	6 11/16	4	3/4	5/8	1 1/2	5/8
10	200	29	1/2	7 9/16	4	3/4	5/8	1 1/2	1/2
20	256	30	1/2	8 5/16	4	3/4	5/8	1 1/2	1/2
30	332	37	1/2	7 5/16	5 9/16	3/4	3/4	2	3/4
40	446	38	1/2	7 15/16	5 9/16	3/4	3/4	2	5/8
50	598	39	1/2	8 5/8	5 9/16	3/4	3/4	2	3/4
60	798	57	5/8	8 13/16	6 5/8	15/16	1	2	13/16
70	1064	63	5/8	9 3/4	6 5/8	15/16	1	2	7/8
80	1426	67	5/8	10 1/4	6 5/8	15/16	1	2	7/8
90	1900	123	3/4	10 7/8	8 5/8	1 1/16	1 1/4	3	7/8
100	2470	137	3/4	12 1/8	8 5/8	1 1/16	1 1/4	3	7/8
110	3230	125	7/8	9 15/16	8 5/8	1 1/4	1 1/4	3	1 11/16
120	4276	137	1	10 9/16	8 5/8	1 3/8	1 1/2	4	1 3/8
130	5700	175	1 1/8	13 1/8	8 5/8	1 9/16	1 1/2	4	13/16
140	7600	183	1 1/8	13 1/4	8 5/8	1 9/16	1 1/2	4	11/16
150	10260	224	1 1/4	13 3/4	8 5/8	1 7/8	2 1/8	4	1 15/16
160	14250	270	1 1/2	16 1/16	8 5/8	2 3/16	2 1/8	4	2 3/8
170	19000	326	1 3/4	18 1/8	8 5/8	2 7/16	2 1/8	4	2 9/16
180	25290	630	2	18 1/8	12 3/4	2 13/16	2 3/8	4	2 15/16
190	33610	723	2 1/4	20 3/8	12 3/4	3 1/16	2 5/8	4	3 5/16
200	44650	933	2 1/2	23 5/8	12 3/4	3 5/16	2 7/8	4	3 9/16
210	59376	1137	2 3/4	26 5/16	12 3/4	3 11/16	3 1/8	4	4
220	79182	1436	3	32 3/8	12 3/4	3 15/16	3 3/8	4	4 5/16

Figure 13-3. Continued.

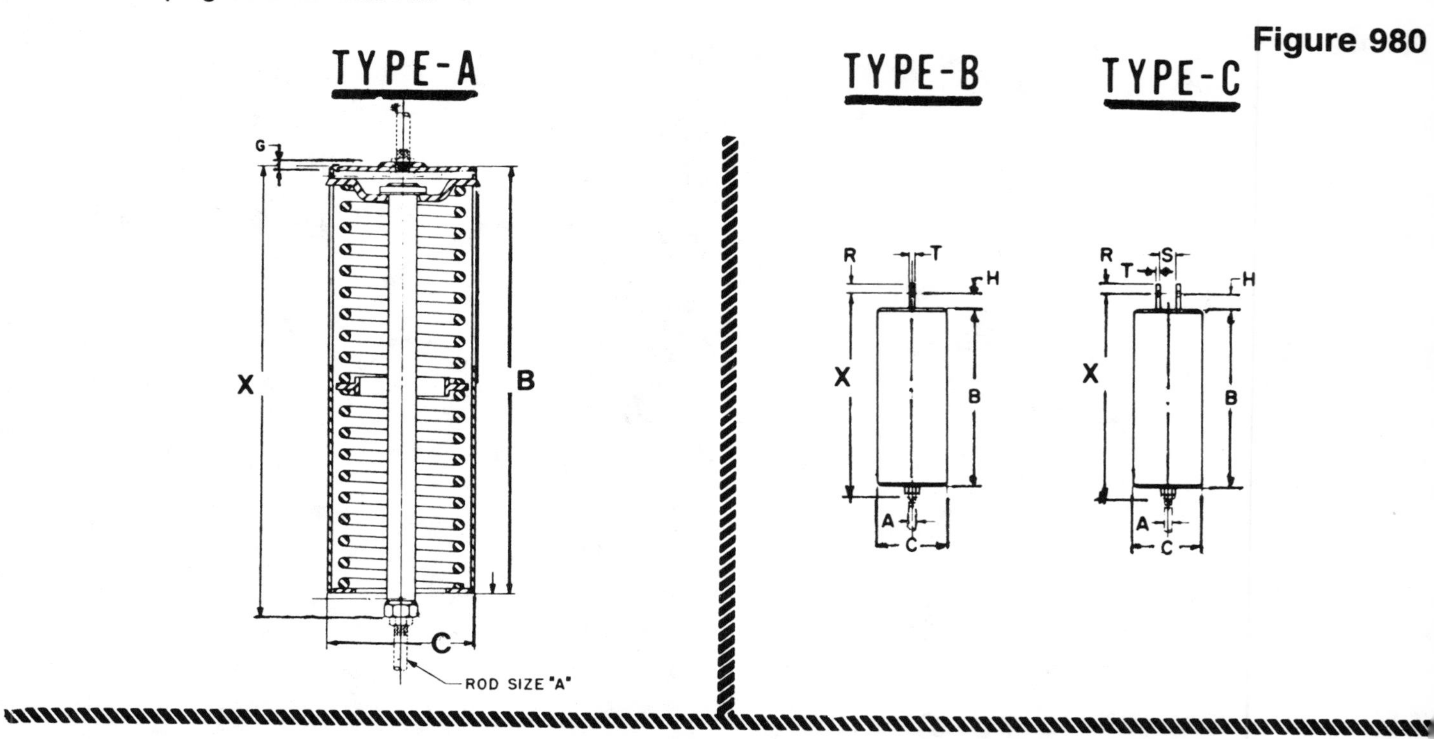

Type A springs are furnished with a threaded bushing in the top plate, providing for a simple rod attachment for the upper connection.

Type B and C springs are unfurnished with one or two lugs as shown, welded to the top cap of spring. These types are designed for use where headroom is limited, as these springs can be attached directly to building steel by a pair of angles, eye rod or a single plate.

hanger size	rod size A	casing length B A, B, C D, E, G	casing diam C	types B, C: lug hole size	types B, C: height of pin H	types B, C: R	types B, C: clevis opening S	types B, C: thickness T	loaded length X: type A min	loaded length X: type A max	loaded length X: types B, C min	loaded length X: types B, C max	loaded length X: type F min	loaded length X: type F max	weight (approx) lb, each: types A, B, C	weight (approx) lb, each: types D, E	weight (approx) lb, each: type F	weight (approx) lb, each: type G
00	1/2	12 5/8	4	11/16	1 1/2	1 1/4	7/8	1/4	14 5/16	19 5/16	17 1/16	22 1/16	14 1/4	16 1/4	11	11	19	35
10	1/2	14 3/8	4	11/16	1 1/2	1 1/4	7/8	1/4	16 1/16	21 1/16	18 13/16	23 13/16	15 15/16	17 15/16	13	13	20	39
20	1/2	15 7/8	4	11/16	1 1/2	1 1/4	7/8	1/4	17 9/16	22 9/16	20 5/16	25 5/16	17 7/16	19 7/16	15	15	22	43
30	1/2	14	5 9/16	11/16	1 1/2	1 1/4	7/8	1/4	15 9/16	20 9/16	18 5/16	23 5/16	15 5/8	17 5/8	20	19	33	51
40	1/2	15 1/4	5 9/16	11/16	1 1/2	1 1/4	7/8	1/4	17 1/16	22 1/16	19 13/16	24 13/16	16 7/8	18 7/8	23	22	37	57
50	1/2	16 5/8	5 9/16	11/16	1 1/2	1 1/4	7/8	1/4	18 5/16	23 5/16	21 1/16	26 1/16	18 1/4	20 1/4	25	24	39	61
60	5/8	16 11/16	6 5/8	13/16	1 1/2	1 1/4	1 1/16	1/4	18 5/8	23 5/8	21 3/8	26 3/8	18 3/8	20 3/8	38	37	59	87
70	5/8	18 5/8	6 5/8	13/16	1 1/2	1 1/4	1 1/16	1/4	20 5/8	25 5/8	23 3/8	28 3/8	20 5/16	22 5/16	46	45	69	103
80	5/8	19 9/16	6 5/8	13/16	1 1/2	1 1/4	1 1/16	1/4	21 1/8	26 1/8	23 7/8	28 7/8	21 1/4	23 1/4	58	49	72	127
90	3/4	20 3/16	8 5/8	15/16	1 1/2	1 1/4	1 1/4	3/8	21 15/16	26 15/16	24 11/16	29 11/16	21 3/4	23 3/4	87	84	126	187
100	3/4	22 5/8	8 5/8	15/16	1 1/2	1 1/4	1 1/4	3/8	24 7/16	29 7/16	27 3/16	32 3/16	24 3/16	26 3/16	104	98	140	221
110	7/8	18 1/4	8 5/8	1 1/8	2	1 1/4	1 7/16	3/8	20 1/8	25 1/8	23 3/8	28 3/8	19 13/16	21 13/16	88	85	124	189
120	1	19 1/2	8 5/8	1 1/4	2	1 1/2	1 5/8	1/2	21 3/16	26 3/16	24 11/16	29 11/16	21 1/16	23 1/16	98	94	134	213
130	1 1/8	24 5/8	8 5/8	1 3/8	3	1 1/2	1 13/16	1/2	26 5/16	31 5/16	30 13/16	35 13/16	26 3/16	28 3/16	134	129	171	285
140	1 1/8	24 7/8	8 5/8	1 3/8	3	1 1/2	1 13/16	1/2	26 13/16	31 13/16	31 5/16	36 5/16	26 7/16	28 7/16	143	137	178	303
150	1 1/4	25 1/4	8 5/8	1 1/2	3	2	2	5/8	28 1/4	33 1/4	33 1/4	38 1/4	26 9/16	28 9/16	158	149	187	342
160	1 1/2	29 7/8	8 5/8	1 3/4	3	2 1/2	2 3/8	3/4	33 1/8	38 1/8	38 5/8	43 5/8	31 3/16	33 3/16	204	188	227	434
170	1 3/4	34	8 5/8	2	3	2 1/2	2 5/8	3/4	37 5/8	42 5/8	43 1/8	48 1/8	35 5/16	37 5/16	259	233	273	544
180	2	33 1/8	12 3/4	2 3/8	4	3	2 7/8	3/4	37 3/16	42 3/16	44 3/16	49 3/16	34 1/16	36 1/16	482	447	520	996
190	2 1/4	37 5/8	12 3/4	2 5/8	4 1/2	3	3 1/8	3/4	41 13/16	46 13/16	49 5/16	54 5/16	38 9/16	40 9/16	570	518	594	1171
200	2 1/2	44 1/8	12 3/4	2 7/8	4 1/2	4	3 3/8	1	48 11/16	53 11/16	57 3/16	62 3/16	45 1/16	47 1/16	772	693	777	1573
210	2 3/4	48 7/8	12 3/4	3 1/8	4 1/2	4	3 5/8	1	52 7/8	57 7/8	61 3/8	66 3/8	49 7/8	51 7/8	910	815	842	1905
220	3	61	12 3/4	3 3/8	5	4	3 7/8	1	66 1/16	71 1/16	75 1/16	80 1/16	62	64	1210	1110	1154	2506

Figure 13-4. Spring supports. (Courtesy Support Technology Products, Inc. and Piping Technology Products, Inc.)

Figure 980

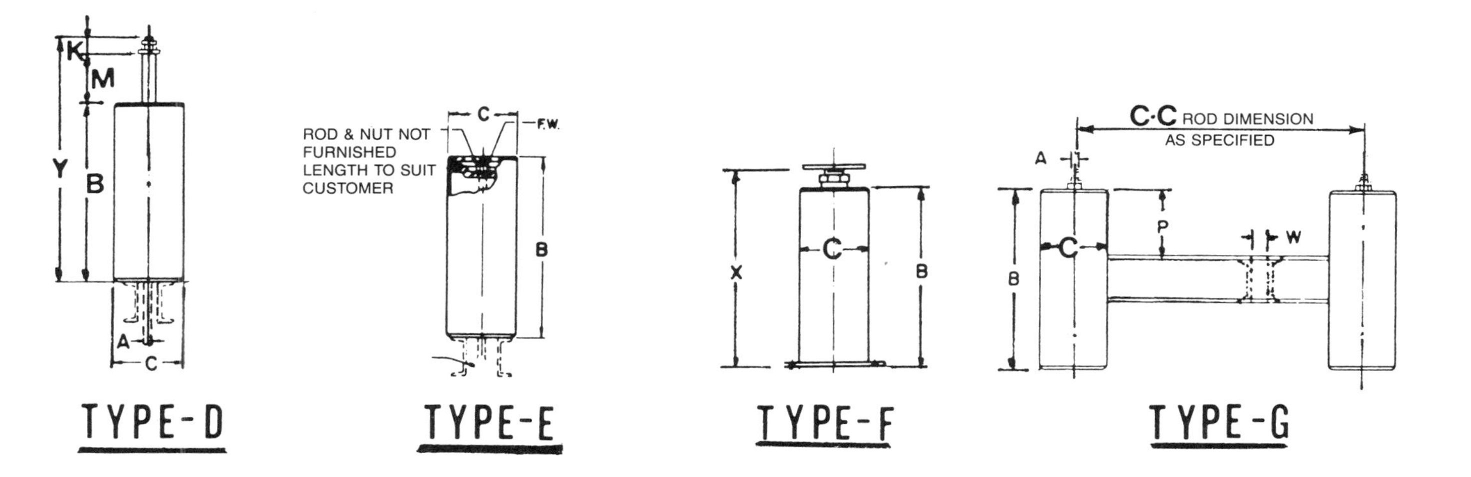

hanger size	type D: rod length Y	type D: allowance for nuts K	type D: height of space M	type F: bottom flange square	type F: bottom flange bolt circle min	type F: bottom flange bolt circle max	type F: bottom flange bolts	type F: thick. bottom flange	type F: load col. diam	type F: load flange diam D•	type F: thick. of load flange•	type G: space between channels W	type G: P
00	19⅜	1¼	5½	7½	7	8¾	⅝	¼	1.900	3 13/16	3/16	⅝	1½
10	21⅛	1¼	5½	7½	7	8¾	⅝	¼	1.900	3 13/16	3/16	⅝	1½
20	22⅝	1¼	5½	7½	7	8¾	⅝	¼	1.900	3 13/16	3/16	⅝	1½
30	20¾	1¼	5½	7½	7¾	8¾	¾	¼	2.875	5¼	3/16	¾	2
40	22	1¼	5½	7½	7¾	8¾	¾	¼	2.875	5¼	3/16	¾	2
50	23⅜	1¼	5½	7½	7¾	8¾	¾	¼	2.875	5¼	3/16	¾	2
60	23 11/16	1½	5½	9	8	10⅞	¾	⅜	3.50	6 5/16	¼	1	2
70	25⅝	1½	5½	9	8	10⅞	¾	⅜	3.50	6 5/16	¼	1	2
80	26 9/16	1½	5½	9	8	10⅞	¾	⅜	3.50	6 5/16	¼	1	2
90	27 7/16	1¾	5½	13¼	10 9/16	16½	¾	½	4.50	8¼	½	1¼	3
100	29⅞	1¾	5½	13¼	10 9/16	16½	¾	½	4.50	8¼	½	1¼	3
110	25¾	2	5½	13¼	10 9/16	16½	¾	½	4.50	8¼	½	1¼	3
120	27¼	2¼	5½	13¼	10 9/16	16½	¾	½	4.50	8¼	½	1½	4
130	32⅝	2½	5½	13¼	10 9/16	16½	¾	½	4.50	8¼	½	1½	4
140	32⅞	2½	5½	13¼	10 9/16	16½	¾	½	4.50	8¼	½	1½	4
150	33¾	3	5½	13¼	10 9/16	16½	¾	½	4.50	8¼	½	2⅛	4
160	38⅞	3½	5½	13¼	10 9/16	16½	¾	½	4.50	8¼	½	2⅛	4
170	43½	4	5½	13¼	10 9/16	16½	¾	½	4.50	8¼	½	2⅛	4
180	43 3/16	4 9/16	5½	17¼	15¾	22	¾	⅝	5.563	12½	½	2⅜	4
190	48⅛	5	5½	17¼	15¾	22	¾	⅝	5.563	12½	½	2⅝	4
200	55 3/16	5 9/16	5½	17¼	15¾	22	¾	⅝	5.563	12½	½	2⅞	4
210	60⅝	6¼	5½	17¼	15¾	22	¾	⅝	5.563	12½	½	3⅛	4
220	73⅛	6⅝	5½	17¼	15¾	22	¾	⅝	5.563	12½	½	3⅜	4

Figure 13-4. Continued.

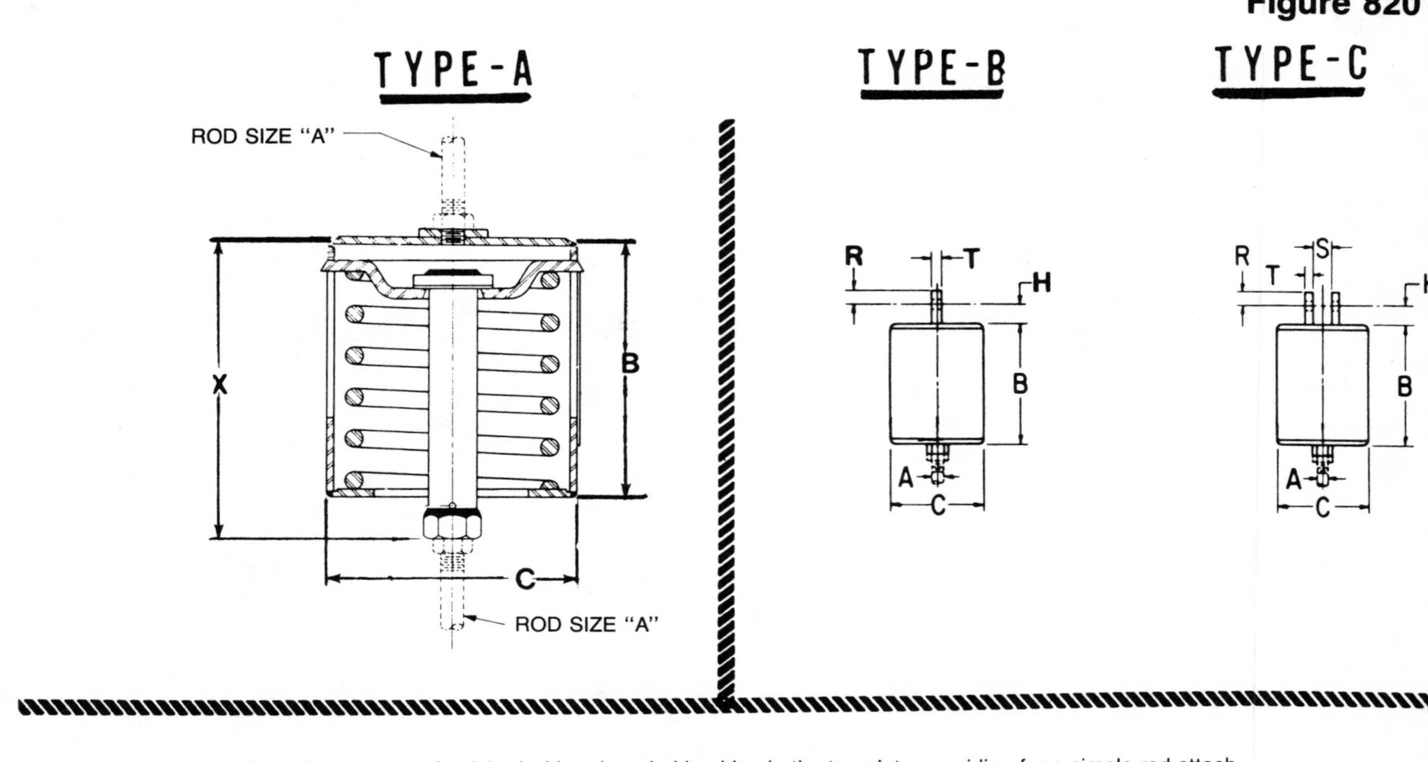

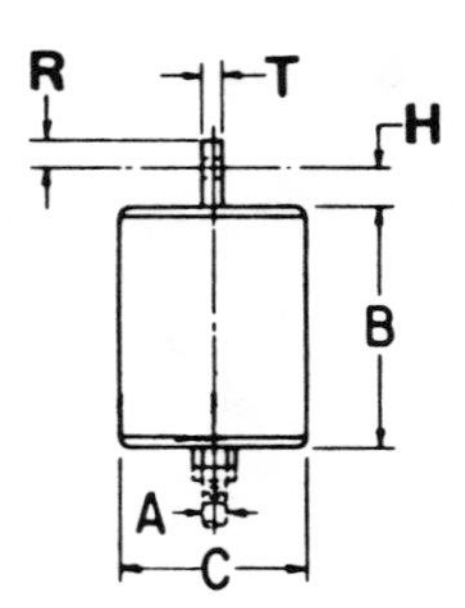

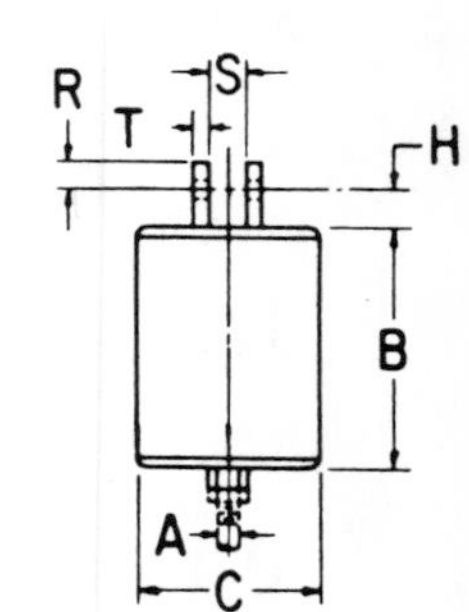

Type A springs are furnished with a threaded bushing in the top plate, providing for a simple rod attachment for the upper connection.

Type B and C springs are unfurnished with one or two lugs as shown, welded to the top cap of spring. These types are designed for use where headroom is limited, as these springs can be attached directly to building steel by a pair of angles, eye rod or a single plate.

				types B, C					loaded length X						weight (approx) lb, each			
		casing length B							type A		types B, C		type F					
hanger size	rod size A	A, B, C D, E, G	casing diam C	lug hole size	height of pin H	R	clevis opening S	thickness T	min	max	min	max	min	max	types A, B, C	types D, E	type F	type G
00	1/2	4 1/2	4	11/16	1 1/2	1 1/4	7/8	1/4	5 5/16	6 9/16	8 1/16	9 5/16	6 1/16	6 9/16	5	4	10	25
10	1/2	4 3/4	4	11/16	1 1/2	1 1/4	7/8	1/4	5 9/16	6 13/16	8 5/16	9 9/16	6 5/16	6 13/16	6	5	10	25
20	1/2	5 3/8	4	11/16	1 1/2	1 1/4	7/8	1/4	6 1/16	7 5/16	8 13/16	10 1/16	6 15/16	7 7/16	7	8	11	27
30	1/2	4 7/8	5 9/16	11/16	1 1/2	1 1/4	7/8	1/4	5 9/16	6 13/16	8 5/16	9 9/16	6 1/2	7	9	8	17	29
40	1/2	5 1/4	5 9/16	11/16	1 1/2	1 1/4	7/8	1/4	6 1/16	7 5/16	8 13/16	10 1/16	6 7/8	7 3/8	10	9	18	31
50	1/2	5 5/8	5 9/16	11/16	1 1/2	1 1/4	7/8	1/4	6 5/16	7 9/16	9 1/16	10 5/16	7 1/4	7 3/4	11	10	19	32
60	5/8	5 13/16	6 5/8	13/16	1 1/2	1 1/4	1 1/16	1/4	6 3/4	8	9 1/2	10 3/4	7 1/2	8	17	16	30	45
70	5/8	6 7/16	6 5/8	13/16	1 1/2	1 1/4	1 1/16	1/4	7 1/4	8 1/2	10	11 1/4	8 1/8	8 5/8	20	19	32	51
80	5/8	6 11/16	6 5/8	13/16	1 1/2	1 1/4	1 1/16	1/4	7 1/2	8 3/4	10 1/4	11 1/2	8 3/8	8 7/8	21	20	33	53
90	3/4	7 3/4	8 5/8	15/16	1 1/2	1 1/4	1 1/4	3/8	8 9/16	9 13/16	11 5/16	12 9/16	9 5/16	10 5/16	46	42	68	105
100	3/4	8 1/4	8 5/8	15/16	1 1/2	1 1/4	1 1/4	3/8	9 1/16	10 5/16	11 13/16	13 1/16	9 13/16	10 13/16	52	48	74	117
110	7/8	6 15/16	8 5/8	1 1/8	2	1 1/4	1 7/16	3/8	7 15/16	9 3/16	11 3/16	12 7/16	8 1/2	9 1/2	45	41	66	101
120	1	7 1/4	8 5/8	1 1/4	2	1 1/2	1 5/8	1/2	8 3/16	9 7/16	11 11/16	12 15/16	8 13/16	9 13/16	48	43	68	112
130	1 1/8	8 5/8	8 5/8	1 3/8	3	1 1/2	1 13/16	1/2	9 11/16	10 15/16	14 3/16	15 7/16	10 3/16	11 3/16	59	53	71	134
140	1 1/8	8 7/8	8 5/8	1 3/8	3	1 1/2	1 13/16	1/2	9 15/16	11 3/16	14 7/16	15 11/16	10 7/16	11 7/16	62	55	81	139
150	1 1/4	9 3/8	8 5/8	1 1/2	3	2	2	5/8	11 5/8	12 7/8	16 5/8	17 7/8	10 11/16	11 11/16	74	65	86	172
160	1 1/2	10 5/8	8 5/8	1 3/4	3	2 1/2	2 3/8	3/4	13 1/4	14 1/2	18 3/4	20	11 15/16	12 15/16	88	77	98	202
170	1 3/4	11 7/8	8 5/8	2	3	2 1/2	2 5/8	3/4	14 11/16	15 15/16	20 3/16	21 7/16	13 3/16	14 3/16	106	91	112	238
180	2	12 7/8	12 3/4	2 3/8	4	3	2 7/8	3/4	16	17 1/4	23	24 1/4	13 13/16	14 13/16	229	196	240	488
190	2 1/4	13 7/8	12 3/4	2 5/8	4 1/2	3	3 1/8	3/4	17 5/16	18 9/16	24 13/16	26 1/16	14 13/16	15 13/16	256	216	245	539
200	2 1/2	16	12 3/4	2 7/8	4 1/2	4	3 3/8	1	19 13/16	21 1/16	28 5/16	29 9/16	16 15/16	17 15/16	320	272	314	669
210	2 3/4	17	12 3/4	3 1/8	4 1/2	4	3 5/8	1	20 5/16	21 9/16	28 13/16	30 1/16	18	19	371	309	318	827
220	3	21 1/4	12 3/4	3 3/8	5	4	3 7/8	1	24 13/16	26 1/16	33 13/16	35 1/16	22 1/4	23 1/4	460	401	413	1006

Figure 13-5. Spring supports. (Courtesy Support Technology Products, Inc. and Piping Technology Products, Inc.)

Figure 820

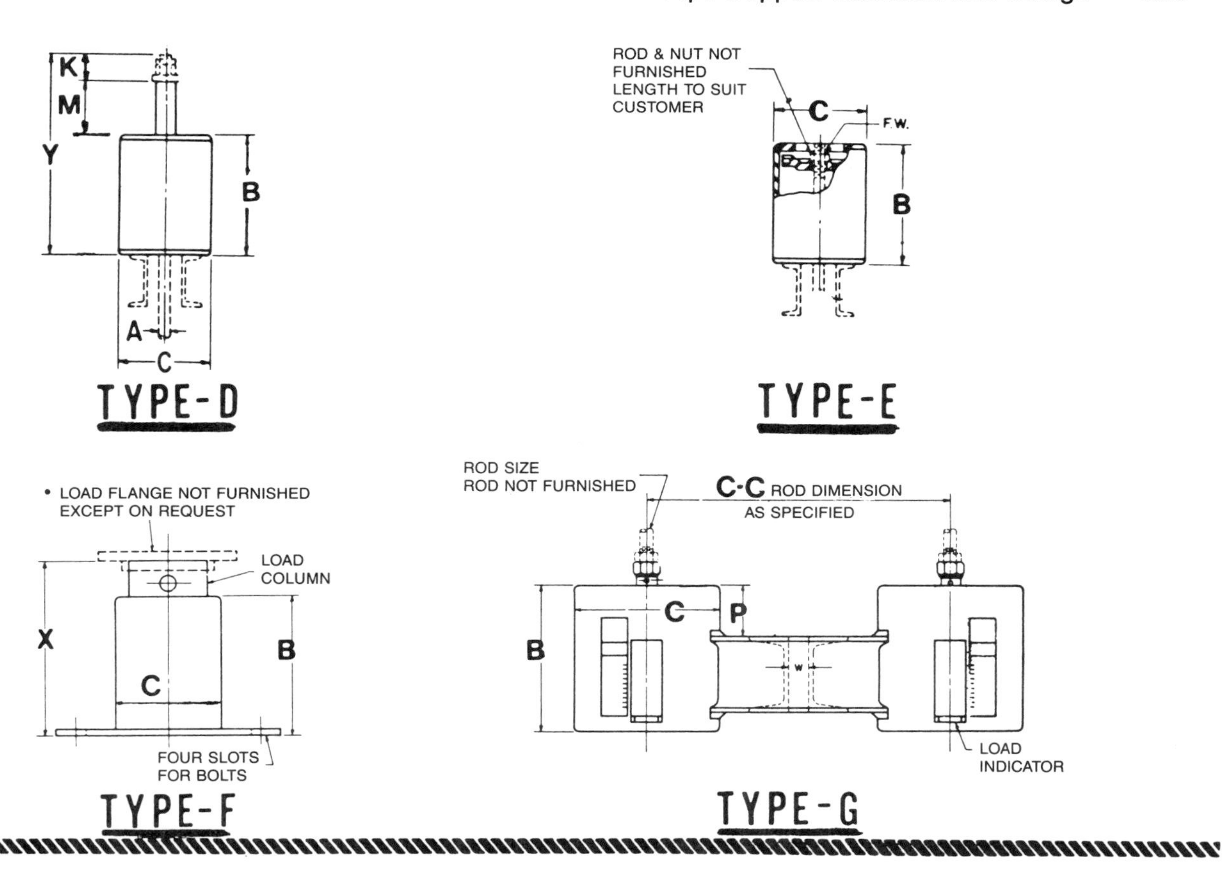

	type D			type F								type G	
hanger size	rod length Y	allow-ance for nuts K	height of spacer M	bot-tom flange square	bottom flange bolt circle min	bottom flange bolt circle max	bot-tom flange bolts	thick bot-tom flange	load col diam	load flange	thick. of load flange	space between chan-nels W	P
00	7½	1¼	1¾	7½	7	8¾	⅝	¼	1.900	3 13/16	3/16	⅝	1
10	7¾	1¼	1¾	7½	7	8¾	⅝	¼	1.900	3 13/16	3/16	⅝	1
20	8⅜	1¼	1¾	7½	7	8¾	⅝	¼	1.900	3 13/16	3/16	⅝	1
30	7⅞	1¼	1¾	7½	7¾	8¾	¾	¼	2.875	5¼	3/16	¾	1
40	8¼	1¼	1¾	7½	7¾	8¾	¾	¼	2.875	5¼	3/16	¾	1
50	8⅝	1¼	1¾	7½	7¾	8¾	¾	¼	2.875	5¼	3/16	¾	1
60	9 1/16	1½	1¾	9	8	10⅞	¾	⅜	3.50	6 5/16	¼	1	2
70	9 11/16	1½	1¾	9	8	10⅞	¾	⅜	3.50	6 5/16	¼	1	2
80	9 15/16	1½	1¾	9	8	10⅞	¾	⅜	3.50	6 5/16	¼	1	2
90	11¼	1¾	1¾	13¼	10 9/16	16½	¾	½	4.50	8¼	½	1¼	2
100	11¾	1¾	1¾	13¼	10 9/16	16½	¾	½	4.50	8¼	½	1¼	2
110	10 11/16	2	1¾	13¼	10 9/16	16½	¾	½	4.50	8¼	½	1¼	2
120	11¼	2¼	1¾	13¼	10 9/16	16½	¾	½	4.50	8¼	½	1½	1½
130	12⅞	2½	1¾	13¼	10 9/16	16½	¾	½	4.50	8¼	½	1½	3
140	13⅛	2½	1¾	13¼	10 9/16	16½	¾	½	4.50	8¼	½	1½	3
150	14⅛	3	1¾	13¼	10 9/16	16½	¾	½	4.50	8¼	½	2⅛	1
160	15⅞	3½	1¾	13¼	10 9/16	16½	¾	½	4.50	8¼	½	2⅛	2
170	17⅝	4	1¾	13¼	10 9/16	16½	¾	½	4.50	8¼	½	2⅛	2
180	19 3/16	4 9/16	1¾	17¼	15¾	22	¾	⅝	5.563	12½	½	2⅜	½
190	20⅝	5	1¾	17¼	15¾	22	¾	⅝	5.563	12½	½	2⅝	1
200	23 5/16	5 9/16	1¾	17¼	15¾	22	¾	⅝	5.563	12½	½	2⅞	1
210	25	6¼	1¾	17¼	15¾	22	¾	⅝	5.563	12½	½	3⅛	1
220	29⅝	6⅝	1¾	17¼	15¾	22	¾	⅝	5.563	12½	½	3⅜	3

Figure 13-5. Continued.

SERVICE: Recommended for light loads where vertical movement does not exceed 1¼ inches.

APPROVALS: Complies with Federal Specification WW-H-171D (Type 49) and Manufacturers Standardization Society SP-69 (Type 48).

INSTALLATION: Designed for attachment to its supporting member by screwing a rod into the top cap of the hanger the full depth of the cap.

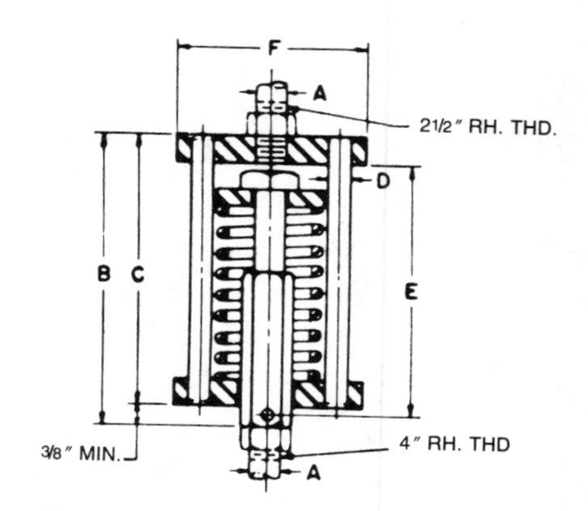

LIGHT DUTY SPRING HANGER

Carbon Steel Spring Coil and Cage

The Light Duty Spring Hanger is used for the support of miscellaneous field run piping systems subject to slight (up to 1/4") vertical displacement. It is designed for incorporation in rod hangers with a load coupling provided for spring loading. The unit does not have a load scale and travel indicator. Amount of spring loading can be approximated by relating "B" dimension with spring deflection rate.

Selection of correct spring size is normally done by approximate methods taking into account weight of pipe, covering, contents and major fittings.

Ordering: Order by part number and spring size number.

DIMENSIONS IN INCHES

Spring Size No.	A	B		C	D	E	F	Maximum Deflection	Maximum Load Pounds	Spring Deflection Lbs. per in.	Weight Lbs. per 100
		Min.	Max.								
1	3/8	4 1/2	6 1/2	4 1/8	1/4	3 3/4	2 3/8	2	52	26	160
2	3/8	4 1/2	6 1/4	4 1/8	5/16	3 3/4	3 1/8	1 3/4	115	66	238
3	1/2	5 7/8	7 3/4	5 1/2	3/8	5	2 3/4	1 7/8	163	87	287
4	1/2	5 7/8	7 5/8	5 1/2	3/8	5	3 1/4	1 3/4	266	152	350
5	5/8	6 3/4	8 3/4	6 3/8	1/2	5 3/4	4 1/8	2	400	200	680
6	3/4	8 3/8	10 7/8	8	1/2	7 3/8	4 5/8	2 1/2	600	240	982

Figure 13-6. Spring supports. (Courtesy Support Technology Products, Inc. and Piping Technology Products, Inc.)

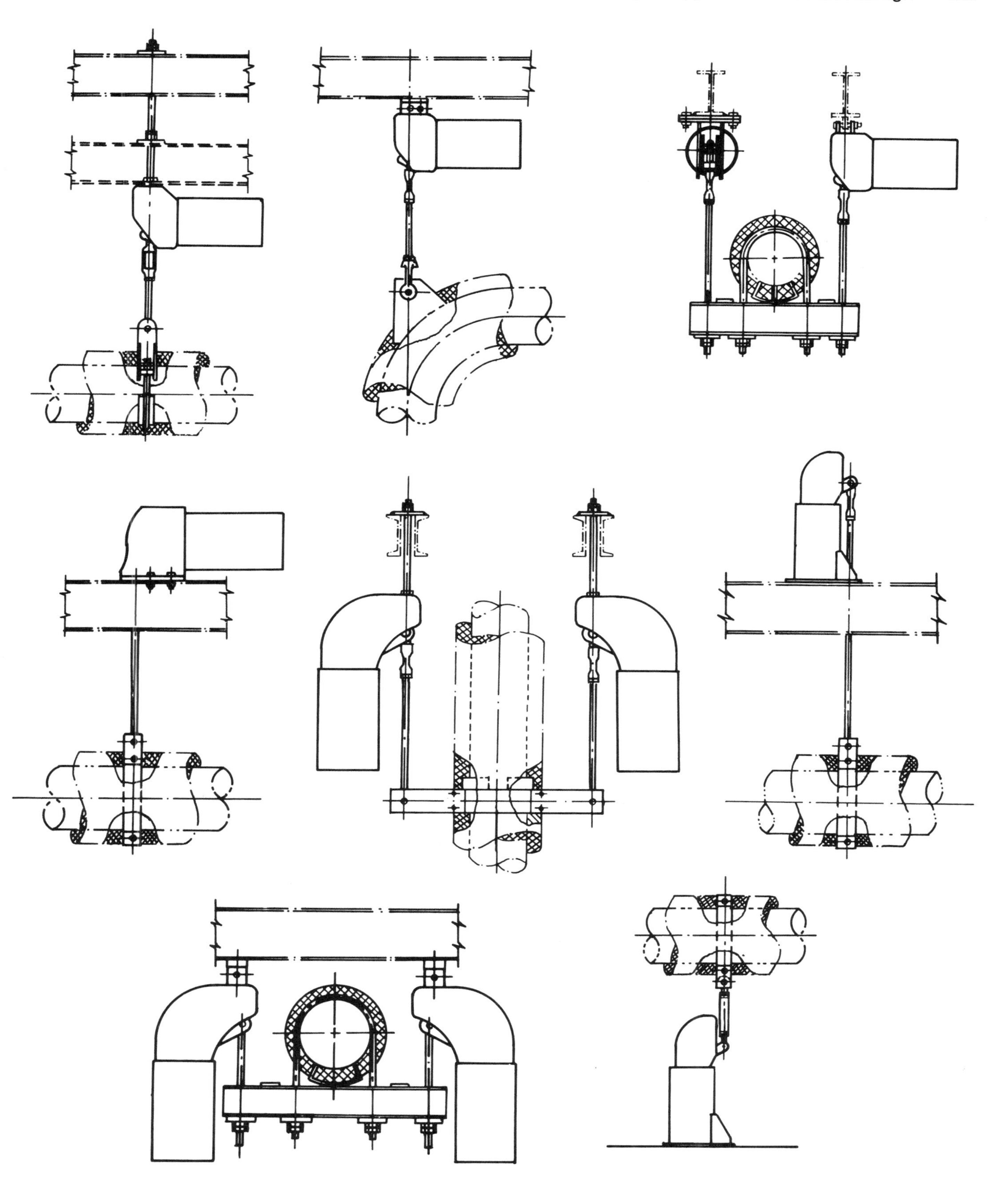

Figure 13-7. Typical arrangements of constant supports. (Courtesy of Elcen Metal Products Company.)

Table 13-2
Load Table for Constant Spring Supports
(lb for total travel in in.)

hanger size no.	load in pounds for total travel in inches														
	1½	2	2½	3	3½	4	4½	5	5½	6	6½	7	7½	8	8½
1	144	108	86	72	62	54	48	43	39	36	33	31	29	27	
	173	130	104	87	74	65	58	52	47	43	40	37	35	33	
2	204	153	122	102	87	77	68	61	56	51	47	44	41	38	
3	233	175	140	117	100	88	78	70	64	58	54	50	47	44	
4	280	210	168	140	120	105	93	84	76	70	65	60	56	53	
5	327	245	196	163	140	123	109	98	89	82	75	70	65	61	
6	373	280	224	187	160	140	124	112	102	93	86	80	75	70	
7	451	338	270	225	193	169	150	135	123	113	104	97	90	85	
8	527	395	316	263	226	198	176	158	144	132	122	113	105	99	
9	600	450	360	300	257	225	200	180	164	150	138	129	120	113	
10	727	545	436	363	311	273	242	218	198	182	168	156	145	136	
11	851	638	510	425	365	319	284	255	232	213	196	182	170	160	
12	977	733	586	489	419	367	326	293	267	244	226	209	195	183	
13	1177	883	706	589	505	442	392	353	321	294	272	252	235	221	
14	1373	1030	824	687	589	515	458	412	375	343	317	294	275	258	
15	1573	1180	944	787	674	590	524	472	429	393	363	337	315	295	
16	1893	1420	1136	947	811	710	631	568	516	473	437	406	379	355	
17	2217	1663	1330	1109	950	832	739	665	605	554	512	475	443	416	
18	2540	1905	1524	1270	1089	953	847	762	693	635	586	544	508	476	
19															448
		2025	1620	1350	1157	1013	900	810	736	675	623	579	540	506	476
20		2145	1716	1430	1226	1073	953	858	780	715	660	613	572	536	505
21		2335	1868	1557	1334	1168	1038	934	849	778	718	667	623	584	549
22		2525	2020	1683	1443	1263	1122	1010	918	842	777	721	673	631	594
23		2710	2168	1807	1549	1355	1204	1084	985	903	834	775	723	678	638
24		2910	2328	1940	1663	1455	1293	1164	1058	970	895	831	776	728	685
25		3110	2488	2073	1777	1555	1382	1244	1131	1037	957	889	829	778	732
26		3310	2648	2207	1891	1655	1471	1324	1204	1103	1018	946	883	828	779
27		3630	2904	2420	2074	1815	1613	1452	1320	1210	1117	1037	968	908	854
28		3950	3160	2633	2257	1975	1756	1580	1436	1317	1215	1129	1053	988	929
29		4270	3416	2847	2440	2135	1898	1708	1553	1423	1314	1220	1139	1068	1005
30		4535	3628	3023	2591	2268	2016	1814	1649	1512	1395	1296	1209	1134	1067
31		4795	3836	3197	2740	2398	2131	1918	1744	1598	1475	1370	1279	1199	1128
32		5060	4048	3373	2891	2530	2249	2024	1840	1687	1557	1446	1349	1265	1191
33		5295	4236	3530	3026	2648	2353	2118	1925	1765	1629	1513	1412	1324	1246
34		5525	4420	3683	3157	2763	2456	2210	2009	1842	1700	1579	1473	1381	1300
35			4696	3913	3354	2935	2609	2348	2135	1957	1806	1677	1565	1468	1381
36			4968	4140	3549	3105	2760	2484	2258	2070	1911	1774	1656	1553	1461
37			5240	4367	3743	3275	2911	2620	2382	2183	2015	1871	1747	1638	1541
38			5616	4680	4011	3510	3120	2808	2553	2340	2160	2006	1872	1755	1652
39			5988	4990	4277	3743	3327	2994	2722	2495	2303	2139	1996	1871	1761
40			6360	5300	4543	3975	3533	3180	2891	2650	2446	2271	2120	1988	1871
41			6976	5813	4983	4360	3876	3488	3171	2907	2683	2491	2325	2180	2052
42			7588	6323	5420	4743	4216	3794	3449	3162	2919	2710	2529	2371	2232
43			8200	6833	5857	5125	4556	4100	3727	3417	3154	2929	2733	2563	2412
44			8724	7270	6231	5453	4847	4362	3965	3635	3355	3116	2908	2726	2566
45			9284	7737	6631	5803	5158	4642	4220	3868	3571	3316	3095	2901	2731
46			9760	8133	6971	6100	5422	4880	4436	4067	3754	3486	3253	3050	2871
47			10376	8647	7411	6485	5764	5188	4716	4323	3991	3706	3459	3243	3052
48			10988	9157	7848	6868	6104	5494	4995	4578	4226	3924	3663	3434	3232
49			11600	9667	8286	7250	6444	5800	5273	4833	4462	4143	3867	3625	3412
50				10367	8886	7775	6911	6220	5655	5183	4785	4443	4147	3888	3659
51				11067	9486	8300	7378	6640	6036	5533	5108	4743	4427	4150	3906
52				11847	10154	8885	7898	7108	6462	5923	5468	5077	4739	4443	4181
53				12623	10820	9468	8415	7574	6886	6311	5826	5410	5049	4734	4455
54				13400	11486	10050	8933	8040	7309	6700	6185	5743	5360	5025	4730
55				14713	12611	11035	9809	8828	8026	7356	6791	6306	5885	5518	5193
56				16023	13734	12018	10682	9614	8740	8011	7396	6867	6409	6009	5655
57				17333	14857	13000	11555	10400	9455	8666	8000	7429	6933	6500	6118
58				18423	15791	13818	12282	11054	10049	9211	8503	7896	7369	6809	6503
59				19510	16723	14633	13007	11706	10642	9755	9005	8362	7804	7316	6886
60				20600	17657	15450	13733	12360	11236	10300	9508	8829	8240	7725	7271
61				21890	18763	16418	14593	13134	11940	10945	10103	9382	8756	8209	7726
62				23176	19865	17383	15451	13906	12642	11588	10697	9933	9270	8691	8180
63				24463	20968	18348	16309	14678	13344	12231	11291	10484	9785	9174	8634

Table 13-3
Load Table for Constant Spring Supports
(lb for total travel in in.)

hanger size no.	loads in pounds for total travel in inches														
	9	9½	10	10½	11	11½	12	12½	13	13½	14	14½	15	15½	16
1															
2															
3															
4															
5															
6															
7															
8															
9															
10															
11															
12															
13															
14															
15															
16															
17															
18															
19	423 450	401 426	381 405												
20	477	452	429												
21	519	492	467												
22	561	532	505												
23	602	571	542												
24	647	613	582												
25	691	655	622												
26	736	697	662												
27	807	764	726												
28	878	832	790												
29	949	899	854												
30	1008	955	907												
31	1066	1009	959												
32	1124	1065	1012												
33	1177	1115	1059												
34	1228	1163	1105												
35	1304	1236	1174	1053 1118	1005 1067	962 1021	922 978	885 939	851 903	819 870	790 838				
36	1380	1307	1242	1183	1129	1080	1035	994	955	920	887				
37	1456	1379	1310	1248	1191	1139	1092	1048	1008	970	936				
38	1560	1478	1404	1337	1276	1221	1170	1123	1080	1040	1003				
39	1663	1576	1497	1426	1361	1302	1247	1198	1151	1109	1069				
40	1767	1674	1590	1514	1445	1383	1325	1272	1223	1178	1136				
41	1938	1836	1744	1661	1585	1516	1453	1395	1341	1292	1246				
42	2108	1997	1897	1807	1724	1649	1581	1518	1459	1405	1355				
43	2278	2158	2050	1952	1863	1782	1708	1640	1577	1518	1464				
44	2423	2296	2181	2077	1983	1896	1817	1745	1678	1615	1558				
45	2579	2443	2321	2210	2110	2018	1934	1857	1785	1719	1658				
46	2711	2568	2440	2324	2218	2122	2033	1952	1877	1807	1743				
47	2882	2730	2594	2470	2358	2255	2162	2075	1995	1921	1853				
48	3052	2891	2747	2616	2497	2389	2289	2198	2113	2035	1962				
49	3222	3053	2900	2762	2636	2522	2417	2320	2231	2148	2071				
50	3456	3274	3110	2962	2827	2704	2592	2488	2392	2304	2221	2001 2145	1934 2073	1871 2006	1813 1944
51	3689	3495	3320	3162	3018	2887	2767	2656	2554	2459	2371	2289	2213	2142	2075
52	3949	3741	3554	3384	3231	3090	2962	2843	2734	2632	2538	2451	2369	2293	2221
53	4208	3986	3787	3606	3442	3293	3156	3030	2913	2805	2705	2612	2524	2443	2367
54	4467	4231	4020	3828	3654	3495	3350	3216	3092	2978	2871	2772	2680	2593	2513
55	4904	4646	4414	4203	4012	3838	3678	3531	3395	3269	3152	3044	2942	2847	2759
56	5341	5060	4807	4518	4370	4180	4006	3846	3698	3561	3433	3315	3204	3101	3004
57	5778	5474	5200	4952	4727	4521	4333	4160	4000	3852	3714	3586	3466	3355	3250
58	6141	5818	5527	5263	5024	4806	4606	4422	4251	4094	3947	3811	3684	3565	3454
59	6503	6161	5853	5574	5320	5089	4877	4682	4502	4335	4180	4036	3902	3776	3658
60	6867	6505	6180	5885	5618	5374	5150	4944	4754	4578	4414	4262	4120	3987	3863
61	7297	6912	6567	6254	5969	5710	5472	5254	5051	4864	4690	4529	4378	4236	4104
62	7725	7319	6953	6621	6320	6046	5794	5562	5348	5150	4965	4795	4635	4485	4346
63	8154	7725	7339	6989	6671	6381	6116	5871	5645	5436	5242	5061	4892	4734	4587

Table 13-4
Load Table for Constant Spring Supports
(lb for total travel in in.)

hanger size no.	load in pounds for total travel in inches																
	4	4½	5	5½	6	6½	7	7½	8	8½	9	9½	10	10½	11	11½	12
64	19225	17089	15380	13982	12816	11831	10986	10253	9613	9047	8544	8094	7690	7323	6990	6686	6408
65	20100	17866	16080	14618	13400	12370	11486	10720	10050	9459	8933	8463	8040	7657	7308	6991	6700
66	22068	19615	17654	16049	14711	13580	12610	11769	11034	10385	9808	9291	8827	8406	8024	7675	7356
67	24033	21362	19226	17478	16021	14790	13733	12817	12016	11310	10681	10119	9613	9154	8738	8359	8011
68	26000	23111	20800	18909	17333	16000	14857	13866	13000	12236	11555	10947	10400	9904	9454	9043	8666
69	27635	24564	22108	20098	18423	17007	15792	14738	13818	13005	12282	11635	11054	10527	10048	9611	9211
70	29268	26015	23414	21286	19511	18011	16725	15609	14634	13773	13008	12323	11707	11149	10642	10179	9755
71	30900	27466	24720	22473	20599	19016	17657	16480	15450	14542	13733	13010	12360	11770	11235	10747	10300
72	32835	29186	26268	23880	21889	20207	18763	17512	16418	15452	14593	13825	13134	12508	11939	11420	10945
73	34768	30904	27814	25286	23177	21396	19868	18542	17384	16362	15452	14639	13907	13244	12641	12092	11589
74	36700	32622	29360	26691	24466	22585	20972	19573	18350	17271	16311	15452	14680	13980	13344	12764	12233
75	38800	34489	31040	28218	25866	23878	22172	20693	19400	18259	17244	16336	15520	14780	14108	13495	12933
76	40900	36355	32720	29746	27266	25170	23372	21813	20450	19248	18178	17221	16360	15580	14871	14225	13633
77	43000	38222	34400	31273	28666	26462	24572	22933	21500	20236	19111	18105	17200	16380	15635	14955	14333
78	45335	40297	36268	32971	30222	27899	25906	24178	22668	21335	20149	19088	18134	17269	16484	15768	15111
79	47668	42371	38134	34668	31779	29335	27239	25422	23834	22432	21185	20070	19067	18158	17332	16579	15889
80	50000	44444	40000	36364	33332	30770	28572	26666	25000	23530	22222	21052	20000	19046	18180	17390	16666
81	52500	46666	42000	38182	35000	32309	30000	27999	26250	24707	23333	22105	21000	19998	19089	18260	17500
82	55000	48888	44000	40000	36665	33847	31429	29333	27500	25883	24444	23157	22000	20951	20000	19129	18333
83	57500	51111	46000	41819	38332	35386	32858	30666	28750	27060	25555	24210	23000	21903	20907	20000	19166
84			49200	44728	40998	37847	35144	32799	30750	28942	27333	25894	24600	23427	22361	21390	20500
85			52400	47637	43665	40309	37429	34932	32750	30824	29111	27578	26200	24950	23816	22781	21832
86			55400	50364	46165	42616	39572	36932	34625	32589	30777	29157	27700	26379	25179	24085	23082
87			58400	53091	48665	44924	41715	38932	36500	34354	32444	30736	29200	27807	26543	25389	24332
88			61400	55819	51165	47232	43858	40932	38375	36119	34111	32315	30700	29236	27906	26694	25582
89			66000	60000	54998	50771	47144	43999	41250	38825	36666	34736	33000	31426	29997	28694	27500
90					61331	56617	52572	49065	46000	43295	40888	38736	36800	35045	33451	31998	30665
91					67164	62002	57573	53732	50375	47413	44777	42420	40300	38378	36633	35041	33582
92					73500	67848	63001	58799	55125	51884	49000	46420	44100	41996	40087	38345	36749
93					80830	74617	69287	64665	60625	57060	53888	51051	48500	46187	44087	42171	40415
94					87500	81540	75716	70665	66250	62355	58888	55788	53000	50472	48177	46084	44165
95							78930	73665	69063	65002	61388	58156	55250	52615	50222	48040	46040
96							82145	76665	71875	67649	63888	60525	57500	54757	52268	50000	47915
97							85360	79665	74688	70296	66388	62893	59750	56900	54313	51953	49790
98							87500	82665	77500	72943	68888	65261	62000	59043	56358	53909	51665
99								85998	80625	75884	71666	67893	64500	61423	58631	56083	53748
100								87500	83750	78826	74444	70524	67000	63804	60903	58257	55831
101									86875	81767	77221	73156	69500	66185	63176	60430	57914
102									87500	84708	80000	75787	72000	68566	65448	62604	60000
103										87500	83610	79210	75250	71661	68402	65430	62706
104											87221	82629	78500	74756	71357	68256	65414
105											87500	86050	81750	77851	74311	71082	68122
106												87500	85000	80946	77265	73908	70831
107													87500	84469	80628	77125	73914
108														87500	83992	80342	77000
108															87446	83646	80163
110															87500	86950	83330

Table 13-5
Load Table for Constant Spring Supports
(lb for total travel in in.)

hanger size no.	load in pounds for total travel in inches															
	12½	13	13½	14	14½	15	15½	16	16½	17	17½	18	18½	19	19½	20
64	6152	5915	5696	5492	5303	5126	4961	4806								
65	6432	6184	5955	5742	5544	5359	5187	5025								
66	7062	6790	6538	6304	6087	5884	5694	5517								
67	7690	7394	7120	6966	6629	6408	6201	6008								
68	8320	8000	7703	7428	7172	6933	6709	6500								
69	8843	8503	8188	7895	7623	7369	7131	6909								
70	9366	9005	8671	8361	8073	7804	7552	7317								
71	9888	9507	9155	8828	8523	8239	7973	7725								
72	10507	10103	9728	9380	9057	8755	8473	8209								
73	11126	10697	10301	9932	9590	9270	8971	8692								
74	11744	11292	10873	10484	10123	9786	9470	9175								
75	12416	11938	11496	11084	10703	10346	10012	9700								
76	13088	12584	12118	11684	11282	10906	10554	10225								
77	13760	13230	12740	12284	11861	11466	11096	10750								
78	14507	13949	13432	12951	12505	12088	11698	11334								
79	15254	14666	14123	13618	13149	12710	12300	11917								
80	16000	15384	14814	14284	13792	13332	12902	12500								
81	16800	16153	15555	14998	14482	14000	13547	13125								
82	17600	16922	16295	15712	15171	14665	14192	13750								
83	18400	17692	17036	16427	15861	15332	14837	14375								
84	19680	18922	18221	17569	16964	16398	15869	15375								
85	20960	20153	19406	18712	18068	17465	16902	16375								
86	22160	21307	20517	19783	19102	18465	17869	17313								
87	23360	22461	21628	20855	20136	19465	18837	18250								
88	24560	23614	22739	21926	21171	20465	19805	19188								
89	26400	25384	24443	23569	22757	21998	21288	20625								
90	29440	28307	27258	26283	25377	24531	23740	23000								
91	32240	31000	29850	28782	27791	26864	25998	25188								
92	35280	33922	32665	31496	30411	29397	28449	27563								
93	38800	37306	35924	34639	33446	32330	31287	30313								
94	42400	40768	39257	37853	36549	35330	34190	33125								
95									32119	31175	30285	29442	28647	27894	27179	26500
	44200	42498	40924	39460	38100	36830	35642	34531	33482	32498	31570	30691	29863	29078	28332	27625
96	46000	44230	42590	41067	39652	38330	37093	35938	34845	33822	32856	31941	31080	30262	29486	28750
97	47800	45960	44257	42673	41204	39829	39545	37344	36209	35145	34141	33191	32295	31446	30640	29875
98	49600	47690	45923	44280	42755	41329	40000	38750	37572	36468	35427	34441	33511	32631	31794	31000
99	51600	49613	47775	46066	44479	42996	41609	40313	39087	37939	36855	35830	34862	33946	33076	32250
100	53600	51536	49627	47851	46203	44662	43221	41875	40602	39409	38284	37219	36214	35262	34358	33500
101	55600	53459	51479	49637	47927	46329	44834	43438	42117	40880	39712	38607	37565	36578	35640	34750
102	57600	56382	53330	51422	49651	47995	46447	45000	43632	42350	41141	39996	38916	37894	36922	36000
103	60200	57882	55738	53744	51892	50162	48544	47031	45602	44262	42998	41801	40673	39604	38588	37625
104	62800	60382	58145	56065	54134	52328	50640	49063	47571	46174	44855	43607	42429	41315	40255	39250
105	65400	62882	60552	58386	56375	54495	52737	51094	49541	48085	46712	45412	44186	43025	41921	40875
106	68000	65382	62960	60707	58616	56661	54834	53125	51510	50000	48569	47218	45943	44736	43588	42500
107	70960	68228	65700	63350	61168	59127	57220	55438	53752	52173	50683	49273	47942	46683	45485	44350
108	73920	71074	68441	65992	63719	61594	59607	57750	55994	54350	52797	51328	49942	48630	47383	46200
109	76960	74000	71255	68706	66340	64127	62059	60125	58297	56585	54969	53439	52000	50630	49331	48100
110	80000	76920	74070	71420	68960	66660	64510	62500	60600	58820	57140	55550	54050	52630	51280	50000

Figure 550

VIBRATION CONTROL AND SWAY BRACE

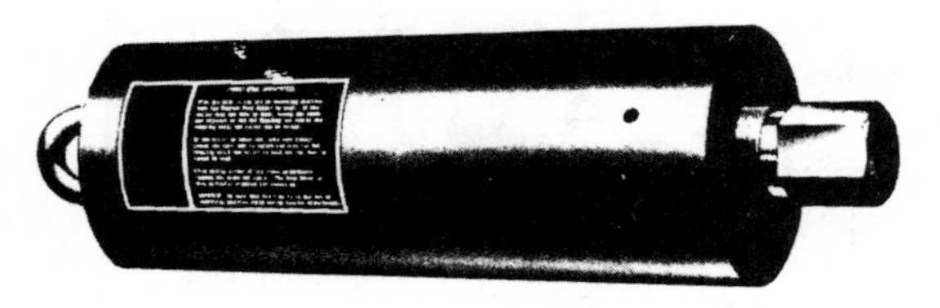

The FIG 550 vibration control and sway brace presents a neat, compact appearance

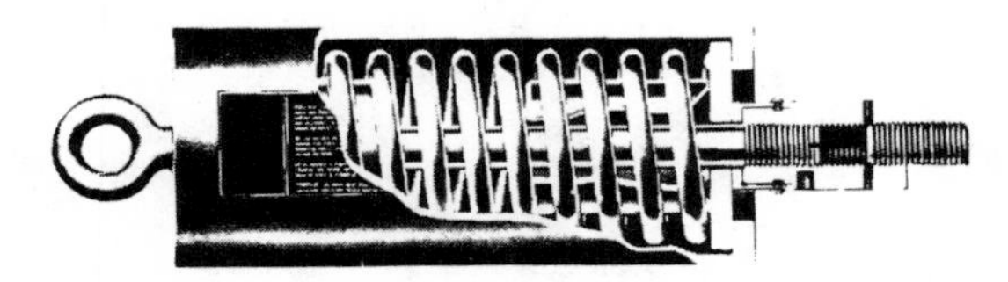

Cut-away section shows simplicity of exclusive single spring design

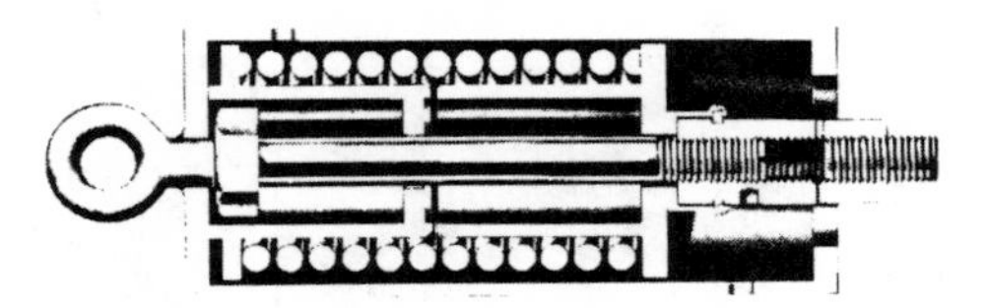

Deflection of single spring occurs when thrust exceeds pre-compression

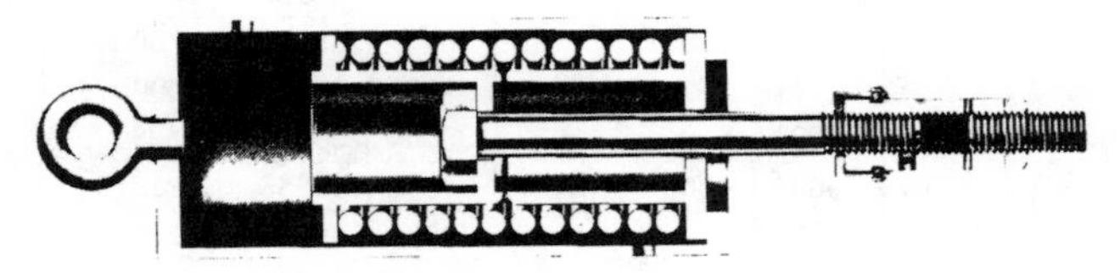

Tension causes deflection of single spring in opposite direction

Size Range: For pipe sizes 2 through 24 inch.

Service: Recommended for controlling vibration; absorbing shock loadings; guiding or restraining the movement of pipe resulting from thermal expansion; bracing a pipe line against sway.

Installation: Shipped ready for installation

Adjustment: The sway brace should be in the neutral position when the system is Hot and operating, at which time the tension test collar should be hand tight. If it is not, the sway brace should be adjusted to the neutral position by use of the load coupling. The screws in the tension test collar need not be loosened, since they serve only to secure it to the load coupling.

Features:

- Vibration is opposed with an instantaneous counter force bringing the pipe back to normal position.
- A single energy-absorbing pre-loaded spring provides two way action.
- One spring saves space and simplifies design.
- Spring has 3-inch travel in either direction.
- Accurate neutral adjustment assured.
- Enclosed spring excludes dirt and gives a clean, compact appearance.

Specifications: Fulfills the requirements of the ASA Code for Pressure Piping as to fabrication details and materials.

Figure 13-8. Vibration control and sway braces. (Courtesy Support Technology and Piping Technology Products, Inc.)

Size Selection: The vibration control and sway brace gives full deflection forces from 200 to 1800 pounds and has initial precompressed spring forces from 50 to 450 pounds to dampen vibrations, oppose pipe sway and absorb shock forces.

The exact amount of energy needed to control piping should be in proportion to the mass, amplitude of movement, and nature of disturbing forces acting on the pipe. When it is possible to calculate the exact restraining force required, the size of the vibration control and sway brace capable of providing this force should be selected.

To simplify the selection of size, engineers have designed the vibration control and sway brace in three sizes that are readily related to nominal pipe size. For pipe sizes 3½-inch and smaller, the small size is recommended; for 4 to 8-inch, the medium size; and for 10-inch and larger, the large size.

Installation: The vibration control and sway brace is shipped ready for installation. The rod coupling rotates with slight resistance and the tension test collar can be rotated by hand while holding the rod coupling stationary.

Important: Rod lengths should be cut and final tension adjustments made for the hot or operating position of the pipe. If, with the pipe in its hot position, the tension test collar can not be turned by hand or if it turns very freely, loosen the jam nut adjacent to the rod coupling and rotate the coupling until the collar can just be turned by hand. Retighten the jam nut.

When correct tension adjustments are completed, the brace exerts no force on the pipe in its operating position. Under shut-down conditions, the brace allows the pipe to assume its cold position. It exerts a nominal cold strain force equal to the pre-load force plus the amount of travel from the hot to cold position, times the spring scale of the particular size of the vibration control and sway brace.

vibration control and sway brace

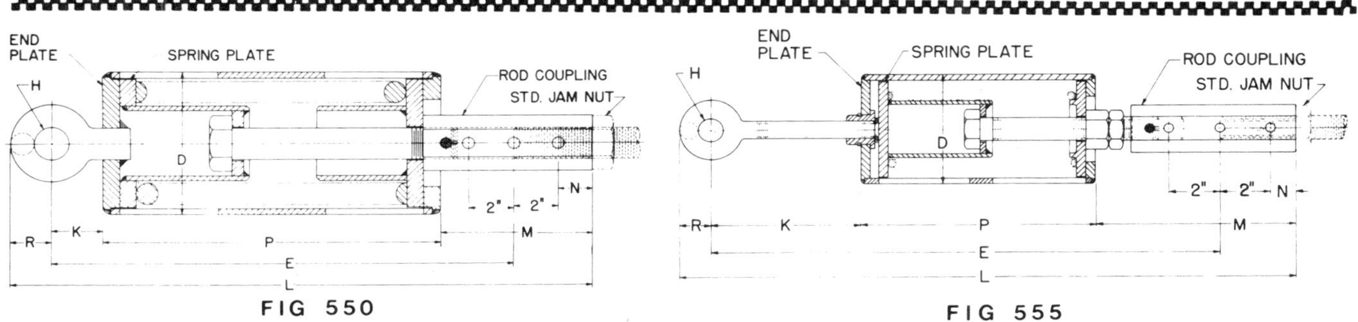

loads • weights • dimensions (inches)

FIG. 550

sway brace size	for pipe size	preload and spring scale, lb	max force, lb	weight (approx) each, lb	rod size,	pipe size,	eye, H diam hole	eye, H thickness	D	rod take-out E	K	L	M	N	P	R
1	2 to 3½	50	200	22	¾	1½	1	¾	4½	13⅝	1⅝	17⅞	6⅛	1	8⅞	1¼
2	4 to 8	150	600	25	1	2	1	¾	4½	14⅜	1⅝	18⅝	6⅛	1	9⅝	1¼
3	10 to 16	450	1800	36	1	2	1	¾	4½	17¾	1⅝	22	6⅛	1	13	1¼
4	18 to 24	900	3600	64	1¼	2	1½	1½	6⅝	17	2¼	22 5/16	6¾	1½	11½	1 13/16
5	▲	1350	5400	79	1½	2½	1½	1½	6⅝	18½	2¼	23 13/16	6¾	1½	13	1 13/16
6	▲	1800	7200	95	1½	2½	1½	1½	6⅝	20½	2¼	25 13/16	6¾	1½	15	1 13/16

FIG. 555

sway brace size	for pipe size	preload and spring scale, lb	max force, lb	weight (approx) each, lb	rod size,	pipe size,	eye, H diam hole	eye, H thickness	D	rod take-out E	K, max	L	M, min	N	P	R
1	2 to 3½	50	200	23	¾	1½	1	¾	4½	20	5 15/16	24¼	7⅞	1	9 3/16	1¼
2	4 to 8	150	600	26	1	2	1	¾	4½	20¾	5 15/16	25	7⅞	1	9 15/16	1¼
3	10 to 16	450	1800	38	1	2	1	¾	4½	24⅛	5 15/16	28⅜	7⅞	1	13 5/16	1¼
4	18 to 24	900	3600	67	1¼	2	1½	1½	6⅝	24 5/16	6 9/16	29⅝	9¼	1½	12	1 13/16
5	▲	1350	5400	82	1½	2½	1½	1½	6⅝	25 13/16	6 9/16	31⅛	9¼	1½	13½	1 13/16
6	▲	1800	7200	98	1½	2½	1½	1½	6⅝	27 13/16	6 9/16	33⅛	9¼	1½	15½	1 13/16

▲ As specified by customer.

Figure 13-8. Continued.

FIG 550A

recommended when W dimension is 2 ft 0 in. or less

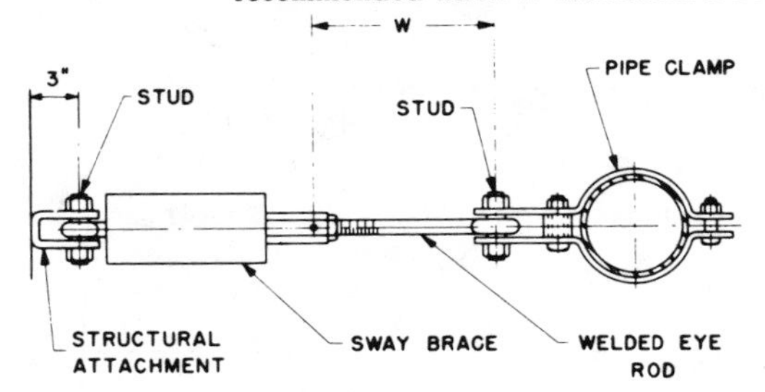

FIG 555A

recommended when W dimension is 2 ft 0 in. or less.

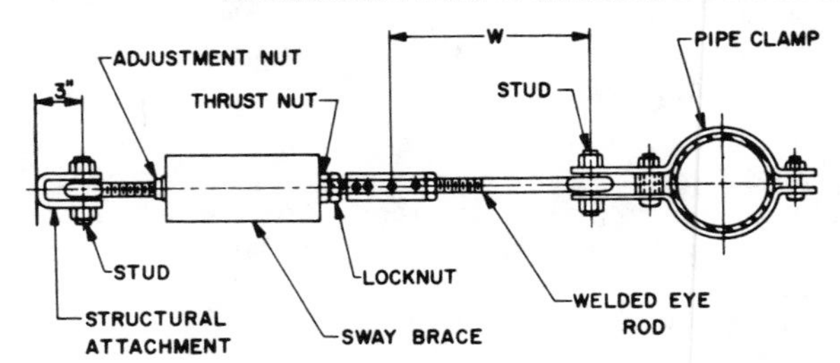

FIG 550B

recommended when W dimenson is 2 ft 1 in. or more

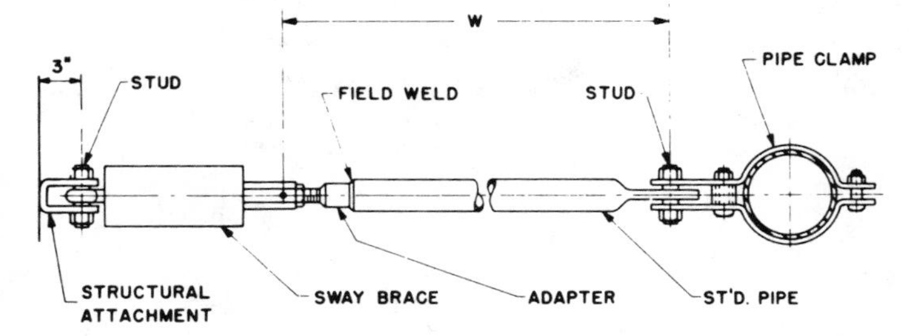

FIG 555B

recommended when W dimension is 2 ft 1 in. or more

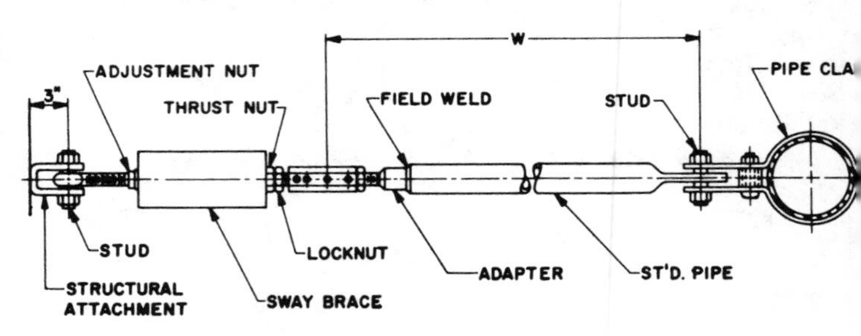

nominal pipe size	sway brace size	distance center of pipe to outside stud of pipe clamp
2	1	5⅛
2½		5⅜
3		5 15/16
3½		6 3/16
4	2	6½
5		7
6		8 9/16
8		9 9/16
10	3	10⅝
12		11⅝
14		12 11/16
16		13 11/16
18	4	14 11/16
20		15⅞
24		17⅞

Dimensions for assemblies for larger pipe sizes available on application.

♦ See paragraph "How to size assemblies" above.

Figure 13-8. Continued.

ing system. The thickness of the polyurethane support should match that of the line pipe.

- Support load.
- Environmental conditions—The exposed cradle may require special coatings or galvanizing.

From these design conditions, a suitable foam density is selected for the supports. Tables 13-6 through 13-11 include some typical properties of molded rigid polyurethane foam used to fabricate supports.

Examining these tables, it is apparent that as the foam density at ambient temperature is increased, both the thermal conductivity factor and the compressive strength also increase. At cryogenic temperatures, however, higher density rigid polyurethane foam has approximately the same thermal conductivity factor as lower density foam. This results from the fluorocarbon within the foam cells becoming a liquid at the cryogenic temperature, thus creating a partial vacuum. Thus the normal support design procedure involves first determining the required K factor to insulate the piping based upon the thickness of the matching pipe insulation. Secondly, the foam density needed to produce the required K factor is selected. Lastly, the length of the support needed to support the pipe is determined using the selected density.

Molded rigid polyurethane foam supports may also be used to support other types of piping systems where the medium being transferred in the pipe is to be maintained at a high temperature and protected from a cold environment. This type of application is typical of a pipeline pumping oil at a design temperature of 180°F through a cold environment at approximately −50°F. The insulating properties of the polyurethane foam are necessary to keep oil in a low viscous state for pumping over long distances. The supports for this type of application are designed in the same manner as those for cryogenic applications.

Insulated Anchors

For special designs where it is necessary to anchor the piping system, it is also necessary to avoid the metal-to-metal contact for the conditions already stated. Anchors are fabricated for this application by foaming between an actual piece of the line pipe and an outer jacket. See Figure 13-10.

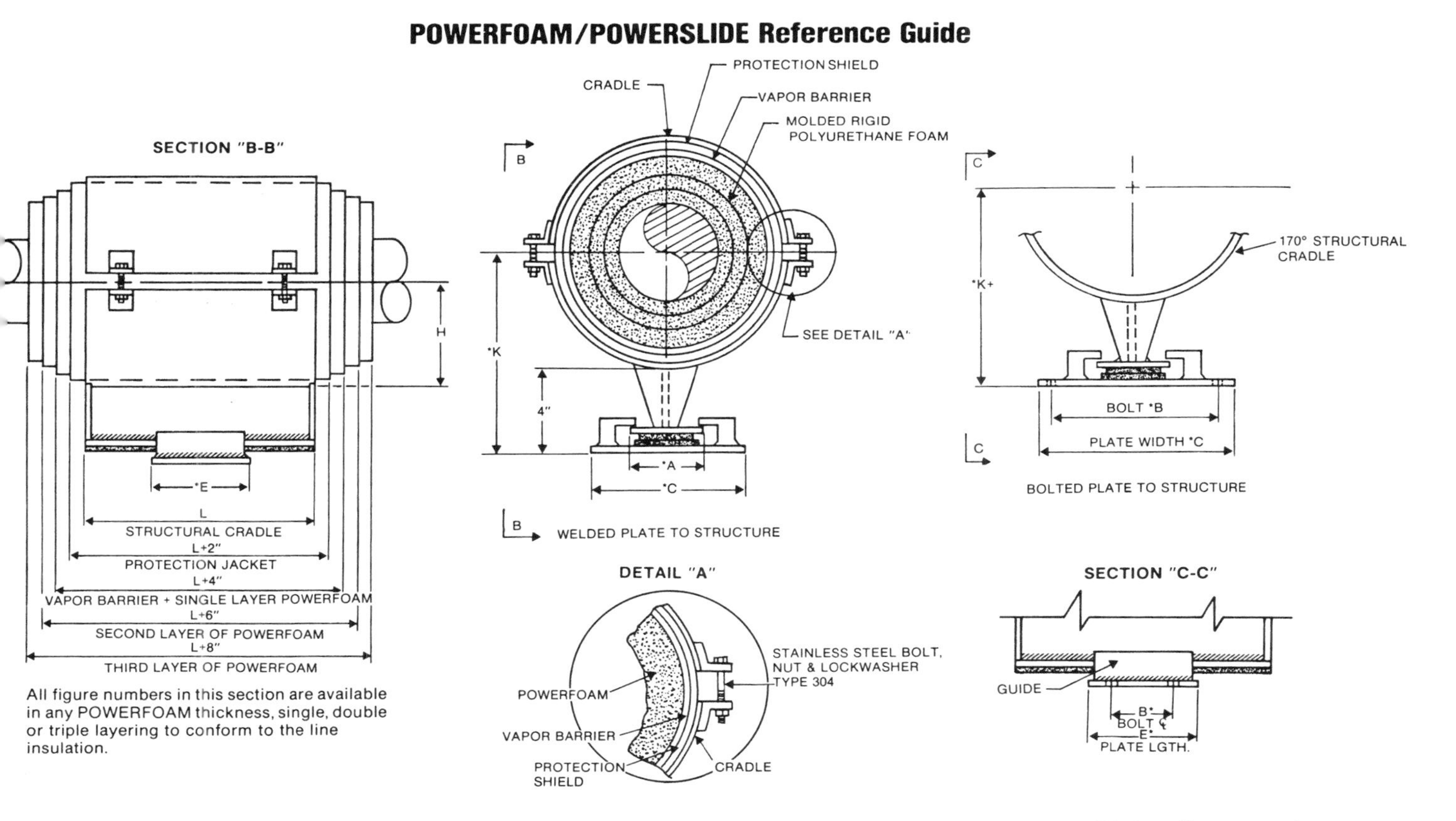

Figure 13-9. POWERFOAM/POWERSLIDE™ reference guides. (Courtesy of Power Piping Company.)

POWERFOAM Insulated Pipe Anchor

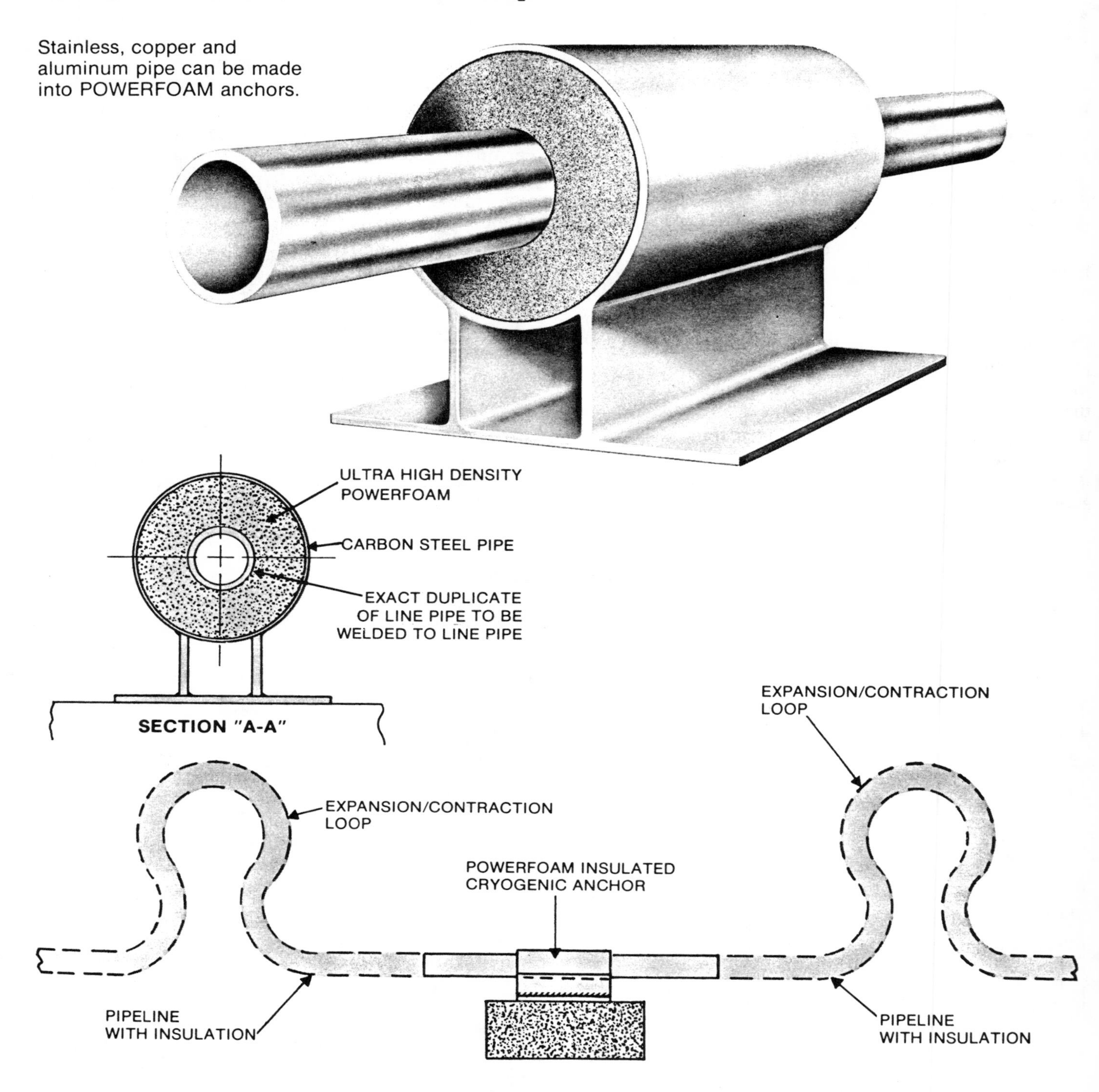

Figure 13-10. POWERFOAM™ insulated pipe anchor. (Courtesy of Power Piping Company.)

Table 13-6
POWERFOAM™ Thermal Properties

Powerfoam Densities		Temperature in Centigrade °C			Temperature in Fahrenheit °F			Power Input Amount of Energy Power Loss To Maintain Delta "T"/2 ft. l.		Apparent Thermal Conductivity Aged Powerfoam	
lb./cu.ft.	Kg./cu. m.	Hot Face	Cold Face	Mean	Hot Face	Cold Face	Mean	Watts	Btu/Hr.	Watts/ Meter °Kelvin	"K" Factor Btu. In. Hr. Ft.2 °F
10	160.0	+43.5	-193.7	-75.1	+110.3	-316.7	-103.2	26.0	88.7	0.0213	0.147
10	160.0	+42.9	-162.9	-60.0	+109.2	-261.2	-76.0	23.2	79.2	0.0219	0.152
14	224.0	+41.6	-193.4	-75.9	+106.9	-316.1	-104.6	28.9	98.6	0.0241	0.167
14	224.0	+42.8	-159.6	-58.4	+109.1	-255.3	-73.1	25.2	86.0	0.0244	0.169
20	320.0	+44.3	-193.4	-74.6	+111.7	-316.1	-102.2	35.7	121.7	0.0297	0.206
20	320.0	+38.7	-157.6	-59.4	+101.7	-251.7	-75.0	31.8	108.6	0.0321	0.223

Courtesy of Power Piping Company.

Table 13-7
POWERFOAM™ Physical Properties

Powerfoam Densities		Pipe Temp.		Test Pieces Foam Length		Load At Yield		Load At 1% Deflection		Compressive Strength At Yield		Compressive Strength At 1% Deflection		Deformation At Yield in % Of Thickness	Compressive Modulus		Engineering Data Strength Compressive At Yield With A Safety Factor Of 5:1	
lb./cu. ft.	Kg./cu. m.	°F	°C	in.	mm.	lbs.	Kg.	PSI	Kg./cm. 2	PSI	Kg./cm. 2	PSI	Kg./cm. 2		PSI	Kg./cm. 2	PSI	Kg./cm. 2
10	160.0	-256	-160	6.0	152	5900	2676	2625	1191	534	38	238	17	2.8	19500	1371	106.8	7.51
10	160.0	-318	-194.5	6.0	152	4500	2041	2550	1157	408	29	231	16	1.9	22100	1483	81.6	5.74
14	224.0	-256	-160	6.0	152	9200	4173	3675	1667	833	59	333	23	3.1	27200	1912	166.6	11.71
14	224.0	-318	-194.5	6.0	152	9200	4173	2800	1270	833	59	254	18	3.2	27000	1898	166.6	11.71
20	320.0	-256	-160	6.0	152	14600	6622	4200	1905	1322	93	380	27	3.2	40000	2812	264.4	18.59
20	320.0	-318	-194.5	6.0	152	18000	8165	3900	1315	1630	115	354	25	4.8	34900	2453	326.0	22.92

Courtesy of Power Piping Company.

POWERFOAM Ambient Temperature Compressive Strength at Yield

10#/Ft.^{3}, 129 PSI • 14#/Ft.^{3}, 223 PSI • 20#/Ft.^{3}, 530 PSI

Table 13-8
POWERFOAM™ Temperature Range

Powerfoam Densities		Maximum (Hot) Service Temperature		Minimum (Cryogenic) Service Temperature	
lb./cu.	Kg./cu. m.	°F	°C	°F	°C
10	160.0	+275	+135	-425	-245
14	224.0	+275	+135	-425	-254
20	320.0	+275	+135	-425	-254

Courtesy of Power Piping Company.

Data is all based on tests performed on POWERFOAM made with our formula and molding techniques.

Independent testing laboratory corroborating test data available upon request.

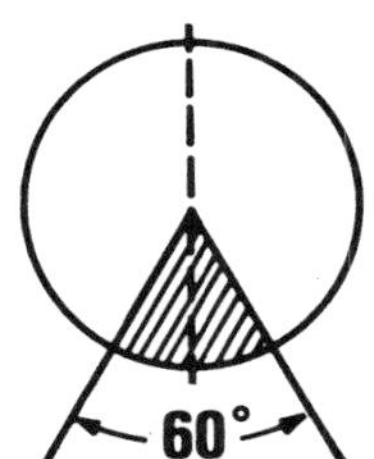

SUPPORT CONTACT
60° — 30° each side of vertical center line.

SUSTAINABLE LOAD FORMULA:

$$\left(\frac{\pi \cdot D \cdot L}{6}\right)(C) = \text{Sustainable Load}$$

C = Compressive strength with safety factor
D = Outer diameter in inches
L = Length in inches

Table 13-9
Engineering Data

SCHEDULE 40 PIPE	IPS	WEIGHT OF PIPE, WATER & *INSULATION (PER FOOT)		SUPPORT SPACING (MAXIMUM SPAN)		TOTAL WEIGHT OF SPAN	
	Inches	lb.	Kg.	ft.	meters	lb.	Kg.
	1/2	1.75	.7875	7	2.1336	12.25	5.5125
	3/4	2.2	.99	7	2.1336	15.4	6.93
	1	2.95	1.3275	7	2.1336	20.65	9.2925
	1-1/4	3.81	1.7145	7	2.1336	26.67	12.0015
	1-1/2	4.56	2.052	9	2.7432	41.04	18.468
	2	6.16	2.772	10	3.048	61.6	27.72
	2-1/2	9.05	4.0725	11	3.3528	99.55	44.7975
	3	12.08	5.436	12	3.6576	144.96	65.232
	3-1/2	14.77	6.6465	13	3.9624	192.01	86.4045
	4	17.77	7.9965	14	4.2672	248.78	111.951
	** 4-1/2	—	—	14	4.2672	—	—
	5	24.98	11.241	16	4.8768	399.68	179.856
	6	33.39	15.0255	17	5.1816	567.63	255.434
	** 7	47.19	21.2355	17	5.1816	802.23	361.004
STAND. .375 WALL PIPE	8	52.48	23.616	19	5.7912	997.12	448.704
	** 9	66.31	29.8395	19	5.7912	1259.89	566.95
	10	77.3	34.785	20	6.096	1546	695.7
	** 11	89.59	40.3155	20	6.096	1791.8	806.31
	12	101.69	45.7605	23	7.0104	2338.87	1052.49
	14	117.64	52.938	25	7.62	2941	1323.45
	16	145.49	65.4705	27	8.2296	3928.23	1767.7
	18	175.92	79.164	28	8.5344	4925.76	2216.59
	20	209.11	94.0995	30	9.144	6273.3	2822.99
	** 22	245.11	110.3	30	9.144	7353.3	3308.99
	24	283.7	127.665	32	9.7536	9078.4	4085.28
	** 26	325.09	146.291	32	9.7536	10402.9	4681.3
	** 28	369.18	166.131	32	9.7536	11813.8	5316.19
	30	416.18	187.281	35	10.668	14566.3	6554.83
	36	572.95	257.828	37	11.2776	21199.2	9539.61
	** 40	690.93	310.919	38	11.5824	26255.3	11814.9
	42	754.07	339.332	39	11.8872	29408.7	13233.9
	48	999.82	449.919	40	12.192	39992.8	17996.8
	54	1190.04	535.518	42	12.8016	49981.7	22491.8
	60	1444.75	650.138	44	13.4112	63569	28606.1
	72	2027.61	912.424	46	14.0208	93270.1	41971.5

*3#/ft.3 — 3" thk.
**Are not regular pipe sizes

***SUSTAINABLE LOADS OF INSULATED PIPE SUPPORTS

2 lb./cu. ft. — 32 Kg./cu. m.

COMPRESSIVE STRENGTH = 5.8 PSI (.40774 Kg./Cm.2) WITH 5:1 SAFETY FACTOR (NON-MOLDED FOAM BY OTHERS AMBIENT TEMP.)

IPS PIPE DIA.	6 in. Long		12 in. Long		18 in. Long		24 in. Long	
Inches	lb.	Kg.	lb.	Kg.	lb.	Kg.	lb.	Kg.
1/2	15.3058	6.93966	30.6116	13.8793	45.9174	20.819	61.2233	27.7586
3/4	19.1323	8.67457	38.2646	17.3491	57.3968	26.0237	76.5291	34.6983
1	23.9609	10.8639	47.9218	21.7277	71.8827	32.5916	95.8436	43.4555
1-1/4	30.2472	13.7141	60.4944	27.4282	90.7416	41.1423	120.989	54.8563
1-1/2	—	—	69.2406	31.3937	103.861	47.0905	138.481	62.7874
2	—	—	86.5508	39.2421	129.826	58.8632	173.102	78.4842
2-1/2	—	—	104.772	47.5036	157.158	71.2554	209.544	95.0072
3	—	—	—	—	191.323	86.7457	255.097	115.661
3-1/2	—	—	—	—	218.655	99.138	291.54	132.184
4	—	—	—	—	—	—	327.982	148.707
4-1/2	—	—	—	—	—	—	—	—
5	—	—	—	—	—	—	405.459	183.835
6	—	—	—	—	—	—	—	—
7	—	—	—	—	—	—	—	—
8	—	—	—	—	—	—	—	—
9	—	—	—	—	—	—	—	—
10	—	—	—	—	—	—	—	—
11	—	—	—	—	—	—	—	—
12	—	—	—	—	—	—	—	—
14	—	—	—	—	—	—	—	—
16	—	—	—	—	—	—	—	—
18	—	—	—	—	—	—	—	—
20	—	—	—	—	—	—	—	—
22	—	—	—	—	—	—	—	—
24	—	—	—	—	—	—	—	—
26	—	—	—	—	—	—	—	—
28	—	—	—	—	—	—	—	—
30	—	—	—	—	—	—	—	—
36	—	—	—	—	—	—	—	—
40	—	—	—	—	—	—	—	—
42	—	—	—	—	—	—	—	—
48	—	—	—	—	—	—	—	—
54	—	—	—	—	—	—	—	—
60	—	—	—	—	—	—	—	—
72	—	—	—	—	—	—	—	—

***Based on foam compression (with a 5:1 safety factor), length of supports and pipe sizes.

Courtesy of Power Piping Company.

Table 13-10
Engineering Data

***SUSTAINABLE LOADS OF INSULATED PIPE SUPPORTS

4 lb./cu. ft. — 64 Kg./cu. m.

COMPRESSIVE STRENGTH = 13 PSI (.9139 Kg./Cm2) WITH 5:1 SAFETY FACTOR (NON-MOLDED FOAM BY OTHERS AMBIENT TEMP.)

IPS PIPE DIA. Inches	6 in. Long		12 in. Long		18 in. Long		24 in. Long	
	lb.	Kg.	lb.	Kg.	lb.	Kg.	lb.	Kg.
1/2	34.3062	15.5544	68.6123	31.1088	102.919	46.6632	137.225	62.2176
3/4	42.8827	19.443	85.7654	38.886	128.648	58.329	171.531	77.772
1	53.7055	24.3501	107.411	48.7001	161.116	73.0502	214.822	97.4002
1-1/4	67.7955	30.7385	135.591	61.4769	203.387	92.2154	271.182	122.954
1-1/2	77.5972	35.1826	155.195	70.3652	232.792	105.548	310.389	140.73
2	96.9966	43.9782	193.993	87.9565	290.99	131.935	387.986	175.913
2-1/2	117.417	53.2368	234.834	106.474	352.251	159.71	469.668	212.947
3	—	—	285.885	129.62	428.827	194.43	571.769	259.24
3-1/2	—	—	326.725	148.137	490.088	222.206	653.451	296.275
4	—	—	367.566	166.654	551.349	249.982	735.132	333.309
4-1/2	—	—	—	—	—	—	—	—
5	—	—	454.393	206.022	681.59	309.033	908.786	412.044
6	—	—	—	—	811.708	368.028	1082.28	490.705
7	—	—	—	—	934.23	423.58	1245.64	564.773
8	—	—	—	—	1056.75	479.131	1409.0	638.842
9	—	—	—	—	—	—	1572.37	712.91
10	—	—	—	—	—	—	1756.15	796.237
11	—	—	—	—	—	—	1919.51	870.306
12	—	—	—	—	—	—	—	—
14	—	—	—	—	—	—	—	—
16	—	—	—	—	—	—	—	—
18	—	—	—	—	—	—	—	—
20	—	—	—	—	—	—	—	—
22	—	—	—	—	—	—	—	—
24	—	—	—	—	—	—	—	—
26	—	—	—	—	—	—	—	—
28	—	—	—	—	—	—	—	—
30	—	—	—	—	—	—	—	—
36	—	—	—	—	—	—	—	—
40	—	—	—	—	—	—	—	—
42	—	—	—	—	—	—	—	—
48	—	—	—	—	—	—	—	—
54	—	—	—	—	—	—	—	—
60	—	—	—	—	—	—	—	—
72	—	—	—	—	—	—	—	—

***Based on foam compression (with a 5:1 safety factor), length of supports and pipe sizes.

6 lb./cu. ft. — 96 Kg./cu. m.

COMPRESSIVE STRENGTH = 16 PSI (1.1248 Kg./Cm.2) WITH 5:1 SAFETY FACTOR (NON-MOLDED FOAM BY OTHERS AMBIENT TEMP.)

IPS PIPE DIA. Inches	6 in. Long		12 in. Long		18 in. Long		24 in. Long	
	lb.	Kg.	lb.	Kg.	lb.	Kg.	lb.	Kg.
1/2	42.223	19.1439	84.4459	38.2878	126.669	57.4317	168.892	76.5755
3/4	52.7787	23.9299	105.557	47.8597	158.336	71.7896	211.115	95.7194
1	66.099	29.9693	132.198	59.9386	198.297	89.9079	264.396	119.877
1-1/4	83.4406	37.832	166.881	75.6639	250.322	113.496	333.763	151.328
1-1/2	95.5043	43.3016	191.009	86.6033	286.513	129.905	382.017	173.207
2	119.38	54.1271	238.761	108.254	358.141	162.381	477.522	216.508
2-1/2	144.513	65.5222	289.026	131.045	433.539	196.567	578.053	262.089
3	175.929	79.7662	351.858	159.532	527.787	239.299	703.716	319.065
3-1/2	201.062	91.1614	402.124	182.323	603.185	273.484	804.247	364.646
4	—	—	452.389	205.113	678.583	307.67	904.778	410.226
4-1/2	—	—	—	—	—	—	—	—
5	—	—	559.253	253.565	838.88	380.348	1118.51	507.131
6	—	—	666.017	301.972	999.025	452.958	1332.03	603.944
7	—	—	—	—	1149.82	521.329	1533.1	695.106
8	—	—	—	—	1300.62	589.7	1734.16	786.267
9	—	—	—	—	1451.42	658.071	1935.22	877.428
10	—	—	—	—	1621.06	734.989	2161.41	979.985
11	—	—	—	—	—	—	2362.48	1071.15
12	—	—	—	—	—	—	2563.54	1162.31
14	—	—	—	—	—	—	—	—
16	—	—	—	—	—	—	—	—
18	—	—	—	—	—	—	—	—
20	—	—	—	—	—	—	—	—
22	—	—	—	—	—	—	—	—
24	—	—	—	—	—	—	—	—
26	—	—	—	—	—	—	—	—
28	—	—	—	—	—	—	—	—
30	—	—	—	—	—	—	—	—
36	—	—	—	—	—	—	—	—
40	—	—	—	—	—	—	—	—
42	—	—	—	—	—	—	—	—
48	—	—	—	—	—	—	—	—
54	—	—	—	—	—	—	—	—
60	—	—	—	—	—	—	—	—
72	—	—	—	—	—	—	—	—

***Based on foam compression (with a 5:1 safety factor), length of supports and pipe sizes.

Courtesy of Power Piping Company.

Table 13-11
Engineering Data

***SUSTAINABLE LOADS OF INSULATED PIPE SUPPORTS

8 lb./cu. ft. — 128 Kg./cu. m.
COMPRESSIVE STRENGTH = 22 PSI (1.5466 Kg./Cm.2) WITH 5:1 SAFETY FACTOR (NON-MOLDED FOAM BY OTHERS AMBIENT TEMP.)

IPS PIPE DIA. Inches	6 In. Long		12 In. Long		18 In. Long		24 In. Long	
	lb.	Kg.	lb.	Kg.	lb.	Kg.	lb.	Kg.
1/2	58.0566	26.3228	116.113	52.6457	174.17	78.9685	232.226	105.291
3/4	72.5707	32.9036	145.141	65.8071	217.712	98.7107	290.283	131.614
1	90.8861	41.2078	181.772	82.4156	272.659	123.623	363.545	164.831
1-1/4	114.731	52.019	229.462	104.038	344.193	156.057	458.923	208.076
1-1/2	131.318	59.5398	262.637	119.08	393.955	178.619	525.274	238.159
2	164.148	74.4247	328.296	148.849	492.444	223.274	656.592	297.699
2-1/2	198.706	90.0931	397.411	180.186	596.117	270.279	794.822	360.372
3	241.902	109.679	483.805	219.357	725.707	329.036	967.609	438.714
3-1/2	276.46	125.347	552.92	250.694	829.38	376.041	1105.84	501.388
4	311.017	141.015	622.035	282.03	933.052	423.046	1244.07	564.061
4-1/2	—	—	—	—	—	—	—	—
5	—	—	768.973	348.652	1153.46	522.978	1537.95	697.305
6	—	—	915.773	415.212	1373.66	622.817	1831.55	830.423
7	—	—	1054.0	477.885	1581.01	716.828	2108.01	955.77
8	—	—	1192.23	540.558	1788.35	810.838	2384.47	1081.12
9	—	—	1330.46	603.232	1995.7	904.848	2660.93	1206.46
10	—	—	—	—	2228.96	1010.61	2971.94	1347.48
11	—	—	—	—	2436.3	1104.62	3248.4	1472.83
12	—	—	—	—	2643.65	1198.63	3524.86	1598.17
14	—	—	—	—	—	—	3870.44	1754.86
16	—	—	—	—	—	—	4423.36	2005.55
18	—	—	—	—	—	—	4976.28	2256.24
20	—	—	—	—	—	—	—	—
22	—	—	—	—	—	—	—	—
24	—	—	—	—	—	—	—	—
26	—	—	—	—	—	—	—	—
28	—	—	—	—	—	—	—	—
30	—	—	—	—	—	—	—	—
36	—	—	—	—	—	—	—	—
40	—	—	—	—	—	—	—	—
42	—	—	—	—	—	—	—	—
48	—	—	—	—	—	—	—	—
54	—	—	—	—	—	—	—	—
60	—	—	—	—	—	—	—	—
72	—	—	—	—	—	—	—	—

***Based on foam compression (with a 5:1 safety factor), length of supports and pipe sizes.

10 lb./cu. ft. — 160 Kg./cu. m.
****COMPRESSIVE STRENGTH = 94.2 PSI (6.62226 Kg./Cm.2) WITH 5:1 SAFETY FACTOR (CRYOGENIC AVERAGE TEMP.)**

IPS PIPE DIA. Inches	6 In. Long		12 In. Long		18 In. Long		24 In. Long	
	lb.	Kg.	lb.	Kg.	lb.	Kg.	lb.	Kg.
1/2	248.588	112.71	497.175	225.419	745.763	338.129	994.35	450.838
3/4	310.735	140.887	621.469	281.774	932.204	422.661	1242.94	563.548
1	389.158	176.444	778.316	352.888	1167.47	529.333	1556.63	705.777
1-1/4	491.257	222.736	982.513	445.471	1473.77	668.207	1965.03	890.943
1-1/2	562.282	254.938	1124.56	509.877	1686.85	764.815	2249.13	1019.75
2	702.852	318.673	1405.7	637.346	2108.56	956.019	2811.41	1274.69
2-1/2	850.821	385.762	1701.64	771.524	2552.46	1157.29	3403.28	1543.05
3	1035.78	469.623	2071.56	939.247	3107.35	1408.87	4143.13	1878.49
3-1/2	1183.75	536.713	2367.5	1073.43	3551.25	1610.14	4735.0	2146.85
4	1331.72	603.802	2663.44	1207.6	3995.16	1811.41	5326.88	2415.21
4-1/2	—	—	—	—	—	—	—	—
5	1646.3	746.433	3292.6	1492.87	4938.9	2239.3	6585.21	2985.73
6	1960.59	888.93	3921.18	1777.86	5881.76	2666.79	7842.35	3555.72
7	2256.53	1023.11	4513.05	2046.22	6769.58	3069.33	9026.1	4092.43
8	2552.46	1157.29	5104.93	2314.57	7657.39	3471.86	10209.9	4629.15
9	2848.4	1291.47	5696.8	2582.93	8545.2	3874.39	11393.6	5165.86
10	3181.33	1442.42	6362.66	2884.83	9543.99	4327.24	12725.3	5769.66
11	3477.27	1576.59	6954.54	3153.19	10431.8	4729.78	13909.1	6306.37
12	3773.21	1710.77	7546.41	3421.54	11319.6	5132.31	15092.8	6843.08
14	4143.13	1878.49	8286.25	3756.99	12429.4	5635.48	16572.5	7513.97
16	4735.0	2146.85	9470.01	4293.7	14205	6440.55	18940.0	8587.4
18	5326.88	2415.21	10653.8	4830.41	15980.6	7245.62	21307.5	9660.83
20	—	—	11837.5	5367.13	17756.3	8050.69	23675.0	10734.3
22	—	—	13021.3	5903.84	19531.9	8855.75	26042.5	11807.7
24	—	—	14205.0	6440.55	21307.5	9660.83	28410.0	12881.1
26	—	—	15388.8	6977.26	23083.1	10465.9	30777.5	13954.5
28	—	—	16572.5	7513.97	24858.8	11271.0	33145.0	15028.0
30	—	—	17756.3	8050.69	26634.4	12076.0	35512.5	16101.4
36	—	—	21307.5	9660.83	31961.3	14491.2	42615.0	19321.7
40	—	—	—	—	35512.5	16101.4	47350.0	21468.5
42	—	—	—	—	37288.2	16906.4	49717.5	22541.9
48	—	—	—	—	42615.0	19321.7	56820.0	25762.2
54	—	—	—	—	—	—	63922.5	28982.5
60	—	—	—	—	—	—	71025.0	32202.8
72	—	—	—	—	—	—	—	—

***Based on foam densities (with a 5:1 safety factor), length of supports and pipe sizes.

****Compressive strength of POWERFOAM only.

Courtesy of Power Piping Company.

14

Fundamentals of Expansion Joints

Thermal movements in pipelines and ducting result from variations in temperature of the flowing medium or from variations in ambient temperature where piping is exposed to weather. If not compensated for in system design, these movements may cause high stresses, possibly resulting in failure of the piping or connected equipment.

Compensation for thermal movement in a piping system can be achieved by three basic methods:

1. Designing a flexible piping system that utilizes changes of direction to absorb movement.
2. Using pipe loops or bends to absorb the movement.
3. Using expansion devices, such as expansion joints, swivel joints, ball joints, and flexible hose.

There are two general categories of expansion joints—the slip type and packless (or bellows) type. The packless, corrugated metal expansion joint is most frequently used in modern piping applications. It does not require maintenance, and its inherent flexibility to absorb thermal movements in several planes permits greater freedom in piping design. The slip joint, a pair of telescoping sleeves made pressure tight by a packing gland, can absorb a greater amount of axial movement than a comparable bellows-type joint. However, it requires periodic maintenance and is restricted to axial movement only.

Types of Joint Movements

Expansion joints installed in piping systems are subject to three types of movement—axial movement, angular rotation, and lateral deflection. These movements can occur individually or in combinations. The four examples in Figure 14-1 show how single and universal expansion joints absorb these movements.

Nomenclature and Symbols

Standard nomenclature used in discussing expansion joints and the symbols used in applications drawings are presented in Figure 14-2.

Types of Expansion Joints

The type of expansion joint used depends on the type of movement to which it will be subjected.

Single Expansion Joint

This is the simplest type of expansion joint. As its name implies, it is constructed with one bellows and is used mostly to absorb axial movements. A single joint can also be used to absorb angular and lateral movements, as well as a combination of these three basic movements.

Figure 14-3 typifies good practice in the use of a single expansion joint to absorb axial movement. Note that the expansion joint is placed between two main anchors (MA) and that it is located near one of the anchors. (Notice also that the first alignment guide (Gl) is placed close to the joint. The second guide (G2) is close to the first, and intermediate alignment guides (G) are provided along the balance of the line.

Double Expansion Joint

This consists of two single joints joined by a common connector that is anchored to a rigid part of the structure by means of an anchor support base. Double expansion

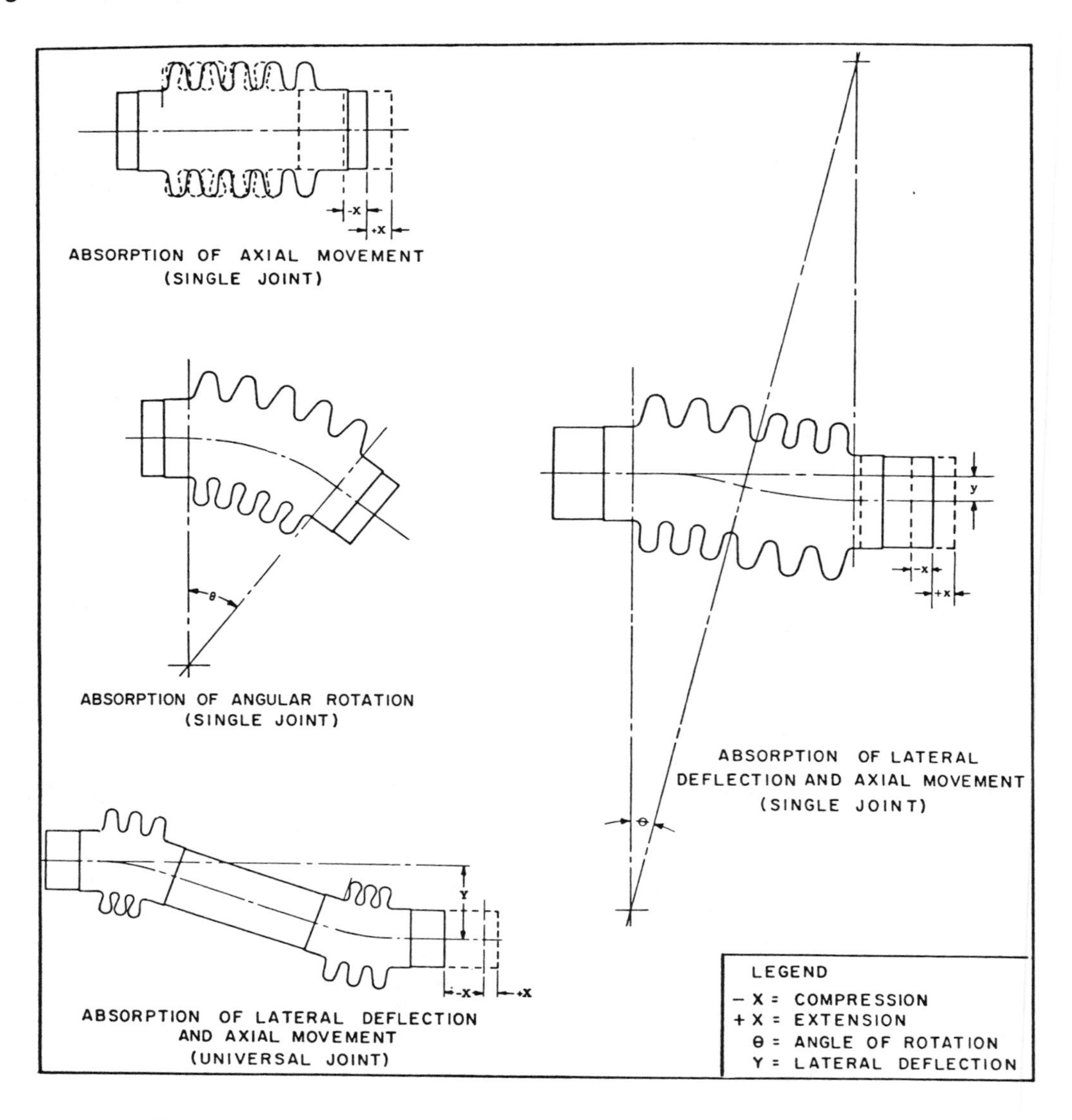

Figure 14-1. Expansion joint movements. (Courtesy of Badger Expansion Joint Company.)

joints are supplied with or without an anchor support base depending on the customer's preference. See Figure 14-4.

A double joint is used when the axial movement to be absorbed is too large to be handled by a single joint. The intermediate anchor on the center nipple divides this movement so that each bellows of the double joint is usually located in the center of a pipe run; so both ends are subjected to the same movements and have the same number of corrugations.

Universal Expansion Joint

This consists of two bellows joined by a common connector which is not anchored to the structure. This permits the universal expansion joint to absorb any combination of three basic movements—axial, lateral, and angular—where these movements are too great to be handled by a single joint.

Universal joints usually have tie rods with stops that distribute the movement between the bellows and stabilize the common connector. The joints find increasing use in steam and hot-water distribution systems because there are impressive cost savings for the large amounts of movement they can absorb with a minimum of guiding and anchoring.

Figure 14-5 illustrates a universal expansion joint used to absorb lateral deflection in a single plan Z bend. Both anchors are intermediate anchors because the pressure loading is absorbed by the tie rods. Only directional guid-

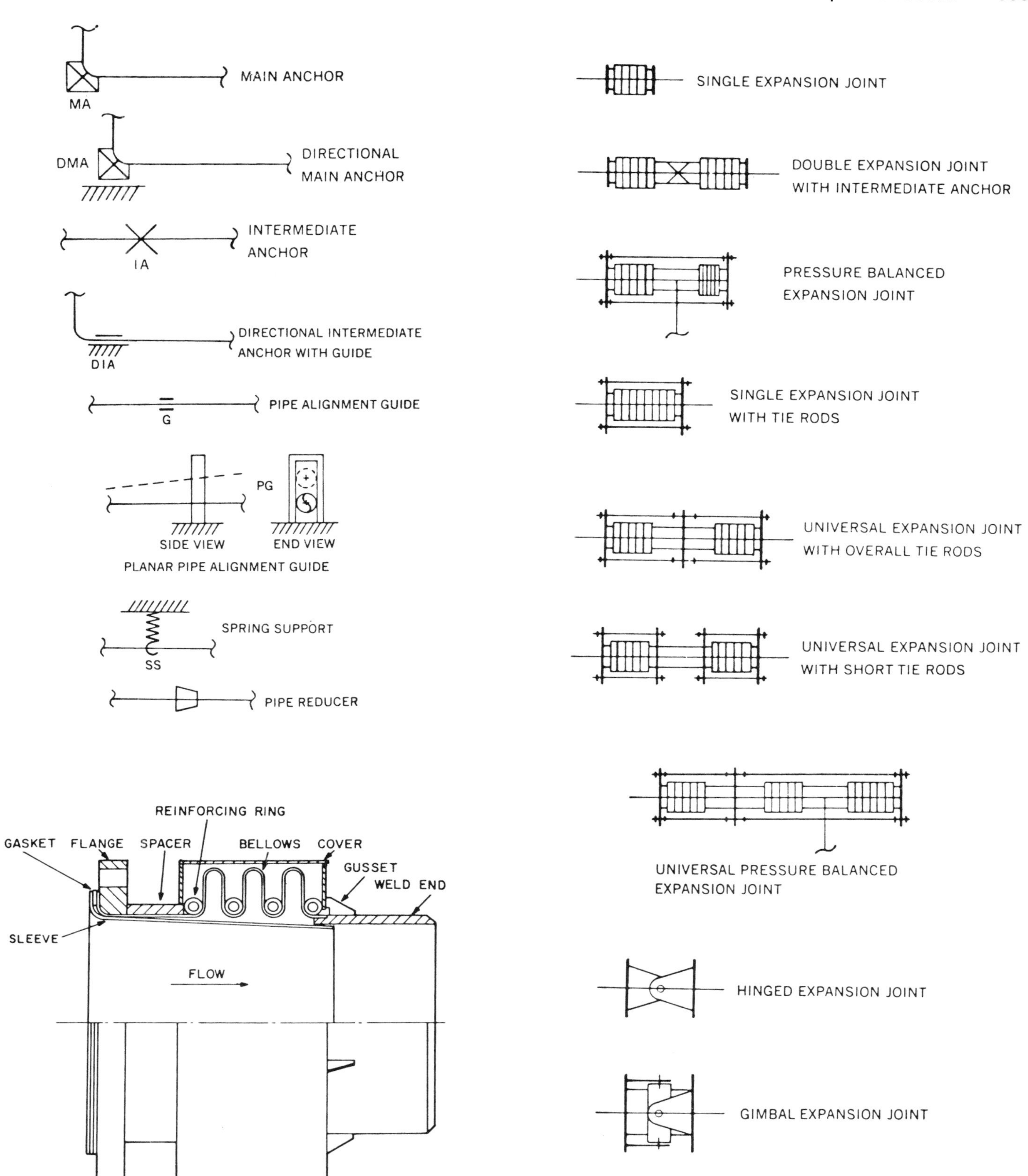

Figure 14-2. Expansion joint symbols. (Courtesy of Badger Expansion Joint Company.)

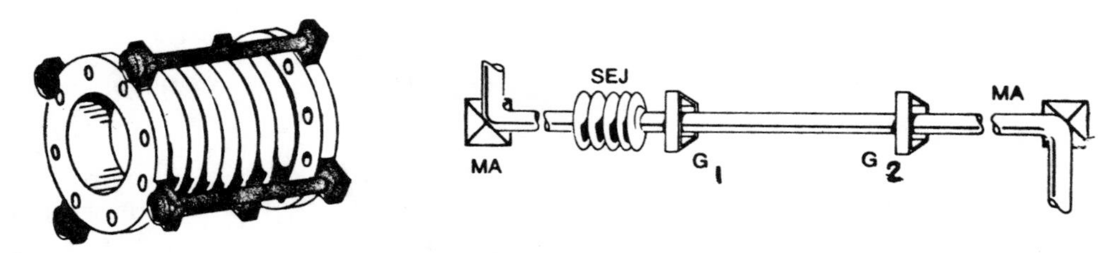

Figure 14-3. Single expansion joint. (Courtesy of Badger Expansion Joint Company.)

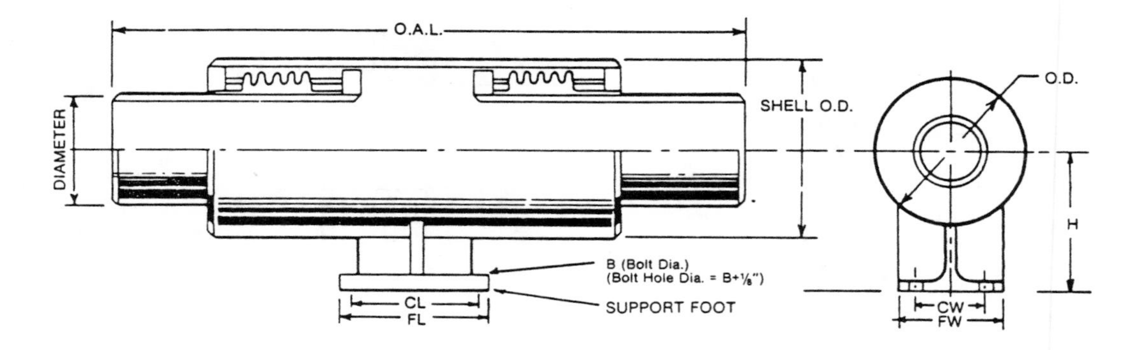

Figure 14-4. Double expansion joint. (Courtesy of Badger Expansion Joint Company.)

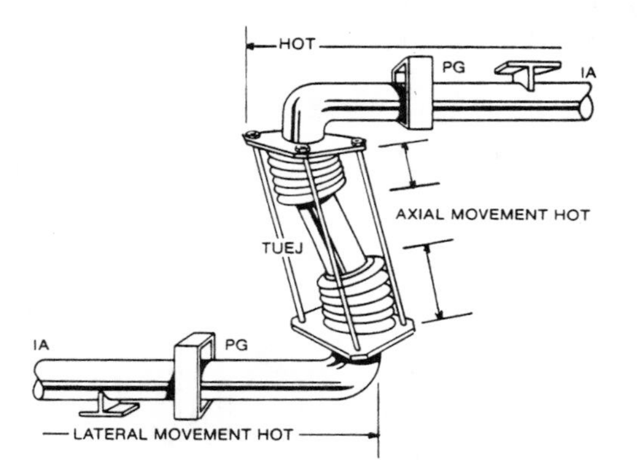

Figure 14-5. Universal expansion joint. (Courtesy of Badger Expansion Joint Company.)

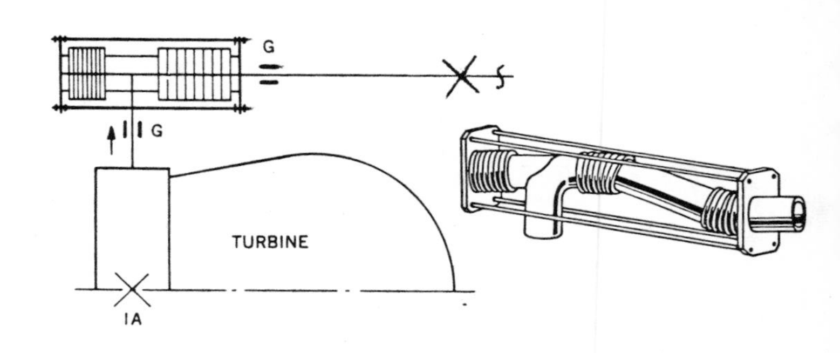

Figure 14-6. Pressure balance expansion joint. (Courtesy of Badger Expansion Joint Company.)

ing, if any, is required because the compressive load on the pipe consists only of the force necessary to deflect the expansion joint.

Where dimensionally feasible, the expansion joint should be designed to fill the entire offset leg so that its expansion is absorbed within the tie rods as axial movement.

Pressure Balanced Expansion Joint

This is a combination of single joints that oppose each other in the same way the internal pressure loads oppose the other. This prevents excessive loading due to pressure thrust from being transmitted to pipe anchors, turbines, or process equipment. The compressive forces of the two bellows are additive, but these are usually negligible in comparison with the pressure forces. This type of joint is used where a pipeline changes direction. It absorbs axial or a combination of axial and lateral movements.

Figure 14-6 shows a typical application of a pressure-balanced expansion joint for combined axial movement and lateral deflection. The anchor on the piping run and that on the turbine are intermediate anchors, and only directional guiding is required. By proper design, the guide directly above the turbine can be made to absorb the axial movement forces of the expansion joint without transmitting these to the turbine. The only force imposed on the turbine is that which is required to deflect the expansion joint laterally.

Hinged Expansion Joint

This is a single expansion joint designed to permit angular rotation in one plane only by use of a pair of pins through hinge plates attached to the expansion joint ends.

Hinged joints are used in sets of two or three to absorb pipe movement in one or more directions in a single plane piping system. Each individual joint in the system is restricted to pure angular rotation by its hinges. However, each pair of hinged joints, separated by a section of piping, will act together to absorb lateral deflection in much the same manner as a universal expansion joint in a single-plane application.

Expansion joint hinges are designed to transmit the full pressure thrust of the expansion joint and, in addition, may be designed to support the weight of piping and equipment, and absorb thermal loads, wind loads, and other external forces. A hinged system permits large movements to be absorbed with the minimal anchor forces.

Figure 14-7 illustrates a two-hinge expansion joint system. In this application the expansion joints absorb only the differential vertical growth between the vessel and pipe riser. Any horizontal movement due to piping expansion, vibration, wind loads, etc. will be absorbed by bending of the vertical pipe leg. A planar guide may be installed near the top of the vessel to protect the hinged joints from wind loads at right angles to the plane of the piping.

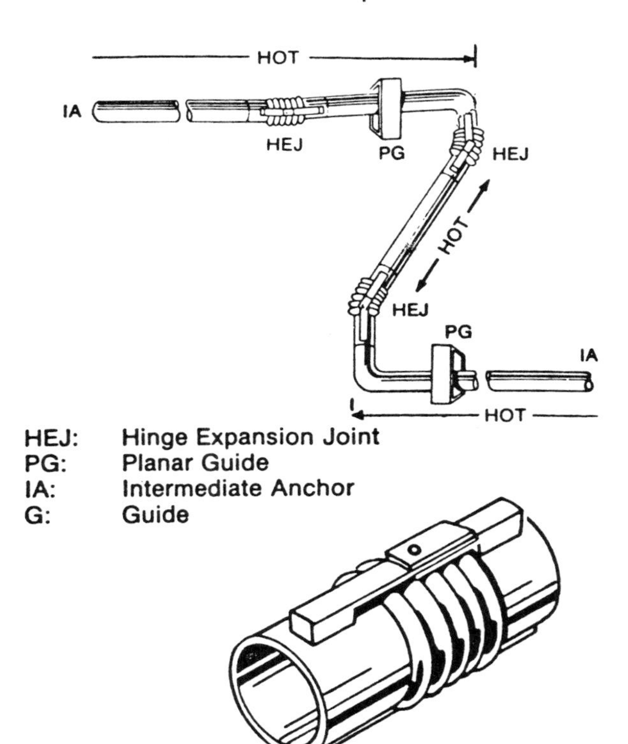

Figure 14-7. Hinged expansion joint. (Courtesy of Badger Expansion Joint Company.)

Gimbal Expansion Joint

This is a single expansion joint designed to permit angular rotation in any plane by the use of two pairs of hinges affixed to a common floating gimbal ring. Unlike the hinged joint which can absorb angular rotation in a single plane only, the gimbal joint can absorb angular rotation in any plane. The ability of the gimbal expansion joint to absorb angular rotation in any plane is most often applied by using two gimbal joints which act together to absorb movement. Gimbals, like hinges, are designed to transmit the pressure thrust and are used in pairs, or in conjunction with a hinged joint.

Figure 14-8 illustrates a gimbal-joint application. Because pressure loading is absorbed by the gimbal structure, only intermediate anchors are required. Planar guides are provided to restrict the movement of each piping leg. As in a hinged-joint installation, the location of pipe supports is simplified by the load-carrying ability of the gimbal.

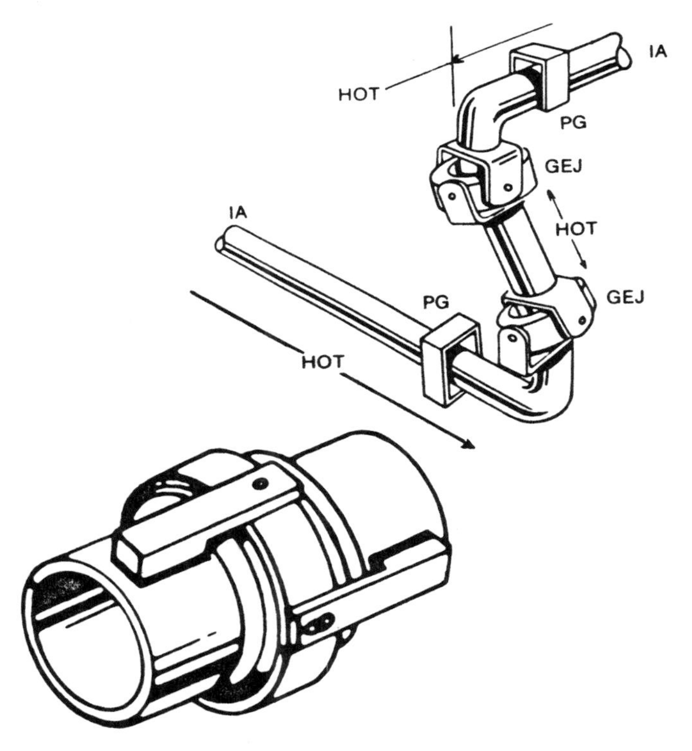

Figure 14-8. Gimbal expansion joint. (Courtesy of Badger Expansion Joint Company.)

Anchors, Guides and Supports

Pipe Anchors

The function of pipe anchors is to divide a pipeline into individual expanding sections. Since thermal movement cannot be restrained, it is the function of pipe anchors to limit and control the movement that expansion joints, located in the line between the anchors, must absorb.

In some applications, major pieces of connected equipment such as turbines, pumps, compressors, and reactors, if designed to withstand the forces acting upon them, can function as anchors. Additional pipe anchors are commonly located at valves, at changes in pipe direction, at blind ends of pipe and, at major branch connections. Expansion devices must be installed in each of the pipe sections to provide flexibility.

Pipe Guides

A pipe guide is a sleeve or frame fastened to a rigid structure that permits the pipeline to move only along its own axis. The guide is needed to prevent the pipeline from buckling due to the pressure thrust or flexibility of the expansion joint—or both.

A planar pipe guide is a pipe guide modified to permit limited movement in one direction other than longitudinal. It is used in "L" or "Z" piping configurations (see Figure 14-5) where the expansion joints are subjected to lateral deflection or angular rotation.

Pipe guides should be located and spaced carefully in a piping system. (See Figure 14-9.)

A pipe support carries the dead weight of the insulation, piping, and its contents. Pipe supports are not pipe guides. Supports do not limit the free movement of piping or contribute to guiding it in any way. The recommendations for pipe anchors and guides given in this chapter represent the minimum requirements for controlling pipelines containing expansion joints. However, standard piping practice usually requires additional pipe supports between guides.

Forces and Moments

To calculate the loads on piping, supports, and equipment, the forces and moments to move an expansion joint must be known. The expansion joint manufacturer will provide axial, lateral, and angular spring rates.

Cold Springing of Expansion Joints

"Cold springing" means prestraining the elements of a piping system at the time of installation so that thermal stresses occurring when the piping is hot are appreciably reduced. The purposes of cold-springing expansion joints may be considerably different, although the mechanics are basically the same. Cold springing is generally applied to expansion joints absorbing only lateral deflection or angular rotation.

Cold springing should not be confused with "precompressing" or "presetting" an expansion joint. The latter terms apply to adjusting an expansion joint in an axial direction to allow for specified amounts of axial compression or extension without physical interference between the corrugations or overextending the corrugations, which might damage them. If desired, cold springing can be done at the factory before shipment to facilitate installation.

The endurance or cyclic life of an expansion joint is dependent on the maximum range of stress to which the bellows is subjected, the numerical maximum stress value being a far less significant factor. Cold springing an expansion joint to reduce the maximum numerical stress would not result in any great improvement in cyclic life. There are, however, a number of other reasons for cold-springing expansion joints as follows:

Force Reduction

In a wide range of applications, the force required to deflect an expansion joint is significant. Where the expansion joint is used to relieve the loading on sensitive equipment, where anchor structures are limited to extremely small loads, and in other similar cases, cold-springing the expansion joint at installation can cut the maximum deflection force in half. In some cases, a 100% cold spring will reduce deflection forces to a minimum at extremely high operating temperatures.

Stability

Figure 14-1 shows the movements of bellows due to angular rotation and/or lateral deflection. In both cases, one side of the bellows is extended and the other compressed, so the bellows may become distorted when subjected to

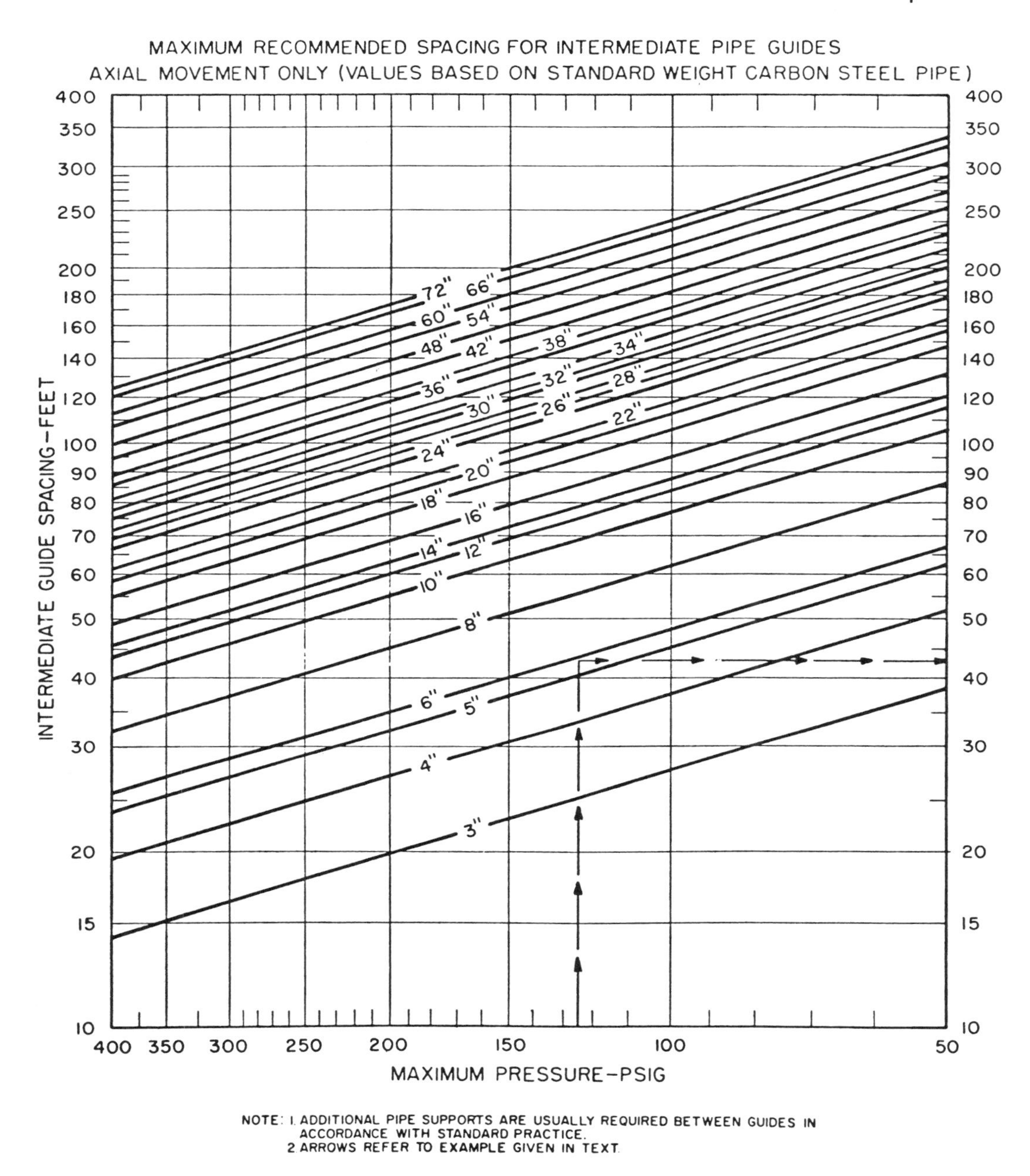

Figure 14-9. Spacing for guides with expansion joint. (Courtesy of Badger Expansion Joint Company.)

internal pressure. Reducing either the internal pressure or the displacement of the corrugations will improve the stability of the expansion joint. By cold springing the expansion joint 50% at installation, the maximum displacement per corrugation is cut in half and the expansion joint is far more stable. For this reason, where expansion joints are subjected to large lateral deflections, or where operating pressures are high, it is good practice to install the joint in a 50% cold-sprung condition.

Component Clearances

Where an expansion joint is furnished with internal sleeves, external covers, or tie devices spanning the bellows, these components must have enough clearance to accommodate the lateral deflection or angular rotation of the joint. The required clearance can be reduced to a minimum if the joint is cold sprung 50%. By this means, internal sleeves of maximum diameter can be furnished, the overall diameter of an expansion joint incorporating external covers or tie devices minimized, and the design of external structures simplified.

Use of Internal Sleeves in Expansion Joints

Internal sleeves should be specified in expansion joints in the following cases:

1. When smooth flow and/or minimum friction losses are desired.
2. Where flow velocities are high.
3. Where there is a danger of pitting or erosion.
4. In high-temperature applications.
5. When copper bellows are used and the application is for high-pressure drip, super-heated steam, hot water or condensate, or where there is any possibility of flashing.

Internal sleeves should not be used where tars or other highly viscous fluids are flowing. These may cause "packing up," "coking," or "caking" and result in joint failure. If purging will prevent these conditions, sleeves should be used in conjunction with purging connections.

Tie Rods, Hinges, and Similar Accessories

In a piping system with expansion joints, it is often impractical to provide main anchors to absorb pressure thrusts. In these cases, tie rods, hinges, or gimbals may solve the problem as long as their attachments are designed to transmit the forces imposed by pressure in the expansion joint.

Method of Attachment

Tie rods, hinges, and gimbals are attached in two basic ways:

1. By a structure whose function is to transmit the loads to the pipe or equipment. This concentrated loading may introduce high localized stresses into the piping in addition to the stresses due to internal pressure.
2. By direct attachment to flanges, which then carry the loads on the rods or hinges in addition to their normal flange load. In this method the total load is transmitted through the flange bolts to the mating flange and then to the connecting pipe.

In some instances cold springing is recommended to keep tie rods closer to the bellows, thereby minimizing moments. When ordering, advise if joints are to be insulated. If so, specify the insulation thickness, because this will affect the hardware design.

Consideration must also be given to the crushing of piping. Attachments must be designed to distribute the load as much as possible. In some cases it becomes necessary to increase the thickness of the pipe wall and/or the lengths of the pipe nipples in order to distribute the load.

Proper design of attachments is extremely important, particularly for critical applications with high pressures and temperatures. In such cases, hardware can cost as much as or more than the expansion joints. For greater system reliability, it is important that emphasis be put on engineering design rather than price. Upon receipt of pertinent application data, special requirements can be determined.

Calculation of Forces and Loads

The forces or loads to be calculated for tie rods, hinges and attachments are:

1. Pressure thrust.
2. Force to extend or compress the expansion joint due to thermal growth within its tied length.
3. Weight of joint.
4. Unsupported weight of piping and insulation between a pair of bellows.
5. Weight of fluid carried in the joint and unsupported piping. In large joints, consideration should be given to the weight of water used in hydro testing.
6. Wind loading effects, if present.

In addition, effects of temperature and flow conditions must be accounted for.

Cycle Life Expectancy

The cycle life expectancy of an expansion joint is affected by various factors in physical construction. These are:

1. Operating pressure.
2. Operating temperature.
3. Bellows material.

4. The movement per corrugation.
5. The thickness of the bellows.
6. The center-to-center distance of the corrugations.
7. Depth and shape of the corrugation.

Any change in these factors will result in a change in the life of the expansion joint.

The life expectancy is defined as the total number of complete cycles that can be expected from the expansion joint based on data tabulated from tests performed at room temperature under simulated operating conditions. A cycle is one complete movement from the full-open to the full-closed to the full-open position. It should be noted, however, that laboratory tests rarely if ever duplicate actual service conditions. Cycle life is only one factor in the design of an expansion joint and may be the least important. Many life cycle tests have been conducted and expansion joints can be manufactured to meet any specification. However, experience has shown that few applications have a real need for high cycle-life design, which adds unnecessary costs to the expansion joint.

Corrosion

Corrosion can significantly reduce the service life of an expansion joint. The design and operating characteristics of expansion joints are such that they may be exposed to corrosive attack under conditions that do not affect piping and fittings of similar materials.

Types of corrosion most frequently experienced in expansion-joint applications are as follows:

1. Stress-corrosion (a cracking of the material as the result of a combination of stress and corrosive environment).
2. Intergranular-corrosion, characterized by a preferential attack along the grain boundaries in metals.
3. Pitting, which is a localized attack on metals.
4. General corrosion or the gradual eating away of the metals in a system.
5. Impingement and corrosion erosion, associated with the impact of a liquid or gas medium on the surface of the material under attack.
6. Elevated temperature oxidation, most commonly encountered in hot air and exhaust lines.

The corrosion resistance of stainless steel depends on the formation of a thin, unbroken, chromic oxide surface, which will form slowly in the atmosphere on clean stainless steel. Particles of steel from welding spatter should be prevented by covering the bellows and using an anti-spatter compound when welding.

External conditions should also be considered. External corrosion can result from fumes or sprays that may contact the bellows or in tunnel and manhole installations where water is allowed to collect. Direct application of insulation to the expansion-joint bellows and direct burial in the ground are not recommended. Many corrosion problems encountered in the field can be reduced, if not completely eliminated. Where corrosion problems are complex, consult a qualified corrosion engineer.

Erosion

This is the mechanical wearing away of the metal surfaces in a joint. It usually results from the impact of solid particles entrained in the flowing medium. Where there is a possibility of severe erosion, such as in lines carrying abrasive media, heavy liners should be used to protect the bellows of the expansion joint.

Calculating Thermal Expansion

Metallic, packless expansion joints are normally designed to move in axial compression only, and unless otherwise specified, the minimum and installation temperatures are assumed to be 60°F.

Here is how to determine the amount of thermal expansion in a piping system:

Example

Assume a 10-in. steam line fabricated from carbon steel is carrying superheated steam at 300 psig and the distance between pipeanchors is 140 ft–0 in. The minimum ambient temperature is 70°F and the maximum operating temperature is 460°F.

Solution

From Chapter 2, Table 2-1, we find that the expansion of carbon steel pipe at 460°F is 3.25 in. per 100 ft, and at 70°F the expansion per 100 ft is 0 in.

$$\text{Total expansion: } \frac{(140 \text{ ft})\ (3.25 \text{ in.}) - 0 \text{ in.}}{100} = 4.55 \text{ in.}$$

Therefore, we find that we should select an expansion joint that will absorb at least 4.55 in. of axial compression.

Precompression

If the minimum operating temperature is lower than the anticipated installation temperature, the expansion joint will be subjected to both extension and compression during operation. Because most expansion joints are designed to function in compression only, any expansion joint used in such an application must be precompressed (prior to installation) to prevent extension of the expansion joint beyond its original, overall length.

If advised of the minimum, maximum, and installation temperatures when the order is placed, the expansion joint will be factory precompressed and may be installed as received.

In the case of expansion joints specified for low-temperature service only, the installation and maximum temperatures are normally the same, so the joints function entirely in extension. Where such service conditions are clearly specified, the expansion joint will always be factory precompressed, ready for installation.

Where it is not possible to anticipate the installation temperature, the expansion joint may be precompressed in the field. The amount of precompression is determined as follows:

$$P = \frac{A_r\ (T_2 - T_1)}{(T_3 - T_1)}$$

where P = Total amount of precompression, in.
A_r = Total rated axial movement of the expansion joint, in.
T_1 = Minimum temperature
T_2 = Installation temperature determined by actual temperature reading of adjacent piping. Do not use the ambient atmospheric temperature for this purpose.
T_3 = Maximum temperature

Example

Assume that the installation temperature will be 70°F. The required precompression is then calculated as follows:

$$P = \frac{6(70°F - 0°F)}{(460°F - 0°F)} = 0.913 \text{ in.}$$

Note: If the amount of precompression is very small (1/8 in. per corrugation or less), it may be neglected. When precompression is required, remember to deduct the amount of this precompression from the normal overall length dimensions.

Application

Pipe Anchors

The first step is to determine the tentative locations of pipe anchors. By proper location, any piping system can be reduced to a number of individual expanding pipe sections having relatively simple configurations. The number and location of pipe anchors will depend upon piping configuration, amount of thermal expansion, the proximity of structural members suitable for use as anchors, and the location of pipe fittings, connected equipment, and branch connections.

Start out with the assumption that single expansion joints in straight axial compression will provide the simplest and most economical layout. Wherever possible, the distance between anchors and amount of expansion should be kept uniform so that the expansion joints used will be interchangeable. To minimize the number of expansion joints adjust the distance between anchors so that expansion joints having a maximum number of corrugations in each bellows (consistent with stability) can be used.

Calculation of Forces Acting on Main Pipe Anchors

A main pipe anchor must be designed to withstand the forces and moments imposed upon it by each of the pipe sections to which it is attached. In the case of the installation illustrated in Figure 14-10, the force acting on the main anchor consists of the full line thrust due to pressure, the force required to deflect the expansion joint, the rated

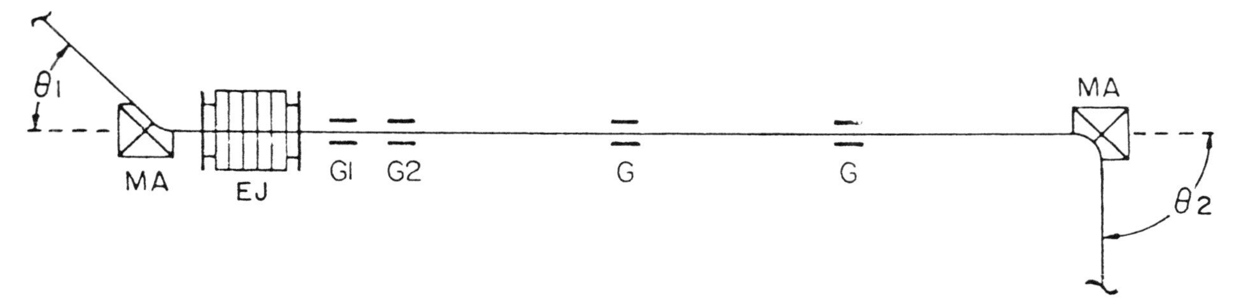

Figure 14-10. Diagram illustrating the forces that act upon the main anchor.

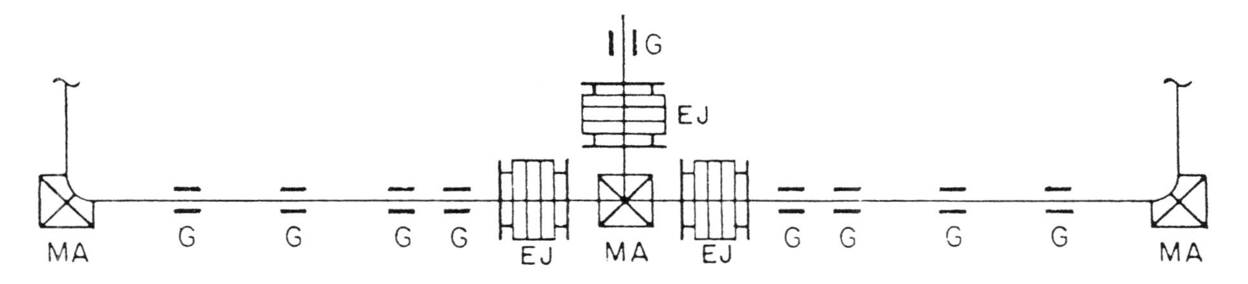

Figure 14-11. Diagram illustrating the forces that act upon the main anchor in applications involving straight pipe selections and in applications involving anchors at pipe bends and elbows.

movement, and the frictional force due to the pipe alignment guides. Formulas for calculating anchor forces in various applications follow.

The steps for calculating the main anchor forces for applications involving straight pipe sections (see the center anchor in Figure 14-11) are:

1. Calculate the full line thrust:

$$F_s = AP$$

where F_s = Static thrust due to internal pressure, lb
A = Effective pressure thrust area (in.^{2}) taken from data sheet
P = Maximum pressure (psi) based on the most severe conditions whether design, operational or test

2. Assuming that the weight of the pipeline and its contents are carried by supports. To calculate the total force imposed on the main anchor (F_{ma}) by any one pipe section use the following equation:

$$F_{ma} = F_s + F_m + F_g$$

where F_{ma} = Force on main anchor, lb
F_s = Static thrust due to internal pressure, lb
F_m = Force (from data sheet) required to extend or compress the expansion joint, lb
F_g = Frictional force due to pipe alignment guides. Note: This can be obtained from the manufacturer of the guides.

To determine the net load on the anchor, it is necessary to add vectorially the forces imposed upon it by each of the three pipe sections to which it is attached.

To calculate the main anchor forces for applications involving straight pipe sections containing expansion joints of different diameters (see center anchor in Figure 14-12), use the following equation:

$$F_s = (A_1 - A_2)P$$

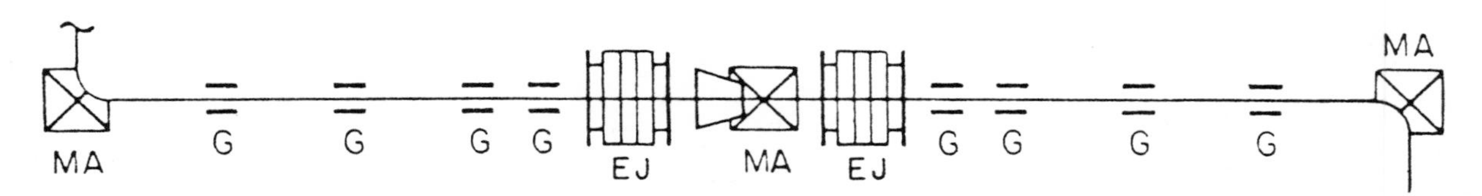

Figure 14-12. Diagram illustrating the forces that act upon the main anchor in applications involving straight pipe selections containing expansion joints of different diameters.

where A_1 = Effective area, corresponding to the mean diameter of the corrugations of the expansion joint in the larger pipe section, $in.^2$

A_2 = Effective area, corresponding to the mean diameter of the expansion joint in the smaller pipe section, $in.^2$

P = Maximum pressure (psi), based on the most severe conditions, whether design, operational, or test.

Here again, it is necessary to consider the differences in the forces required to extend or compress the expansion joints and the differences in the frictional forces due to pipe alignment guides and supports. Thus, the total force on the center anchor will be:

$$F_{ma} = F_s + F_{m1} + F_{g1} - F_{g2}$$

where F_{m1} = Force (from data sheet) required to extend or compress the expansion joint in the larger pipe section, lb

F_{m2} = Force (from data sheet) required to extend or compress the expansion joint in the small pipe section, lb

F_{g1} = Frictional force (from guide manufacturer) due to pipe alignment guides in the larger pipe section, lb

F_{g2} = Frictional force (from guide manufacturer) due to pipe alignment guides in the smaller pipe section, lb

To calculation the main anchor forces for applications involving anchors at pipe bends and elbows (see Figure 14-10) the following calculation must be used.

In the case of an anchor located at a pipe bend or elbow, it is necessary to consider the forces imposed by the pipe sections on both sides of the anchor. Thus, assuming that each section contains an expansion joint, the line thrust due to pressure (F_s = AP) and the forces F_m and F_g, explained previously, become biaxial components and must be added vectorially. In addition, the effect at the elbow of the centrifugal thrust (F_p) due to flow, must be considered. F_p may be calculated as follows:

$$F_p = \frac{2ADV^2}{g} \sin\frac{\emptyset}{2}$$

where A = Internal area of pipe, ft^2

D = Density of fluid, lb/ft^3

V = Velocity of flow, ft/sec

g = Acceleration due to gravity, 32.2 ft/sec^2

$\emptyset$ = Angle of pipe bend

Calculation of Intermediate Pipe Anchor Forces

An intermediate pipe anchor must be designed to withstand the force and moments imposed upon it by each of the pipe sections attached to it. However, an intermediate anchor does not have to be designed to withstand the full line pressure thrust, because this force is always absorbed by main anchors or by devices on the expansion joint, such as limit rods, tie rods, gimbals, or hinges.

Assuming that the weight of the pipeline and its contents is carried by supports, the following calculation will determine the forces acting on an intermediate pipe anchor in a pipe section containing expansion joints (see Figure 14-13):

$$F_{IA} = F_{m1} + F_{g1} + F_{m2} + F_{g2}$$

where F_{m1} = The force (from the data sheet) required to extend or compress expansion joint EJ1 shown in Figure 14-13.

F_{g1} = The total force due to friction of all the pipe alignment guides installed on the pipe section to the right of the intermediate anchor in Figure 14-13.

F_{m2} = The force required to extend or compress expansion joint EJ2 shown in Figure 14-13.

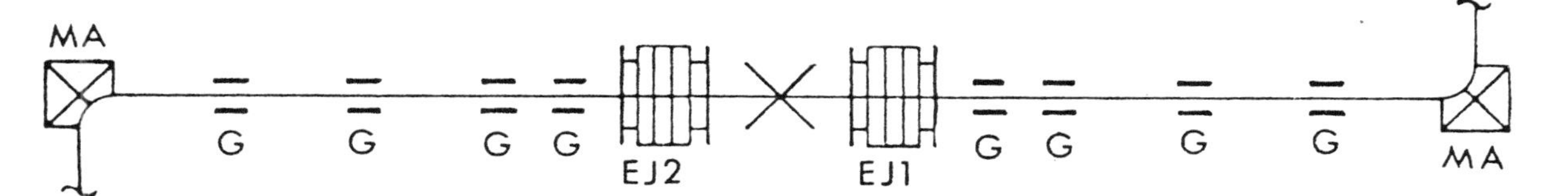

Figure 14-13. Diagram illustrating the forces that act upon an intermediate pipe anchor in a pipe section containing expansion joints.

F_{g2} = The total force due to friction of all the pipe alignment guides installed on the pipe section to the left of the intermediate anchor in Figure 14-13.

Note: The frictional force due to pipe alignment guides can be obtained from the manufacturer of the guides.

If the pipe is the same diameter on both sides of the intermediate anchor, and if the guides on both pipe sections are similar in number and design to F_{m2} and F_{g1}, respectively, but opposite in sign, F_{1A} will be equal to zero. However, it is possible that the pipeline may heat up gradually from one end, thereby causing one of the pipe sections to expand before the other. It is therefore considered good practice to design the intermediate anchor to resist the forces exerted by one of the two pipe sections (i.e., $F_{1A} = F_{m1} + F_{g1}$).

Pipe Guides and Guiding

A pipe alignment guide is a sleeve or frame fastened to some rigid structure that permits the pipeline to move freely along its own axis and limits it to this type of motion. A roller support, U bolt, or pipe hanger, which only supports the weight of the pipe, cannot be substituted for a pipe guide.

Pipe guides are required to prevent buckling of the pipeline. Buckling is caused by compressive loading on the pipe due to the internal pressure thrust and the flexibility of the expansion joint which causes the pipe to act like a column with end loading.

In axial movement applications, avoid using a single pipe-alignment guide because such a guide may act as a fulcrum, which might impose lateral deflection or angular rotation on the expansion joint due to movement of the piping in a direction other than axial.

Planar pipe guides are modified to permit limited movement and/or bending of the piping in one plane. These are used only in applications involving lateral deflection or angular rotation resulting from L- or Z-shaped pipe configurations.

Proper alignment is very important in the installation of all expansion joints. Expansion joints will not function properly unless the pipeline in which they are installed is securely anchored and guided.

Spacing of Pipe Guides

Where an expansion joint is located close to an anchor, the first pipe guide should be located no more than four pipe diameters from the moving end. The second should be located no more than fourteen pipe diameters from the first. The recommended spacing for intermediate guides along the balance of the pipeline can be determined from Figure 14-9. For any known pressure and pipe size, the guide spacing can be determined by locating the pressure on the scale at the bottom of Figure 14-9. Follow the pressure line vertically until it intersects the diagonal line for pipe size. From this intersection, follow across horizontally to the guide spacing column (left to right) and read the recommended spacing. For example, the recommended intermediate guide spacing for a 6-in. pipeline containing an expansion joint under a pressure of 125 psig is 43 feet. The first guide should be no more than 24 in. from the expansion joint, and the second pipe guide 84 in. from the first.

Location of Expansion Joints

Wherever possible, an expansion joint should be located immediately adjacent to a pipe anchor. If it is not possible to locate the expansion joint near a pipe anchor, pipe guides should be used on both sides of the expansion joint in accordance with the instructions given in the preceding paragraphs under "Spacing of Pipe Guides."

Figure 14-10 shows the preferred practice in the use of a single expansion joint (EJ) to absorb axial pipeline expansion. Note the use of one expansion joint between two main anchors (MA), the nearness of the expansion joint to an anchor, the closeness of the first alignment guide (G_1), the spacing between the first alignment guide and the second alignment guide (G_2), and the spacing of intermediate guides (G) along the balance of the line.

Expansion joints should not be located immediately downstream from turbulence-producing devices (such as butterfly valves), plug valves, and sudden increases in pipe size, mitered elbows, etc. If it is impossible to locate the expansion joint an adequate distance away from tubulence producers, the joint should be equipped with a heavy sleeve. Figures 14-14 and 14-15 show the information required for standard and special expansion joints specification sheets.

End Connections

The type of end connections selected depends upon the operating conditions and the customer's requirements. See Figure 14-16 for illustrations. The following is a brief description of the various types available.

Van Stoned Flanges (Type V)

The flanges are slipped over the ends of the bellows and the bellows material is flared out or "Van Stoned" over the faces of the flanges. The Van Stones are roughly equivalent to the raised faces on standard forged steel flanges. The flanges are loose and free to rotate, thus permitting easy alignment with the mating pipeline flanges.

This construction is generally used in applications involving product purity or corrosion, because the only material in contact with the flowing medium is the corrosion-resistant bellows material.

Welding Ends (Type W)

The ends of the expansion joint are supplied with pipe suitably beveled for welding to connecting equipment or piping. Standard joints are supplied with carbon steel weld ends. See individual data sheets for grade and type. Other thicknesses, lengths, and grades of carbon steel weld ends are available on order. Where alloy pipe is used, it may be advantageous to use weld ends that are shorter and thinner than carbon steel standards. Consult the factory for recommendations when alloy pipe is used.

Fixed Flanges (Type SF)

The flanges are welded directly to the bellows material without the use of intermediate pipe nipples. In this construction the flanges are in direct contact with the flowing medium.

Fixed Flanges (Type F)

The flanges are welded to pipe nipples, thereby providing greater overall length. In this construction both the pipe nipples and flanges are in direct contact with the flowing medium.

Combination Ends

Expansion joints can be supplied with one weld end and one flanged end to meet installation requirements.

Covers

Covers protect expansion joints from mechanical damage and serve as a base for insulation.

Sleeves

Sleeves minimize pressure drop and also streamline the flow of gas or fluid through an expansion joint, thereby reducing friction losses and turbulence. They are recommended for all expansion joints, except in applications where high-viscosity fluids such as tar are involved. Sleeves are required whenever the velocity of flow exceeds the following values:

Nominal Pipe Size	Medium in Pipe	Velocity of Flow
3 to 6 in.	Steam	1,000 ft/min/in. dia
> 6 in.	Steam	6,000 ft/min
3 to 6 in.	Air (other gases)	250 ft/min/in. dia
> 6 in.	Air (other gases)	1,500 ft/min

For additional data use the sheet for supplemental information for special expansion joints.

Customer ______________________ Date ______________________
Project ______________________ Inquiry/Job No. ______________________

1. Item No.
2. Quantity
3. Size
4. Flowing Medium*
5. Flow Velocity
6. Int. Design Pressure, psig
7. Int. Text Pressure, psig
8. Maximum Temperature, °F
9. Minimum Temperature, °F
10. Installation Temperature, °F
11. Axial compression, in.
12. Axial extension, in.
13. Lateral deflection, in.
14. Angular rotation, deg.
15. Pipe specification
16. Weld end specification
17. Flange specification
18. Type or catalog number
19. Internal sleeves
20. External covers
21. Anchor base
22. Limit rods

Use manufacturer's standard unless otherwise specified by purchaser.

23. Bellows material
24. Equalizing ring material
25. Total corrugations
26. Length limitation

* If flowing medium is corrosive, erosive, or viscous explain in detail.

Figure 14-14. Standard expansion joint specification sheet.

Customer ______________________ Date ______________________
Project ______________________ Inquiry/Job No. ______________________

1. Item No.
2. External design pressure, psig
3. External test pressure, psig
4. Pipe purge, instr. connection
5. Vibration amplitude
6. Vibration frequency

Special Flange Design

7. Material
8. Facing
9. O.D.
10. I.D.
11. Thickness
12. B.C. diameter
13. No. holes
14. Size holes
15. Hole orientation

Design Restrictions

16. Length
17. Maximum O.D.
18. Minimum I.D.
19. Axial force
20. Lateral force (Shear)
21. End moment
22. Cyclic design life
23. ASME Code partial Data forms required
24. Applicable codes and specifications

Figure 14-15. Supplemental information for special expansion joints, to be used with the standard expansion joint specification sheet.

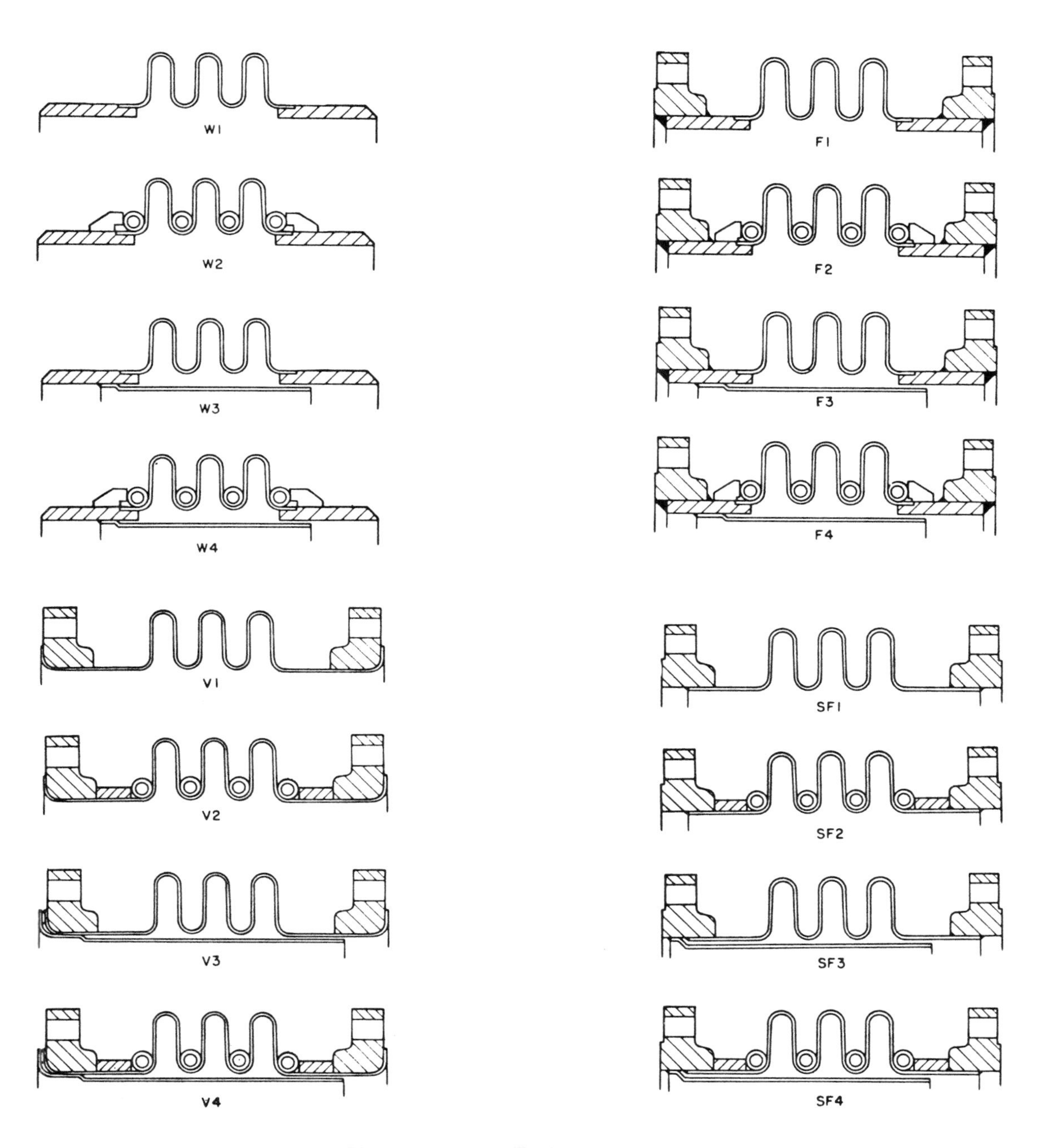

Figure 14-16. End connections.

15
Glossary

Aging—The term originally applied to the process or sometimes to the effects of allowing a metal to remain at ordinary temperatures. Heat treatment at temperatures above room temperature for the purpose of accelerating changes of the type that might take place during aging at ordinary temperature is called artificial aging. The changes taking place during artificial aging are due to the precipitation treatment. Aging is an approach to the attainment of equilibrium from an unstable condition induced by a prior operation. The fundamental reaction involved is generally one of precipitation, sometimes submicroscopic. The method employed to bring about aging consists of exposure to a favorable temperature subsequent to (1) a relatively rapid cooling from some elevated temperature (quench aging) or (2) a limited degree of cold work (strain aging).

Alclad—The common name for a type of clad-wrought aluminum product with coatings of high purity aluminum; or an aluminum alloy different from the core alloy in composition.

Alloy—A metallic substance consisting of two or more elements, of which at least one is metal, and in which all elements are miscible in the molten state and do not separate when solid.

Alloying elements—Chemical elements constituting an alloy. In steel, usually the elements added to modify the properties of the steel.

Annealing—A heating and controlled operation to impart specific desirable properties generally concerned with subsequent fabrication of the alloy, such as softness and ductility. When annealing follows cold working for the purposes of stress removal, it is called stress annealing.

Arc welding—Welding accomplished by using an electric arc formed between a metallic or carbon electrode and the metal being welded, between two separate electrodes, or between two separate pieces being welded (also called fusion welding).

Austenite—A solid solution in which gamma iron is the solvent, having a face-centered cubic crystal structure.

Austenitic steel—Steel, which due to its composition has a stable structure at normal (room) temperatures; as for example: the 18-8 types. It is not hardened by thermal treatment.

Bend test—A test commonly used to determine relative ductility of a sample by bending it over a given radius and through a given angle.

Billet—A semi-finished rolled ingot of rectangular or nearly rectangular cross section.

Brass—A copper-base alloy in which zinc is the principal added element.

Brazing—Joining metals by fusion of nonferrous alloys with melting points above 800°F but below the melting point of the metals being joined.

Brinell hardness—A hardness number determined by applying a known load to the surface of the material to be tested through a hardened steel ball of known diameter. Note: Not suitable for measuring the hardness of strip and sheet because of insufficient thickness.

Brittleness—A tendency to fracture without appreciable deformation.

Carbon steel—Steel in which carbon provides the properties without substantial amounts of other alloying elements.

Carburizing—Diffusing carbon into the surface of iron-base alloys by heating in the presence of carbonaceous materials.

Case hardening—Carburizing, nitriding, or cyaniding and subsequent hardening by suitable heat treatment, if necessary, all or part of the surface portions of a section of iron-base alloy.

Casting—Pouring molten metal into a mold or a metal object so produced.

Cementite—An iron-carbon compound with the chemical formula Fe3C often called iron carbide.

Charpy test—A pendulum-type impact test in which a notched specimen, supported at both ends as a simple beam, is broken by the impact of the falling pendulum. The energy absorbed in breaking the specimen, as determined by the decreased rise of the pendulum, is a measure of the impact strength of the metal.

Chemical analysis—Separating an alloy into its component elements and identifying them. In quantitative analysis, the proportion of each element is determined.

Chromium—A hard crystalline metal used as an alloying element to give resistance to heat, corrosion, and wear and increase strength and hardenability.

Cold working—Permanent deformation of a metal below its recrystallization temperature. Also defined as plastic deformation of a metal at a temperature low enough to ensure strain hardening. Mechanical properties, such as tensile strength, hardness, and ductility, are also altered.

Compressive strength—The ability to withstand compressive stresses.

Compressive stress—Stress caused by a compressive load or in fibers compressed by a bending.

Cooling stresses—Stresses caused by uneven contraction, external restraint, or localized plastic deformation during cooling.

Corrosion—Gradual chemical or electrochemical attack on a metal by atmosphere, moisture, or other elements.

Corrosion embrittlement—Embrittlement in certain alloys caused by exposure to a corrosive environment.

Corrosion fatigue—Combined action of corrosion and fatigue in which local corroded areas act as stress concentrators, causing failure at the point of stress concentration and exposing new metal surfaces to corrosion. The failure is progressive and rapid.

Creep—Plastic flow of metal, usually occurring at high temperatures, subject to stress appreciably less than its yield strength. It progresses through first, second, and third stages to fracture or results in stress relaxation.

Cyaniding—A process of case hardening a ferrous alloy by heating in a molten cyanide salt bath, thus causing the alloy to absorb carbon and nitrogen simultaneously. Cyaniding is usually followed by quenching to produce a hard case.

Ductility—That property of metal which allows the metal to be permanently deformed before final rupture.

Elastic limit (limit of elasticity)—Maximum stress to which a metal can be subjected without permanent deformation at the point of stress.

Electrochemical corrosion—Localized corrosion that results from exposure of an assembly of dissimilar metals in contact with or coupled with one another; or of a metal containing microscopic areas dissimilar in composition or structure. The dissimilar elements form short-circuited electrodes. The corrosive medium is the electrolyte, and an electric current is induced, which results in the disolution of the electrode that has the more anodic solution potential, while the other is unattacked.

Elongation—The amount of permanent extension in the tensile test, usually expressed as a percentage of the original gage length, (e.g., 25 percent in 2 inches). It may also refer to the amount of extension at any stage in any process which continuously elongates a body, as in rolling.

Endurance limit—A limit of stress below which metal will withstand stress without fracture; a specified large number of applications of such stress.

Eutectoid steel—A carbon steel containing 0.80% carbon that becomes a solid solution at any temperature in the austenite temperature range between 1,333°F and 2,500°F.

Fatigue—The tendency of a metal to fracture under conditions of repeated cyclic stressing below the ultimate tensile strength but above the yield strength.

Ferrite—A solid solution in which alphas iron is the solvent and having a body-centered cubic crystal structure.

Ferritic steel—Steel which, due to its composition, is not hardenable by heat treatment. Such stainless types as 405, 430, and 448 are essentially ferritic steels.

Free machining—The property of steel imparted by additions of sulphur, selenium, or phosphorus which promote chip breakage and permit increased machining speeds. Additions of sulphur or selenium also help to decrease friction between the chips and the tool face.

Galling—The damaging of one or both metallic surfaces by removal of particles from localized areas during sliding friction.

Galvanic corrosion—Corrosive action occurring when two dissimilar metals are in contact and are joined by a solution capable of conducting an electric current, a condition which causes a flow of electric current and corrosion of the more anodic of the two metals. (Also see *Electrochemical Corrosion*.)

Gas welding—Welding in which heat is supplied by a manually or automatically controlled torch flame of oxyacetylene or oxyhydrogen (also called fusion welding).

Grains—Individual crystals in metal.

Hardenability—In a ferrous alloy, the property that determines the depth and distribution of hardness induced by heat treating and quenching.

Hardness—Resistance to indentation by standard balls, diamonds, etc., under standard loads. Also, the degree of cold working.

Heading—An upsetting process used to form rivet, screw, and bolt heads in making these products from wire or rod.

Heat treatable—Refers to an alloy that may be hardened by heat treatment.

Heat treatment—A combination of heating and cooling operations timed and applied to metal or alloy to produce desired properties.

Homogenizing—A process of heat treatment at high temperature to eliminate or decrease chemical segregation by diffusion. Attainment of austenite that has a uniform distribution of carbon.

Hooke's Law—Stress is proportional to strain in the elastic region.

Hot forming—Working operations performed on metals heated to temperatures above room temperature.

Hot working—Hot forming above the recrystallization temperature.

Hydrogen embrittlement—A brittleness sometimes engendered by contact with plating and pickling solution acid due to absorption of hydrogen by the metal. The embrittlement is more evident in hardened parts, and can be removed by aging or heating the steel for a prescribed period.

Hypereutectoid steels—Steels containing from 0.80% to above 2.0% carbon.

Hypoeutectoid steels—Carbon steels containing less than 0.80% carbon.

Impact test—A test designed to determine the energy absorbed in fracturing a test bar at high velocity. The usual impact test specimen is a standard size square bar with a V or keyhole type notch. (See Charpy test and Izod test.)

Intergranular corrosion—Corrosion that tends to localize at grain boundaries, usually under conditions of prolonged stress and certain environments, and in association with poor heat treating or welding practice that has caused the precipitation of a more easily attacked constituent at these boundaries.

Izod test—A pendulum-type of notched-bar impact test in which the specimen is supported at one end as a cantilever beam and the energy required to break off the free end is used as a measure of impact strength.

Machinability—The rate and ease with which a metal can be machined.

Magnetic particle testing—This method of inspection consists in suitably magnetizing the material and applying a prepared magnetic powder which adheres along lines of flux leakage. On properly magnetized material, flux leakage develops along surface nonuniformities. This method is not applicable to high manganese or austenitic stainless steels and nonferrous alloys, which are nonmagnetic.

Martensite—An unstable constituent in quenched steel, the hardest of the transformation products of austenite.

Martensitic steel—Steel which, due to its composition, has martensite as its chief constituent after cooling. The hardenable stainless types are all martensite steels.

Mechanical properties—Those properties that reveal the reaction, elastic or plastic, of a material to an applied stress or that involves the relationship between stress and strain; for example, Young's modulus, tensile strength, fatigue limit. These properties have often been designated as physical properties, but the term mechanical properties is technically more accurate and therefore preferred.

Modulus of rigidity—The ratio of the unit shear stress to the unit angular strain in the elastic range.

Nitriding—A process of surface hardening in which a ferrous alloy is heated in an atmosphere of cracked ammonia gas or other suitable nitrogenous material thus allowing nitrogen to diffuse into the surface metal. Nitriding is conducted at temperatures below the critical temperature range and produces surface hardening of the metal without quenching.

Normalizing—A process in which steel is heated to a suitable temperature above the transformation range and is subsequently cooled in still air at room temperature. This operation is used for grain refining or to develop specified mechanical properties.

Notch sensitivity—The reduction caused in nominal strength, impact or static, by the presence of a stress concentration, usually expressed as the ratio of the notched to the unnotched strength.

Permeability—Magnetic permeability is the ratio of the magnetic induction to the intensity of the magnetizing field.

Physical properties—Those properties familiarly discussed in physics, exclusive of those described under *Mechanical Properties;* for example, density, electrical conductivity; coefficient for thermal expansion. The term has often been used to describe mechanical properties, but such usage is not recommended.

Pickling—Immersion in dilute acid or other suitable media for the removal of oxide scale from hot-rolled or otherwise sealed surfaces.

Plasticity—The ability of a metal to be deformed extensively without rupture.

Plating—Deposition of a thin film of a metal or alloy on a different base metal from a solution containing ions of the plating metal.

Poisson's ratio—Ratio expressing the relation of strain normal to the applied load as a proportion of direct strain within the elastic limit. Also relates moduli of elasticity and rigidity.

Precipitation hardening—Hardening of metallic alloys, by aging, which results from the precipitation of a constituent from a supersaturated solid solution, usually nonferrous alloys. Also termed as hardening. (See *Aging*.)

Process annealing—An annealing operation carried out at a constant temperature just below the critical transformation temperature (also referred to as subcritical annealing).

Proof stress—In a test, stress that will cause a specified permanent set in a material, usually 1% or less.

Proportional limit—The highest stress at which the material still follows Hooke's Law, similar to elastic limit.

Quenching—A process of rapid cooling from an elevated temperature.

Radiography—The use of X-rays or gamma radiation to detect internal structural defects in metal objects.

Reduction of area—In a tensile test, the difference between the original cross-sectional area and that of the smallest area of the point of rupture. It is usually stated as a percentage of the original area. Also called contraction of area, it is not applicable to the mechanical testing of sheet and strip. It is also a measure of cold work.

Refractory metals—Metals such as tungsten, columbium, tantalum, and molybdenum, which have relatively high melting temperatures.

Residual stress—Stresses locked in a metal after the completion of nonuniform heating or cooling, working, etc. due to expansion, contraction, phase changes, and other phenomena.

Resistance welding—A welding process in which the work pieces are heated by the passage of an electric current through the contact area, combined with pressure causing joining by fusion.

Rockwell hardness test—This test consists of forcing a cone shaped diamond or hardened steel ball into a metal specimen to determine the degree of penetration and, hence, the hardness.

Rupture stress—The true stress given by dividing the load at the moment of incipient fracture by the area supporting that load.

Salt spray test—An accelerated corrosion test in which the metal specimens are exposed to a fine mist of salt water solution.

Scaling—Surface oxidation caused by heating in an oxidizing atmosphere.

Seam welding—Resistance welding that consists of a series of overlapping spots forming a continuous weld.

Shear—Plastic deformation in which parallel planes of metal crystals slide so as to retain their parallel relationship. Also called angular elastic strain.

Shear stress—Stress acting on a shear plane.

Solution treating—A condition of complete solubility resulting in a single phase for compositions of two or more alloying elements at temperatures lower than the solids. Solid solutions may be limited in extent with respect to range of alloy composition or can be continuous, extending throughout an alloy series.

Specific gravity—A numerical value representing the weight of a given substance compared with the weight of an equal volume of water.

Spot welding—A resistance-welding process in which the fusion is limited to a small circular or oval area.

Stabilization—Prevention of the formation of carbides at the grain boundaries of austenitic stainless steels. Dimensional control of nonferrous castings.

Strain—Deformation expressed in units per unit of length produced by strain.

Strain aging—Load per unit of area.

Stress concentrator or stress raiser—Any notch, scratch, sharp change of contour, slot groove, hole, defect, or other discontinuity in an engineering material that has the effect of concentrating the stresses applied to the material or generated in it by heating or cooling.

Stress corrosion—Corrosive action induced and accelerated by the presence of stresses.

Stress rupture—A test to destruction at elevated temperature, by which it is possible to determine the stress that causes failure at a given temperature and with the lapse of a given period of time.

Temper—A condition produced in a metal or alloy by mechanical or thermal treatment and having characteristic structure and mechanical properties.

Temper brittleness—Brittleness that results when certain steels are held within or slowly cooled through a certain range of temperature below the transformation range. The brittleness is revealed by a notched-bar impact test at room temperature or lower temperatures.

Tempering—The process of reheating quench hardened or normalized steel to a temperature below the transformation range and then cooling at any rate desired. This operation is frequently called stress relieving. "Drawing" is synonymous with tempering, but the latter is the preferred usage.

Tensile strength—The maximum load in pounds per square inch, based on the original cross section, which may be developed in tensile testing. (See also *Ultimate Strength*.)

Thermal stresses—Stresses in metal, resulting from nonuniform temperature distribution.

Through-hardening—Thermal description of alloys that harden completely, so the center of a hardened section exhibits hardness similar to the surface.

Torsion—Strain created in an object by a twisting action or the stresses created by such an action.

Toughness—Ability to absorb considerable energy before fracture, usually represented by the area under a stress-strain curve and therefore involving both ductility and strength.

Ultimate strength—The maximum strength or stress before complete failure or fracture occurs.

Vacuum melting—A process by which alloys are melted in a near perfect vacuum to prevent contamination by atmospheric elements.

Vickers hardness test—An indentation hardness test utilizing a diamond pyramid and useful over the entire range of common metals.

Welding—A process of joining metals whereby partial melting of the parent metals occurs except in the case of pressure welding when heating is only sufficient to cause recrystallization across the interface.

Yield point—The load per unit or original cross section at which a marked increase in deformation occurs without increase in load. In stainless and heat-resisting steels, this occurs only in the martensitic and ferritic chromium types. In the austenitic stainless and heat-resisting steels, the yield point is the stress corresponding to some definite and arbitrary total deformation, permanent deformation, or slope of the load deformation curve; this is more properly termed the yield strength.

Yield strength—Stress corresponding to some fixed permanent deformation such as 0.1 or 0.2% offset from the modulus slope.

Index